PELICAN BOOKS

A714

THE ARCHITECTURE OF MATTER

Dr Stephen Toulmin, who is married to June Goodfield, was born in London in 1922 and educated at Oundle School and King's College, Cambridge, where he read mathematics and physics. After wartime work in radar, he took his Ph.D. in philosophy at Cambridge, becoming a university lecturer at Oxford in 1949 and Professor of Philosophy at Leeds University in 1955. His longstanding interest in the wider relevance of science to our ideas led him, in 1960, to set up for the Nuffield Foundation a new Unit for the History of Ideas, to produce books and films on the development of scientific thought. Since 1965 he has been Professor of the History of Ideas and Philosophy at Brandeis University, near Boston, and he is also a Counsellor of the Smithsonian Institution in Washington. He has written extensively, and is at present preparing a book on *The Evolution of Understanding*.

Dr June Goodfield was born at Stratford-on-Avon in 1927, and attended University College, Nottingham, where she read zoology before going on to post-graduate research at Oxford. Later she taught at Cheltenham Ladies' College, before going to Leeds to take her Ph.D. in the History and Philosophy of Science. She was a Leverhulme Research Fellow and subsequently a lecturer in this subject at the University of Leeds. Between 1960 and 1964, she directed the film programme of the Unit for the History of Ideas, and is now Rebecca Bacharach Treves Professor of the History and Philosophy of Science at Wellesley College, near Boston. Her books include *The Growth of Scientific Physiology*, and she has written science programmes for the BBC television programme, *Horizon*.

When in England, the Toulmins live on the Sussex Downs.

This is a companion volume to *The Fabric of the Heavens* and *The Discovery of Time*, already available as Pelicans.

STEPHEN TOULMIN
JUNE GOODFIELD

THE ARCHITECTURE
OF MATTER

with sixteen plates

PENGUIN BOOKS
by arrangement with Hutchinson of London

Penguin Books Ltd, Harmondsworth, Middlesex, England
Penguin Books Australia Ltd, Ringwood, Victoria, Australia

—

First published by Hutchinson 1962
Published in Pelican Books 1965
Reprinted 1968

—

Copyright © Stephen Toulmin and June Goodfield, 1962

—

Made and printed in Great Britain
by Hazell Watson & Viney Ltd,
Aylesbury, Bucks
Set in Monotype Times

Contents

CONTENTS

CONTENTS

Acknowledgements I

For permission to reproduce half-tone illustrations the authors are indebted to the following:

Plate 1: Dr J. S. Needham, F.R.S., Ho Ping-Yü, The Society for the Study of Alchemy and Early Chemistry, and the editor of *Ambix* (Vol. VII, No. 2, 1959); *Plate 2:* The University of Chicago Press, Lazarus Ercker *Treatise on Ores and Assaying* translated by A. G. Sisco and C. S. Smith; *Plates 3 and 10:* The Trustees of the British Museum; *Plate 4:* Mr Osvaldo Bohm; *Plates 5 and 6:* The Trustees of the Tate Gallery; *Plates 7 and 9:* The Science Museum, London; *Plate 8:* The Syndics of the University Press, Cambridge, *The Evolution of Physics* (Einstein and Infeld) (a) Lastowiecki and Gregor, (b) Loria and Klinger; *Plate 11:* Professor G. Causey and E. & S. Livingstone Ltd., *Electron Microscopy*; *Plate 12:* Dr J. W. Menter; *Plate 13:* Professor P. Köller and George Allen & Unwin Ltd, *The Handling of Chromosomes* (Darlington and La Cœur); *Plate 14:* Dr M. H. F. Wilkins; *Plate 15:* Dr R. C. Valentine and the Royal College of Surgeons; *Plate 16:* Mr John Freeman and the Natural History Museum.

And for permission to reproduce line drawings in the text:

Dr Martin Levey, Dr Harry Woolf, and *Isis* (Vol. 51, March 1960), *page 32*; The Harvard University Press, The Loeb Classical Library, and William Heinemann Ltd, *A Source Book in Greek Science* (M. R. Cohen and I. E. Drabkin), *page 115*; F. Sherwood Taylor and Taylor & Francis Ltd, 'The Origin of the Thermometer' from *Annals of Science* (Vol. 5, 1947), *page 234*; Professor Read and George Bell & Sons Ltd, *Through Alchemy to Chemistry*, *page 145*; Dr J. S. Needham, F.R.S., Ho Ping-Yü, The Society for the Study of Alchemy and Early Chemistry, and the editor of *Ambix* (Vol. VII, No. 2, 1959), *page 148* and accompanying text; Librairie Gallimard, *Encyclopédie de la Pléiade*, *page 238*; The Science Museum, London, from the original in the Manchester

ACKNOWLEDGEMENTS

Literary and Philosophical Society, *page 262*; Dannemann, *Die Naturwissenschaften in ihrer Entwicklung und in ihrem Zusammenhange*, Leipzig, *page 276*; George Gamow and Harper & Brothers, *Biography of Physics, page 284*; *Man's World of Sound* by John R. Pierce and Edward E. David, Jr. Copyright © 1958 by John R. Pierce and Edward E. David, Jr. Reprinted by permission of Doubleday & Company, Inc. (slightly modified), *page 285*; The Syndics of the University Press, Cambridge, *The Newer Alchemy* by Lord Rutherford, *page 316*; Dr John R. Baker, Dr Donald Parry and the Company of Biologists Ltd, *Quarterly Journal of Microscopical Science* (Vol. 94, Part 4, December 1953), *page 391*.

Acknowledgements II

For permission to reprint copyright extracts the authors are indebted to the following:

Siegfried Sassoon and Faber & Faber, the sonnet 'Grandeur of Ghosts' from his *Collected Poems*; J. Chadwick, W. N. Mann and Blackwell Scientific Publications Ltd, *The Medical Works of Hippocrates*; B. T. Batsford Ltd, *Picasso* by Gertrude Stein; R. C. Trevelyan and the Syndics of the University Press, Cambridge, *De Rerum Natura* (Lucretius); Lawrence Durrell and Faber & Faber Ltd, *Mountolive*; K. J. Franklin and Blackwell Scientific Publications Ltd, *De Motu Cordis* and *On the Circulation of the Blood* (Harvey); The Macmillan Company of New York, Cajori's edition of the *Principia* (Newton); D. McKie and Edward Arnold Ltd, *Essays of Jean Rey*; Princeton University Press and P. P. Wiener, *The Aim and Structure of Physical Theory*; A. S. Eve and the Syndics of the University Press, Cambridge, *Rutherford*; Blackie & Son Ltd, *Theoretical Physics* by Joos, translated Freeman; Professor David Bohm and Routledge & Kegan Paul Ltd, *Casualty and Chance in Modern Physics*; Stanford University Press and Oxford University Press, *Disease, Life and Man* by Virchow, translated by L. J. Rather; Faber & Faber, *Fundamental Problems of Nuclear Science* by W. Heisenberg.

ACKNOWLEDGEMENTS

In addition, the authors must acknowledge their debt for modified extracts to the following:

A. Pi Suñer and Sir Isaac Pitman & Sons, *Classics of Biology*; Professor E. H. Warmington, The Loeb Classical Library and William Heinemann, *Hesiod*; Martin Levey and D. Van Nostrand Co. Inc., *Chemistry and Chemical Technology in Ancient Mesopotamia*; R. J. Forbes and Heinemann of New York, *Studies in Ancient Technology*; The Harvard University Press, The Loeb Classical Library, and William Heinemann, *A Source Book in Greek Science* (M. R. Cohen and I. E. Drabkin).

When I have heard small talk about great men
I climb to bed; light my two candles; then
  Consider what was said; and put aside
  What Such-a-one remarked and Someone-else replied.

They have spoken lightly of my deathless friends
  (Lamps for my gloom, hands guiding where I stumble),
Quoting, for shallow conversational ends,
  What Shelley shrilled, what Blake once wildly muttered. . . .

How can they use such names and be not humble?
I have sat silent; angry at what they uttered.
The dead bequeathed them life; the dead have said
What these can only memorize and mumble.

Grandeur of Ghosts – SIEGFRIED SASSOON

Soul of the World, inspir'd by Thee,
The jarring Seeds of Matter did agree.
Thou didst the scatter'd Atoms bind,
Which, by thy Laws of True Proportion join'd,
Made up of various Parts
                    One Perfect Harmony.

Ode for St Cecilia's Day – NICHOLAS BRADY

Philosophy begins when men are perplexed. At first they puzzle about things near at hand, then gradually extend their questioning to greater matters. A man who is puzzled and amazed recognizes his own ignorance. Thus, since men turned to philosophy in order to escape from a state of ignorance, their aim was evidently understanding, rather than practical gain.

Metaphysics, I. II – ARISTOTLE

Authors' Foreword

WE published the first volume of this series (*The Fabric of the Heavens*) with some trepidation: knowing that our story had been told a number of times before, we had to hope that it was worth telling again from our own particular point of view. In embarking on the present volume we have felt an equal but different trepidation, for this time our story is both vast and largely unfamiliar. To the best of our knowledge, in fact, this is the first recent attempt to give a coherent general account of the whole field we have called 'matter-theory' (i.e. the physics, chemistry, and physiology of material things, both inanimate and animate) as it has evolved since the very beginning of science.

Until recently, many scholars doubted whether the continuity ideas evident in astronomy and dynamics had any counterpart in the history of chemistry and physiology – rather, these sciences seemed to them to have evolved independently and from scratch in the years following A.D. 1600. Recent research by historians of scientific thought makes it possible, however, to paint a more unified and more intelligible picture; and five years of first-hand work have convinced us that in matter-theory also there exist continuous traditions coming down from Ionia to the present day. Over the centuries, there has been a continuity of problems, of interests, of questions, of answers – in short, a continuity in *modes of thought*. If this fact has not always been evident, that seems to be because historians have so often considered the different sub-branches of matter-theory (e.g. atomic physics, chemistry, and physiology) in isolation, instead of recognizing them as united by a common body of problems and concepts.

Current research is already beginning to fill in some of the details of our story: for example, Henry Guerlac's book *Lavoisier, the Crucial Year*, which makes clear beyond doubt the paramount importance of Stephen Hales' ideas for the development of Lavoisier's thought, appeared while this volume was in press. In the next ten years the whole picture we have sketched here in first outline may be expected to become far crisper and more precise. Meanwhile we hope that, where the details are still obscure today, our first dotted lines will prove to have been reasonably well placed.

We were very grateful to all those colleagues who, after the appearance of *The Fabric of the Heavens*, took the trouble to write to us drawing attention to questionable statements and interpretations in the original edition. We have tried to meet their criticisms in the American edition of the book, and the necessary revisions will be incorporated (together with an index) in all subsequent English editions. We shall, of course, continue to welcome similar criticisms and suggestions for improving the present volume. We are already in considerable debt to a number of friends who have read and commented on parts of the typescript; as well as to Miss Helen Mortimer, Mrs Ann Goddard, and Mrs A. Alvarez, for their marathon feats of transcription and retyping. But our greatest debt – as always – is to all the historians and philosophers of science on whose researches any general survey such as ours is inevitably dependent. It is because of the reliable and scholarly tradition which they are so rapidly establishing that the history of scientific thought is at last winning in the world of learning the recognition it rightly deserves.

STEPHEN TOULMIN
JUNE GOODFIELD

London 1962

INTRODUCTION
The Problems of Matter-Theory

Men are by nature inquisitive: turning their eyes and their minds at times on the celestial backcloth to their lives, at times on the objects and creatures whose world and fate they share, at times on the historical process in which they – and all things – are involved. A persistent curiosity about the scale and layout of the cosmos has ultimately forced them (by the arguments we studied in *The Fabric of the Heavens*) to contemplate spatial dimensions larger than the imagination could at first contain. In the present volume, we must watch the same persistent search for understanding shrinking the focus of attention to dimensions as unimaginably small.

This search for understanding has created – science. And, by now, the development of man's cosmological ideas has established the chief spatial relationships in his universe so firmly that they have become part of our 'common sense'. In this way, the Frame of Nature has been defined. Yet the sequence of events by which this came about has had an almost fictional simplicity, which must be recognized and discounted if one is not to approach the history of other sciences with false expectations.

From the very outset, the heavens presented men with a clear contrast and a crucial problem. The unrelenting sweep of the constellations led them to believe in a natural order, binding all things together in a harmonious system. In direct contrast, the planets moved across the sky in a manner irregular, anomalous, for long unpredictable and for even longer inexplicable. Their movements struck them as perfect examples of those out-of-the-ordinary events which cried out for explanation. And this theme, announced at the opening, dominates the counterpoint of astronomical theory right up to the time of Einstein. So the story of astronomy has a natural unity and form, from the

Babylonian ephemerides and Plato's Myth of Er to Newton and beyond.

But if the history of cosmology imitates fiction, the story of matter-theory is more like real life – at once more rambling and more confusing. For our experience of material things is varied and complex. Their behaviour displays no single outstanding regularity nor any single striking anomaly. Instead a variety of happenings and changes, processes and techniques demand to be understood, and incorporated into a common framework of ideas The craft of the iron-smelter and the art of the physician; the ripening of crops and the vagaries of the weather; earthquakes and rainbows; birth, growth, and death; the amber and the magnet; freezing and evaporation – men faced this bewildering carnival of Nature with no immediate clues to guide their attention. Consequently, the first chapters in the story we have now to examine were bound to be tentative and spasmodic. The starting-points for a theory of matter took a long time to locate. Initially, all possible and plausible views about the nature of material things did equally much, and equally little, to explain the facts of everyday experience.

Long before the birth of science, men were acquainted with snow, wind, rain, mist, and cloud; with heat and cold, light and dark; with salt and fresh water, wine, milk, blood and honey, ripe and unripe fruits, fertile and infertile seeds. Farmers were familiar with birth, growth, and decay; craftsmen knew how to liquefy or solidify; techniques for smelting ores, for producing gold ornaments, glass, perfumes, and medicines were well established. To our eyes, this list appears a mixed bag, containing changes and processes of many different kinds, which we broadly distinguish as physical, chemical, and biological. Yet the distinctions we now draw, and regard as fundamental, are not self-evident: they could be established only in the light of experience. Even some of the most obvious properties and processes took the longest to explain. The colours of flames emitted by different substances were well-known from early times, yet only in the last few years have they found a full and precise explanation in terms of the quantum theory; and the equally familiar process by which wounds heal is one which, even today, presents physiologists with a whole range of unsolved problems. So, whereas the men who first speculated about the heavens could at once grapple with a problem of crucial theoretical importance, those who contemplated the nature of material things were less fortunate. Where should they begin? What distinctions should they draw? Which phenomena should they study first? There was really no way of telling.

This overriding complexity in the world of material change inevitably affects both the story to be told in this volume, and the manner of telling it. The plot has no natural and inevitable thread; and, if our account is to be coherent and intelligible, we shall have to exercise the historian's prerogative and determine for ourselves what – in any period – are the significant episodes to recount.

How shall we make our choice? By what criteria can we identify 'significant' episodes? There is always a temptation to make this selection retrospective: that is, in the light of subsequent discoveries and of our contemporary theoretical insights. Knowing, for instance, the light shed by the study of combustion on the theoretical problems of eighteenth-century chemistry, we might attempt to chronicle the changes in ideas about burning, trusting that the results would adequately reflect the development of our ideas about matter in general. But such a selection is unprofitable, for it inevitably suggests that everything in matter-theory before 1630 was so much chaos and folly. In this way, we are distracted from the more fundamental question, why combustion – of all processes – ultimately turned out to be the simplest and most revealing starting-point for the construction of a chemical theory.

All attempts to follow the story of matter-theory backwards lead to a similar result. The doctrine of atomism can likewise be traced to the seventeenth century; but apart from isolated appearances in the ancient world, it was largely unfashionable – and unconvincing – before that time. And, if it was unfashionable for so long, this must not be put down to the blindness of earlier philosophers and scientists. Rather, one should ask, what particular merits finally commended the atomistic view to scientists, and what part has it played in the development of contemporary ideas about matter? We need here some principle of selection which will allow us to penetrate behind the changing doctrines that scientists have put forward to a more fundamental level.

Only then can we hope to understand how the focus of interest has shifted, and why the forms of the best-attested scientific theories have altered so drastically over the centuries.

As in our earlier volume, we shall attempt to capture the intellectual attitudes of our predecessors. We must try once again to reconstruct the problems of men for whom all our own inheritance of ideas was ... something in the future. For these men, our common-sense distinctions about matter, far from being established and fundamental, were still *unmade*; and only by setting aside these distinctions, at any rate initially, can we hope to see the material world through their eyes. Then at last we may be able to recognize the truly significant figures in our story, placing them in the context of their own times, rather than looking only for those thinkers who apparently anticipated the doctrines of today.

The basic difficulty is to acknowledge to oneself just how many intellectual skins must be sloughed off in the process. It is easy to ignore the hyperons, mesons, and other sub-atomic particles of modern physics. Nor, for that matter, is it hard to forget the results of Dalton's work, and to look at the world through the eyes of men for whom chemical atomism itself was still highly speculative. Even the distinction between elementary substances, compounds, and mixtures can be laid aside without too much heart-break; for it really makes very little difference to our vision of the world whether we regard iron as the element and rust as the compound, or vice versa. Yet to have got so far – to have cast off the basic categories of today's elementary chemistry – is merely to have *begun* the necessary intellectual undressing. For there are other, deeper ideas which have taken so firm a hold on all our minds that the textbooks no longer bother to mention them.

E. M. Forster has written an entertaining essay about Voltaire's scientific work, depicting that great Frenchman embarking – barely two hundred years ago – on a vain series of experiments to determine 'the weight of fire'. Voltaire burnt substances of different kinds, weighing them before and after the process. In some cases the weight increased, in some cases it diminished, and in a few it remained (so far as he could tell) unaltered. He was extremely perplexed by this result, and did not know what to make of it. Any twentieth-century schoolboy could tell him: the point

Voltaire found so obscure was soon afterwards cleared up by Lavoisier. (Fire is not a form of ponderable matter, on a par with water or air – still less with iron, or hydrogen, or sulphur.) Yet if we laugh at Voltaire now we must do so sympathetically, for he was not just a literary man meddling in something he did not understand. He had a thorough grasp of the ideas current among the leading scientists of his time, and his account of the scientific work of Isaac Newton was the channel by which Newtonian theories at last achieved a foothold in France.

Voltaire's experiments thus pose a problem for us, as well as for him. One could not have explained to him just what *was* at fault with his investigations, in terms which he – or the best-trained scientists of the time – could have accepted. The difficulties were finally resolved only when a radically new theory had been introduced.

A scientific colleague of ours, when asked how he would have persuaded Voltaire that his experiments were pointless, replied light-heartedly: 'I should have told him to use his common sense.' But the common sense of Voltaire's time was not, and could not have been, identical with the common sense of our own period. For Lavoisier helped to *create* our contemporary common-sense ideas about matter, just as Newton, earlier, had helped to establish our common-sense picture of the planetary system. If, in retrospect, it seems to us obvious that fire is not a substance, we should regard this 'obviousness' with grave suspicion. Indeed, we need only list the great chemists – ranging from Robert Boyle up to Lavoisier himself – who provided either fire or heat or both with some sort of material incarnation, to realize what a profoundly difficult and important achievement it was to establish the distinction between *processes* (such as burning) and *substances* (such as coal and smoke and flame).

If we can already take for granted a theoretical revolution less than two hundred years old, how much more firmly rooted are the ideas and distinctions established earlier. We never question, for instance, the belief that elementary chemical substances are inanimate, and normally changeless, rather than developing like living organisms. Iron is iron, and will remain so, turning into rust only if acted on from outside. It is, no doubt, capable of changing its physical nature also if interfered with violently – e.g.

by the beam from a linear accelerator – but the interference does have to be definite and violent. Its natural tendency (we all assume) is to remain the substance it is. Yet before 1650 this distinction between physico-chemical change and biological development was far from clear: it was firmly established only after 1780, and it is still open to reinterpretation. And, if we are to start our enquiry from scratch, we must strip off from our minds this further layer of theory, and abandon for once the distinction between inert, physico-chemical substances and self-developing organisms.

Our starting-point is a world in which material things apparently come into being, change and disappear spontaneously; and one over which we have acquired a certain degree of control. To understand this world, we need a consistent and embracing set of ideas which will make intelligible both spontaneous material changes and the deliberate manipulations of the craftsman. The central question of all matter-theory thus becomes: 'In what sort of terms should we think about the architecture of Nature and the activities of material things?'

This question has faced men with a tangled skein of problems, which have only gradually been unravelled into separate strands. Yet certain recurrent questions and themes – certain patterns of thought – have arisen repeatedly in different contexts. Three such themes can usefully be stated at the outset. There is, first, the contrast between two groups of theories: those that treat the development of living creatures as the pattern characteristic of all material change, and those which find the fundamental pattern in the behaviour of passive, inanimate objects. A second, and related, contrast marks off 'structural' theories from 'functional' ones: the one explaining the behaviour of material things by showing how they are constructed, the other accounting for their form and design by the purposes they have to serve. Lastly, there has been a continuous oscillation between 'atomistic' and 'continuum' theories: some scientists treating material things as aggregates of corpuscles or particles, others choosing as their intellectual model a continuous fluid or field. Though other sub-plots will be important from time to time, these three fundamental problems serve as central strands for the story that follows.

PART I
POSSIBLE WORLDS

1

Crafts and Rituals

BEFORE we start to look at the earliest theories about matter and material things, we must go back a little further in history. For the period of conscious theorizing was preceded by an earlier, more practical phase; and this did something – but only something – to influence the speculations of later, more intellectual centuries.

To begin with, the relations between 'natural philosophy' and the craft tradition were distant ones, and their union into our contemporary scientific technology is something quite new in history. The alliance is still not entirely easy, for there is a natural opposition between the practical craftsman and the speculative scientist, which nowadays we tend to forget. The basic crafts – agriculture, medicine, metal-working, weaving, dyeing, perfumery and glass-making – are among the oldest elements in human society, and the proudest. There one can still hear the voice of the authentic practical man, suspicious of upstart theories only a few centuries old. For five thousand years and more, men have been tilling the soil, working metals, and brewing beer; they have developed well-tried recipes, experimented with most of the imaginable variations; and they are at first sceptical whenever an outsider presumes to tell the guild how better to conduct its business. Such men manipulate Nature skilfully, ingeniously, and economically: they are prepared to leave abstract speculations to more rarefied souls.

In this, they have some justification. For, however spectacular the influence of science on a few branches of technology, one can easily exaggerate its impact on industry at large. Hero of Alexandria made hydraulic toys for his patrons, Galileo made calculations about the strength of beams, but the age of applied science proper began only after A.D. 1850. In the interaction between theory and practice, science has again and again been in the position of debtor, drawing on the craft tradition and profiting from its experience rather than teaching craftsmen anything new. It has been said that 'science owes more to the steam-engine than the steam-engine owes to science', and the same thing is true more generally. In its early stages, especially, the craft tradition was – so far as we can tell – devoid of anything which we would recognize as scientific speculation.

The Sources of our Knowledge

When no written records have survived, past ideas can be reconstructed only painfully and partially: intellectual activities have an enduring existence only in their expression, and affect our practical activities indirectly. About practical skills and crafts we can be more certain: even where no recorded recipes or other written documents have survived, the end-products remain and are sufficient testimony. So, by examining the material relics of earlier societies, we can discover a fair amount about their technical understanding of material substances, and the manner in which they manipulated them. From these clues it is clear that, as early as 3500 B.C., men had become highly competent – above all, in the techniques of metal-working.

In many cases the products of craftsmen are our *chief* evidence of life in early periods. Archaeologists have for a long time labelled the stages of human development as 'the Middle Stone Age', 'the Early Bronze Age', and so on – referring to the most advanced craft-techniques in use at each time. The reason is clear. For, of all the things that men contrive, shaped objects of stone and metal are the most enduring. Pottery, too, though fragments need to be reconstructed, will survive for thousands of years; and, for their more detailed time-divisions, archaeologists frequently rely on the 'typology' of ceramics – recognizing the age and affiliations of a particular site by the shapes and decorative patterns of its pottery. Metals and pottery apart, the processes of decay quickly do their work; and only by special good fortune do books and parchments, fabrics, furniture, or even houses survive for more than a thousand years. In looking back to the ancient civilizations of Mesopotamia and Egypt, we are to some extent fortunate: the sand of Egypt has yielded papyri which in a more humid climate would have disintegrated long since, and the baked-clay tablets of Mesopotamia, with their cuneiform inscriptions, have likewise survived for a remarkably long time. But the prime evidence of early technology still comes from tools, weapons, and pottery fragments.

The justification of archaeology, as of any other science, is the questions it enables us to answer; and the imaginative scrutiny of such finds can teach us much about the practical knowledge and techniques at the command of early man. We can photograph the surface of ancient metallic objects through a microscope, and study the crystalline structure of the surface: this tells us the temperature at which the objects were cast or moulded, and whether they were hammered or annealed. And, by analysing the alloys used in their tools, we can establish (for instance) that as early as 3000 B.C. Mesopotamian craftsmen deliberately mixed pure copper with varying amounts of tin, to produce bronzes suitable for different purposes.

Archaeological finds are, however, not the only source of our knowledge. Some written records are also available. Early Egyptian papyri depict farmers and craftsmen at work, though these pictures are usually so sketchy or stylized that their interpretation calls for a good deal of guess-work. Some early handbooks of instructions and recipes have also survived: notably a tablet dating from the seventeenth century B.C. which records a recipe for making green glaze. Apart, however, from the computational methods of astronomy, craft-techniques were rarely committed to writing. Cuneiform records were laborious and expensive to produce, and the art of writing was mastered by only a small minority of the population, being used principally for State documents, legal records, contracts, and religious texts. So the average craftsman was probably illiterate and could obtain a permanent record of his procedures only with the help of a professional 'scribe'.

Then, as later, craftsmen learned the arts of their trades by apprenticeship – living with a master and progressively acquiring the skills by word and by example. To this day, the industrial arts and crafts have not yet been reduced to infallible, written recipes. The kitchen is not the only place where individual experience can crucially affect the quality of the end-product, and a master brewer (for instance) has to exercise his personal judgement similarly – telling by eye as much as by the thermometer when to cut short a particular fermentation. To the early craftsman, accordingly, permanent written records were of less importance than training, practice, and experience. Yet, even given the records we have, our knowledge of ancient technology might be greater than it is. Few scholars have mastered the ancient scripts and languages of the Middle East, and only a handful of these know enough about the industrial arts to interpret the technical documents that have already come to light. Half a dozen qualified scholars who deliberately gave their attention to the available tablets and papyri could make a great difference to our knowledge.

For the moment, then, our resources are as follows. From both Egypt and Mesopotamia, we have metal and pottery objects dating from before 3000 B.C. From Mesopotamia, we have cuneiform tablets, of which a few refer directly to technical processes. Some early medical texts are preserved on Egyptian papyri, together with a number of pictures of early craftsmen at work. The material relics from Crete and Greece date well before 1000 B.C. – and for much longer in the case of the Minoan Empire. Written records also survive from Minoan Crete and Mycenean Greece, but until recently these have been useless to us, for the scripts in which they were written had not even been deciphered. In the case of China and India, too, we have archaeological remains dating back to around 1500 B.C., but the labour of interpreting the literary records is only beginning.

So any picture built up from the material at present available inevitably contains large blank areas. Still, its general form can be sketched in with reasonable confidence, especially where it concerns the relationship between science, craft, and religion. What follows is an attempt to draw such an outline picture.

The Artificial Crafts in Antiquity

Our practical skills and activities fall into two general classes, which may be called the *natural arts* and the *artificial crafts*. In every age, the farmer and the doctor are concerned with natural processes which would continue, of their own accord, whether we interfered with them or no. Their task is to exploit these natural processes to the best of their ability – to steer them in a favourable direction, and to remedy the worst disasters that afflict our agriculture or health: in these natural arts, all we can hope to do is to take advantage of certain natural powers stronger than ourselves. But the men who run factories and produce artefacts have more direct control over the timing and end-products of their activities. Left to itself gold does not turn into helmets, nor malachite into copper; but provided that we manipulate these materials in the correct way, we can bring about these changes whenever we please. This distinction between natural and artificial techniques may not be absolute, since no craft can be divorced entirely from the influence of the environment; yet in the ancient world we do find rather different attitudes towards them, and it will be convenient to discuss them here separately.

We have substantial knowledge about three ancient crafts: metal-working, glass-making, and perfumery. The Sumerian society of southern Iraq was firmly established soon after 4000 B.C., and we have metal objects displaying a high degree of craftsmanship dating from about that time. The Sumerians learned to handle two metals with great skill – gold and bronze. To begin with they obtained the gold from alluvial deposits of gold-dust, later by extraction from crushed rocks; while the first bronze, too, was probably made from copper found naturally in metallic form. Around 3500 B.C., the potters of Mesopotamia possessed kilns producing temperatures of at least 1100°C., and from then on copper ores could be smelted, and bronze alloys formed, by melting together copper and tin. (The first genuine 'tin-bearing' bronzes we know to date from 3150 B.C.) Once this point had been reached, the chief methods of the craft were quickly developed. Charcoal was introduced into the crucible to speed the smelting process, bellows were employed to create a forced draught, and bronze objects began to be cast in moulds of sand. (The moulds were formed around beeswax cores of the desired shape, and these were subsequently melted out to leave space for the metal. This 'lost wax' process was certainly in use by 2800 B.C.) Most significantly, by photographing the bronze and gold objects through a microscope, one can show that the mixtures used for each alloy were carefully controlled, copper being alloyed with different amounts of tin, and gold with silver and copper: indeed, a complex nomenclature grew up for referring to the different varieties of 'gold' in current use.

In the case of metals, we have the end-products of the craft and many indirect references in texts, but few direct accounts of the processes employed. So we cannot reconstruct the attitude of the ancient metal-workers towards their craft and materials. In the case of glass we have been more fortunate. A cuneiform tablet recovered from a site near Baghdad and written during the reign of Gulkishar (1690–1636 B.C.) preserves a recipe for the manufacture of green glaze. The text is fragmentary, yet what remains is striking enough: it can be transcribed as follows:

Take a mina [pound] of 'zuku-glass' [the basic glass made from sand and ash] together with ten shekels [one-sixth lb.] of lead, fifteen shekels [one-quarter lb.] of copper, half a shekel of saltpetre, and half of lime. Fire them together in the kiln and the result will be 'lead santu-glass' [a red glass].

Take a mina of zuku-glass, together with ten shekels of lead, fourteen shekels of copper, two shekels of lime and a shekel of saltpetre: fire them in the kiln and the result will be 'Akkadian santu-glass'.

Green the clay [to be glazed] by keeping it in vinegar and copper, taking it out on the third day when it deposits a bloom. Pour off the liquid and dry the clay: if it appears marbled, all is well. Now take equal parts of Akkadian and lead santu-glass, and blend them together. When they are melted together, blend them further with a mina of the molten mixture formed from a shekel and a half of zuku-glass, seven and a half grains of saltpetre, seven and a half grains of copper and seven and a half grains of lead. Melt them together, keep the mixture for one day, and then take it out and cool it . . .

Here follows an obscure sentence, apparently referring to 'embryos', which we can leave aside for the moment. The recipe continues:

Dip the pot in this glaze, then lift it out, fire it and leave it to cool. Inspect the result: if the glaze resembles marble, all is well. Put it back into the kiln again . . .

[As an over-glaze] take a mina and two shekels of zuku-glass, together with fifteen grains of copper, fifteen grains of lead and fifteen grains of saltpetre: no lime should be included. Examine the resulting glaze, then place it for storage in an old wine-skin.

This tablet is the property of Liballit-Marduk, son of Ussur-an-Marduk, priest of Marduk, a Babylonian. Dated on the twenty-fourth day of the month of Tebet, in the year after Gulkishar became king.

This recipe is a remarkable document for two reasons. First despite the antiquity of the tablet – the procedure it describes is one which can be repeated to this day. Though there are slight ambiguities about the raw materials, the recipe has been followed step by step using modern materials, and it gave a wholly adequate result. The pot to be glazed was placed in a solution of copper acetate, until it acquired a layer of verdigris; and the resulting 'greened' clay was then glazed twice in succession. The first glaze resulted in a dull finish, but when heated up to 1000°C. the second over-glaze gave a bright smooth surface.

The second remarkable point about this tablet is this: the bulk of the text consists of a straightforward technological recipe. The writer lays down the steps to be followed, confident that the procedure specified will lead to the desired result, without any particular need for Divine assistance or intervention by the Gods. At this point in the text, we have left behind the realm of spells, prayers, or rituals: effective command has been achieved over the techniques in question.

The same is true of the glass-recipes recovered from the library of the Assyrian king Assurbanipal, who reigned a thousand years later. Once again we are here given a series of practicable and ingenious recipes, presented in the spirit of a craftsman – not to say a chef. (The language is, after all, very much that of a cookery book: 'Do this: and the result will be that.') The whole thing is severely workman-like, and the documents contain no trace of philosophical or theoretical speculation.

A similar housewifely precision reappears in the surviving perfumery-texts, which date from about 1200 B.C. Indeed, there is evidence that in Mesopotamia this craft was practised by women, and even that it grew out of the kitchen. The post of court perfumier was held by a woman, and many instruments of the craft resemble earlier cooking-vessels.

The techniques employed by these perfumiers have one special interest. Here, for the first time, we find evidence of *distillation*, a technique which was to play a special part in alchemy and chemistry much later. Until very recently, scholars believed that true stills were first employed only in the Alexandrian period, around the beginning of our era. However, we now have evidence that, as early as 3000 B.C., primitive pots were in use for extraction and distillation. These pots had double rims, and the secret of their operation lay in the circular trough enclosed between them. In the extraction-pot this trough was perforated by a number of drainage-holes which led back to the body of the pot: plants from which oils were to be extracted were crushed and placed in the trough. The pot was filled with water and placed on the fire: steam condensed on the lid and percolated back through the plants into the pot by way of the drainage-holes. The process was kept going until all the oils had been extracted, the principle being precisely that of a modern coffee-percolator.

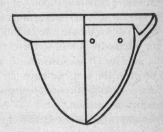

Mesopotamian
extraction-pot from the
fourth millennium B.C.*

Other pots contained no drainage-holes, and were used for straightforward distillation. The mixture was brought to the boil and the liquid condensing on the lid ran down into the trough for collection.

In the light of these discoveries, we can make much clearer sense of the early perfumery-texts. Evidently liquids were distilled repeatedly, so as to increase their concentration:

The thirteenth time the ingredients are mixed together, remove the oil and purify the body of the still. Heat water, clean out a storage pot, pour the water into the pot and then add two cupfuls of balsam condensate. Leave it to stand all day. At the end of the day, transfer the mixture to a shallow bowl and add a pint of balsam. Leave it to stand overnight, and in the morning wipe out a still-pot, and place into it the soaked aromatic material which stood in the shallow bowl overnight. Light a fire under the still: the aromatic material will become hot.

* See article by Martin Levey in *Isis*, Vol. 51, March 1960

Pour in the oil, stir and cover. Do not remove the plants or the charcoal. As the fire burns up, the oil will begin to bubble. Keep wiping round the trough of the still with a hand-cloth.

The shape of the pot gives us a clue to the process. The last sentence is an instruction to soak up the distilled fluid in a cloth, from which it can be wrung out into a separate vessel. And the same process became part of the craft tradition of the Middle East, remaining in use for at least two thousand years. The real innovation in Alexandrian times was the development of a still having a head with 'beaks', through which the distillate could run off continuously into collecting-vessels.

A closely related technique was that of sublimation, in which vapours were driven off from solid substances directly instead of first liquefying and then evaporating. (This transformation occurs naturally on a fine day in winter, when a bank of snow turns directly into water-vapour, without forming water on the way.) Sublimation was especially used for the production of mercury from cinnabar – the sulphide of mercury found in Nature. In the Chinese 'rainbow vessel', shown in Plate 1, the mineral cinnabar was heated: metallic mercury sublimed off, condensed in the top half of the pot, and then ran down into collecting-tubes.

One other artificial craft familiar from early times was later to influence men's theoretical ideas. This was the craft of dyeing. Many substances were used for this purpose – animal, vegetable, and mineral: scarlet from cochineal-insects, purple from the shellfish *Murex*, tree-bark, shrubs and plants, lime and chalk. Clothes of fine bright colours were expensive and sought after, and Joseph's 'coat of many colours' may have been the cause of his undoing, for a young man who so conspicuously came from a rich family and went around unprotected was an obvious target for robbers.

One thing links many of the early crafts. Metal-workers, glass-makers, and dyers alike had the task of *imitating* Nature, and of creating products which were indistinguishable by eye from the best natural materials. The earliest glass objects known are certain Egyptian beads, which were used as personal ornaments in place of precious stones; even then they were known as 'sparklers'. Glass-making thus began as the production of artificial jewels, and since gold and jewels were always in short supply men continued to think of the crafts in this light as late as classical times. The metal-workers of Alexandria, for instance, produced silver and copper alloys having the appearance and properties of gold; and they developed for this purpose a whole range of techniques for depositing a durable golden colour on a relatively cheap alloy. There was nothing necessarily fraudulent about these techniques. Men were paying for the appearance, not for the 'atomic weights', so that craftsmen and customers alike were entitled to be satisfied with the results. But, though there were many other kinds of gold on the market – green gold, white gold, and red gold – natural gold remained the most valued, being untarnishable, and having the greatest density. The best natural gold usually cost six times as much as silver, and three thousand times as much as copper; and when, much later, Archimedes of Syracuse devised his hydrostatic balance, he relied on the greater density of natural gold to prove that the king's original crown had been replaced by an imitation. The fraud lay, of course, not in passing off an alloy as a chemical element, but in substituting a cheaper substance for a more valuable one.

The Natural Arts

In ancient times, however, the artificial crafts played a much smaller part in men's lives than the natural arts. Given flint tools and weapons, and some pottery, life was supportable at a primitive level without metal, glass, or perfumes, even in an English winter. It was much more urgent for men to master the arts of medicine, agriculture, and husbandry, and this obliged them to relate their practical activities to their wider beliefs about the universe. Smelting, dyeing, and the like exploited self-contained processes, which could be carried out with the same results at any time of the day or the year. The situation in medicine and agriculture was very different: there, all a man's efforts were in vain, unless he acted at the correct time, in step with the ruling cycles of natural change.

From the moment that people settled in the valleys of great rivers, and began to improve their agriculture by cooperative irrigation, the fundamental problem became to keep in step with these natural cycles. The first achievements were inevitably precarious. For the soil, the sea, and the sky were unpredictable, and seemingly wilful. They could be wonderfully beneficent, or implacably destructive. Settled agriculture and social life were at the mercy of natural forces and agencies: if the new communities were to survive, their life had to be synchronized with the tides and seasons. From this necessity sprang the myths by which people in the Middle East interpreted their experiences, and the great cycles of ritual by which they governed their lives. These things were, in fact, two aspects of a single phenomenon.

Reading about the pre-classical myths in books, we are in danger of divorcing them from the pattern of social life out of which they grew; and, as a result, of regarding them as merely arbitrary and fantastic. But the men concerned did not first record the recurrent cycles of natural changes, as detached observers might do, and then *subsequently* postulate concealed divinities as theories by which these cycles might be explained. In describing Nature mythologically, they were simply speaking of what they knew – testifying to the undeniable existence of natural powers with which they were forced to wrestle, and which they sought to propitiate; and, understandably, they spoke in the terms to which they were most accustomed, namely, the language of personal relations. So there was nothing hypothetical or speculative about the statement that Demeter sprang from the union of Zeus and Gaia: it reported the essential fact on which an understanding of agriculture depended – that the corn-harvest depended on the soil being fertilized by rain from the sky. The name 'Zeus' called to mind the many-sided capacity of the heavens to influence our lives; and the same manner of speaking persisted in later centuries, when changes in the weather were no longer regarded as the deliberate expression of a divine will. (Aristotle – as we shall see – while insisting that the rain does not fall from choice, but because it must do, still retained the old vocabulary: 'Zeus rains, not in order to make the crops grow, but of necessity.')

The secret of a successful life lay, therefore, in walking the tightrope between the various natural agencies which could affect one's fortunes. People who believed that these powers could be influenced by 'diplomacy' set a corresponding importance on acts of intercession and propitiation; yet even those who were sceptical about sacrifices as a means of changing the weather were exposed to the same practical necessities. It was still essential to understand the seasons and to order one's life in step with them.

The documents which enshrine this point of view remind us less of recipes in a cookery book than of the traditional sayings in which country lore is customarily preserved: there is in both cases the same mixture of sound sense and credulity. We possess a Greek poem, dating from before 800 B.C., which gives a good idea of this attitude – Hesiod's *Works and Days*. In places, the poet is content to record the traditional time-table of the farmer's year:

When the Pleiades, daughters of Atlas, are high in the sky [i.e. early in May], start on your harvest, and plough when they are about to set [i.e. in November]. For forty nights and days they are hidden: when they first reappear after the turn of the year, sharpen your sickle. This is the rule which holds for the plains, and for those living near the sea, and for those further from the sea who live on rich country or in valleys or protected places: strip for sowing, and strip for ploughing, and strip for the harvest, if you wish to gather in all Demeter's gifts in due time. . . .

When the Sun's sharp strength and humid heat abate, all-powerful Zeus brings the rains of autumn [i.e. in October] and men begin to feel far more comfortable . . . then, when the trees lose their leaves and stop growing, the timber you cut will be least liable to worm. So remember to cut your wood then: that is the season for such work. . . .

When you start on your ploughing – holding the end of the plough in your hand and driving the oxen as they haul on the yoke by the harness – pray to Zeus of the earth, and to Demeter the pure, to make her holy seed sound and heavy. Arrange for a hand to follow behind you with a mattock, hiding the seed to make trouble for the birds: good husbandry serves men best, bad husbandry the worst. So, if Olympian Zeus himself finally gives a good yield, your corn will bow its ears to the ground, and, sweeping the spiders' webs from your cornbins, you will take in your harvested crop with joy. In this way you will be well provided for until grey springtime comes round once more. You will not need to envy others: others will need your help. But if you leave ploughing the good ground until the winter solstice [December], you will reap a sparse harvest, by hand, bound into rough sheaves, and have no cause for joy, as you bring home your single basketful: few will then admire you.

Elsewhere Hesiod gives more general advice. This is the usual mixture of useful and sensible tips ('Do not get yourself known as being either over-hospitable or inhospitable', 'Do not relieve yourself into springs'), with others whose value is less obvious ('At a wine-party, never place the ladle on top of the punch-bowl, for it brings bad luck') and others which are now ambiguous ('Do not eat or wash from un-blessed [unsterilized?] pots: there is mischief in them').

Only at the end of the poem does it become clear how far Hesiod accepted a complete harmony between terrestrial and celestial happenings. The motion of the sun, moon, and planets, going through their endless permutations, determined for him the 'character' of each moment: and the cycle of the month brought with it a sequence of auspicious and inauspicious days.

Everyone praises a different day, but few fully understand their nature. One day may be like a stepmother, another like a mother. A man will be happy and lucky if, having an eye to all these things, he completes his work without offending the gods, reads the omens of the birds and avoids all transgressions.

The twelfth day of the month Hesiod recommended for shearing sheep or reaping crops; and the twenty-seventh day as the best for opening a wine-jar. The thirteenth was bad for sowing, yet the best for setting plants. Boars and bulls should be gelded on the eighth day, but mules on the twelfth. You should bring your bride home on the fourth day of the month, provided the other omens are favourable, and this was also a good day for laying down a ship. And, even though the calendar no longer possesses all its former tyranny over men's lives, countryfolk to this day associate special taboos and obligations with the full moon.

Ritual and Cosmology

We are faced here with a curious blend of good sense and astrology; and a similar mixture can be found in the medical texts of ancient Mesopotamia and Egypt, where one and the same papyrus could record both effective prescriptions for dealing with wounds and also ritual incantations or spells. For the foundation of all successful arts and crafts consisted in a proper understanding of the natural powers; and, if the support of these powers could be assured by libations or sacrifices, so much the better. Sir Arthur Grimble has told how Gilbert Islanders today, when secretly slipping a drug into an enemy's food, will take care to utter the appropriate spell to ensure its efficacy. In our eyes, this murmuring of words is a needless formality: if the drug is going to work, it will do so whether the spell has been uttered or not. But this point of view is a modern one, relying on recent physiology for its justification. It is better to be safe than sorry, and craft traditions have always preferred to err on the conservative side. So long as there is any chance of this drug failing to act through his neglecting to utter the spell, the Gilbert Islander must in all prudence utter it. When one is employing a practical procedure hallowed by long tradition, deep theoretical insight is required before one can justifiably omit even a single step of the traditional recipe.

To some extent, a ritual element can be found also in the artificial crafts of the ancient world, where at first sight the recipes looked so much more direct. For example, in the Mesopotamian recipes for glass and glazes referred to earlier, instructions for the necessary technical procedures are accompanied by other injunctions of a ritual kind. The recipes from the library of Assurbanipal (seventh century B.C.) begin by explaining that the glass-furnace must be built at the auspicious time: a shrine to the appropriate Gods must be installed, and care must be taken to keep the goodwill of the deities in the daily operation of the workshop:

When laying out the ground-plan for a glass-furnace, find out a favourable day in a lucky month for such work. While the furnace is being built, supervise the workers and work alongside them yourself. In the furnace-building, place figures of the embryo-gods. Do not allow any stranger to enter the building, nor should anyone who is unclean walk before them. Offer the due libations to the gods daily. On any day when you put minerals into the furnace, make an offering to the embryos, setting a censer of pine-incense before them, and pouring out beer to them. Then kindle a fire underneath the furnace and put the minerals into it. The men whom you employ to supervise the furnace shall purify themselves, before you set them to work.

The reference to 'embryo-gods' has a history. In the earlier set of recipes, dating from 1600 B.C., there is a very obscure passage in which some scholars have seen evidence that actual human embryos – possibly still-born infants – were buried in the furnace. What could have been the point of this? There is little contemporary evidence, but perhaps we may read back into this association beliefs which are quite explicit later on. For, if one contrasts the brilliancy and cohesion of new-poured glass or metal ingots with the dirty and chaotic pile of ore, ash, and sand from which they are made, the change is most striking: it is as though one had transformed a dull, lifeless agglomeration into a living unity. The sparkle of gold and glass had something of the vital spark visible in the human eye, so that it was not mere fancy to see, in the artificial production of these materials, the creation of something superior – if not actually alive.

This, at any rate, was the interpretation placed on these processes by the alchemists of the early Christian era:

There is nothing incredible [wrote Aeneas of Gaza, in the sixth century A.D.] about the metamorphosis of matter into a higher state. For men who are skilled in the material crafts take silver and tin, change their appearance and transform them into an excellent gold. Glass, likewise, is manufactured from fragmented sand and soluble soda-ash, which are transformed into something quite new and shining.

In the regeneration of sand and ash to form glass, the embryos might well have a part to play. The life which in them had been frustrated could be transferred to the glass-maker's mix, and find an alternative mode of fulfilment through his agency.

As the centuries passed, men's beliefs about the 'sympathies' between divine and terrestrial things hardened into a complete intellectual system – notably in Babylonia. A cosmological picture was eventually built up in which the seven chief heavenly bodies (the sun, moon, and planets) moved and changed in harmony with seven metallic substances on the earth, seven principal parts of the human body, seven colours and seven days of the week; and each group was apparently associated with a particular pattern of numbers, arranged in the forms still known to mathematicians as 'magic squares' (see Plate 13). And it is possible that this whole system of beliefs found a material embodiment in the *ziggurats* of Mesopotamia – that these giant temples each comprised seven superimposed platforms, with areas corresponding to one of the seven magic squares, each platform symbolizing also one of the seven colours, and one of the seven metals. The ascent from ground level to the pinnacle of the temple took place (it seems) in seven stages, each with its appropriate ritual; and the progress of the soul itself involved passing through seven successive stages of enlightenment, from the lowest and basest state symbolized by lead, to the most noble and untarnishable represented by gold.

As an intellectual system, the result was something more than a naïve mythology, but something less than a scientific theory. It reflected a genuine conviction that happenings in different realms of Nature are connected – as they indeed are – but it over-simplified their relationships. In Alexandrian times, we shall find these ideas playing a more influential and more nearly scientific part. For the moment, the tradition was almost entirely practical, and the centre of the picture was still occupied by the craftsmen.

Technique and Understanding

It will be convenient to clarify the relationship between the crafts and the natural sciences before we go any further; otherwise, some aspects of our later story may appear needlessly surprising. Again and again we shall find the intellectual tradition of science exploiting the skills, instruments, and experience of the craftsmen, while yet maintaining a quite independent existence. So any picture which presents matter-theory as growing directly out of a craft background, and immediately serving the practical needs of industry in return, is seriously unbalanced. Theoretical chemists have, of course, found subjects for research in the workshop or the factory, and they have also (though only recently) been able to propose technical innovations; but craft experience has been only one of many separate stimuli giving rise to reflective thought about matter. Never in the past has it been a necessary test of a good scientific theory that it should at once lead to the improvement of industrial processes and techniques.

The spirit of the early craftsmen was throughout that of a medieval guild, rather than that of a scientific academy. In one craft after another, we find the same formula repeated: 'The initiated may tell this to the initiated, outsiders shall not have it explained'; and, on top of this declaration of secrecy, the cryptic abbreviations and the use of a dead language (Sumerian, of course, rather than Latin) remind us of modern medical prescriptions. We are emphatically in the world of practical men.

What is missing in all this? The answer is: any persistent attempt to theorize about, or make general sense of, the inherited experience of the guilds. The iron-founder, for instance, needs to know only that the smelting of iron ore can be accelerated by adding charcoal to the melt. The theoretical chemist seeks to understand *why* this is so, by relating this observation and others to a common general theory. The efficacy of techniques – whether metallurgical, agricultural, medical, or astronomical – in this way provides scientists with fresh phenomena: for these practical achievements are evidence of natural relations and connexions which are being exploited without being understood.

So, while the connexion between matter-theory and the crafts is unquestionable, it is nevertheless indirect. The instruments and procedures developed by craftsmen during the first millennia of settled society became the common property of all their successors; and, in due course, we shall find the natural philosophers of Ionia and Athens citing as evidence not only observations of Nature but also contemporary techniques. Brick-making, sculpture, medicine, and agriculture were as familiar to them as rainbows, constellations, and earthquakes. But in drawing on this body of common knowledge they were not acting as craftsmen, nor did they see themselves as such. They wanted, not to *make* things, but to *make sense* of them.

The task of winning practical men over to the cause of natural science has been a slow one. Before A.D. 1850, intellectual advances within the sciences of matter no more led to immediate improvements in the crafts than had Newton's theory of planetary motion at once led to better planetary forecasting. If, during the last few decades, scientists have at last been able to supplement, and even to revolutionize, the age-old craft traditions, this has been an incidental – and largely uncovenanted – fruit of scientific success. For it was necessary first that disinterested men should spend many centuries developing a theoretical insight into the nature and structure of matter, whose soundness could be established by observation, reason, and experiment, quite independently of its technological dividends.

In the present chapter, we have been concerned with two kinds of human activity: crafts – the development of techniques designed to serve men's practical needs; and rituals – the attempt to control the powers of Nature, not only for comfort or convenience, but rather so that man shall live in harmony with the cosmic order. So far as we know, these represented the whole of man's understanding of the material world, until about the year 600 B.C. After that time, we find a parallel, *intellectual* tradition growing up, with very different aims. The growth of this intellectual tradition, and the manner in which its ideas were eventually re-applied for practical ends, will be our theme for the remainder of this book.

FURTHER READING AND REFERENCES

For the general historical background to the ancient empires of the Middle East, see:

V. Gordon Childe, *What Happened in History*, Max Parrish, 1960

J. H. Breasted, *Ancient Times*, Harper, 1926

Leonard Woolley, *The Sumerians*, Clarendon Press, 1928

The most up-to-date and penetrating discussions of craft techniques in Egypt and Mesopotamia are to be found in:

R. J. Forbes, *Studies in Ancient Technology*, E. J. Brill, 1955

Martin Levey, *Chemistry and Chemical Technology in Ancient Mesopotamia*, Elsevier, 1959

The Babylonian glaze-recipe from the seventeenth century B.C. quoted in this chapter has been followed in modern times by H. Moore (see his article in *Iraq*, Vol. 10, 1948).

The relationship between crafts and rituals is touched on in:

H. Frankfort, *Before Philosophy* (*The Intellectual Adventure of Ancient Man*), Penguin Books, 1949.

W. K. C. Guthrie, *The Greeks and their Gods*, Methuen, 1950

For modern parallels in a primitive society, see:

Sir Arthur Grimble, *A Pattern of Islands*, John Murray, 1952

Ancient Chinese technology is analysed in detail in:

Joseph Needham, *Science and Civilization in China*, Cambridge University Press, 1954

The volumes of *Ambix* contain many articles bearing on the subjects discussed in this chapter: notably, those by R. Campbell Thompson and H. F. Stapledon.

2

First Principles

NEW ideas are the goals of science, not its end-product. They do not *guarantee* deeper understanding, yet our grasp of Nature will be extended only if we are prepared to welcome them and give them a hearing. If at the outset exaggerated claims are made on their behalf, this need not matter. Enthusiasm and deep conviction are necessary if men are to explore all the possibilities of any new idea, and later experience can be relied on either to confirm or to moderate the initial claims – for science flourishes on a double programme of speculative liberty and unsparing criticism.

The enthusiasts who first declared that 'Everything is water ... or atoms and the void ... or number' were in the same position as – say – today's advocates for the ideas of cybernetics: the scientists who translate all descriptions of natural events into their own novel terminology of 'negative feed-back', 'entropy', and 'bits of information'. There is in each case the same passionate belief in a new principle of order, intended to carry us beyond former perplexities to a new level of understanding. Yet just how much does any new theory achieve? Only time and experience can show. The indispensable motive is this initial conviction: the faith that there *are* unchanging principles of Nature, about which a rational theory can be built up – principles that are within our intellectual reach, and can actually be stated and discussed.

This new approach, and the critical curiosity associated with it, were the foundations of 'natural philosophy' among the classical Greeks. In their speculations about the nature of matter, as in their astronomy, the first philosophers did not question the existence of 'eternal principles': the point at issue between them was, how they should be conceived. It may seem surprising that, for all their acute observations and painstaking arguments, they remained so divided. Yet this surprise would be misplaced. Confronted by the full complexity of Nature, the Greeks were fully

43

occupied in exploring the possibilities and implications of different types of theory. All their conceptions promised new understanding in one direction or another: it was – inevitably – a task for later generations to discover in what fields each of these ideas would yield most intellectual profit.

The New Climate of Thought

The most profound historical changes rarely come about because earlier social or intellectual systems have been torn down and rebuilt from the ground. They are more often the result of quite small readjustments operating by a kind of leverage. For the moment comes when changes which, individually, had been too small to have any lasting effect suddenly combine to produce radical changes in men's outlook. When this happens, we need to look less for the initial *cause* of the historical change than for the attendant *circumstance* which allowed it to have effect.

Something of this pattern can be discerned when we turn to classical Greece and study the origin of the speculative tradition in science. For this did not begin with a flood of revolutionary ideas: the crucial change lay, rather, in men's attitudes towards the existing tradition. People have been tempted to picture philosophy before the days of Socrates as a deliberate attack on earlier mythologies by a group of angry young rationalists – a brand-new liberal enlightenment sweeping away reactionary superstitions about Marduk and Thoth, Jahweh and Zeus. Closer examination shows a different picture. At the beginning we find not so much a torrent of new ideas as a change in emphasis. The long-term results were certainly to be far-reaching, but this was chiefly due to intellectual opportunities which opened up during the next three hundred years. For, in science as elsewhere, original thought acts like a yeast. Placed in one environment it will be stifled: in another, it will produce a ferment.

Individual men in the great Middle-Eastern empires were (as we know) quite capable of speculating in novel scientific ways; yet, by itself, this did not create a tradition of scientific theorizing. For the ideas were not perpetuated, and no intellectual chain-reaction followed: circumstances discouraged the spread of heterodox ideas about the natural powers at work in the world.

The Greek experience was different. Even though scientific and philosophical argument remained activities of a minority, and were regarded by some as heretical or dangerous, novel ideas nevertheless had the opportunity to spread and make their way. So it was possible for the new conceptions about Nature, fanning out from Ionia and Italy in the years after 600 B.C., to be criticized, developed, and incorporated into wider systems of matter-theory, first in Athens during the fourth century and later in Rome and Alexandria.

To begin with, there was little in the way of a head-on attack. The philosophers wanted to rationalize the earlier traditions, rather than to destroy them – sifting them by critical thought and logical examination in the hope of placing them on a firmer foundation. They were quite prepared to take over many of the traditional ideas and, if they were dissatisfied with the mythological tradition, this was on account of its methods rather than its ideas. For they were no longer content with bare assertions. Aristotle, for instance, discussed the dogma that the 'first principles' are either Gods or born of Gods, those things which did not taste nectar and ambrosia becoming mortals. To this, he objected:

> But it is not worth scrutinizing too seriously the subtleties of mythologizers. Instead, we must find out how the same principles could possibly give rise both to immortal and to perishable creatures, by cross-questioning *those who are prepared to offer arguments* for this view.

In due course, it is true, the new philosophical movement did attract men with an iconoclastic cast of mind. The sun – if regarded as the supreme arbiter of human destiny – might well be numbered among the undying divinities, or 'Natural Powers': when reduced to the status of a lump of flaming rock it was at best a 'natural power'. Anaxagoras, by making this suggestion, was certainly redirecting men's attitudes drastically: and this scepticism was carried further by Epicurus when he argued that men need no longer regard the Gods with fear, since they had better things to do than worry about the human race. Even the medical men, pragmatic as always, picked up the same critical attitude. People suffering from fits had hitherto been regarded as 'possessed by spirits', and the Delphic Oracle herself delivered 'divinely inspired' prophecies while in a state of induced frenzy. So epilepsy and other conditions in which the patient was temporarily 'out of his mind' seemed to be quite unlike those other diseases whose causes were clearly physical. But by the middle of the fifth century, the great physician Hippokrates could dismiss this belief as superstitious. Writing of epilepsy, he said:

> I do not believe that the so called 'Sacred Disease' is any more divine or sacred than any other; on the contrary, it has specific characteristics and a definite cause. . . . All diseases are alike divine and all human: each has its own nature and character, and there is nothing in any disease intrinsically unintelligible or resistant to treatment.

So the determination of the philosophers to regularize and make sense of the older tradition was fated, in the end, to destroy it. At the outset, they were prepared to distinguish two kinds of myths: well-founded rational myths, and baseless implausible ones. But, as time went on, the suspicion arose that all myths of the traditional type – involving the personification of natural forces – were equally doomed. Those 'rational myths' which survived into the new era did so in the form of impersonal theories.

The continuity of the 'mythological' and 'scientific' traditions is apparent in the ideas of the very first natural philosopher. As Aristotle tells us, Thales of Miletos

> . . . declared that water was the underlying principle of things . . . probably deriving this opinion from the fact that all things are nourished by moisture, even heat being generated by it . . . and also from the fact that the seeds of all creatures are moist by nature, water being the underlying element in all moist things.

Yet the idea itself was not novel:

> The men of the very earliest times, who first speculated about the Gods long before the present age, accepted the same view of nature. They made Okeanos and Tethys the parents of creation and the oath of the Gods was by water, under the name of Styx.

The same primary belief is found in many Middle-Eastern Creation stories, as in the Hebrew *Book of Genesis*. There, the dry land appeared directly out of the waters, while in the Sumerian account the Gods built a reed-mat as a first habitation. In each case the beginning was the same: a formless chaos consisting entirely of that liquid, mutable, ubiquitous, fertilizing substance – water.

In one further respect the first systems of natural philosophy resembled the earlier myths which they were to displace. Questions about the ultimate structure of things were still closely interwoven with questions about the original creation of the universe. The very same word (*archai*) was used, not only for the 'origins' of the world and for the 'axioms' of a scientific theory, but also for the basic 'units' or ingredients from which the material world was built. The philosopher saw his task as a double one: to identify the fundamentals of material objects, and at the same time to explain how, at the very beginning, these came to be organized as they are – forming the earth, the sea, and the sky with which we are familiar. In this respect, the first theories were indeed rational *myths*.

Yet, at the same time, they were *rational* myths. Though the philosopher's job was to produce a rival to the *Book of Genesis*, he imposed on himself one fresh, crucial demand: the new tale must not be dependent on miracles or Divine commands, 'too deep for human understanding'. The Jehovah of the Old Testament had only to issue his orders: 'God said, Let there be Light, and there was Light'. In Plato's *Timaeus*, the Creator was no longer free to work in so arbitrary a manner. His world had a rational, logical, and *discoverable* structure; and, by using their intelligence, men could indeed discover it. So what mattered now about the Creation was not the Deity's initial act of will, but the rational specification to which His Creation conformed.

What sorts of problems, then, faced the Greek philosophers when they set out to explain the nature of the material world? These were *not* practical problems of technique or control, originating in any craft or art, for Greek philosophy began, essentially, as an intellectual movement – though one which always had some religious associations. The craftsman, as we have seen, need not demand rational understanding of natural processes: 'the point is, to change the world, not to understand it'. But, as Aristotle firmly insisted, the motive of the original philosophers was quite different:

Men begin to philosophize in the first place – and still do – out of perplexity. To begin with, they puzzled about problems near at hand; then went on, bit by bit, to perplexities about larger things: for instance, the phases of the moon, the motions of the sun and stars, and the origin of the universe. Now, a man who is puzzled recognizes his own ignorance – so that, in a sense, even a man with a taste for myths is a sort of philosopher, a myth being made up of wonders. Thus, since men turned to philosophy in order to escape from a state of ignorance, their aim was evidently knowledge, rather than any sort of practical gain. The evidence of history confirms this: for, when the necessities of life were mostly provided, men turned their minds to this study as a leisure-time reaction.

And what sort of understanding were the philosophers seeking? Once again, Aristotle is quite explicit, and his account still holds good of modern scientists.

In some ways, the effect of achieving understanding is to reverse completely our initial attitude of mind. For everyone starts (as we said) by being perplexed by some fact or other: for instance, the behaviour of automata, or the turning-back of the sun at the solstices, or the fact that the diagonal of a square is incommensurable with the side. Anyone who has not yet seen why the side and the diagonal have no common unit regards this as quite extraordinary. But one ends up in the opposite frame of mind . . . for nothing would so much flabbergast a mathematician as if the diagonal and side of a square were to become commensurable!

The nature of intellectual understanding has rarely been better described, and this 'reversal of attitude' is strikingly paralleled elsewhere – for instance, in our aesthetic experience. Encountering a new school of painting or a new style of music for the first time, we often find that we 'can make nothing of it'. The picture appears formless, and the noise tuneless. Yet, once we have acquired the ability to follow the music or understand the painting, our whole frame of mind alters and we can no longer put ourselves back in our former position. The forms in the painting and the tunes in the music now 'stick out a mile', and we wonder how anyone could miss them. As Gertrude Stein wrote in her biography of Picasso:

It is strange about everything, it is strange about pictures, a picture may seem extraordinarily strange to you and after some time not only does it not seem strange but it is impossible to find what there was in it that was strange.

So paint comes, with the growth of experience, to present itself to the creative eye as a woman's face; and a sequence of sounds hitherto strange comes to be heard as a cadence. Science in the same way has as its goal an intellectual grasp based not just on bare theories, but on a new vision of Nature – a new harmony of the reason and the senses, by which we can not only *state*, but *see* with our own eyes, the working-out of natural principles.

The Problem of Change

The tradition of matter-theory springs ultimately from certain general problems which perplexed the Greek philosophers. Certainly, some individual phenomena caught their interest – the phases of the moon, the mathematical properties of the square, and so on – but these specific problems were important chiefly on account of their general implications. For a satisfactory conception of the material world should, they felt, unify our understanding of all the variety in Nature. The mainspring of their science (which has been one of the motive forces in all subsequent science) was the search for this 'unifying principle'. To a man without a theory, the world is no more intelligible than the sequence of patterns in a kaleidoscope. As the Greeks put it, experience presents us with a *flux*. The fundamental problem was to discover the enduring, unchanging entities behind this flux: for, if we could only understand the ways in which these entities interacted and developed, we should then be able to make sense of the world around us.

This approach to Nature gave rise to problems at three levels, so 'the problem of change' was for the Greeks a multiple one.

(i) In the first place, there was one entirely general question. Any theory of the natural world must have two contrasted features: it must *both* give an account of the unchanging ingredients in things, *and* explain how these unchanging ingredients can give rise to the changing flux we perceive. In other words, one's explanations must contain both elements of stability and elements of change. It was very difficult, as they soon found, to define the 'enduring elements' in Nature, and in some respects their problem is still with us – for instance, in the persistent difficulties that arise when we try to characterize the unity of a human personality. (If the infant of 1880 and the greybeard of 1950 are both Rupert Jones, what continuing element is responsible for this common identity?)

(ii) At a slightly less abstract level, they were faced with another question: How can we frame a set of concepts which will apply universally, so that we can explain all kinds of change in terms of a common vocabulary? In building up their new theories, experience offered them many starting-points, and intelligence thought up many lines of attack. The immediate problem was not to search for one single, correct account: it was, rather, to find the most promising starting-point and direction. Should we cast all our explanations in the 'eternally true' formulae of mathematics? If so, how can these formulae be related to the changes in the flux? Or are the persisting elements in Nature, perhaps, unobservable particles, lacking all properties detectable by the senses? If so, how can our account explain the actual colours and smells of the objects around us?

(iii) Only when they had satisfied themselves about these general questions, did the Greek philosophers turn to specific scientific problems: such as the cause of earthquakes, the formation of the rocks, the action of fire, the relation between liquids and gases, or the mechanism of vision. And in every field they were faced as much by problems of *method* as by problems of substance. They were not yet in a position to ask questions of the form: 'Given that perception involves physical processes between the object and the eye, what are the detailed mechanisms that enable us to see?' Instead they had to ask the preliminary question: 'Is perception to be explained as a physical process, or as a psychological one?' At the first stage, the exact potentialities and limitations of each sort of explanation were impossible to foresee.

To recount all the ways in which the Greek philosophers tried to meet these difficulties would involve us in the whole history of Greek philosophy, including metaphysics. For our present purpose, what matters is this: they introduced for the first time certain patterns of thought which have been, ever since, the staple of scientific speculation about the nature of matter.

The Raw Materials of the World

The starting-point for the men of Miletos – Thales, Anaximander, and Anaximenes – was provided by everyday objects and substances familiar to them; and initially they looked for an equally familiar type of explanation – what might be called a 'culinary' explanation. As we ourselves might contemplate a remarkable new plastic, or a delectable soufflé, and wonder what ingredients had gone into it, so, too, the Ionians began by asking: 'What are the raw materials or ingredients which go to form the objects of that natural world?'

At first glance, of course, different things seem to be made of quite different stuffs – flesh and bone, water and ice. Yet to some extent these substances are evidently capable of changing into one another. This fact was at once suggestive: for perhaps they might all turn out to share a common material basis. And, immediately, we find Thales and his followers putting forward speculations of the greatest daring and generality, only to find that these gave rise to almost insuperable difficulties. The resulting debate is still continuing.

Thales (we saw) regarded water as the fundamental substance of the world, and the reason is not far to seek. Undoubtedly the first mythologizers and the first philosophers were impressed by the same thing: the crucial part played by water and watery liquids in so many familiar natural processes. Water is widespread in Nature, occurs in many different forms and plays a central part not only in the weather and the cycle of the seasons, but also in the lives of animals and men. It appeared to surround the world in which men lived entirely, both welling up out of the ground and falling down from above: so that many of the traditional mythologies placed the earth mid-way between 'the waters above the firmament' and another equally extensive, subterranean ocean. Furthermore, it occurred naturally in all three states – solid, liquid, and vapour – and, far from appearing a sterile, inanimate substance, composed only of inorganic elements in combination, it seemed to be both alive and versatile – the indispensable agent of germination and growth. Finally, as candidate for the position of 'basic stuff', water had a particular philosophical merit, and one which Anaximander was shortly to turn against Thales. It was in many ways indeterminate: colourless, tasteless, transparent, and without any shape of its own. Yet it could easily be given both a colour and a taste, and it would take up the shape of any vessel into which it was poured.

At this point the difficulties began. Any unique 'basic stuff' must have the powers both of a chameleon and of a magician. The trouble was that even water could not be sufficiently versatile. As Werner Heisenberg still points out, a 'universal stuff' can be satisfying to the intellect only if it is entirely devoid of *all* individual properties of its own. And in that case (as Anaximander retorted) it could not even be 'water'.

We possess only fragments of the arguments by which Anaximander criticized Thales, but the same point was to be made later in Plato's *Timaeus*:

Consider first the stuff we call water. When this is compressed, we observe it – or so we suppose – turning into earth and rock, and this same stuff, when evaporated and dispersed, turns into wind and air; the air catches fire and turns to flame; while, reversing the process, the fire will revert to the form of air by being compressed and extinguished, the air condensing once more as cloud and mist. From these, still more compressed, flows water; and from water come earth and rock again: so that (as it seems) they take part in a cycle of reciprocal transformation.

Now, since no one of these material substances ever retains its original character unchanged throughout these transformations, which of them can we without embarrassment assert to be the real 'this' – the ultimate constituent of the thing in question?

If all liquids contained water, this fact might explain their common liquidity; but it would do so precisely by contrasting substances which contained much water, and were liquid, with others which contained less and were solid. When the presence of water is used to account for the special properties of liquids, it cannot at the same time be used to explain the properties of solids, flames, and vapours also. Accordingly, the basic substance cannot be identified with common water, or fire, or any other determinate stuff: rather, it must be capable of taking on liquid or fiery properties interchangeably.

One may reconstruct Anaximander's arguments as follows. Thales was right in looking for some unchanging element behind the cycles of birth and death, summer and winter, but he was mistaken when he attributed these entirely to the transformations of water. The world as we know it alternates between wet and dry, hot and cold, and neither gets the upper hand – for, surely, a world composed entirely of water must be predominantly wet.

The different kinds of matter are opposed to one another – air is cold, water moist, flame hot – so, if any one of them were unlimited [in quantity and power], the others would by now have ceased to exist. The unbounded material of the world is, accordingly, something distinct from the four elementary substances [earth, air, flame, and water]. It is eternal and ageless, and encompasses all worlds. And into it the elementary substances pass away once more, as is only fitting; since – putting it somewhat poetically – they in this way make reparation and satisfaction to one another, as time requires, for their former inequities.

So, at the very outset, the fundamental starting-point of all matter-theory was faced with its fundamental difficulty. As the price for being completely universal, any explanation in terms of a basic stuff threatened to become completely abstract.

Greeks being Greeks, this was the beginning of a prolonged dispute, and in the debate which followed three alternative theories were put forward. Each tried to improve on Thales' doctrine in a different way, and each is the ancestor of an intellectual tradition that has lasted down to the present day.

(i) *The Pendulum Theory*

For Anaximander, as we have seen, the basic stuff was something entirely characterless: an anonymous neutral basis, from which everyday substances were formed by a 'separating-out' of opposing qualities. (Its nearest modern equivalent is the physicist's generalized idea of 'energy'. In itself, energy is neither magnetic nor electric, neither kinetic nor potential, neither matter nor radiation; but it is capable of manifesting itself alternatively, either as electromagnetic radiation, or as mass, or as the energy of motion.)

Anaximander applied his idea to account for the cycle of the seasons. Summer and winter represented alternate swings of a pendulum, upsetting the equilibrium between hot and cold, wet and dry. Such 'inequities' were only temporary. For having gone to one extreme, the pendulum turned back, so the separating-out of opposites was never complete or permanent. The force of Anaximander's model will be obvious to anyone who has built a sand-castle at the tide's edge. You begin with a mixture of solid and liquid. You dig a trench to hold back the water, and pile the sand up in a mound. But the more you separate the two substances, the more rapidly they in turn undo your work. As the mound of sand gets higher and the trench of water deeper, they revert ever faster to the original undifferentiated sludge.

Only in one case was there a permanent separation of the different forms of matter. At the Creation, the sea and the land, the atmosphere and the fiery matter of the heavens, were set apart in an enduring manner; and this stability was maintained by the whirling of the heavens. These formed a sort of centrifuge, in perpetual rotation, the denser and more sluggish stuff remaining at the centre, while the more volatile substances were flung out to the periphery. It was this eternal motion which brought about the original stratification of the universe, and so long as the motion continued the different layers of the cosmos would never fall together again. (For the relevant passages from Anaximander and Anaxagoras, see *The Fabric of the Heavens*, pp. 65–9.)

(ii) *The Breath Theory*

Anaximenes, Anaximander's immediate successor, put into circulation two further influential ideas. He accepted both the picture of the heavens as a whirling eddy and the concept of a single basic, undifferentiated stuff. But this common substance (which he called the *pneuma*) was not, after all, completely distinct from more familiar substances, for it possessed many properties of the ordinary atmosphere. Both were material, invisible, colourless, and odourless:

Anaximenes said that the underlying substance . . . was pneuma (air). From this, there first arose the things whose existence is eternal – past, present, and future – the gods and the divine things; while other things came from these in turn. Just as the soul, being a kind of air [or breath], holds our bodies together, so the universal pneuma encompassed the whole universe.

Pneuma takes the following forms. When it is entirely homogeneous, we cannot see it; but the effect of heat and cold, moisture and motion, is

54

to make it visible. It is always in a state of change; for otherwise it would not alter its form so much.

What distinguishes the pneuma in different substances is its degree of rarefaction and condensation. When it is so dilated as to be extremely thin, it becomes fiery; while, by contrast, compression of the pneuma causes the winds. Felting of the pneuma [i.e. a multiple compression or squeezing together of the layers] produces clouds – and these, still further compressed, turn to water. Water, when compressed even more, turns to earth; and this, when compressed to its greatest extent, to rock.

In this passage we see Anaximenes employing two distinct ideas, which were later to become the starting points of rival intellectual traditions: atomism and the continuum theory. His view that different states of matter correspond to dilated or compressed states of a single basic stuff was later to be taken over by the atomists. (They thought of solids as composed of atoms packed closely together, and of vapours as formed of the same atoms separated far apart.) Yet, unlike the Greek atomists, he recognized the need for some agency capable of maintaining things in a stable pattern. His concept of the pneuma was to be greatly developed by the Stoics, and it has most recently evolved into the 'force-fields' and 'wave-functions' of contemporary matter-theory.

But Anaximenes had not really escaped the objections pressed against Thales. As the basic form of matter, air was just as arbitrary as water; and, significantly enough, one finds Herakleitos of Ephesos making out an equally plausible case on behalf of fire half a century later.

(iii) *The Mixture Theory*

The third alternative was the most successful, and, though it may seem obvious now, it was none the less revolutionary at the time. Its fundamental supposition was that the raw material of the world is not all of one single kind, but comes naturally in several different varieties, which are free to mix and combine, dissociate and separate, in varying proportions.

The reputed author of this view was Empedokles, who lived at Akragas in Sicily in the fifth century B.C. Like Pythagoras, who had left the island of Samos (across the straits from Miletos) and established a fraternity in southern Italy, Empedokles was a religious teacher as well as a philosopher and doctor: he has, in fact, been called a 'medicine-man'. He may even have been a heterodox follower of Pythagoras, for his preaching resembled Pythagoreanism (and Buddhism) in its doctrine of rebirth and *nirvana*. Like other religious teachers before and since, he combined preaching with healing, and ended up convinced of his own immortality. According to a hostile rumour, he leapt into the crater of the volcano Etna, in the hope of strengthening his reputation for divinity – and so became the subject of a poem by Robert Browning.

His teachings formed a series of poems some five thousand verses in length. Only three hundred and fifty verses have survived from his poem *On Nature* yet, even so, the relics are more substantial than those from any other early Greek philosopher. From them we can extract a theory which, in its own distinctive way, tackles all three central problems of Greek science. As we have seen, the questions were: (a) What are the stable *principles* behind the flux? (b) What *process* is responsible for the changes in the flux? (c) What *agencies* control this process? To these questions Empedokles replied in turn: (a) The enduring principles in the natural world are the four basic types of matter – solid, liquid, fiery, and aeriform. These are 'the four roots from which all material things spring', they are conserved in all material transformations. (b) Change comes about through the mingling and separation of these four basic materials, which unite in different proportions to produce the familiar objects around us. (c) The agents responsible for this process are two universal powers acting in opposition, which he called, allegorically, Love and Strife.

Empedokles wrote his poetry in the tradition of Hesiod, and it is not surprising that he speaks of his four basic stuffs as personified natural powers. (Zeus certainly represented the fire and light of the sky, but scholars are still arguing about the identification of Hera, Aidoneus, and Nestis.)

Hear, first, about the four roots of all things: gleaming Zeus, and life-bringing Hera, and Aidoneus, and Nestis whose tears form a spring of water for mortals. And let me tell you another thing: in the birth of mortal things nothing is really created, nor in dreadful death is there any true destruction. All that occurs is a mixture, and an exchange of ingredients; and 'substance' is only a name given to things by mankind. For, when the elements have been mixed and come to light in the form of a man, or as some kind of wild animal, or plant, or bird, then men declare that these have 'come into existence'; and when the elements separate, men call this sad destiny 'death'. . . .

Fools! For they do not take the long view: imagining that things can be born which had previously no existence at all, or that things which die are utterly destroyed. From what is wholly non-existent, nothing can arise: and for what truly exists, to perish is impossible and inconceivable; for it must always continue to exist wherever one may put it.

The elements alone truly exist; but, coursing through one another, they develop into the forms of men and the other breeds of animals. Sometimes, under the influence of Love, they are united into an organized whole. At other times, through the action of hostile Strife, they are forced apart; until once more they grow into a unity and are governed. So, through their ability to form units out of parts, and in due course to separate once more, they may be said to 'come into existence' and to be 'mortal'; yet in another sense, taking part as they do in a continual exchange, they exist continually unaltered, as they follow out the cycle of changes.

The importance of this theory for the origins of science lies in the conception of material things as mixtures of several distinct stuffs, which are conserved throughout all natural changes, and which from time to time combine to form different organized wholes. Empedokles' list of elementary substances is, no doubt, far too short by our standards. Still, the originality and significance of his theory must not be underestimated. For this was the first appearance in our scientific tradition of an important intellectual model. However much we have to qualify it, the theory that all material things are *organized mixtures* of different elementary substances ultimately derives from this poem by Empedokles. No doubt some practical conception of this sort was common form among craftsmen, yet, as an explicit *theory*, this is its first appearance on our intellectual stage. Having said this, we must add two immediate qualifications. Empedokles' poem was as much a rewriting of *Genesis* as a contribution to chemistry and physiology. Also, when he came to apply his ideas to actual examples, they inevitably lost a good deal of their first precision; for he was determined to extend his theory to cover all natural happenings – the origin of species, human embryology, the mechanisms of vision and comparative anatomy, as well as astronomy and meteorology. Yet, in its essential form, the theory of mixtures and combinations is undeniably there. And, as developed by his contemporary Anaxagoras, and later by the atomists, this type of matter-theory has been in circulation ever since.

Empedokles' formative agents, Love and Strife, remained personified natural powers, like the three Fates in Plato's Myth of Er, who kept the heavenly spheres spinning. And this, as Aristotle in due course complained, left the creation of material objects from the four elements essentially mysterious. Once again, this objection does not entirely destroy the significance of Empedokles' doctrine. For a theory which prompts us to ask fruitful questions has great merits and, provided it does this, we can excuse a few vague answers. Led by Empedokles, philosophers were now able to turn their enquiries in profitable directions: asking, in the first place, how many (and of what kinds) the underlying elementary substances were; and, in the second, what sorts of agencies and forces caused them to unite into organic wholes – whether living or non-living. Indeed, these further questions were immediately taken up by other thinkers.

Philosophy had already come a long way in the century or more since Thales. By the time of Empedokles and Anaxagoras, men possessed a whole arsenal of ideas with which to attack the problems of the flux, and the central issues of matter-theory were emerging with some clarity. The philosophy of matter was still far from being 'physics' or 'chemistry', as we know those subjects, but it had at any rate established itself as a hopeful field for rational enquiry.

The Ultimate Units

The doctrines we have looked at so far concentrated on questions about the ultimate *ingredients* of material things. From shortly before 500 B.C., however, an alternate intellectual tradition was developing, whose approach was less 'culinary' and more abstract. It originated with the mathematical teachings of Pythagoras and, in contrast to earlier theories, looked for a quantitative account of material change. The world was composed of fundamental *units*, whose nature could be fathomed only by studying their numerical or geometrical properties. The flux of the world was an illusion, which resulted from our relying too much on the evidence of our senses. Colours, sounds, tastes, and smells no doubt varied continually, but the man of insight looked past these sensory changes to the stable mathematical order behind.

The founding fathers of Greek science reached a great deal further than they could grasp, and none more so than Pythagoras. Again and again they felt they were on the verge of explaining all the manifold processes of Nature, but, when it came to the point, they could show only that their ideas provided a *possible* account of the nature of things, and over questions of detail they were forced to rely more on imagination than on solid proof.

In the case of Pythagoras, the gap between promise and achievement was almost grotesque. His conviction that the crucial properties of material things were mathematical, and best expressed in formulae, in due course bore fruit which his original groundwork alone made possible. But to begin with (as we saw in *The Fabric of the Heavens*) even geometry resisted the Pythagoreans' assaults, and Aristotle commented unkindly on their lack of progress. It was harmless enough to say that material objects were 'describable in mathematical terms', or 'constructed according to numerical ratios' – and that, according to Pythagoras' widow, was all he had meant to claim. But, watered down in this way, the view was too vague, for at once the question arose: *In what respects* are the objects of the everyday world describable in mathematical terms, and *how* do numerical ratios and formulae apply to the architecture of Nature? It was the further step, of declaring that *all* objects in the natural world 'are' or 'are made up from' numbers, which landed them in insuperable difficulties. And these Aristotle kept rubbing in:

There are some people who would even construct the whole universe out of numbers, as do some of the Pythagoreans. Yet manifestly, physical objects are all heavier or lighter, whereas unit-numbers [being weightless] cannot go to make up a body or have weight, however you put them together.

In matter-theory, then, the more enthusiastic Pythagoreans underestimated the gulf between pure mathematics and the world of Nature. This gulf could be bridged only by discovering fundamental material units, which could serve as physical counterparts of their mathematical units. And this was one starting-point for the novel, and profoundly influential, system known as atomism, an intellectual novelty which was first introduced in the fifth century B.C., by the philosophers Leukippos and Demokritos.

It must be emphasized straight away that the original atomistic theory was neither more nor less 'scientific' than the speculations of the Ionians and Empedokles. If, since A.D. 1800, Demokritos has acquired a reputation for being somehow more of a scientist than other Greek philosophers, this is only because of a transient and partial similarity between his doctrines and those of nineteenth-century science. (The physics of our own day, as we shall see later, rests on fundamental concepts of a very different form.) The atomists, like other philosophers, were solely concerned to construct a plausible and *possible* system of Nature.

The ultimate constituents of the world, as Leukippos taught, were:

. . . innumerable, ever-moving units, viz. the atoms. There is an infinite number of them, and they are invisible on account of their small size. The material of the atoms themselves is packed entirely close, and can be called *what is*; while they are free to move through the void (which may be called *what is not*). By coming together in association, they are responsible for the creation of material things: by separation and dissociation, for their disappearance.

These atoms had several well-defined properties, First, they represented the limit beyond which no homogeneous substance could be divided. The word 'atom', indeed, originally meant 'uncuttable', and those physicists who in the 1920s were said to have 'split the atom' proved – in Greek terms – that the chemical elements are not made up of true atoms after all. Secondly, the atoms were separated by 'the void' – i.e. regions of space devoid of all properties whatever – so they could affect one another only by direct contact, collision, or interlocking. Thirdly, although all atoms were composed of the same stuff – the usual undifferentiated 'sludge' – individual kinds of atoms had different shapes and sizes, *whose number and variety were unlimited*. Finally, every homogeneous substance had atoms of its own characteristic shape, and the sensory qualities it appeared to have simply reflected the effects produced on our bodies by interacting with these atoms.

The theory based on these axioms had great intellectual power. For, instead of vague references to 'mixture' or 'Love', one could now suggest detailed mechanisms to explain how material objects came into being.

These atoms exist in the unbounded void, being entirely separate from each other; they differ in shape, size, position, and arrangement; and they move through the void, overtaking each other and colliding. Sometimes they bounce off in random directions, at others – because they fit together in shape, size, position, or arrangement – they become interlocked and so remain in association. *This is the origin of composite bodies.* . . .

The atoms have all kinds of shape, appearance, and size. . . . Some are rough in texture, others shaped like hooks; some are concave, others convex; and there are innumerable other varieties.

We do not know how far Leukippos and Demokritos developed their theory, since their views are now known only from second-hand fragments – the passage just quoted, for instance, comes from Simplicius, nine centuries later. The only complete statement of atomism to have come down to us from antiquity is Lucretius' long poem *On the Nature of Things* (*c.* 50 B.C.), and even this was greatly influenced by the work of other philosophers much later than Demokritos. Only on a few subjects can we reconstruct the original doctrine with some degree of confidence.

This first atomistic theory was still only a beginning. And it is interesting that the cosmological picture accepted by its founders was far cruder than that taught by non-atomists, such as Anaxagoras. But the significant thing for our present purpose is the *general form* of the theory, not its detailed application to particular facts; and, in its intellectual methods, it introduced two novelties which were later to be of the highest importance. One of these was made explicit by Demokritos: the other, though to begin with only implied, was stated clearly by Epicurus about 300 B.C.

The first of these innovations has become a commonplace: namely, the idea that the sensory qualities of material objects are as dependent on the properties of our bodies as on the inner make-up of the objects themselves. So far as we know, Demokritos was the first man to distinguish clearly between 'primary' qualities – those which figure in a physicist's description of an object – and 'secondary' qualities, which arise from its interaction with the sense-organs of an observer. (This distinction was revived in the seventeenth century by Galileo and Locke.) As authentic primary qualities Demokritos would recognize only size, shape, motion, and arrangement: tastes and colours were qualities of the secondary kind.

Galen quotes a famous remark by Demokritos and comments on it:

'Sweetness exists only by convention, bitterness by convention, colour by convention: the atoms and the void alone exist in reality. . . . We have no accurate knowledge of anything in reality, but can be aware only of the changes which correspond to it in the conditions of our bodies, and of those things that flow on to the body and collide with it.'

That is what Demokritos tells us, and he adds that all the qualities of the objects we perceive result from these atomic collisions. In reality, there is no whiteness or blackness or yellowness or redness; nor any bitterness or sweetness. For his phrase 'by convention' means 'in our usage' or 'from our point of view', as contrasted with 'as things really are'.

Demokritos' second novelty sprang from the implications of his first. Most of his atoms were invisibly small, and our senses could not penetrate far enough to observe them directly. It followed that the way to acquire true knowledge of the realities of the world was not by sensory observation, but only by rational, theoretical enquiry:

There are two kinds of undertaking, one authentic, the other bastard. Sight, hearing, smell, taste, and touch all belong to the latter: but reality is distinct from this. When the bastard kind can help us no further – when we can no longer see, nor hear, nor smell, nor taste, nor feel more minutely – and a higher degree of discrimination is required, then the authentic variety of understanding comes in, giving us a tool for discriminating more finely.

This doctrine has one further important consequence. Only by using our reason to 'discriminate more finely' can we adequately explain the properties of visible and tangible objects. With our intellects as the only guide, we must explore the world of the invisibly small, where the motions, shapes, and interlockings of the atoms are the only true reality.

This intellectual method – of explaining directly-observable happenings by appealing to insensibly minute but *hypothetical* constituents – has played a key part in the development of physics and chemistry; and, from its earliest days, it gave rise to philosophical questions which are still with us. Supposing the constituent atoms of things *are* insensibly minute, how can we know anything about them? Are they just too small to be seen? Or should they be regarded solely as creations of the intellect? Even in Demokritos himself, there is a certain ambiguity about their status. Sometimes he speaks as though their minute size alone prevented us from seeing or feeling them. At others, he argues that both *do* and *must* escape our senses – that we could never possibly discover anything about them, except by inference, since 'Man is severed from Reality'.

On the first of these interpretations, it follows that creatures blessed with finer and more discriminating senses could see and feel what we can only infer. The second interpretation, on the other hand, implies that atoms are purely 'theoretical' entities – fictions or hypotheses, rather than real bricks. Atomism then becomes a kind of fable, which interprets the world of Nature allegorically, aud we are not justified in making any downright assertions about the granular structure of the natural world.

As things were, Demokritos exploited both interpretations. Like Eudoxos, whose celestial spheres had a similar ambiguous status, he invited men to think about his atoms in two ways. They were, he implied, unobservable *both* for reasons of fact *and* as a matter of philosophical principle. Although they really existed, they were too small to be seen; and, in any case, they only 'existed' in a manner of speaking, since one could discover what was *really* going on in the world only by hypothesis and rational inference.

This ambiguity in atomism has never been wholly resolved. Whenever scientists have introduced hypothetical, sub-microscopic entities in order to explain their experiments or observations, two alternative schools of interpretation have grown up. One school hesitates to treat these entities as any more than hypotheses – the *dramatis personae* in a scientific fable representing one stage along our march towards understanding. The other school takes the entities entirely seriously and literally, attributing their unobservability solely to the limitations of our senses and instruments. And there are reasons to believe that this ambiguity can never be finally resolved. This oscillation between the 'phenomenalistic' interpretation, which makes the entities creatures of our minds, and the 'realistic' interpretation, which treats them as tiny bricks, seems itself to be part of the process by which scientific understanding advances.

The Debate is Thrown Open

By 400 B.C., then, the main characters in Greek matter-theory had made their appearance. From then on, the philosophical schools were to serve as a perpetual court, in which rival claims were pleaded. For the beginning period, we are lucky to have Aristotle as a self-appointed, though severe, Clerk of Court. His records may not always be complete, or completely just; but, by comparing them with other ancient sources, we can reconstruct the essentials of the debate with reasonable confidence.

As Aristotle saw, each of the earlier theories had great attractions, and could be supported by powerful arguments. Yet, somewhere along the way, the original ambition of natural philosophy – to find some single conception which could do justice to *all* our experience – had suffered shipwreck. To give a satisfactory account of the natural world, men must evidently face problems more profound and more varied than they had realized when they set out.

Consider, first, the 'culinary' approach of the Ionians. To this, one can immediately reply: a list of ingredients alone is not a recipe. It is undoubtedly important to recognize the fundamental materials of Nature, but that is only the beginning. A comprehensive account will have also to explain how these raw materials take the forms of men and beasts, trees, rocks, and stars. Moreover, our resulting picture must be something more than a 'snapshot': we are entitled to ask for a 'cinematographic' account (Aristotle's own word is 'kinetic'), which will make sense of the continually-changing character of the flux.

If Aristotle is to be believed, philosophers soon became aware of these difficulties:

One might suppose [on the Ionian view] that the only explanatory factor required was the 'raw material'. But, as they followed up this idea, the very nature of the case forced further enquiries on them: for if all things are formed from, and fall back into, some one substance (or perhaps several), how does this come about and what is the explanation? The underlying substance itself is surely not responsible for its own transformations. I mean: neither wood nor bronze (say) has the power to transform itself, so that the wood turns into a bed or the bronze into a statue. No, something else is responsible for this transformation. The study of this problem is the search for the second kind of 'natural principle' – the 'origin of change', as we should say.

Yet this 'origin of change' must not be too abstract or general. Our explanations must show, not just that the universal matter *can be* shaped into a man or a tree, but why it takes one form on one occasion and a different form on another.

These early thinkers seem to have grasped two of the necessary explanatory factors: the material basis of things, and the agent of change, but only dimly and uncertainly. Like untrained recruits in a battle, who wander about and occasionally strike excellent blows, these thinkers display the same lack of understanding, and do not appear to be entirely at home even with their own doctrines: for evidently they found little or no occasion to apply them. Anaxagoras, for instance, brings in Mind as an artifice to account for the order in Nature, dragging it in when he is stuck for any other explanation but at other times using anything rather than Mind to explain the way things develop.

As for the Pythagoreans and the atomists, Aristotle found their suggestions interesting and worth considering, but concluded that, at most, they gave us only a part of the truth:

Leukippos and his disciple Demokritos . . . hold that 'atomic variables' are the explanation of everything else. There are three variables, they say: shape, order, and placing . . . for instance, A and N differ in shape, AN and NA in order, and H and ⊐ in placing. But as for *change* – how and why it affects things – this they casually pass over in the same way as the others.

Aristotle's verdict, though fierce, is understandable. At this stage, a great deal of thought had been given to the *possible* forms which a matter-theory might take, but the dispute between the different approaches remained a rather barren rivalry. The remarkable thing is that, during their discussions, the early Greek philosophers should have put into circulation so many of the ideas which recent science has exploited. Certainly Demokritos did not *anticipate* Dalton: for before A.D. 1700 nobody could distinguish between physical and chemical processes, still less recognize the basic facts of chemical change that Dalton in due course explained. Yet Leukippos and Demokritos *did* launch some of the ideas which Dalton put to good use later: these men created an intellectual tradition which, as a consequence of Dalton's work, rooted itself firmly in our knowledge of Nature. And the same point can be made about other novel ideas; such as the pneuma of Anaximenes and the mathematics of Pythagoras. All these traditions, created by the Greeks, have developed down the centuries to provide the vocabulary of theoretical discussion during the modern scientific period.

It was becoming clear around 400 B.C. that if men wished to go further, they must abandon – at least temporarily – some of the ambitions of the first philosophers. The ambition to find stable principles behind the flux remained, but a comprehensive picture of matter could not be built up using only one single basic principle – whether material, mathematical, or atomistic. For none of the initial theories was in itself rich enough to cover bodies and processes of all kinds. Instead, a composite theory was required – one which brought together explanatory factors and intellectual conceptions of several different kinds. The next step was not to multiply the number of rival theories still further, but to arrange the pieces already in circulation into a more comprehensive and convincing pattern.

FURTHER READING AND REFERENCES

The origins of natural philosophy in classical Greece can conveniently be studied with the help of the standard works on the subject:

F. M. Cornford, *From Religion to Philosophy*, Edward Arnold, 1912

J. Burnet, *Early Greek Philosophy*, A. & C. Black, 1892 (4th ed. 1930)

S. Sambursky, *The Physical World of the Greeks*, Routledge & Kegan Paul, 1956

For the surviving texts of the Ionian and Italian philosophers consult the indispensable book:

G. S. Kirk and J. Raven, *The Pre-Socratic Philosophers*, Cambridge University Press, 1951

For the medical tradition in Aegean Greece, see:

J. Chadwick and W. N. Mann, *The Medical Works of Hippocrates*, Blackwell Scientific Publications, Oxford, 1950

The bearing of early Greek conceptions of matter on the physical theories of modern times is the subject of two fascinating and profound chapters in:

W. Heisenberg, *Philosophical Problems of Nuclear Science*, Faber & Faber, 1952

On the atomism of Demokritos, see in particular:

A. G. von Melsen, *From Atomos to Atom* Harper, 1960

Cyril Bailey, *The Greek Atomists and Epicurus*, Clarendon Press, 1928

The film *The God Within*, prepared in conjunction with this volume, surveys the environment, attitudes, and theories of the first Greek scientists.

3

Atoms and Organisms

SOME scientific problems are born, resolved, and forgotten within a century. Others, like the poor, are always with us. The project of weaving into a single fabric the separate intellectual threads spun by the scientists of Ionia and Italy at once ran up against one fundamental snag; and the resulting quandary, far from being easily resolved, has persisted in one form or another ever since. For a comprehensive 'philosophy of matter' has to embrace in its categories material things from the simplest to the most complex, from the utterly inert to the most animate and rational, from the completely uniform to the most delicately and exquisitely structured. It must show us stones and leaves, air and men, all patterned within a consistent framework of ideas and exemplifying the same basic principles.

That was the task the Ionians had set themselves from the very beginning, and it was already proving a tall order. For it meant finding the intellectual link between the shapeless raw materials of the world – the 'four roots' of Empedokles – and such finely ordered structures as the human eye. And what could this link be? Had solids, liquids, flames, and vapours the capacity to form themselves into organisms unaided? Or must some immaterial agency act on them from outside, moulding them into the shapes and consistencies on which the proper functioning of the organism depends? Both views involved difficulties. Either one could refuse to recognize any essential distinction between animate and inanimate, structured and homogeneous things; in which case it had to be explained how uniform matter could transform itself into living creatures. Or alternatively one could treat these distinctions as absolute, and regard the structure of organs as something imposed on the inert raw materials from outside; and in that case some clear and intelligible account was required – less vague and poetic than the 'Love and Strife' of Empedokles – of the agency responsible for this transformation.

In the two following chapters we shall see how, in their different ways, the Greek philosophers of succeeding generations came to terms with this problem. But first it is important to locate the point of difficulty more exactly. We can best illustrate it by showing how it affected the atomistic system taught by Demokritos and Epicurus in Greece and later by the Roman poet Lucretius. For the classical atomists, however 'scientific' they may now appear, did not escape this problem. On the contrary, it floored them. The difficulties about organization and organisms arose for them in a peculiarly sharp form, which they were never able to cope with at all satisfactorily. They did their best to embrace the structure and behaviour of living things within their theories, but the range of their ideas was too limited, and they ended by evading the central issues instead of meeting them. This was no historical accident: rather, it was a direct consequence of the very purity of their doctrines. For there is something in the internal logic of a *purely* atomistic theory which necessarily debars it from solving the problems of organization and directed activity. If we are to see why the later development of matter-theory took the course it did, we must understand the nature of this obstacle – since at the time it made atomism as implausible as the heliocentric astronomy of Aristarchos, and left the field wide open for the *continuum* theories which were to eclipse atomism for nearly two thousand years.

The claim that pure atomism cannot explain the organization of living things must not be misunderstood. Biologists today, of course, accept modern atomic theory as wholeheartedly and sincerely as do physicists and chemists, nor do they despair of applying it to biological structure and activity. Why, then, was Greek atomism incapable of solving these problems?

The answer is easily given. Our own atomism – first sketched by Newton and Boyle, and later developed into the basis of chemistry by John Dalton – is not the pure atomism of the Greeks. For them, it was axiomatic that the individual atoms of the world, when left to themselves, raced freely through the void in straight lines without interacting. Only if they collided or became interlocked did they produce any effect on one another. So a pair of atoms had only three possible states. Either they were not in contact at all, in which case their mutual influence was zero; or they were colliding and rebounding; or, finally, they were jammed together, their excrescences interlocked, and would remain so until knocked apart. With the laudable obstinacy of all Greek scientists, the atomists were determined to keep their theories consistent, and refused to compromise on these principles. Interlocking and impact were the sole permissible modes of interaction between atoms, and nothing as intangible as the electrical or gravitational fields of modern physics was admitted into their system. Our own atomic theory presents a striking contrast. Its great explanatory powers are a direct result of the very *variety* of interactions which it admits. Far from recognizing impact alone, the theory acknowledges gravitational, electric, and magnetic fields, not to mention 'exchange forces', and other more recondite influences. Indeed this variety of bonds, attractions, and fields sometimes threatens to obscure the unit 'bricks' between which the interactions take place.

But to return to our earlier assertion: if we follow Lucretius' account of the atomistic world-picture, in his poem *On the Nature of Things* – beginning with the simple physics and gradually moving over to biology and psychology – we shall see how the critical obstacles press more and more into the foreground.

At first the theory is entirely convincing. Just because atoms cannot be seen, Lucretius argues, it does not follow that they are not there:

> Lest you yet
> Should tend in any way to doubt my words
> Because the primal particles of things
> Can never be distinguished by the eyes,
> Consider now these further instances
> Of Bodies which you must yourself admit
> Are real things, and yet cannot be seen.
> First the wind's violent force scourges the sea,
> Whelming huge ships and scattering the clouds ...
>
> Winds therefore must be invisible substances
> Beyond all doubt, since in their works and ways
> We find that they resemble mighty rivers
> Which are of visible substance. Then again
> We can perceive the various scents of things,
> Yet never see them coming to our nostrils:

70

Heats too we see not, nor can we observe
Cold with our eyes nor ever behold sounds:
Yet must all these be of a bodily nature,
Since they are able to act upon our senses.
For naught can touch or be touched except body.

Behind all natural phenomena, however static they appear, lies
the random jostling of the atoms. And the results of this movement may even sometimes be visible:

An image illustrating what I tell you
Is constantly at hand and taking place
Before our very eyes. Do but observe:
Whenever beams make their way in and pour
The sunlight through the dark rooms of a house,
You will see many tiny bodies mingling
In many ways within those beams of light
All through the empty space, and as it were
In never-ending conflict waging war,
Combating and contending troop with troop
Without pause, kept in motion by perpetual
Meetings and separations; so that this
May help you to imagine what it means
That the primordial particles of things
Are always tossing about in the great void.

Such waverings indicate
That underneath appearance there must be
Motions of matter secret and unseen.
For many bodies you will here observe
Changing their course, urged by invisible blows,
Driven backward and returning whence they came,
Now this way and now that, on all sides round.

So far, so good: the properties of vapours may well be explained by the random motion of atoms. But solid materials –
ordinary stones and metals, for instance – are coherent and rigid.
How does Lucretius account for this contrast? The most rigid
solids present few difficulties:

Furthermore things which seem to us hard and dense
Must needs be made of particles more hooked
One to another, and be held in union
Welded throughout by branch-like elements.

First in this class diamond stones, inured
To despise blows, stand in the foremost rank,
And stubborn blocks of basalt, and the strength
Of hard iron, and brass bolts which, as they struggle
Against their staples, utter a loud scream. . . .
The closest unions are formed by those bodies
Whereof the textures mutually correspond
In such wise that the cavities of the one
Reciprocally fit the other's solids.
Moreover it is possible that some things
Are held together linked and interwoven
As though by rings and hooks; which seems more likely
To be what happens with this iron and stone.

Yet in other cases this appearance of utter solidity may be misleading. A striking analogy shows how an unchanging visible outline may conceal a flux of independent atomic movements below the level of our vision:

Thus often on some hill the woolly flocks
Creep onward cropping the glad pasturage
Whichever way the grass pearled with fresh dew
Tempts and invites each, while the full-fed lambs
Gambol and butt playfully; yet they all
Seem to us, blent by distance, to stand still
Like a white patch upon the green hillside.
Again, when mighty legions fill wide plains
With rapid movements, waging mimic war,
A glitter rises therefrom to the skies, . . .
And horsemen, wheeling suddenly about,
Gallop across the middle of the plains
Shaking them with the violence of their charge.
And yet high up among the hills there must be
Some point from which they seem to stand quite still,
Resting a patch of brightness on the plains.

The image is attractive, but the first discrepancies are already creeping in. The sheep in a pen may seem to resemble the atoms of an enclosed vapour; but – unlike those atoms – they do not disperse in all directions when the 'container' is removed. The very gregariousness of sheep makes them crucially unlike pure atoms. They are not mechanically interlocked, nor are their motions entirely random: to our modern eyes, they resemble much more closely the molecules of a liquid.

Indeed, the Greek atomists found the liquid state itself hard to explain. Of the three normal states of matter, only the solid and gaseous fitted naturally into their system. In a solid, the greater part of the atoms had become so rigidly interlocked that the over-all shape of the body remained the same; while in a vapour the atoms were dissociated and, apart from elastic collisions, were moving freely. Since interlocking and collision were the *only* permitted interactions, the atoms of a solid, when separated, should at once go over into the gaseous state: forming, so long as they were still close together, a sluggish gas, but a gas none the less. And the very existence of liquids can be reconciled with atomism only by supposing – as we do – that *attractive forces* act between neighbouring particles even when they are not in contact.

Over magnetism, another non-mechanical action, similar difficulties arose; and we find Lucretius putting forward a view which the atomists of sixteenth-century Europe were to revive with no greater success. On this theory, magnets are continually sending out streams of minute particles capable of moving the bodies on which they impinge; but they can do so only if the 'pores' in those bodies are neither too large nor too small to be affected by the magnetic particles.

> [Some materials]
> Stand firm by their own weight, gold for example;
> Others again, because theirs is a body
> So porous that the current unresisted
> Flies through them, can in no wise be propelled;
> And to this class wood, it is clear, belongs.
> Between these two then lies the nature of iron:
> So when it has absorbed certain minute
> Bodies of brass, then the Magnesian stones
> Are able to propel it with their steam.

In magnetism and electric attraction the Greeks were already encountering two of those species of 'action at a distance' which ultimately compelled Newton to dilute the concepts of atomism with concepts of force. But the irremediable weaknesses of un-diluted atomism are most clearly revealed when Lucretius turns to the problems of biological integration and the action of the mind. As he admits, an animated body is quite unlike a mindless or lifeless corpse:

> Moreover by itself the body never
> Is born, nor grows, nor is it seen to last
> Long after death. For never in the way
> That water's liquid often throws off heat
> Which has been given it, yet is not itself
> For that cause riven in pieces, but remains
> Uninjured – never thus, I say, when once
> The soul has left it, can the frame endure
> That separation, but it perishes
> Utterly, and riven in pieces, rots away.

In trying to explain the self-maintenance of the living body and the operations of the mind, Lucretius at any rate knew what view he would *not* accept:

> Some would have it that the sense of the mind
> Resides in no fixed part, but deem it rather
> A kind of vital habit of the body,
> Which by the Greeks is called a harmony,
> Something that causes us to live and feel,
> Though the intellect is not in any part;
> Just as good health is often spoken of
> As though belonging to the body, and yet
> It is not any part of a healthy man.

This view made the mind something intangible. But, if it was to act on the body at all, then it must do so only in those ways a good atomist would recognize. This meant treating the mind as one more material – and therefore atomic – part of the human frame:

> The intellect, wherein resides the reasoning
> And guiding power of life, I assert to be
> No less a part of man than feet and hands
> And eyes are part of the whole living creature. . . .

> Its seat
> Is fixed in the middle region of the breast.
> For here it is that fear and panic throb:
> Around these parts dwell joys that soothe. Here then
> Is the intellect or mind. The rest of the soul,
> Dispersed through the whole body, obeys and moves
> At the will and propulsion of the mind.

The fundamental difficulty is now apparent. The 'mind' was brought in to account for the integration of living parts and activities: but in Lucretius' hands, it has simply become one more thing to be integrated. Where before we had to explain how eyes, ears, hands, and heart operate in harmony, we are now faced with the more complex question, how all these organs *and the 'mind-stuff'* remain integrated. Lucretius is trembling on the verge of a 'regress' – a string of pseudo-explanations each of which merely describes the phenomena to be explained in a more complicated way than its predecessor.

For a little while he postpones the evil moment, by discoursing about the wonderfully fine atoms of this 'mind-stuff':

> And now, what is the substance of this mind,
> And of what elements it is composed,
> I will go on to explain to you. First I say
> It is extremely subtle, and is formed
> Of particles exceedingly minute.
> That this is so, if you consider well,
> You may be thus convinced. No visible action
> Takes place with such rapidity as the mind
> Conceives it happening and itself begins it . . .

> But that
> Which is so very mobile, must consist
> Of seeds which are quite round and quite minute. . . .
> A light and gentle breath has force enough
> To blow down a high heap of poppy seed
> From top to bottom, but on a pile of stones
> Or corn-ears it has no effect at all.
> Therefore the mobility of bodies
> Is in proportion to their littleness
> And to their smoothness; while the greater weight
> And the more roughness bodies may possess,
> The stabler will they be. Since then we have found
> The mind's nature pre-eminently mobile,
> It needs must be composed of particles
> Exceedingly minute and smooth and round.

But to say only that the mind consists of minute, smooth, round particles is no explanation of life or mental activity. Lucretius is obliged to go further.

Let us not think however that this substance
Is simple; for a certain tenuous breath,
Mingled with heat, quits dying men: moreover
The heat draws with it air; since there can be
No heat with which air also is not mixed:
For seeing that the nature of heat is rare,
There needs must be many atoms of air
Moving about within it. Thus we have found
The substance of the mind to be threefold.

Yet all these three combined are not enough
To create sensation, since indeed the mind
Does not admit that any one of these
Is able to create sense-giving motions,
Far less the thoughts it ponders in itself,
So to these must be added some fourth substance.

By now, the 'mind-stuff' has become a complex of at least three
substances – breath, heat, and air – which, if the mind itself is not
to fall to pieces, in turn require integrating: and this despite the
fact that it was introduced in the first place simply to explain the
integration of the body.

So to these must be added some fourth substance.
And this is altogether without name:
Than this nothing more mobile can exist,
Nothing more subtle, nor composed of smaller

And smoother elements . . .
Nor is there anything within our body
Farther beneath our ken than this; and so
This is the very soul of the whole soul.

Just as mingled together within our limbs
And our whole body are latent the mind's force
And the soul's power, because they each are formed
Of small and few particles; so, you see,
This force without a name, being composed
Of minute particles, is lying hidden;
Nay, in a sense, it is the very soul
Of the whole soul, and rules throughout the body.

The source of the regress should now be obvious. Even this
nameless agency, introduced to hold together the component

substances of the 'mind-stuff', is itself 'composed of minute particles'. How are we to account for the inner cohesion linking *these* particles? If Lucretius had pursued the matter, his principles would have compelled him to introduce yet a fifth, more anonymous substance, itself corpuscular; whose constituent particles were held together by a sixth, even more anonymous substance, itself corpuscular. . . .

But in this direction there is no end, nor any true enlightenment. It was a mistake to introduce the 'mind-stuff' in the first place. So long as we confine ourselves to a *purely* atomistic picture, the integration of organic behaviour will remain mysterious, however subtle and mobile we suppose the 'mind-stuff' to be. Yet the problem of the mind was only an extreme illustration of the general problem which proved fatal to Greek atomism. Whether we are discussing molecules, chromosomes, cells, organs, or organisms, we can retain the atomistic picture *only* by supplementing collision and interlocking with other kinds of interaction.

To say this is, of course, to be wise after the event. The best the atomists could do to explain the structure and working of organisms, without abandoning their fundamental axioms, was to offer the hypothesis of a corpuscular 'mind-stuff'. This being so, it is not surprising that most philosophers from Plato right up to Descartes looked elsewhere for an understanding of living things. And they were right to do so. In astronomy the heliocentric theory put forward by Aristarchos of Samos was neglected until Copernicus' time only because enough evidence was not then available to establish its soundness: Aristarchos had in that sense 'guessed right'. But the same cannot be said on behalf of Demokritos and Epicurus. Atomism in the ancient world was too narrow a system, and the axioms on which it was based were too inflexible, to explain any but simple physical processes. The range of interactions it admitted – the collision, jamming, and unlocking of solid atoms – was too restricted to account for many familiar experiences; and modern scientists could no more abandon their 'fields of force', and go back to the pure principles of Demokritos, than they could give up the hundred material elements of chemistry for the four of Empedokles.

Why did the Greek atomists not explore for themselves the new pathways we now take for granted? What made it so important for them to restrict the interactions between atoms to collisions and interlocking? The reason is that their theory had metaphysical tasks to perform as well as scientific ones. Leukippos wished to explain (as the Greeks put it) the difference between 'what is' and 'what is not', between those things that can claim some enduring reality and those which cannot. Reality, he declared, was synonymous with 'volumes fully occupied by matter'; and a volume entirely full of matter, of whatever shape, was in his terminology an *atom*. All the rest was void – empty space, devoid of matter, the home of 'what is not', and so incapable of either acting or transmitting action. For how could anything produce (or hand on) physical effects unless it was real? And what was reality but the atoms? . . . This was the intellectual circle within which the Greek atomists were trapped, and more recently science has broken out from it only at the cost of postponing the metaphysical questions which had highest priority for the Greeks.

FURTHER READING AND REFERENCES

The quotations from Lucretius in this chapter are taken from the translation of his poem *De Rerum Natura* by R. C. Trevelyan, Cambridge University Press, 1937. Another translation is available also in the Penguin Classics.

4

Likely Stories

IN 600 B.C., when Thales of Miletos was in his twenties, the traditional mythologies had not yet been seriously questioned. Two hundred years later the intellectual environment was very different. Athens had become the focal point of Greek intellectual life, drawing to itself philosophers with utterly-contrasted outlooks; and any serious-minded Athenian with a critical interest in the workings of Nature – for instance, Plato, who was born in 429 B.C. – was faced with an embarrassing variety of rival world-pictures. He could follow Parmenides, the metaphysician from Elea in southern Italy, whose conversation with Socrates later became the subject of one of the dialogues; or the radical Anaxagoras from Klazomenae in Ionia, who taught Pericles and lived in Athens for some years, until the unpopularity of his views led to his banishment. Alternatively he could study the mathematical doctrines of Pythagoras, or the intellectual novelties of the atomists – for Demokritos still had thirty years to live.

The raw materials of the Ionians, the logical axioms of the Eleatics, the unit-numbers of the Pythagoreans, the atoms of Leukippos and Demokritos – how was one to choose between them? Socrates himself, concluding that this chaos of opinions could not be resolved, gave up the attempt. Philosophers, he declared, should concentrate on problems of personal and political conduct, and he was not alone in his scepticism. One group of men as intelligent and articulate as the philosophers shared his attitude – namely, the doctors. Hippokrates of Kos was well aware of the new theories, particularly those of Empedokles who tried to apply his ideas to medicine. But he could see no medical value in them, arguing that they stood in the way of impartial reporting, and that their application led to no cures. The conscientious physician could not afford to waste time on such hypotheses.

In all previous attempts to speak or to write about medicine the authors have introduced certain arbitrary suppositions into their arguments and have reduced the causes of death and the maladies that affect mankind to a narrow compass. They have supposed that there are but one or two causes; heat or cold, moisture, dryness or anything else they may fancy. From many considerations their mistake is obvious; indeed, this is proved from their own words. ... I do not think that medicine is in need of some new hypothesis dealing, for instance, with invisible or problematic substances about which one must have some theory or another in order to discuss them seriously. In such matters medicine differs from subjects like astronomy and geology, of which a man might know the truth and lecture on it without he or his audience being able to judge whether it were the truth or not, because there is no true criterion.

Fortunately, two great teachers at least did not take the easy way out – of complete scepticism. Faced with all these rival doctrines, they tried to combine the merits of earlier theories into more comprehensive systems, instead of setting them in opposition. Where Hippokrates expressed the enduring scepticism of the craftsman towards theoretical speculation, Plato and Aristotle were to be the prophets of future scientific ideas. Both men realized that an all-embracing system of thought must be built up around certain novel theoretical conceptions, which could provide a 'logical skeleton' for scientific explanation. But they approached Nature with different backgrounds and preoccupations, and this affected everything else in their theories.

Plato found his inspiration in geometry. According to him, an account of the natural world would be intellectually satisfying only if it took the form of an ordered mathematical system – like electromagnetic theory or quantum mechanics today. The scientist then had a double task. In the first place he had to explore the logical consequences of his different ideas *in the abstract* – so as to find out what properties any circle or cube (or chair, for that matter) must have, as a result of being a circle, cube, or chair. In this way a body of knowledge would be built up whose validity was established by the reason alone; and Plato hoped that the greater part of science would respond to treatment in this mathematical way. But there was also a second task. For in some fields pure mathematical reasoning was not entirely conclusive, and one could conceive alternative explanations for the same phenomenon all equally possible. In these cases, a scientist could not hope for the full certainty of mathematics; all that he could ask for was a *plausible* account. As Plato makes Timaeus say:

So, Socrates, if there are many things about the world – the nature of the divine powers, and the origin of the cosmos – of which we cannot give an entirely precise and self-validating explanation, you must not be surprised. Provided the explanation we give is as plausible as any other we should be satisfied, seeing that I, the speaker, and you, my critics, are only human: in these matters, it is appropriate that we should accept the *likely story* and demand nothing more.

Aristotle, on the other hand, did not believe that all theories should be based on abstractions of a mathematical kind. On the contrary, the 'unchanging principles' of mathematics would apply only to similarly unchanging objects in Nature – such as the planets. To understand the creatures of earth, which are born, mature, and die, one needed conceptions whose form reflected the processes of development and change. So he himself worked from a quite different starting-point: his first-hand knowledge of living things. The life of any individual develops through a sequence of stages which – if not drastically interfered with – succeed one another in a constant, natural order. Even single organs go through their own phases of development and have parts to play in this life-cycle. Now we cannot lay down in the abstract what kinds of living creature there *must* be, and just how the phases of their life-cycles *must* succeed one another: we can discover such things only by reflecting on our observations, and distinguishing the essential features of the typical life-cycle from the accidents which affect the lives of individuals.

Thus Plato and Aristotle embarked on science with very different ideals and explanatory models. For Plato, the logical backbone of science was to be provided by geometry; for Aristotle, by classification. Both men incorporated into their systems the positive achievements of their predecessors but, working on such different principles, they ended by arranging them in very different patterns. And the contrast between their methods, and their conclusions, is particularly striking in the field of matter-theory.

Plato's Theory of Matter

Plato's account of the nature of material things in his dialogue, the *Timaeus*, falls into two sharply contrasted halves. The first part deals with the raw materials of the world, the second with the structure of organized beings – especially the human frame. He evidently saw no way of relating the forms of organs and organisms to the properties of homogeneous substances alone, and the explanations he gave in the two cases were of radically different kinds.

He presented the first part of his theory, not as axiomatic and self-evident, but only as 'a likely story'. One could certainly explain the properties of geometrical figures, and possibly the motions of the planets also, in mathematical terms alone; but the nature of the differences between solids, liquids, flames, and

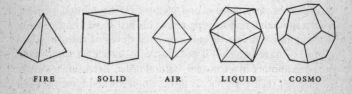

FIRE   SOLID   AIR   LIQUID   COSMO

vapours could be established only with the help of some intelligent guess-work. As a result, the theory of matter could give a *plausible* explanation of the differences between these substances, but that was all one was entitled to expect. Whereas the steps within a mathematical system were rigorous deductions, whose validity could be checked for certain, when we applied such systems to explain the properties of materials our results must inevitably remain tentative and provisional.

With this qualification, Plato set out to fit Empedokles' four elements into his own intellectual framework. His ambition was to match the familiar properties and transformations of these material substances to more fundamental – geometrical – principles. The stepping-stone he required was provided by Theaetetus – his discovery that there are, and can be, only five regular convex solids: the tetrahedron, the cube, the octahedron, dodecahedron, and icosahedron. Taking this theorem as his starting-point, Plato saw how a highly plausible account could be given of the characteristic properties of matter.

He argued that, since material substances were three-dimensional, the units of which they were composed must similarly be three-dimensional: i.e. solids of characteristically different shapes. And he proceeded to ask what set of relations in the eternal world of geometry could then be correlated with the properties of the four basic kinds of matter. He tried out the following hypothesis: Each of the four Empedoklean forms of matter is associated with one of the regular solids, the differences between them arising from the geometrical properties of their atoms. On this basis, the first problem was to decide which solid goes with which element.

Three of the solids have triangles for their faces, whereas the cube is bounded by squares; and this gave him his first clue.

To the solid state let us allot the cubical shape; for earth is the least mobile of the four kinds [of matter] and retains its shape best. This description calls for a shape having the most stable base, and . . . the square is certainly a more stable base than the triangle, both in parts and as a whole.

So our theory will maintain its plausibility if we allot this shape to the solid state; and – as to the others – give water the least mobile, fire the most mobile, and air the intermediate shape. Again, we may assign the smallest shape to fire, the largest to water and the middling one to air; or the sharpest-cornered one to fire, the next to air, the last to water.

Now, of the figures we have taken, the one with the fewest faces [tetrahedron] must be the most mobile, for in every direction its edges and corners are the sharpest, and it is also the lightest, being made up of the smallest number of unit-triangles. On all these counts, the octahedron stands second, and the icosahedron third. So we seem to have real [i.e. mathematical] grounds, as well as plausible guesswork, to justify choosing the pyramid from among the regular solids as the atom or seed of fire; the second figure [octahedron] as that of air; and the third [icosahedron] as that of water.

These unit-bodies must be thought of as being so minute that a single atom of any one form is too small to be visible to us, though a large number taken together form a mass which we can see. And, as for their numbers, motions, and other properties, we must assume that the Creator determined these in the most appropriate manner.

In this theory, Plato wove together separate threads from three earlier philosophers: the mathematics of Pythagoras, the atomism of Demokritos, and the four elements of Empedokles. As happens with the best scientific syntheses, the resulting theory transformed the components from which it started, and was intellectually more powerful than any of them. For these geometrical atoms differed from those of Demokritos in having a *limited* number of definite shapes, governed by precise mathematical theorems; and, furthermore, they were no longer immutable, but could change into one another in ways that could be related back to their geometrical compositions. As a result, Plato could envisage transmutations of a kind that Demokritos did not allow for, and so introduced a new, quantitative element into the analysis of material change.

In Plato's view these transformations were a direct consequence of the geometrical shapes of the ultimate units into which matter

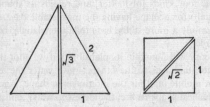

can be analysed. For the regular solids can all be built up from two simple triangles, and these plane figures – rather than the solids themselves – were the fundamental elements of his theory.

Anyone can recognize that earth, air, fire, and water are material bodies, and all body has volume. Further, a volume must be bounded by a surface, and any surface bounded by straight lines can be made up from triangles. Now, all triangles can be constructed from two basic triangles, each of which has one right angle, the other angles being acute. One of these two triangles, being isosceles, has base angles of 45°: the other has unequal sides, and so unequal base angles.

The first triangle he employed was the 'half-square', with angles of 90°, 45°, and 45° respectively. The other triangle now had to be identified.

There is only one right-angled triangle with equal [short] sides, but an endless number having unequal sides. If we are to make any progress from our first principles, we must choose the most suitable out of this innumerable collection. . . . For our own part, leaving the rest aside, let us postulate as the most appropriate of these triangles one particular sort – namely, the half-equilateral triangle [i.e. the triangle having angles of 90°, 60°, and 30°, two of which placed side by side form an equilateral triangle].

The reason for this choice is too long to tell at present; and if anyone should look into the matter and establish that our view is incorrect, he is very welcome to the credit for his discovery. So much, then, for the selection of our basic triangles, out of which are constructed the shapes of fire and the other substances – one of them isosceles [the half-square], the other having its shorter sides in the ratio $\sqrt{3}:1$ [the half-equilateral].

Now the atomic shapes corresponding to the four kinds of matter had to be constructed. Three of the regular solids can be formed from triangles of his second sort, while only one of them (the cube) is formed from half-squares. The pyramid (or tetrahedron), the octahedron, and the icosahedron, which have equilateral triangles as their faces, can all be made from half-equilateral triangles. By rearranging these triangles, it should in principle be possible to change matter from one form to another; and Plato specified two ways in which this might happen:

When liquid matter is broken up under the action of fire, or perhaps air, its parts may be recombined to form one atom of fire and two of air: while a single unit atom of air dissociates into fragments that can form two atoms of fire.

These 'reactions' correspond exactly to possible reshufflings of unit-triangles. Atoms of the liquid state had twenty faces (i.e. forty half-equilateral triangles), compared with eight faces (sixteen units) for aeriform matter, and four (eight units) in the case of fire. So, when liquid atoms were broken down into their units and these were reordered to form atoms of air and fire, each atom of liquid provided triangles for two of air and one of fire.

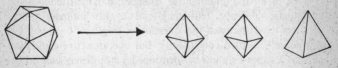

$$L \rightarrow 2A + F \ (40 = 2 \times 16 + 8).$$

Similarly, each atom of air could be converted to two of fire:
$$A \rightarrow 2F \ (16 = 2 \times 8).$$
But the triangles composing the cube are of a different shape from the others, so that solids could only be transformed into other solids.

Solid matter, on colliding with fire, is dissociated, on account of the sharpness of the fiery atoms, either into its invisible atoms or even further into its basic triangles: and it then drifts about within the surrounding mass of fire, air or water, until its constituent parts somewhere meet again and are combined and become earth once more; for they can never be transformed into any other sort of matter.

One effect of these transmutations was to produce an exchange of matter between the different parts of the cosmos:

For, while the greater part of each different kind is separated out to its own region on account of the cosmic motion, those parts which are at any moment changing their nature are sifted out and carried towards the region appropriate to their new form.

A water atom, being heavy, will run down to the sea; but the atoms of air and fire into which it divides will move in the opposite direction into the atmosphere and the heavens.

Up to this point, one of the five regular solids has been ignored – the dodecahedron, whose twelve faces are pentagons, and cannot simply be broken down into the two unit-triangles of Plato's theory. Since this last figure did not seem to correspond to any substance *within* the cosmos, Plato associated it with the boundary of the universe, each of the faces corresponding to one of the twelve principal constellations. (The close approximation of the dodecahedron to a sphere was well known to the Greeks, who made their footballs from pentagons of leather sewn together in sets of twelve.)

Why, of all the innumerable triangles, did Plato choose the half-square and the half-equilateral as his ultimate units? Scholars have discussed this question at length, and probably it can never be settled conclusively. But one attractive suggestion of Karl Popper's should be mentioned, since it may help to explain why Plato hesitated to claim more for the theory than he did. The arithmetical system of Pythagoras had run into difficulties over the discovery that $\sqrt{2}$ is an 'irrational' number (which can be expressed numerically only as the unending decimal $1\cdot414\ldots$) and this irrationality provided a strong motive for Plato to build his own theory on geometrical rather than arithmetical foundations. Now, if some of the ultimate units of matter were half-squares, that would provide a natural place for this number which had caused such intellectual heart-break, since the sides of the half-square are in the proportion $1:1:\sqrt{2}$. But the same difficulties which arose over $\sqrt{2}$ reappeared in the case of other irrational numbers, e.g. $\sqrt{3}$ ($1\cdot732\ldots$) and π ($3\cdot142\ldots$). By using the half-equilateral triangle as his other 'atomic shape', Plato found a place in his world-system for multiples of $\sqrt{3}$ also, since its sides are in the ratio $1:2:\sqrt{3}$. And perhaps he hoped to do even more – to find a place for π, and all other irrational numbers as well. The Greeks had no way of calculating the value of π exactly; and if one adds $\sqrt{2}$ to $\sqrt{3}$ the resulting number ($3\cdot146\ldots$) is very close to their best estimates. It was a daring speculation that *all* irrational numbers could be expressed as sums or multiples of $\sqrt{2}$ and $\sqrt{3}$; and Plato acknowledged that he could not prove it. In the end, it turned out to be wrong, but if it had proved well founded it could have been the heart of a dramatic union of mathematics with atomic theory.

What is the positive significance of Plato's theory of homogeneous material substances? Two things about it should be emphasized. First, he succeeded in showing that the views of earlier scientists could not only be reconciled, but could reinforce one another. What principles govern the shapes of the atoms, and how do these affect their properties? On these questions, Demokritos had been vague, but Plato – marrying atomism with geometry – could be more explicit. How, and why, do different forms of matter change into one another? Once again, Plato envisaged possibilities which his predecessors never foresaw. His theory might still be tentative – and certainly did not carry one to a point where craftsmen would have taken much notice of it. All the same, like a skilful chairman guiding the deliberations of an unruly committee, he ordered the rival views of earlier philosophers into a more comprehensive intellectual framework than had seemed possible.

So, around 350 B.C., we find ourselves for the first time with a mathematical atomism. In all its details, Plato's own theory has died a natural death. Yet its method – of starting from observed properties of matter, and conceiving a mathematical structure of invisible units to account for them – is one that the modern atomists were to revive. For Plato as for Newton, mathematical atomism provided the bricks from which the Creator constructed His universe. Plato supposed that at the Creation the precise 'numbers, motions, and other properties' of the atoms were settled by the Divine Architect 'in the most appropriate manner', so as to produce a truly harmonious world. And this view was to be echoed by Newton two thousand years later:

All these things being consider'd, it seems probable to me, that God in the Beginning form'd Matter in solid, massy, hard, impenetrable, movable Particles, of such Sizes and Figures, and with such other Properties, and in such Proportion to Space, as most conduced to the End for which he form'd them.

Yet, for all its scope, Plato's geometrical atomism did not provide him with a *fully* comprehensive theory of matter. The differences between wine and honey, flame and light, gold and water, might indeed depend on the figures of their constituent atoms alone. But in the structure and behaviour of living things he saw clear evidence of design, which could be understood only by going beyond matter and atoms to explanations at another level. The organs of the body conformed to a plan, which seemed to have been framed deliberately, as it were by an architect or landscape gardener.

Next the Higher Powers ... constructed throughout the body a network of conduits like irrigation channels in a garden with which it might be (so to speak) watered by the incoming fluids.

In Plato's system, then, the science of matter remained divided. About the raw materials of the world he was prepared to offer a geometrical theory, specifying the fundamental shapes of their atoms and the mechanisms by which they combined and separated. But he could give no such mechanical account of the *organization* of the world: that was something decreed at the original Creation.

All these raw materials, then, with the properties determined by their constitution, were employed by the Maker of the best and most beautiful of mortal creatures [i.e. the cosmos] when He created the universe as a self-sufficient and perfect divinity. He subordinated these materials to the *functions* which He Himself contrived for all His creatures.

All things in the universe worked together for good, and had been given forms appropriate to their functions. So the scientist must work out the nature of these 'forms' – the blueprints – according to which the objects of the natural world were made. For instance: the function of the gullet is to serve as a funnel, channelling the food from the mouth into the digestive tract. This being so, it is only reasonable that it should have the *form* of a funnel: only by being made with that form could it perform its allotted function. Indeed, one could even *define* the gullet as 'the funnel by which food passes from the mouth to the stomach'. Having said that much, Plato supposed, no further explanation of its structure need be sought. For everything essential to an understanding of the bodily organs would follow from similar specifications, as certainly as the properties of geometrical figures followed from their initial definitions.

Aristotle's Conception of Science

Plato's account of the natural world had made use of two contrasted patterns of thought: mathematical and functional. In Aristotle's system, functional explanation was given a greatly extended scope, and acquired a more fundamental importance. In this respect, Aristotle was perhaps a truer disciple of Socrates than Plato. For Socrates had not been much interested in mathematics. The foundation of his teaching was a conviction that even men have a function to perform, both in the state of which they are citizens and in the wider universe. A proper definition of 'man' would specify these functions, and so enable us to reason out the principles which should govern our conduct. And this idea was developed by Aristotle into a general principle of all science.

During the period after Plato's death, Aristotle left Athens for Macedonia and Asia Minor. There, working in his favourite field of marine biology, he tried to apply the principles that he had learned from Plato in Athens. But he soon despaired of accounting for the things he discovered in terms of abstract mathematical principles, and in the end was forced to conclude that his teacher's programme could not be realized. Plato, he argued, had been led astray by the analogy between mathematical ideals and other theoretical conceptions. One cannot simply *define* animals, organs, and bodily fluids, and explain their behaviour in the abstract – as one can do for geometrical figures. The understanding of living Nature calls for a detailed and profound study of the processes going on under our eyes. The quasi-mathematical study of 'eternal forms' can throw no light on the directed development by which organisms grow, mature, and die. 'Philosophy', Aristotle commented tartly, 'has turned into mathematics for present-day thinkers, despite their claim that mathematics is to be treated as a means to some other end.'

It is evidently not *shapes* that mark the different elementary substances off from one another. The most important distinctions between different bodies lie in the properties and functions and capacities which we recognize as characteristic of every natural creature. *These* are the things to which we must pay attention first.

There can be no doubt that Aristotle underestimated the possibilities of a mathematical science. Yet there is something true and important in his objections. If we preoccupy ourselves exclusively with the physical aspects of Nature, we may even today conclude that, when these have been mastered, the whole story will have been told. Yet this is rarely the case. Consider, for instance, colour : we can account for the formation of rainbows, the colours of different materials, and so on, using the theories of mathematical physics. Yet there is a whole side to the study of colour which optics and atomic physics leave untouched; and two important groups of questions at least can be answered only by looking in other directions. There are, in the first place, questions about the physiology of colour vision; and, in the second, psychological questions about colour sensations. So a complete account of any natural process must mention factors of several different kinds, and the material make-up of a body or the shapes of its constituent atoms represents only one of the relevant factors. Aristotle in fact distinguished *four* sorts of explanatory factor, all of which had legitimate places in science, and in later centuries these came to be known as his 'four causes'. The name is unfortunate, since nowadays we usually restrict the term 'cause' to one of his four types of factor alone: they would have been better called his 'four *be*causes' – since he was concerned to distinguish, not the different varieties of cause and effect, but rather the different senses in which the question 'Why?' can be asked in science.

Suppose, for instance, we build a fifty-foot statue from butter, to be displayed as an object-lesson in human frailty. We erect it in the cool of the night: calculating that next day, as the sun warms the butter, it will soften and the statue will collapse. In reply to the question 'Why did the statue collapse?' we could then give four different answers, whose relevance would depend on our precise interpretation of the question. We could refer to:

(i) The material constitution of the statue, or 'From what?' – 'It collapsed because it was made of butter.'

(ii) The form, essence, or 'What was it?' – 'It collapsed because it was an oversized statue.'

(iii) The precipitating cause or 'By what?' – 'It collapsed because the sun's warmth softened it.'

(iv) The end, or 'In aid of what?' – 'It collapsed as a portent to men.'

These four types of explanation are not necessarily rivals. Factors of all four types can frequently be cited without inconsistency. Indeed, apart from a few phenomena, such as eclipses, which have no function and so 'just happen', Aristotle thought that *all* natural events called for explanation in all four ways.

Of these four kinds of explanatory factor, Aristotle himself was predominantly interested in the second and the fourth, and his whole conception of science was built around them. The mechanical interactions between atoms were irrelevant to the problems which were his chief concern, and any attempt to discover universal elements composing all things whatever struck him as running too far ahead. The first task was *taxonomy*: to classify all the different things in the world. The second was *physiology*: to study the stages by which the individual comes to maturity, and the contributions made to this growth by the different parts of the body.

A satisfactory explanation would start by identifying the object of study as being (or being part of) an individual of a particular species – whose characteristic nature or form was known. Common observation revealed that living creatures of different kinds displayed quite different sets of capacities; and the 'form' would specify, among other things, the set of capacities (or *psyche*) with which mature members of the species were endowed. Most plants have only a fairly primitive psyche, comprising the capacities to grow and reproduce alone. Animals are endowed with powers of motion, vision, hearing, and touch, and have therefore a more complex psyche. Finally in the higher animals, such as man, powers of thought and reasoning also appear, for these forms of life possess a 'rational' psyche in addition to 'sensitive' and 'vegetative' ones.

Any particular structure or activity must now be related to the life-cycle of the individual in question: by showing that it was either a manifestation of the adult form, or a typical immature phase in which the adult was as yet only 'potential'. Taking the life-cycle as a whole, the adult state was the destination (or *telos*) in which both bodily structure and behaviour were at last fully realized. This was the goal of all development, both its conclusion and its fulfilment; and the central part which this notion of the telos played in Aristotle's work explains why his ideal of explanation is often labelled 'teleological'. The point at issue can be misleading, but it is important. The oak-tree is the telos of the acorn: but if one translates 'telos' as 'final cause', one may give the impression that the future somehow exerts a compulsion on the present – the acorn being obliged by some mysterious psychic force to turn into an oak-tree. Aristotle, however, was not concerned with hidden forces or psychic mechanisms: he was preoccupied, rather, with the *conditions* of development. The future oak-tree does not exert any moulding influence on the present acorn: but the existence of the acorn is an indispensable condition for the ultimate appearance of the adult oak-tree. A full account of the nature of an acorn must include this reference to the future. Only in later centuries, when Aristotle's ideas had been taken over by other philosophers, was the psyche transformed into an 'immaterial agency', forcibly directing the organism towards its telos.

Aristotle's Functional Matter-Theory

In his own particular fields of interest, Aristotle's intellectual methods served him well very and, if we too confine our attention to zoology and physiology, we find his way of thinking congenial and intelligible. But, when we follow him into the chemical field, his whole approach appears strange. During the last two hundred years, the mathematical and atomist approaches have succeeded so dramatically that Aristotle's physiological approach to matter-theory has been entirely displaced, and it is only by a conscious effort that we can set aside more recent ideas and see what he was trying to do.

Where Plato had treated earth, air, fire, and water as distinct types of material substance having atoms of different shapes, Aristotle treated them as species of a genus: instead of asking questions about the units from which matter is composed, he was concerned with the characteristic qualities marking off one substance from another. In this, he was simply applying his general method to the particular field of chemistry. For if animals can be classified in a natural system, why not substances equally? (Centuries later, Mendeleev was to do just that.) The only problem was to discover the *significant* properties of different substances, which can best be used as a basis of classification. Whereas, in the case of an animal, the most fundamental questions had been 'Does it have red blood?' and 'Are its young born alive or in eggs?', the corresponding questions about a material substance were 'Is it hot or cold?' and 'Is it wet or dry?' On these principles, substances fell naturally into four main groups: hot and dry, hot and moist, cold and moist, and cold and dry; and Aristotle at once identified these as corresponding to fiery, aeriform, liquid, and solid respectively.

Aristotle regarded heat and cold as 'active' qualities, whose function was to promote growth and decay, combination and separation; while moisture and dryness were 'passive'. But a theory of matter could not limit itself to classifying *forms*: it must also identify *functions*. This was easy enough when the substances concerned came from organisms, for secretions such as blood and chyle play identifiable parts in the working of the body. But it is far less easy to identify 'functions' for substances in general, and when Aristotle applied his physiological analogies in inanimate substances in detail, he was led into unavoidable ambiguities. He himself remarked on this difficulty in the case of vinegar. The unformed material was clearly water, which is turned into grape-juice by the vine. This grape-juice is in its turn an 'infantile' substance, which has to mature, and its proper nature is manifested only when it achieves the 'adult' form of wine. Yet, as Aristotle sees, if we are going to say that water or grape-juice is the 'embryonic' substance of wine, ought we not also to say that wine is the 'adolescent' substance of vinegar? Perhaps some of the potential qualities of wine are still concealed, being finally realized only when the wine has turned to vinegar. Yet, though he saw the difficulty, he had few qualms about his answer.

A living man is not potentially a corpse. Death and decay are not part of the proper development of a man, but an accident that overtakes him. The corpse is just a successor to the living body, not its fulfilment. So also with wine and vinegar: wine turns into vinegar, not by maturing further, but simply by going bad. Vinegar is, so to speak, the corpse of wine.

Although extending physiological modes of explanation to matter-theory in general gave rise to difficulties, the programme had its attractions. For the parallels between organic and inorganic processes are extensive and striking. The Greeks knew the similarity between combustion and respiration, and it is natural to ask: Why did Aristotle not draw our modern conclusion – namely, that the chemical processes going on inside animals are essentially similar to those in the inorganic world? The answer is: *he did* – but, having done so, he *interpreted* the conclusion in the reverse direction to ours. Instead of treating inorganic reactions as the fundamental model or 'paradigm', and going on to explain physiological processes in terms of these, he took *organic* development as his paradigm for explaining all material change: any parallels between organic and inorganic processes only served to reinforce his initial commitment to the physiological model.

While there was nothing mysterious about the ripening of crops or the growth of an infant, the action of heat outside living bodies was something greatly in need of explanation. He dealt with this particular problem by his theory of 'concoction'. Concoction was his term for the process by which heat caused bodies to ripen, cook, or otherwise mature.

Concoction, then, is the production of a mature form out of passive material by the action of a body's natural heat. For a thing becomes fully mature when it has been concocted. The process of maturation originates in the body's own heat, even though it may be assisted by outside agencies – e.g. digestion may be helped by taking hot baths and the like, but the principal cause remains the body's own heat. . . .

Ripening is a kind of concoction: this is the name we give to the concoction of the nutriment in fruit. Since concoction produces maturity, ripening is complete when the seeds in the fruit are capable of producing another fruit of the same kind. . . .

Roasting and boiling are of course artificial processes, but generally-similar processes occur in nature – for the changes that take place are similar, although we have no word for them. In this way human arts imitate nature: the digestion of food in the body, for instance, resembles boiling, being produced in a hot, moist medium by the action of bodily heat.

The consistency and apparent ease with which Aristotle applies his physiological model to the most far-fetched examples is almost exasperating. Yet what about the motion of heavenly bodies? This – surely – was an entirely non-functional process, devoid of anything resembling organic development, and governed by purely mechanical principles. Unfortunately, the very examples which in retrospect appear as fatal exceptions to theories often seemed to confirm what in our eyes they refute. So, while it is second nature for us to regard the heavenly bodies as inanimate, unthinking chunks of matter, the picture presented by Aristotle is very different.

The fact is that we are inclined to think of the stars as mere bodies or units, having a certain order about them but completely lifeless; whereas we ought to think of them as possessing both life and initiative.

What appears to us mere lifelessness, Aristotle interpreted as ultimate maturity: the divine cosmos and its celestial inhabitants 'enjoying without interruption the best and most independent life for the whole aeons of their existence'. Exempt from the changes and chances of our mortal earth, the heavenly bodies were able to continue in a state of maturity indefinitely, free from alteration and the accident of death.

Had the elements of the heavens been the same as the ordinary terrestrial elements, then, of course, some change would have been inevitable; and Aristotle used this to support one further conclusion – that the matter of the heavens must be of some different kind. Over and above the four terrestrial elements, there must therefore be a fifth, distinct type of matter, having an unchanging form or essence of its own. This was the 'quintessence', and everything composed of it shared its eternal unchangeability. Before long, the quintessence was destined to play an important part, not only in matter-theory, but in genetics and theology also.

The Inheritance of the Psyche

The problem which confronted Aristotle over the material constitution of the heavenly bodies was waiting for him, also, in his own field of biology. Given the belief that air, flame, water, and earth are the pure forms of raw matter, there is nothing to explain either the permanent stability of the heavenly bodies or the more limited stability of living organisms and species. At first Aristotle could afford to ignore the biological aspect of the problem. Having dismissed as irrelevant all attempts to relate material properties to invisible micro-structures, he could take the existence of plants, animals, and humans as a fundamental fact of nature and the very starting-point for science. Nature just was the totality of organized beings, each developing towards its own individual destination. Only at one point did he find himself in grave difficulty – over the problem of *heredity*.

In the case of the simpler organisms, the problem was not particularly acute. Aristotle envisaged the spontaneous generation of the lowest forms of life as a process which took place continually under the influence of heat, along the banks of rivers and in compost heaps. (There is a reference to this belief in Shakespeare's *Antony and Cleopatra*, during the drunken banquet:

Antony: Thus do they sir: they take the flow of the Nile
By certain scale, in the pyramid; they know
By the height, the lowness, or the mean, if dearth
Or foison follow. The higher Nilus swells,
The more it promises; as it ebbs, the seedsman
Upon the slime and ooze scatters his grain,
And shortly comes to harvest.

Lepidus: You've strange serpents there.

Antony: Ay, Lepidus.

Lepidus: Your serpent of Egypt is bred now of your mud by
the operation of your sun; so is your crocodile.)

But in the case of higher organisms the problem is inescapable. The resemblances between parents and offspring cry out for explanation; and, faced with this problem, Aristotle could no longer utilize the pattern of explanation – the individual's life-cycle – which up to this point had served him so well. For, clearly, you cannot give a full explanation of conception by relating it solely to the life-cycle of *either* the parent *or* the child. Given Aristotle's basic method of explanation, conception was – inevitably – a point of mystery; and, for once, he was compelled to consider questions about the material basis of life.

The material link between father and child is the semen; and how the father's capacities and potentialities – in a word, his psyche – can be transmitted to the offspring in a drop of liquid was a problem which Aristotle could no more escape than we. His belief that the form of the offspring is determined entirely by the paternal contribution, while the mother provides solely the matter of the infant, is neither here nor there: so long as the father's seed is responsible in part for its form and psyche, the problem of mechanism has to be faced. Once again, he did not believe that the whole answer lay in the four terrestrial elements, for these were bound up in his mind with change and decay. So ultimately he was forced to postulate a novel constituent material to account for the stability of living species. This was the pneuma; and he assumed that it was similar to the quintessence of his astrophysics.

The natural principle in the pneuma is analogous to the element of which the heavenly bodies are composed. Whereas terrestrial fire cannot generate animals, and we never find living things being formed in solid or liquid media through its action, solar heat and animal heat *are* capable of generating them. As well as the heat which is active in the semen, all other organic residua retain in them something capable of generating vital activities [e.g. spontaneous generation in compost heaps]. From these considerations it is evident that vital heat in animals is neither identical with, nor derived from, terrestrial fire.

The properties of the pneuma could be found out only by studying its effects. But it was evident from the start that it was complex, and varied from creature to creature:

Let us return to the material of the semen, which comes away from the male, containing in itself that which carries the principle of the psyche. This principle is of two kinds: one of these is not associated with matter, belonging as it does only to those animals which have something divine about them – viz. rational and intellectual capacities, which do not require bodily limbs and organs for their expression. The other is necessarily associated with matter.

This pneuma, 'inborn' with the new embryo, was present in the organism so long as it lived and, when the time came for a further generation, budded off part of itself. In this way, a material agency was provided to explain the chief facts of heredity: so the stability of the psyche could be preserved from one generation to another, and the constancy of the species would be guaranteed.

The hypothesis of the pneuma completed, and set the seal on, Aristotle's whole matter-theory. This can now be summarized as follows. (i) The raw materials of inanimate terrestrial objects are the four elements of Empedokles. (ii) The terrestrial elements have their own levels and, as a result of their natural motion, form a sequence of superimposed layers. (iii) Heavenly bodies are distinct from them, in their natural movement and in their unchanging appearance. The matter of the outer heavens is the 'fifth essence' or quintessence. (iv) Animate terrestrial bodies manifest different grades of psyche in their directed activities and coherent structures. (v) The activities of the psyche show themselves in the life-cycle of the individual organism, which can transmit to its offspring the capacity to repeat the same life-cycle. (vi) The form and the psyche are not themselves material.

They are, rather, the *patterns of structure and activity* characteristic of the species. (vii) However, there must be some material mechanism underlying heredity, and this presumably involves a higher-grade material – the pneuma – to 'carry' the psyche from one generation to the next. This material is closely associated, but not identical, with the natural warmth of all higher animals. (viii) There are several varieties of pneuma, corresponding to the different grades of psyche – vegetative, sensitive, and rational. (ix) Regarded as a raw material, the pneuma is closely analogous to the quintessence of the celestial bodies, which shares its power to stimulate the growth of organisms (and even minerals) on the earth.

Thus, rightly or wrongly, Aristotle's matter-theory and cosmology reacted on each other. In preserving the traditional divinity of the heavenly bodies, the final picture was conservative; and the theory of the pneuma eventually imported the notion of divinity into matter-theory also. For when the philosophical theories of Athens crossed the Mediterranean to Alexandria, to be transmuted by that omnivorous fancy which Lawrence Durrell describes in his *Alexandrian Quartet*, they became the intellectual justification both of alchemy and of a novel religious mysticism.

Between the execution of Socrates in 399 B.C. and Aristotle's death in 322, natural philosophy had become a great deal more systematic and methodical. Those philosophers who continued to work in Plato's intellectual tradition were bringing together the isolated discoveries of earlier mathematicians into a coherent scheme of 'axioms' and 'theorems'. Meanwhile, Aristotle had created almost single-handed a method and a tradition for the biological sciences, establishing the techniques of taxonomy and systematics, embryology and physiology. Unfortunately, though the two traditions were potential allies, they were still thought of as competitors, and were slanted from the outset in opposite directions. So we shall find that just as Plato forced all the phenomena of Nature into a mathematical or quasi-mathematical mould, Aristotle's successors in the Middle Ages compressed all experience – with a similar artificiality – into a physiological or quasi-physiological framework.

FURTHER READING AND REFERENCES

Plato's theories about the material world were one of the subjects of his dialogue, *Timaeus*, which is available in English with useful notes as:

F. M. Cornford, *Plato's Cosmology*, Kegan Paul, 1937

On the same subject, see also:

Paul Friedländer, *Plato, an Introduction*, ch. xiv, Routledge & Kegan Paul, 1958

The theory of the basic triangles is discussed in a paper by K. R. Popper in *British Journal for the Philosophy of Science*, Vol. III, and illustrated in the film *The God Within*.

Aristotle's attitude to science is discussed in the general introductions to his philosophy by A. E. Taylor and by J. H. Randall, Jr.

The original quotations from Aristotle discussed in this chapter come from the *Metaphysics*, *Meteorologica*, and *Generation of Animals*, which are available in the Loeb Classical Library, edited by H. Tredennick, H. P. D. (Sir Desmond) Lee, and A. L. Peck respectively. See also:

J. S. Needham, *A History of Embryology*, Cambridge University Press, 1934

d'Arcy Thompson, *Aristotle as a Biologist*, Clarendon Press, 1913

M. R. Cohen and I. Drabkin, *Source Book in Greek Science*, McGraw-Hill, 1948

5

The Breath of Life

In his story *The Man Who Weighed Souls*, André Maurois introduces us to a certain Dr James, who works at a London hospital. Like human beings in all ages, Dr James is much perplexed by the phenomenon of death. Hoping to discover what precisely happens at the moment when life is extinguished, he devises an ingenious apparatus: he attaches the mortuary slab to a delicate balance, so as to display the minutest changes of weight by the motion of a spot of light. Over it he erects a glass dome, which at its peak is constricted to a neck before opening up again into a globe. There is a tap in the neck so that the globe can be shut off from the dome and detached.

Dr James now arranges for patients who are at their last gasp to be transported to the mortuary slab a few moments earlier than is customary; he lowers the dome over the slab, opens the tap and waits. Each time the same thing happens: shortly after the moment of death the spot of light gives a kick – indicating a sudden, though barely perceptible, change in the weight of the newly-dead body. Dr James closes the tap, removes the globe and takes it away for study. The climax of the story comes when two young lovers are brought into the hospital, dying as the result of a suicide pact. In turn they breathe their last below his dome; but this time, instead of changing the globe, he leaves the tap open and detaches it only after they have both expired. And here follows the climax: when the globe is now irradiated, the contents glow with an unearthly beauty.

We do not need to have the point of this story explained to us, and that very fact is significant. The problems of life and death have perplexed man throughout the millennia of his existence and, among the early forms of speculation, one idea is almost universal. 'While there's breath, there's life,' we say; and ever since Old Testament days it has seemed that the breath we inhale and exhale must in some way be the agent or carrier of life itself –

a dollop of lifeless clay being transformed into a living being when the Divine Creator infuses the Breath of Life into its nostrils.

This picture of the living creature as the union of a brute, insensible matter with an all-pervading and sensitive (but invisible) life-breath has a persisting influence. In some parts of the world, when a man dies the window of his room will be opened so that his spirit, released from the mortal clay, may escape to the heavens. And however much we ourselves may dismiss the Breath of Life as being no more than a striking image, we cannot dismiss the problem which it was intended to solve. For, taken by themselves, the *raw* materials of living things do not grow, reproduce, feel or think; and some further explanation is needed of the mechanisms responsible for these capacities. At its widest, we have gone today only part way towards solving this problem, and we should sympathize with the first scientists who stated, faced, and tried to answer the profound and profoundly difficult questions in which it involves us.

The Stoic Theory of the Pneuma

Aristotle died in the year 322 B.C. By A.D. 100, the predominant centre of intellectual discussion had shifted to Alexandria. Between these dates lies a transitional period which is still not fully understood – a period of intellectual cross-currents. During the classical period at Athens, the philosophers – however theological their interests – were nevertheless rationalists. If their arguments led to results conforming with their religious predispositions, so much the better: indeed, many of them took it for granted that this would happen. Still, they were determined, so far as they were able, to follow an argument wherever it might lead them: they did not wish to force science into line with religion, nor to accept revelation or mystical insight as a substitute for arguments and evidence. By the later Alexandrian period, however, salvation had become paramount and men doubted whether, without the benefit of Divine Revelation, their perplexities about Nature and conduct could be resolved at all. Evidence and argument alone could not be relied on to lead to truth: even in scientific matters, understanding would be granted only to the pure in heart, whose state of mind was pleasing to God. The principle for which the classical Greek philosophers had fought – that men who made general assertions about the world must offer cogent arguments in support of their statements – had been abandoned.

In the intermediate period we find currents flowing in several different directions. Such men as Archimedes, Hipparchos, and Euclid retained the rational scientific ideals of the classical philosophers, and carried their analyses to new levels of refinement and sophistication. But alongside their work we find the beginnings of gnosticism – the claim that one can more certainly achieve a reliable knowledge of the truth by way of asceticism, purification, and mystical practices. Between these extremes lie two major schools of philosophers, whose teachings could be interpreted in alternative ways – either as rational systems of natural philsophy or with an eye to their religious significance. These two aspects were already present in the case of Epicurus, from whom atomism was as much a weapon against the terrors of contemporary religion as it was a detailed theory of Nature. And a similar double purpose is apparent in the world-system of the Stoics.

The beginnings of Stoicism date from around 300 B.C.: its doctrines developed for some five centuries, though without fundamentally changing their character, and, though largely eclipsed by neo-Platonism in Alexandria, Stoicism remained an important influence in Imperial Rome: the Emperor Marcus Aurelius himself was the leading Stoic philosopher of the late second century A.D. At the heart of the Stoic doctrine lay a conviction which was, in itself, highly favourable to the development of a systematic natural science. For, first and foremost, the Stoics believed in 'determinism'; there was nothing wilful about Nature, and everything happened according to law. The secret of human life was to fathom the general character of this universal order and to live in harmony with it. This conviction led certain of the Stoics to elaborate the scientific ideas inherited from their predecessors, but at the same time it reinforced them in beliefs which, to our eyes, appear superstitious. (Their belief in astrological divination, for instance, was justified by appealing to the harmony and interaction between celestial and terrestrial events.)

Before going any further we must state as simply as possible the fundamental scientific ideas which were incorporated into the Stoic world-system. For these have a significance, and a later history, quite independent of the Stoic religion which grew up around them. To our own generation, which is still to some extent under the spell of nineteenth-century atomism, the Stoic conceptions are comparatively unfamiliar; and, on that account alone, they may appear obscure and unintelligible unless we come to them step by step.

As our starting-point, we can take the existence of human beings. On the face of it, human beings are genuinely organized systems: men can think, feel, and argue, and their bodies are composed of numerous organs which are connected and interdependent. We habitually talk about human beings as *integral wholes*, in a way which implies that they have properties, and are capable of doing things, as complete individuals. They are intelligent or stupid, cheerful or glum, sick or in good health; and all these descriptions apply, not to one toe-nail, but to the whole functioning system we call the human being.

Now all this might be a sad misunderstanding – human beings perhaps do not really operate as organized wholes at all, and we have supposed that they do only through some kind of a misapprehension. Their appearance of being genuinely organized systems might be an illusion; and this, in effect, was what the Greek atomists implied. The human body was an unusually large conglomeration of atoms which, purely by chance, happened to stay interlocked for as much as sixty or seventy years until – again by chance – they fell apart. The only events in the world significant from a scientific point of view were those which took place at an invisible level: the collision, jamming, and tearing-apart of atoms.

Now this (argued the Stoics) could hardly be the whole story: not surprisingly, they preferred to start at the other end. There *are* genuinely organized systems in the world on several levels; and any comprehensive scientific system must be intellectually rich enough to find room for them. Such organized systems *do* have 'integral properties', which are not derived entirely from the properties of their various parts. (Whereas, for instance, a man's weight is the sum of the weights of his various organs, his glumness is *not* the sum of their respective glumnesses.) At once, the question arose: if these integral properties do not derive entirely from the properties of the tangible parts of the organism, from what do they derive? This question was of central importance to the Stoics.

Their answer should be taken in several steps. To begin with, they would reply: 'They derive, not from the solid and liquid materials which compose the human body, certainly; but rather, from something which is present in the human being through and through.' What is this something? 'This something we call the pneuma.' But to say no more than that is only to give the 'something' a name: what, then, is the pneuma like? 'Strictly speaking, we can discover what the pneuma is like only by studying the effects it produces. It is not itself one more observable organ of the human body, which can be scrutinized directly; it is a continuous, dynamic agency, responsible for maintaining the cohesion of the body; and since it is hypothetical, quite as much as the atoms, it can be described only by producing models and analogies.' (This reply may seem to evade the question, but it is in fact fair enough. The same answer has been given many times in the history of science, notably about Newton's *gravity* and Bichat's *vitality*.)

One such analogy might be the membrane forming the head of a drum. As we tighten a drum-head, the sound it gives out when struck rises in pitch, and this does not happen because the material ingredients of the drum-head have changed: the same solid parts are in fact present all the time. What alters is the tension in the head – that is, the manner in which the various parts are held together – and the different sounds emitted by the drum reflect the varying tensions of the head. Now tension is not itself an additional ingredient of the membrane, solid or liquid: it is a *state*, and this, rather than the ingredients, is what determines the musical properties of the drum. The pneuma likewise exists in various different states of tension or 'tones', and the different integral properties of any genuinely organized system similarly reflect the varying tones of the pneuma in question.

So far, we have indicated only the starting-point of the Stoic theory – the bare intellectual form of the doctrine they put forward. In some respects we can think of this as an extension of the Pythagorean theory of musical harmonies. The Pythagoreans knew how the sound emitted by a string depended on its length and tension, and they used this discovery to explain in a numerical manner the qualitative character of the sounds we hear. Once such 'mixed' explanations were admitted, the Stoics could see no reason to restrict them to sounds and strings. *All* aspects and properties of natural objects could now be associated with different tensions: not only two-dimensional ones – such as those on a drum-head – but also three-dimensional ones, wave-patterns formed throughout the whole volume of a material body by the active tension of the pneuma.

The analogy with a drum-head can also be extended to three dimensions. If you blow across the neck of a bottle, it will resonate at a definite pitch, depending on its size and shape. This happens because the sound-waves travelling to and fro across the bottle do so at a fixed speed, and will reinforce one another only when their wavelengths are an appropriate fraction of the length of the bottle. By exciting the air in the cavity of the bottle, you can store energy within it, in the form of *standing-waves*; and when you stop blowing this energy is dissipated as the resonance dies away. By 'overblowing', you can excite the air at a higher resonant frequency, and so alter the pattern of standing-waves and the pitch of the sound. With waves of pneuma substituted for waves of air, this was just the explanatory model the Stoics relied on to explain the different qualities of material bodies.

Several kinds of pneuma coexisted in any body: each controlled a different aspect of its behaviour, their wave-patterns being (so to speak) superimposed on one another, like coexisting sound-waves or light-waves. The 'cohesive pneuma' was responsible for the unity of a body, and for the fixed pattern of properties typical of its raw materials; the 'vital pneuma' gave it animation; while the third, 'rational pneuma', was present only in men and other thinking beings. In this way, the Stoics developed a strikingly novel picture of material things, different aspects of any individual creature being related to different underlying wave-patterns, and the possible states of the body to alternative tones of the appropriate pneuma.

But the discussion of the pneuma was never entirely confined to this high intellectual plane. From the outset the Stoics also thought of the pneuma in another way, as a special kind of material substance – an extremely tenuous, but none the less physical, agency spread continuously throughout an organism, like an intangible but elastic perspex, or a highly penetrative gas. They did so for several reasons. In the first place, like physicists in all ages, they believed that some genuine material agency must lie behind their abstract theoretical ideas. But they had two further reasons. If the pneuma was capable of producing physical effects at all (they agreed), it must itself have a material character. You cannot, for instance, blow up a balloon using abstractions alone: the fact that it expands when you puff into it is evidence that your breath – though invisible – is nevertheless material. But the changes produced in a balloon by the air we breathe are no more striking than those for which the pneuma was responsible – so the pneuma, it seemed, could hardly be less material than air. Furthermore: the pneuma theory also provided a natural explanation for one other striking contrast – between the tangible forms of matter (solid and liquid) and the intangible ones (fiery and aery). The material ingredients of the body were presumably solids and liquids, and these were customarily classed as 'passive' forms of matter: by comparison, the 'active' forms – fire and air – were intangible, tenuous, imponderable, and elusive. Completing their theory in an elegant way, the Stoics allotted to these forms of matter the active tasks of holding together inert materials in stable, functioning wholes, and concluded that the different sorts of pneuma were composed of varying blends of fire and air.

However, treating the pneuma as a material medium landed one in fresh difficulties. Firstly, it apparently spread not through empty space alone, but equally through ordinary material objects. This implied that several different forms of substance could be present in the same volume at the same time: one of them being solid or liquid, and the remainder, as many as three in the case of human beings, being ethereal. (The Stoics themselves, for instance Chrysippos, grasped this nettle without hesitation. When the ethereal pneuma held the solid parts of a body together in a coherent pattern, it did more than fill the gaps between them: it entered into a 'total union' with them.) Secondly, it was hard to imagine any material as tenuous as the pneuma also being cohesive and elastic enough to hold together the parts of an organism. But in the time of the Stoics the conception of a 'material substance' was not clear-cut, and the differences between fire and breath, life and air, were not understood. So long as this remained so – that is, until the eighteenth century A.D. – this objection to the theory could not be pressed to a conclusion.

Armed with this general theory, the Stoics could attack the problems of physiology in a more comprehensive way than ever before. Aristotle had introduced the pneuma with the restricted task of explaining heredity. Yet, if the elements of Empedokles were too disorganized to carry the psyche at the moment of insemination, they presumably remained unsuitable for this task throughout the whole life of the organism. Some physical agency was required as the material basis of the psyche at *all* times; and, since the psyche itself could hardly act on the bodily frame except in a direct physical manner, the Stoics drew the natural conclusion – that the psyche and the pneuma were simply two aspects of the same thing. Thus, psyche and pneuma became interchangeable terms, which referred equally to a pattern of observable characters and to the hypothetical medium presumed to underlie it.

This same intellectual step was repeated – all the way along the scale which extended from simple inanimate matter to the whole cosmos – to account for every variety of organization and order. At one end, the Stoics drew religious conclusions, which will concern us in the next section. At the other, they recognized and tackled questions in matter-theory which have come to the fore again only in the twentieth century. Consider, for instance, the question: why do the chemical substances existing in the world have fixed constitutions? Why does iron (say) always display the same combination of qualities and properties; and why do we find only a limited range of metals in Nature, instead of substances with every conceivable – and even changing – combinations of density, ductility, tensile strength, colour, and melting-point? Nineteenth-century physicists and chemists never faced these questions. They treated the ninety-two chemical elements as distinct species – as though created by God in fixed kinds, with permanent combinations of properties. Yet the stable patterns of physical properties in the inorganic world (corresponding to different 'tensions' in the stoic 'cohesive pneuma') can no more be taken for granted than the organization of living things, and twentieth-century science has an explanation for them. Significantly enough this has to come, not from chemical atomism, but from the novel theories of quantum mechanics, in which the idea of wave-patterns is once again used to account for the properties of matter.

Stoic Cosmology and Religion

To understand the religious aspects of Stoicism, one must see how the idea of pneuma fitted into the wider framework of their cosmology. For it embraced the whole universe – heavens and earth, Gods and men, body and soul, metals and stones. Once again we must follow out an argument in successive steps.

The first step runs as follows. Every ordered system is the manifestation of a psyche, and every psyche is carried by a pneuma, which holds the parts of the system in their order. The cosmos is an ordered system, in which all things are interlinked. *Ergo*, the universe itself must have a psyche; and this 'World-Soul' must be carried by a universal pneuma, which binds all the objects of heaven and earth in a common destiny. Naturally enough, the Stoics regarded this universal, omnipresent pneuma as belonging to the highest grade of all: it was the ultimate source from which every lesser, localized body drew its individual pneuma and many of them actually identified it with the Deity.

One might have thought that this last doctrine, which treated God himself as a material medium, would have made Stoicism obnoxious to Christian theologians. Yet in many respects the system was congenial to them. First and foremost, it was a mono-theistic view, in a world which was still predominantly poly-theistic: it transformed the personified natural powers of Greek popular religion into so many aspects of an all-embracing agency – the interdependent parts of a single cosmic fabric. Furthermore, the Stoics foreshadowed the Christian doctrine of a Divine Providence, since their 'cosmic organism' was a system of per-fectly co-ordinated organs, ordered in such a way as to operate for the best. Starting as they did from this conception, the medical theories of Galen readily found a place in the intellectual frame-work of early Christianity.

The argument now continues. The pneuma is a compound of fire and air, and these are the two active, celestial forms of mat-ter; the various grades of pneuma differ, presumably, in the ratio of fire to air in their respective constitutions. A higher-grade pneuma contained a larger fraction of fire and a smaller one of air, and the highest grade of all was the pure intellectual pneuma: this could survive the death of the body, and its substance was most like that of the outer heavens.

So the Stoics rejected any *absolute* distinction between the unchanging, super-lunary heavens and the mortal, sub-lunary earth. They believed that similar agencies operated in all parts of the universe, linking heaven and earth in a single causal network. Far from the matter of the heavens being a unique 'quintessence', it was identical with the highest grade of terrestrial pneuma, and consisted almost purely of fire. Thus, the upper regions were composed of the two creative elements; and the 'change and decay' of the terrestrial world were due only to the abundance of the passive elements, earth and water. The difference between the two realms was accordingly only a matter of degree; and even the markings on the surface of the moon could be explained by terrestrial analogies:

The moon consists wholly of a mixture of air with a soft fire ... the appearance [of a face in the moon] comes from a blackening of the air, as when ripples run across the surface of the sea in the middle of a dead calm.

The last step in the argument united the individual human with the cosmos. All life comes from the World-Soul, and eventually returns to it. Where, in Aristotle, the soul had no real existence apart from an organized body (since the psyche was just the individual's integrated pattern of activity) the Stoics by contrast treated the soul as a separable entity – a tenuous substance, which could lead an independent existence. Having entered the individual at conception, the pneuma remained there throughout his life, sustaining itself on draughts of warm air from the surrounding atmosphere. At death, respiration ceased and the pneuma, which alone could prevent decay, departed from the body. Finding their own natural levels, the corpse sank down to the earth, while the fiery vapour of the soul sped freely upwards to the sky. Thus the pneuma, escaping from the prison of the body, was free to rejoin the celestial reservoir from which it had originally sprung.

The Ruler of the Cosmos is fiery and hot by nature, the Deity and the very Creator being a physical agency identical with the powers in fire.

Some of them even predicted an apocalypse – a destruction of the whole world, when the overmastering fire would consume all things in one great conflagration. Afterwards, when the fire quieted down, a new cycle of creation would begin, with a fresh 'separating-out' of the material elements. Each phase in the history of the cosmos began in a state of undiluted fieriness, and ended with a return to the same condition; within each phase, the four elements were first created, shaping themselves into material objects under the influence of the active energy; but, as the cycle approached its end, the balance between fire and the other elements tilted once again, and the very material elements themselves were consumed in a purifying conflagration.

Stoic ideas undoubtedly helped to rehabilitate the ancient 'astral religions', which had long been established in Babylon and Egypt. With the rise of Alexandria, it was this aspect of Stoicism which flourished most readily. For there the claims of astrology had long been accepted without question, and Oriental religion had a prestige at least equal to that of Greek philosophy. From that day to this, in the countries of the Middle East, the conviction has survived that men's fates are intimately bound up with the aspect of the heavens:

How dark it is tonight [says Leila in Lawrence Durrell's Alexandrian novel, *Mountolive*]. I can see only one star; that means mist. Did you know that in Islam every man has his own star which appears when he is born and goes out when he dies? Perhaps that is your star, David Mountolive.

Or yours?

It is too bright for mine; they pale, you know, as one gets older. Mine must be quite pale, past middle age by now, and when you leave us it will become paler still.

The Scientific Legacy of the Stoics

Away from Hellenistic Alexandria – a city rivalled only by Los Angeles in the variety and eccentricity of its religious sects – the scientific side of the Stoic world-picture remained more influential. Until the revival of atomism around A.D. 1600, much of the dominant intellectual tradition, in matter-theory and in medicine alike, can in fact be traced back to the doctrines examined in this chapter. The key word is 'spirits' – the Latin translation of the Greek word *pneuma* being *spiritus* – and as late as the seventeenth century 'spirits' of many different kinds still haunted the theoretical debates in chemistry and physiology.

In the physiological story the most influential figure was Galen, who came from Pergamon to Rome in the second century A.D. and was personal physician to the Emperor Marcus Aurelius. Galen's theories were based on two central ideas, both of them derived from Aristotle by way of the Stoics. One was the belief that the structures of bodily organs are perfectly adapted to their functions, and must be explained in terms of them. (For this, see the note at the end of this chapter.) The other was the pneuma.

In his hands, this notion acquired a more precise and definite physiological role. According to him, two varieties of pneuma sustained the characteristic activities of our bodies, and in due course these became best known from their Latin names, as the 'vital spirits' and the 'animal spirits'. The two agencies were located in the two interpenetrating networks of organs which play so large a part in the operation of the body: the nervous system and the blood-vessels. The functions of these two systems had been studied to some extent in earlier centuries, but Galen brought the results of his predecessors together, and extended them. He cut the spinal cords of animals at various levels, and observed the effects, he established the relations between the blood-vessels and the nerves, and he finally proved that the control of psychic functions was localized in the brain.

With these demonstrations behind him, he distinguished the three primary needs of the bodily tissues – food, breath, and 'nervous stimuli' – and traced the channels by which these were supplied. The continuance of life, as everyone knew, depended upon an animal inhaling some tenuous matter from the surrounding environment: this material, with which the blood became charged in the lungs, Galen called the vital pneuma (or 'vital spirits'). If breathing were forcibly prevented, death would follow quickly, so it was natural to suppose that these vital spirits were drawn from the external reservoir of life – the Stoic World-Soul. The nervous system was equally essential for life. He showed that the cranial nerves, which lead to and from the brain, control the higher sensory and motor activities, whereas the autonomic or sympathetic nervous system is connected with the brain only indirectly. Sensation and deliberate action are maintained only so long as the necessary cranial nerves are intact; and even these functions can be interrupted by stopping the flow of blood to the brain. So the physical agency responsible for these activities must be nourished by the blood, centred in the brain, and carried to and from it through the cranial nerves. This second agency he called the psychic pneuma (or 'animal spirits').

About nutrition, Galen's views were similar to our own, though of course lacking the biochemical detail discovered since 1840. Food was broken down in the digestive system, where the useful part was 'concocted' and absorbed into the blood, leaving the waste products behind. The nutrients were carried from the liver by the bloodstream, some of them being deposited in the tissues 'like silt laid down by a flood tide', while the rest were carried on and returned to the liver again. Galen himself did not regard the solid and liquid nutrients as varieties of pneuma or 'spirits'; they were not 'active' elements in the body, but only 'passive' ones – its raw materials – and they played a part in the life of the body only through the activity of the genuine 'spirits', vital and animal. Only later did the Islamic physicians adopt the term 'natural spirits' as a name for these nutrients: this step perhaps made physiological theory appear more symmetrical, but it did so only at the cost of obscuring the original significance of the pneuma.

The End of an Era

Before leaving Rome and the Stoics for Alexandria and the alchemists, let us take stock. At the beginning of our present enquiry, we posed three questions. The first of these concerned the ways in which men distinguished between the animate and the inanimate. By the beginning of our era, the systematic zoology of Aristotle and Theophrastus, together with the medical tradition of Hippokrates and his followers, had established well enough the special character of organic beings. Whereas men recognized that an eclipse was a merely physical process – a 'co-incidence' – the processes going on in living things had specific functions. And it was in their respective degrees of 'organization', and the functional character of living processes, that the crucial differences between living and non-living things lay. At a 'chemical' level, on the other hand, the Greeks saw *no* absolute distinction between the raw materials of animate and inanimate things, or even between the processes going on within them. Galen himself, in fact, pointed out the parallel between respiration and combustion:

> It is common knowledge that flames, as much as living things, are swiftly extinguished when deprived of air. If a doctor's cupping-glass or some other narrow or concave vessel is placed over the flame so as to prevent the access of air, it is quickly snuffed out.
>
> Now if we could find out why flames are extinguished in these cases, we should perhaps discover how it is that respiration helps to promote animal heat.

Our second question was, how did men in each epoch think about the relation of structure to function? Plato had explained the properties of homogeneous substances by the structures of their minute atomic units, but when he discussed the human frame he anticipated Aristotle and Galen, reversing the procedure and explaining bodily structures by the functions they performed. The Stoic theories blurred the distinction between functional questions and structural ones, by identifying the pneuma and the psyche: faced with the question whether one should account for structure in terms of function or vice versa, the Stoics would probably have replied: 'What is the difference? The pneuma and the psyche are the same thing. If a functional agency is to operate in the body, it must play some part in its structure, so the two terms of the distinction are no more than two faces of a single coin.' In Galen, finally, the emphasis is once again on function. In his hands even the theory of the pneuma lost some of its ambiguity: vital and animal spirits were simply two more material ingredients in the complex framework of the body, and their properties – like those of any other organ – had to be explained in terms of their functions.

Finally, as our third index, we must look at the opposition between atomistic and continuum views. During the three hundred years following the death of Aristotle, this contrast was stated more sharply and clearly than ever before. Epicurus and his followers would admit into their natural philosophy only atoms and the void. Impact and contact were the fundamental processes by which all changes were brought about: other forces

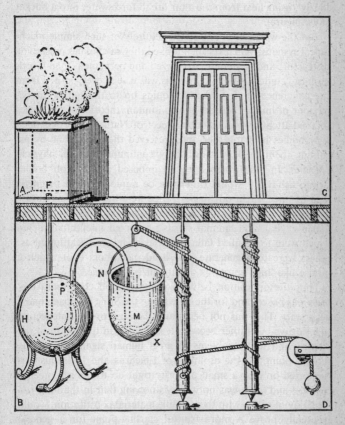

were foreign to their system, and crept into their explanations only inadvertently. Applied to simple physical phenomena, involving mechanical forces only, the resulting theory had great attractions: it could be applied easily and consistently, for instance in hydraulics and the study of air. Hero of Alexandria, in his best-seller on the subject, cited the compressibility of air as evidence of its atomic nature, and went on to propose a series of ingenious machines, operated by air, water, or steam-power: these were designed to flap the wings of a model bird, to rotate a jet-propelled ball, or to open the doors of a temple 'miraculously', using heat from the altar fire to force water into a bucket (M in figure).

But the world does not consist entirely of such simple mechanical systems. Wherever men looked they saw bodies preserving a structure and form more organized and permanent than Greek atomism could easily explain. This was true at every level – from the coherence of the simplest liquids up to the intelligent behaviour of human beings. The continuum theories of the Stoics focused attention on this other aspect of Nature: they explained how bodies held together and preserved their functions by assuming them to be permeated by continuous, active, physical agencies. In part, these agencies imposed patterns on bodies whose behaviour would otherwise be random – as a magnetic field of force might do: in part, they were thought of as diffuse tenuous materials like the nineteenth-century ether. Some, like Galen's 'vital' and 'animal spirits', occupied intellectual niches which were to be filled later by gases or by electrical impulses: others were to degenerate into dead metaphors – of which a phrase like 'high spirits' is one fossilized example.

Thus the opposition between atomistic and continuum theories was posed, and for the time being the Stoic approach had a head start. This was not necessarily because of any intellectual superiority; but rather because it kept man in the centre of the picture, and took problems of great human significance as its starting-point. So the atomism of Epicurus and Lucretius was supported only by a small minority right up to the seventeenth century; and there was no way of knowing that in the long run the study of gases, with their simple material constitution, would eventually prove a more fruitful starting-point for a general theory of matter.

The theories of material substance passed down from classical antiquity to medieval Europe were accordingly dominated by two ideas: first, by Aristotle's conviction that every significant natural process is a kind of development – so that *all* matter is engaged in a process of self-realization and perfection comparable to that of living organisms; secondly, by the Stoic pneuma or spirits, which acted as the material agent of this development. Taken together, these two ideas turned matter-theory away from questions of structure and mechanism, and towards questions of function and development; and this was the direction in which most speculation proceeded for the next fifteen hundred years. A few philosophers carried on the pure tradition of Plato, and kept fresh the geometrical atomism expounded in his *Timaeus*. More of them, however, concentrated on the detailed problems which had arisen in the course of Aristotle's discussions of matter. Others, influenced by theology, identified the pneuma in things with their 'soul', and interpreted all natural processes in animistic terms. Finally, others again married the physiological models of the Athenian philosophers with the practical experience of the Alexandrian craftsmen – and so produced the system of ideas and techniques we know as alchemy. The results of this first marriage between intellect and craft will be our subject in the next chapter.

NOTE: GALEN DEMONSTRATES THE FUNCTION OF THE KIDNEY

Galen's 'principle of perfection' governed his method of enquiry, and shaped his ideal of scientific explanation. 'The forethought and art shown by Nature in relation to animals', he taught, ensures that all bodily organs function in every detail as well as they possibly can. If we are to explain the structure and *modus operandi* of any part, we must discover what it is good for – its *use*: only then shall we fully understand it. We believe nowadays that this principle is sound only with limitations: the human spine, for instance, is imperfectly adapted to the stresses imposed on it since our ancestors adopted an erect posture. Yet, in Galen's own time, this 'teleological' principle was of great value, serving as an indispensable guide to the intellect in both anatomy and physiology. Guided by his faith in the efficacy of the bodily organs, Galen conducted many original experiments, dissections and vivisections, some of which – like Harvey's later – are masterly examples of experimental medicine. In this way he analysed in

117

detail the forms of the principal bodily organs and their contributions to the living process.

The following passage comes from Galen's treatise *On the Natural Faculties*. He asserts that the ureter is a one-way passage which carries urine from the kidneys to the bladder but not in the reverse direction. (This view was disputed by certain followers of Asclepiades, who had tried to apply atomistic and mechanistic doctrines to medicine.) As evidence for his view he quotes the results of an experimental vivisection.

Those who are slaves to dogma do not merely lack all sound knowledge: they will not even stop to learn. Instead of being prepared to listen (as they ought) to the reason why liquid can enter the bladder through the ureters, but cannot return along the same channels – instead of admiring Nature's artistic skill – they refuse to learn. They even go so far as to scoff, maintaining that the kidneys, and many other organs also, have been made by Nature *for no purpose*! Some of them, who had agreed to be shown how the ureters come from the kidneys and are implanted in the bladder, even had the audacity to say that these also had no purpose; while others said that they were spermatic ducts, and that this was the reason why they were inserted into the neck of the bladder rather than into its cavity.

When we had gone on to show them how the *real* spermatic ducts enter the neck of the bladder lower down than the ureters, we supposed that now at least, even if not before, we should wean them from their mistaken suppositions and convert them at once to the opposite view. But they had the presumption to dispute even this: it was no wonder (they said) that the semen remained longer in the latter ducts, for these are more constricted, or that it flowed quickly down the ducts from the kidneys which are well dilated.

We were accordingly compelled to show them clearly, in a living animal, urine passing out through the ureters into the bladder; though we scarcely hoped to put an end to their nonsensical talk, even in this way. The method of demonstration is as follows. First, one must divide the peritoneum in front of the ureters and close these with ligatures: next, having bandaged up the animal, let him go – for he will not continue to urinate otherwise. Subsequently, one loosens the external bandages, to show that the bladder is empty, while the ureters are quite full and distended – in fact, almost on the point of rupturing; when the ligatures are removed, one can plainly see the bladder filling with urine.

After this has been clearly demonstrated, and before the animal urinates again, one must tie a ligature round its penis and then squeeze the bladder all over: still nothing will pass back through the ureters into the kidneys. Evidently, then, the ureters are prevented, not only in a dead animal but equally in a living one, from receiving back urine out of the bladder. When these observations have been made, one next loosens the ligature from the animal's penis and allows it to urinate, then ligatures one of the ureters again, leaving the other free to discharge into the bladder. Then, when some time has elapsed, one can demonstrate plainly that the ligatured ureter is full and distended on the side towards the kidney, while the other – from which the ligature had been removed – is flaccid, having filled the bladder with urine. . . .

Now, if anyone will only test this on an animal for himself I believe that he will condemn the rashness of Asclepiades; and if he recognizes also why nothing flows back from the bladder into the ureters, I believe that this will convince him also of the forethought and art shown by Nature in relation to animals.

These results appeared to Galen to demonstrate that the kidney and bladder *conform to a design*. Certainly he succeeded in showing that the urino-genital system of mammals displays a regular anatomical pattern, and that this pattern is functional – contributing in a highly effective way to the elimination of urine from the body. The question is, whether adding 'So Nature must have made them that way for a purpose', was anything more than a *façon de parler*.

FURTHER READING AND REFERENCES

Few recent studies exist of the Stoic theories of Nature. The outstanding and indispensable book is:

S. Samburksy: *The Physics of the Stoics*, Routledge & Kegan Paul, 1959

On the wider aspects of religion and philosophy in the Stoic and Epicurean period, see:

A. J. Festugière: *Epicurus and his Gods*, Blackwell, 1955

L. Bréhier: *Chrysippe*, Alcan, Paris, 1910

The chief work of Galen to be consulted is his treatise *On the Natural Faculties*, edited for the Loeb Classical Library by A. J. Brock. See also *Source Book in Greek Science*, as before, and the papers by Donald Fleming in *Isis* (1955).

6

The Redemption of Matter

ALCHEMY has too often been given summary justice – dismissed as unworthy of prolonged attention, and scorned the more for being subtle and sophisticated. Men who took for granted the truth of nineteenth-century atomism and the impossibility of transmutation saw in alchemy a lamentable series of errors justified by impenetrable mumbo-jumbo; while its association with religious beliefs of a kind they despised only confirmed their original prejudices. Taking refuge in laughter, they echoed Chaucer's worldly mockery, ridiculing it as a waste of time and money:

> This cursed craft who so wil exercise,
> He shal no good have that may him suffise:
> For al the good he spendeth thereaboute.
> He lose shal, thereof I have no doute.

(Chaucer, one suspects, would have tarred much twentieth-century research with the same brush.) In this way the alchemists could quickly be disposed of as scoundrels, dupes, charlatans, or fools, and their pretended science written off as a bogus parade of verbiage.

To take this particular short cut is, however, not only philistine and unjust, but a serious intellectual blunder; and it is a course we cannot afford to take here. For, if we did, we should pull down the curtain on matter-theory just when men were first attempting to unite natural philosophy with the craft tradition; and we should then snap it up again, around 1600, to reveal the actors on our intellectual stage right in the middle of a scene – in postures which we had disqualified ourselves from understanding. For alchemy was, in fact, a natural and intelligible offspring, bred by Greek philosophy out of Middle-Eastern technology. It provided a direction, an incentive and a terminology for centuries of work in metallurgy and the chemical arts. It conceived, in some form or other, much of the chemical apparatus we know today. And, most important of all, the problems it left unsolved helped to shape the intellectual environment in which seventeenth-century scientists had to work.

The Transition to Alexandria

In all branches of science and philosophy there is a significant change of tone, when the focus shifts from the dry and temperate light of Athens and her intellectual dependencies to the cosmopolitan and iridescent splendours of Hellenistic Alexandria. The difference is plain enough in astronomy and mathematics, where one can contrast the elegant proofs devised by Archimedes of Syracuse (c. 225 B.C.) or the honest perplexity of Hipparchos of Rhodes (c. 125 B.C.) with the more laboured ingenuities of Ptolemy's *Almagest* and *Tetrabiblos*. It is even more striking if one looks instead at ideas about matter: its constitution, purification, transformation, and ultimate destiny. Indeed, the very factors which restored astrology to its former prestige and influence stimulated a new and intense interest in the processes and techniques of chemistry. One man's meat is another man's poison: astrophysics was hampered, speculation about matter encouraged.

What were the operative influences? Some of them were rather general, arising out of historical and social differences between Athens and Alexandria. Such factors as these cannot, of course, shape novel ideas directly; but they can change the focus of men's attention, and in Alexandria they did just that. By diverting men's preoccupations, they encouraged a demand that philosophy should produce not only intellectual insight, but also spiritual salvation. So problems which had never impressed the Athenian philosophers as of great significance now occupied the centre of the stage.

These general influences sprang from the amalgam of ancient and modern, flux and tradition, with which Alexandria was endowed by history and by birth. The circumstances of its founding gave it much of the character of present-day New York. But, unlike New York, it inherited and assimilated strong local traditions; and these, even in 300 B.C., were already more ancient than those of our own so-called Eternal City – present-day Rome.

By comparison with the inhabitants of Alexandria, the classical Greeks were a homogeneous group, with a common language and traditions and a short collective memory. The distinctively pre-Greek elements in Cretan and Mycenaean civilization left few conscious marks on culture and beliefs of classical times: the earliest historical event with a permanent place even in the legends of the Greeks was the Trojan war, which had taken place as recently as 1250 B.C. Yet by that time the settled and recorded life of the Egyptian kingdom had certainly lasted for more than two thousand years. (When Hecateus of Miletos visited the temple at Thebes about 500 B.C., the Egyptian guides deflated his national pride by showing him three hundred and forty-five statues commemorating successive high priests, each of whom had reputedly been the son of the one before.)

In its population, Alexandria was as different from Athens as New York is from London. Greek of a sort was the official language until the Roman conquest in the time of Cleopatra, and it remained the medium of academic discussion as late as A.D. 500; but the people using the language were frequently not Greek at all, either in racial origin or in background. There were, of course, plenty of Greeks: some descended from Alexander's army of occupation, others from the merchants and traders who settled in this great new commercial port. But, as in New York, there was a large Jewish community, which played a notable part in the intellectual life of the city; and there were also Berbers and Libyans, Syrians and Mesopotamians, and Nubians from present-day Sudan, in addition to the indigenous Egyptians or Copts. (The great Arab invasions had not yet taken place.) These varied peoples share no common traditions, and practised a bewildering variety of religions. Furthermore, there was much coming and going between Alexandria and the cities with which it traded – not only with Rome and the other Mediterranean cities, but also with the countries of the East which supplied the luxury markets of the Roman Empire with silks, dyes, and spices. Throughout the Imperial period, in fact, Rome suffered from an adverse balance of payments: there was a continual eastward flow of gold and silver (*librae, solidi,* and *denarii,* the original £ s. d.). Most of this passed through Alexandria and much of it stayed there.

In an environment so different from Athens the position of

scholars and the character of intellectual life were inevitably changed. In Athens scholars and scientists found their pupils among the sons of leading families, and it was quite easy for them to take up the detached and theoretical attitude recommended by Plato and Aristotle. They were free to concentrate on intellectual problems for their own sakes, without particular regard to the demands of commerce or the scruples of religion. In Alexandria things were very different. The rich merchants and traders of the delta, like the meat-packers and automobile-kings of the U.S.A., were happy enough to patronize the arts and scholarship, provided they were presented in a way which meant something to them; but the sons of wealthy and powerful families themselves were less often drawn into the disinterested pursuit of learning.

What sorts of knowledge caught the interest of patrons? Curiously enough, *not* mechanical inventions yielding an immediate financial return. Even so simple a device as the horse-collar, which permits draught-animals to exert their full strength without strangling themselves, came into use in Europe only centuries later. It seems that the reserves of unskilled human strength were so great that people gave little thought to labour-saving gadgets. So practical and intellectual skills found a profitable outlet in other directions: in preparing and imitating precious metals and other luxuries, and in refining the spiritual techniques for personal salvation. In such a society, the atomists found themselves with little to 'sell': they had an advantage only in the realm of hydraulics, and Hero's more perversely ingenious designs for water-powered singing birds may have been intended for the dining-tables of status-seekers. On the other hand, there was an obvious future for any intellectual movement which, at one and the same time, met the demand for religious teaching and consumer goods alike.

The difficulties which plagued astrophysics in the period between Aristotle and Ptolemy themselves helped to redirect men's speculations. Since the Greek philosophers had apparently failed in their attempt to emancipate astronomy from mythology, and to submit even the Gods themselves (i.e. the stars in their courses) to rational scrutiny, older Middle-Eastern traditions could keep their long-standing ascendancy in Egypt despite repeated injections of Greek thought. Within the limited circles of the Museum and Library, individual scholars at Alexandria remained faithful to the rational ideals of Greek philosophy. But out in the busy streets and rich suburbs the public at large looked for something with a more powerful appeal, something it could feel upon its pulse.

One last sociological factor must be mentioned. The Eastern religions had always had a certain vogue at Athens and a social influence comparable to that of Freemasonry, as well as a more direct intellectual influence upon the teachings of Pythagoras and Plato; but the official religion of the Athenian Establishment was the cult of the Olympian deities, and as time went on this was taken less and less seriously. In Egypt religious traditions had to be treated with more circumspection, not only because they were so much stronger but also because the clergy had a monopoly of learning. In the Nile valley as in Mesopotamia, the clergy had served for many hundreds of years both as the religious priest-hood and as the literate minority – they were the 'clerks' as well as the 'clerics'. Metallurgy, astronomy, astrology, medicine, flood-prediction: all these were fostered and developed in the shadow of, and sometimes actually inside, the Temples. And, significantly, the preface to the most famous collection of al-chemical recipes, *On Natural and Secret Things* (originating about 200 B.C.), claimed that it had been found in 'the Temple' – apparently as a guarantee of authenticity.

So began that alliance between religion and technology which makes alchemy so mysterious – and even repellent – to the modern reader. Yet, in seeing here an unnatural union, we are ourselves in danger of one more anachronism: reading back into the Alexandrian way of life distinctions which have won general acceptance only more recently. Until our modern period, only a handful among all the thinkers of Europe and Western Asia – the intellectuals of classical Greece and Rome – had ever dis-tinguished sharply between natural knowledge and religious understanding, or between science and theology.

Oriental religions [write Bidez and Cumont in a recent study] made no separation at all between speculations about the nature of Gods and Men, and investigations into the material world. Faith and learn-ing being closely linked, the theologian was also a scientist. The 'clerks' engaged after their own fashion in research on all three natural kingdoms. Animals, vegetables and minerals were united by hidden affinities with the celestial powers, which conferred mysterious properties on them. Divine wisdom would reveal to devout souls the manner in which these hidden influences gave rise to all the phenomena of nature.

The philosopher Porphyry has preserved a revealing account of the manner in which the Temple priests spent their days under the Roman Empire: he is quoting Cheremon the Stoic, who had first-hand knowledge of the Egyptian priesthood.

They choose Temples as the most suitable places for philosophizing. Their tradition is to remain always near the Temple altars, this proximity being favourable to meditation, and also giving them security. The Holy sanctuary protects them, and everyone honours them as a kind of holy being. So they live in peace, free from contact with the world at large, except at the great festivals and holy days: for at most other times the Temples are barred to profane persons ... These priests, then, have renounced all secular activities, all lucrative work, and give themselves up entirely to meditation, and contemplation of Divine things. Contemplation makes them revered, and imposes on them a tranquil and pious existence; meditation and contemplation together impose on them a somewhat withdrawn and old-fashioned manner of life. ...

Their nights [Cheremon continues] are given up to observing things in the heavens, or to carrying out some holy office; their days to the divine service, which involves singing hymns in honour of the Gods four times a day – at sunrise, at vespers, when the sun is at his zenith, and when he begins to drop towards sunset. For the remainder of their time, they study arithmetic and geometry: they can always be seen at work on some investigation. In short, they give themselves up entirely to the exact sciences.

On winter nights they do the same – giving over their evenings to literary labours, like men uninterested in financial gain, liberated from cruel enslavement to the costs of living. The most impious thing, in their eyes, is to travel far from Egypt, for they fear the softness of foreign fare and the customs of other countries: such travels are permissible, they say, only for those obliged to go abroad in the service of the Kingdom. They place great importance on conformity to traditional practices: if convicted of the smallest offence against them, they are expelled from the Temples.

Unkind readers may see some analogy between the Egyptian Temples and our own Western universities, in the days when all dons were in Holy Orders and unmarried; and this analogy is not entirely far-fetched. For the Temple régime closely resembled that of the monasteries and schools where science and learning were to take root once again in medieval Europe.

Cheremon's description reminds us that the schools and academies of classical Greece were quite exceptional in being organized on a *secular* basis. Elsewhere, learning had always been the property of the sacred hierarchy, and men of scholarly temperament had automatically gone into Holy Orders – as they continued to do in England right up to the nineteenth century A.D. So, except in those restricted circles where the rational impulse behind Greek philosophy kept its original force, it was only to be expected that philosophy in Alexandria should adapt itself more closely to the religious traditions of the Egyptians. Yet one surprise remains – if it really comes as a surprise. The devout souls who looked to Divine Wisdom (*Hagia Sophia*) for an understanding of the nature of matter proved often enough to be skilled, ingenious, and scrupulous craftsmen, practical and inventive in devising recipes, and with the passage of time extending them over a wider and wider range of chemical skills.

This accumulated knowledge was built up within the bounds of a very definite intellectual system. So we must look now, in turn, at the ways in which Greek philosophy changed when transplanted to Alexandria; at the craft-skills which the alchemists inherited and developed; and at the intellectual system in terms of which they interpreted all their practical experience.

The Transformation of Greek Philosophy

In Alexandria the *rapprochement* of philosophy and astral religion was accelerated by the revival of Platonism. However, the Plato we find in the writings of the 'neo-Platonists' was a very different teacher from the geometer, logician, and political theorist of the original dialogues. At every point his system of ideas was now given a twist which fitted them to the preoccupations of the Alexandrians: men looked to his teachings less for a lucid understanding of the heavenly motions and an explicit appreciation of the principles of conduct, than for a spiritual method – a recipe for salvation by self-unification with the Divine Word. Step by step, rational argument was replaced by spiritual exercises. The problem was no longer to free oneself from perplexity and come to understanding: it was now to free oneself from sin and achieve blessedness.

The transformation was gradual. Even in the third century A.D., Plotinos could still protest against the attitude of the gnostics of his time. These men, he grumbled,

no longer accept the old Greek method: the Greeks had clear ideas and spoke without cloudy arrogance of the stages by which the soul climbed from the cavern of ignorance to a contemplation of the highest truth. [Instead, the gnostics] boast of their ability to banish diseases by spells, and make a business of it: this certainly impresses the common herd, who will always gape with admiration at the secret powers of Magi, but men of good sense will not be shaken in their belief that the true causes of diseases are fatigue, over-eating, starvation, corruption and – in brief – changes whose source lies either outside or inside our bodies.

By now, however, the tide was flowing strongly in the other direction. Men of varied creeds and backgrounds – followers of Isis and Mithras, Christians, Jews, and even agnostics – shared a single religious ambition: to purify the soul, preparing it for unity with the Divine Nature by freeing it from dross. Plato had taught that intellectual ideas are quite distinct from – and logically independent of – the material objects of the terrestrial world. Refracted through the Alexandrian prism, this doctrine took on a new shape: the intellect now became the 'immaterial' part of the human being, conferring life and form on the brute matter of the body, but fulfilling its destiny only when separated from it, whether in the after-life or in mystical 'ecstasy'. (The word literally means 'standing-outside'.) His further thesis, that ideas can be grasped by the intellect alone, likewise became a dogma: that only a pure soul is fit to receive the Divine Word. Not for the last time, men began to regard the body as an impediment: a material cage in which the immaterial soul was trapped, a fetter holding it down to the earth. For the pure in heart, death would be an escape; and the wise man would seek peace of mind during life by preparing for this release. Properly pursued, even intellectual enquiries could contribute to this state:

All those – Greeks or Barbarians – who have trained themselves in wisdom by leading a blameless life and are fully determined neither to suffer harm from neighbours nor to cause it in return, avoid both the company of mischief-makers whose time is spent in intrigue, and those places where such men pursue their business – law courts, parliaments, public squares, assemblies: in short, all leagues and meetings of common people. Following a peaceful life, they admiringly contemplate Nature and her creatures, fathoming the secrets of the earth, the sea, the air and the heavens, together with the laws which govern them – accompanying in thought the Moon, the Sun and the choir of planets and fixed stars through their orbits. Though held down to the earth by their bodies, they give wings to their souls. So, traversing the ether, they survey the powers residing there; they have become authentic citizens of the cosmos, making the whole world their city, and regarding all other friends of wisdom [philosophers] as their compatriots.

This union with Eastern religion transformed matter-theory along with the rest of Greek philosophy. The following invocation (c. A.D. 200), originally forming part of a prayer to Mithras, illustrates the use which theology made of Stoic ideas:

First Beginning of my beginning, First Principle of my principle; Breath [pneuma] of breath, First Breath of the breath within me; Fire which, among the compounds which form me, was given by God for my own compound, First Fire of the fire within me; Water of water, First Water of the water within me; Earthy Substance, model of the earthy substance which is within me; O my Perfect Body, fashioned by a glorious arm and an immortal hand in the world of darkness and light, lifeless and living – if it please Thee to transmit and communicate a rebirth to immortality to me, who am still constrained by my natural condition, O that I may, after the violent constraint of my impending Fate [i.e. death], contemplate the immortal Principle thanks to the undying Breath. . . .

(We can stop at this point: the passage quoted represents in the original rather less than half the first sentence!) Here in this prayer, the four roots of Empedokles – the four fundamental forms of matter – have become attributes of the Deity and objects of supplication to be invoked and worshipped. Philosophy has become, in every sense of the metaphor, the 'handmaid of religion'.

For an understanding of alchemy, one thing is especially significant: the connexion between matter-theory and the theme of redemption by regeneration. As we have seen, substances of every sort – inanimate as well as animate – were held together by a pneuma: all of them could be more or less perfect, more or less corrupt. Metals seemed more perfect and 'alive' than the crude ores from which they were manufactured, and there were degrees of perfection even among the metals themselves: gold, which was least readily tarnished and corroded, appeared the 'noblest' of them all. Thus men came to see a parallel between degrees of spiritual perfection in men and degrees of material perfection in substances, and the art of handling ores and metals became a symbolic counterpart of the religious art of self-perfection.

This religious attitude toward matters of 'mere chemistry' may seem less bizarre, if one recalls that – for the philosophers as well as the theologians – things in the heavens and on the earth were bound together in a single causal network. Aristotle himself believed that the same pair of material agents (the two 'exhalations') brought about both atmospheric happenings above ground and mineralogical ones below:

The dry exhalation produces through its heat all the 'fossiles'; for example, all kinds of infusible stones – realgar, ochre, ruddle, sulphur and other substances of this kind. . . . Metals, on the other hand, are produced by the vaporous exhalation, and are all fusible or ductile: for example, iron, gold, copper. . . . They are in one sense liquid and in another sense not: their substance might originally have turned into water, but it can no longer do so – nor are they, like tastes, consequences of a change of quality in water that has already been formed.

As early as Babylon, too, the seven chief metals had been treated as terrestrial counterparts of the sun, moon, and planets: in Chaucer's words,

> Sol gold is, and Luna silver we declare;
> Mars yron, Mercurie is quyksilver;
> Saturnus leed, and Jubitur is tyn,
> And Venus coper, by my fathers kyn.

Transplanted to Egypt and united with Aristotle's teaching, this doctrine became a theory of the *formation* of metals. Proklos of Byzantium (c. A.D. 450) stated this theory quite explicitly:

Gold and silver, as found in nature, as well as all other metals and substances, are engendered in the earth by the celestial Divinities and the effluvia that come from them. The Sun produces gold; the Moon silver; Saturn lead; and Mars iron.

The parallels between the planets and metals were extended to include creatures in every grade of being. Some of the 'astral influences' were obvious enough: for example, the motion of the heliotrope, whose flowers turn to follow the sun in its passage across the sky. Other parallels were less obvious. Yet for Proklos all were equally genuine, providing channels for the action of Divine Power, and needing to be understood if one was to place oneself in harmony with the cosmos and achieve a personal knowledge of the Gods.

By the year A.D. 500 the ideas of the Greek philosophers had been woven into an elaborate network of superstitions. Later neo-Platonism had become a repository, not just for the geometry and astronomy of Euclid and Ptolemy and the logic and zoology of Plato and Aristotle, but also for an extraordinary assortment of pagan doctrines and magical recipes – some of them genuine enough, others frankly in the realm of 'black magic'. This being so, one may perhaps understand better the reasons which prompted Justinian to suppress the Academy. We may regret the suppression, and even regard it as a sad blunder; but we should not suppose that by that time 'philosophy' consisted purely of Platonic and Aristotelian doctrine, or that its exponents were moved any longer by a passion for cool understanding and rational proof alone.

The Craft Element in Alchemy

In our own times there is a clear distinction between the men who work at chemistry and chemical technology and the few remaining adepts who continue to dabble with 'alchemy' – pursuing in secret laboratories at Fez or Marrakesh the Philosophers' Stone or the Elixir of Life; and there is a temptation to apply the same distinction unthinkingly when looking back at earlier periods. Some historians of science have, as a result, supposed that one could distinguish the decent, upstanding, practical-minded craftsmen in Egypt, Islam, and medieval Europe – who made an honest living working in metals or perfumes, and kept their heads free of rubbishy ideas – from a secret fraternity of avaricious fools, wholly lacking in the common sense of the guild craftsmen, who allowed themselves to be deluded by alchemical dreams.

This contrast is in fact artificial. The evidence we possess of chemical and metallurgical techniques in late antiquity comes predominantly from alchemical sources. The processes recorded in these books of recipes take over and extend craft-procedures known for centuries in the earlier empires of Mesopotamia and Egypt. If there is a distinction to be made, it is between those professional craftsmen who accepted the alchemical theories, and those who did not theorize about their art at all. The wildly-impractical *amateur* alchemist, wasting his substance on fruitless researches, was emphatically a creature of medieval Europe: one more by-product of the intellectual indigestion which afflicted Europe from the twelfth century on – resulting from the sudden influx of manuscripts which presented them with a vast but jumbled picture of ancient science and literature.

Again: in presenting the technical side of alchemy, it is not always easy to keep a historical perspective. Some of the basic recipes current in Egypt at the beginning of the Christian era remained virtually unchanged thirteen centuries later – having in the meantime been twice translated, from Greek into Arabic, and from Arabic into Latin. Yet there was a continual growth in the range of techniques available, and in the number of substances known, described and handled. Changes in terminology can also cause trouble. The word 'alcohol' was put into circulation by the Arabic alchemists, but it acquired its present meaning only in the eighteenth century A.D. (Its first appearance in English as a synonym for *aqua ardens* or 'spirits of wine' dates to 1753. Similarly, with its colloquial equivalents – *aqua vitae, eau-de-vie, lebenswassre, aquavit,* or *uisge beatha* (whisky) – this began as a name for the 'medicine of immortality' mentioned by Diodoros of Sicily in the last century B.C.; later it referred to a milky fluid which would allegedly turn silver into gold and prolong life indefinitely; and only in 1309 did Arnald of Villanova identify it with alcohol in the modern sense. Flavoured with rosemary and sage, he declared, this wonderful fluid had a healthy influence on the nerves.)

With these cautions in mind, let us glance briefly at three groups of techniques. The first is concerned with the handling of metals, the second with the production of artificial jewels and dyes, the third with distillation. (Some of the actual recipes appear in the note at the end of this chapter.)

(a) Precious Metals

The early alchemists say little about the business of extracting ores and smelting metals: these techniques they took for granted. They were engaged rather in a 'secondary industry', handling, purifying, and colouring these common primary substances. This has always been the most lucrative side of the metal-worker's craft: from the earliest times men have had to eke out the limited supplies of natural gold and silver, and satisfy some of the public demand for these metals with artificial substitutes. Many of the medieval recipes consist, like their Babylonian precursors, of formulae for producing man-made metals: particularly, *ersatz* substances indistinguishable from – and if possible identical with – the gold and silver found in Nature.

There was, of course, a certain air of sharp practice about the industry, since the man-made metals were in general inferior to natural gold and silver. Like the earliest man-made fibres and artificial silks, which resembled natural wool and silk when new but quickly lost their qualities in use, the alchemists' artificial metals would rarely wear as well, or keep their colours as fast, as natural metals. Yet an element of positive charlatanry entered only comparatively late, and we must not credit the alchemists with conscious dishonesty, at any rate to begin with. Few of the craftsmen supposed that their artificial substances were identical with natural gold; but, since they were required only to pass as 'gold' in commerce, no one was particularly deceived.

The alchemical metal-workers did not, however, restrict their work to producing substitutes for gold and silver. Like an economical housewife who minces meat together with bread to make it go further, they looked for ways of 'inflating' a limited quantity of gold without seriously spoiling its appearance: for instance, adding to gold an equal quantity of silver and a half-quantity of copper leaf, and melting them all together to form an alloy. Other recipes, both more elaborate and more economical, involved repeated meltings and the use of a mixture of substances, some mineral, some animal in origin: for instance, goat's and bull's bile. One whole class involved the use of the mineral known as *auripigmentum* or orpiment, commonly nicknamed 'saffron': this is still called King's Yellow or yellow arsenic – or, in chemical terms, arsenic trisulphide. A third group of metallurgical recipes concerned itself with surface effects: either with cleaning and polishing precious metals, or with producing silver and gold surfaces on baser metals. Then there were recipes for gold and silver inks to be used for illuminating manuscripts, and others for invisible inks. Most schoolboys today know about writing in milk, as suggested in the *Liber Sacerdotum*:

If you wish to w***e *n g**d, either on parchment or on wood, take a jar of milk and mix into it a little saffron. Write letters or figures with it, and put them aside until next day. Then take a small piece of gold and place it on the milk letters you have formed, pushing it to and fro across them with one finger. What you previously wrote will then come up in gilt.

(b) Dye-stuffs and Jewels

Throughout the Roman Empire there was a strong demand for pigments and dyes: white lead, verdigris, blue woad, and especially the rich crimson misleadingly known as 'purple'. The natural purple obtained from the juices of the mollusc *Murex* was unquestionably superior to all imitations, but it was scarce and expensive. So there was the same incentive as with gold and silver to search for substitutes. A long tradition of dyeing and tanning existed in the Middle East, and it is hard to know just how original the alchemical recipes were; but a papyrus at Stockholm dating from the third century A.D. contains one hundred and fifty-two recipes, setting out procedures for dyeing and mordanting fabrics and imitating precious stones. (Many fabrics will not take a dye unless first suitably prepared with a chemical known as a 'mordant': iron dross and pomegranate juice are recommended here.) As one possible artificial purple the recipes prescribe madder, an extract from the root of the plant *Rubia tinctorum*. This remained the principal source of red dye-stuffs throughout

Europe until 1869, and no branch of agriculture has ever been ruined more suddenly and more completely than its cultivation – as a result of the discovery that vivid dye-stuffs could be synthesized cheaply from coal-tar.

The Stockholm papyrus also includes instructions for producing cheap jewellery. Close imitations of the more precious stones were very difficult to achieve, but one could produce coloured glass by following the ancient recipes and subsequently work it into the shape of gems. A cheaper and just passable substitute was produced by coating rock crystal and other semi-precious stones with a colouring agent. This gave something like the desired appearance, at any rate temporarily, and a topaz coated with verdigris could in this way be passed off as an emerald. Techniques of this kind can hardly have had very lasting results, still less the others for producing artificial pearls, but they remain interesting both for the glimpse they give us of the Egyptian craftsmen and on account of the light they throw on the sources of alchemical theory. For the theories of the alchemists also were largely concerned with surface-appearances: the crucial question for them being, how the visible properties of an object – of which colours are the most obvious – are related to its structure and constitution.

(c) *Distillation*

Crude distillation-pots certainly existed in Mesopotamia as far back as 3000 B.C., and presumably their use had been widespread long before 100 B.C. They remained adequate for many purposes, continuing in use in medieval Europe, where they were known by the Arabic name of *aludel*. But the alchemists were interested also in more complex processes. For these it was necessary to work at a higher temperature, keeping the distilling surface at a greater distance from the furnace and cooling it more drastically; so a larger and more elaborate kind of still had to be designed. Typically, this comprised a pot which could be heated in a furnace and supported a tall cylinder: on top of this was the distilling-head, from which one, two, or more 'beaks' led the distillate down into collecting-jars. Very soon, we find water-condensers used to cool the beaks and increase the rate of condensation. Zosimos (third century A.D.) described the 'tribikos' or three-tubed still designed by Maria the Jewess (see p. 149), and the continuity of the technical tradition is evident when we find Abuqasim of Cordova (about A.D. 1100) describing an exactly similar apparatus, for the preparation of rosewater.

Alongside the stills, the alchemist's laboratory contained other essential pieces of equipment. His furnaces were of many kinds. Some processes demanded a fierce heat, with the flames actually playing over the substances being handled. Others required an indirect and gentle heat: for example, the 'rusting' of mercury to form the red calx, which was studied later by Lavoisier. Some of

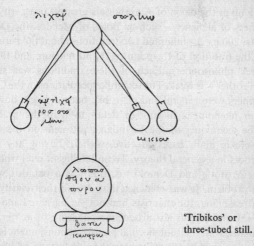

'Tribikos' or three-tubed still.

the alchemist's furnaces would therefore be large and complex, like the furnaces in a modern glass-factory. Others would produce an indirect but closely-controlled heat, by way of sand-baths or water-baths. The water-bath used in our kitchens still preserves the name of its supposed alchemical inventor, Maria the Jewess, being referred to as a *bain-marie*.

Strictly speaking, alchemical procedures of the kind we have been studying here belong in a history of technology rather than of scientific ideas. But they are relevant to the development of scientific thought in two ways. First, they show how in the centuries before A.D. 1600 the range of apparatus and substances in general use increased and widened; so that, when in the eighteenth century the fundamental questions of modern chemistry were stated clearly for the first time, men had ready to hand a whole battery of instruments and techniques. Secondly – and this is more important – the particular selection of processes on which the alchemists concentrated was closely bound up with their system of ideas, and so with the problems which they left to their successors.

The Aims and Axioms of Alchemical Theory

Growing up at the dawn of Alexandria's greatest prosperity, the first fathers of alchemy – such as Bolos of Mendes, the Demokritean (c. 200 B.C.) – inherited two traditions about the nature of matter: the tradition of Egyptian craft and religion, and that of the Greek philosophers. Each of these traditions was strong where the other was weak. The scientific speculations of the Greek philosophers were general and plausible, but rarely got down to particular phenomena in enough detail to help the practical man. The techniques of the Egyptian craftsmen, on the other hand, were in many cases effective, without having any intellectual roots in a general theory. To an intelligent man who had read his Aristotle and Demokritos, this was a paradox which posed a problem. It was evidence that, for all their clarity and force of reasoning, the theorists had not yet mastered and assimilated the craftsmen's less articulate knowledge of matter.

Athenians, with their intellectual preoccupations, might ignore this gap, but in Alexandria, where the whole tone of life and society was more commercial, the paradox was more challenging: by uniting Greek theory with Egyptian craftsmanship, surely one could hope to achieve a new and more powerful understanding of matter. And the crucial thing to recognize about alchemical theory is, in fact, this: that its intellectual principles were derived almost wholly from Greece.

The alchemists, then, were attempting to fit together theoretical ideas and practical experience. Though the results of this attempt were destined ultimately to be rejected, it nevertheless had to be made. For, in the long run, the weakness of Greek natural philosophy could be demonstrated only by pinning its general ideas down in some precise relation to the facts. As with the astronomy of Aristotle, this attempted union of craft and theory was necessary even though premature, and much can be learnt by locating its exact points of weakness. Still more can be learnt by recognizing its points of strength – for in a few, but significant, respects alchemical doctrine was actually sounder than the classical physics and chemistry of the nineteenth century.

The first starting-point for alchemical theory was Aristotle's *principle of development*: the conception that all material things, unless interfered with, will naturally change and develop – turning, when properly fed and nurtured, from an imma'ure to a ripe or adult form. Rather than treating elementary matter as naturally inert and static, they thought of all things equally in a fundamentally *physiological* way. Every material part of the world was developing – animal, vegetable, and mineral, too – while the cosmos in its entirety was like a gigantic organism in course of perfecting itself.

If men were going to apply the physiological mode of explanation to minerals, one question immediately arose: what is the length of the life-span? Any physiological theory of mineral change would be falsified if one could easily demonstrate the stability of inanimate substances, and so show that no such life-cycle was recognizable. But this was not easily done. In the laboratory, chemicals can normally be preserved in a stable condition – even though this may mean drying out, sealing, and even evacuating their containers. But conditions underground, in the mineral strata of the earth, are unlike those in a sterilized bottle with a ground-glass stopper. Slow mineral changes are always going on: pressure, heat, water-seepage, and gas-formation produce inexorable changes in the material content of the earth's crust. The alchemists were well aware of geological change, and recognized how slowly it occurs. This very slowness helped to conceal from them the crucial differences between geological and physiological change. According to Vincent of Beauvais (fourteenth century),

Avicenna explains in his *Alchemy* that gold is produced in the bosom of the earth with the help of a strong solar heat, shining mercury being joined to a clear red sulphur and concocted for a hundred years and more, away from stony minerals.

If a single step in mineralogical development could take a full century, it was difficult, geological records being so short, to find solid evidence against a physiological theory of mineral growth. Pending evidence to the contrary, everything in medieval science inclined men the other way. Mines penetrated into the very 'entrails' of the earth, to the point where the minerals were conceived and gestated:

White mercury, fixed by the virtue of white, incombustible sulphur, engenders in mines a matter which on fusion is turned to silver. Pure sulphur, red and clear, robbed of its burning power, and good clear mercury fixed by the sulphur, engender gold.

And the fundamental idea of this theory, that the earth forms a 'matrix' or 'womb' for the gestation of mineral substances, lasted on for many centuries. We still talk today of 'the womb of the earth', though in our mouths the phrase is a dead metaphor. Yet right up to the eighteenth century men took it literally, believing that, when metals were removed from the earth, the lodes or veins from which they were taken grew again by a subterranean regeneration.

Vincent of Beauvais makes it quite clear how crucial this idea was for the system of alchemical doctrine:

These operations, which Nature achieves on minerals, alchemists set themselves to reproduce: that is the very substance of their art.

If we can take this initial ambition seriously, there is little difficulty in what follows. Suppose minerals were formed under the earth by a kind of gestation: then, provided the natural conditions of their growth were reproduced exactly, the alchemist might hope to manufacture them for himself. Indeed, he might even find ways of accelerating the leisurely development of these geological 'embryos', bringing about in a few days or weeks changes which Nature accomplished only in centuries. At any rate, the idea appeared not impossible, and was worth trying. In all centuries many of the basic processes of industrial chemistry have reproduced and accelerated changes already occurring somewhere in Nature. Indeed, if we ourselves could imitate the conversion of hydrogen to helium which takes place in the sun, we should be very thankful: the possibility of 'thermonuclear' power-stations depends on our devising just such a technique. So, given a physiological theory of chemical change the alchemists set about their own chemical engineering in a perfectly intelligible way.

The aim was: to reproduce in the laboratory the operations which Nature achieves on minerals in the womb of the earth. Artificial embryology called for apparatus in which mineral substances could be incubated. The womb of the earth had to be replaced by an artificial womb: preferably one in which the changes could be watched, to make sure that they took place at the proper speed and in the right order. Clearly, the simplest device was a glass globe with an airtight seal. Such an 'hermetically sealed' vessel would be transparent, and could be heated in a sand-bath or water-bath to a high temperature. Renaissance descriptions of the Great Work (as the quest for artificial gold came to be called) took for granted that the process was an embryological one. A typical seventeenth-century account 'of the appearances in the matras [retort] during the nine months' digestion' describes one phase in the long process:

Next succeeds the reign of Mars, which shows a little yellow, mixed with luteous brownness; these are the chief colours, but transitory ones of the rain-bow and peacocks-tail, it shows most gloriously ... Now the mother being sealed in her infant's belly [sic], swirls and is purified, but because of the present great purity of the compound, no putridness can have place in this regimen, but some obscure colours play their part as the chief actors in this stone and some middle colours do pass and come, pleasant to behold. Now know, that this is the last tillage of our virgin earth, that in it the fruit of the sun might be set and maturated; therefore continue a good heat, and thou shalt see for certain, about thirty days off, this regimen, a citrine colour shall appear, which shall in two weeks after its first appearing, tinge all with a true citrine colour.

To make an artificial womb, and reproduce exactly the necessary mineral processes, was clearly a very complicated and delicate business. Even granted that the fundamental theory was correct it could succeed only with the help of carefully-made furnaces which could be accurately controlled. No wonder that 'pyrotechnics' – the art of managing one's fire so as to produce precisely graded degrees of heat – played an extremely important part in all attempts at transmutation.

There was, however, an alternative way of exploiting the processes by which minerals were supposed to be formed. This was to 'farm', or 'culture', them. It was a popular saying among alchemists that 'gold begets gold, just as corn produces corn, and man engenders man'. They hoped to do for precious metals what today is frequently done in the manufacture of antibiotics and similar substances. One takes a nutrient broth or jelly, places a few spores of the required mould on the surface, and keeps it at the appropriate temperature. The spores feed on the broth or jelly, and proliferate at such a rate that one soon has a regular harvest. Similarly, the alchemists looked for two things which should allow them to culture gold: on one the hand, a suitable nutrient medium, on the other, a fertilizer or catalyst to accelerate the natural process of proliferation. Most frequently, they tried to 'feed' gold on base metals such as lead and copper. The processes by which the Egyptian metal-workers had made a little gold go a long way were then reinterpreted; applying the new theory, that the superior metal would actually digest the baser stuff, and transform it into its own nature.

If a catalyst could have been found which would speed up the natural transformation of baser metals into gold without even a small quantity of gold as a 'seed' or 'starter', that would have been the best solution of all. So, finally, the search for techniques of 'multiplication' gave way to the quest for the Philosophers' Stone, which would function as this crucial catalyst.

A second element in Greek philosophy also provided another starting-point for much in alchemical theory: namely, the analysis of things into a 'soul' and a 'body' – especially the Alexandrian idea that 'the aim of philosophy consists in . . . the separation [by religious exercises] of the soul and the body'. If material substances as well as human beings have a spiritual and a material aspect, then (thought the alchemists) it should be possible to effect the same separation in the case of minerals, by corresponding quasi-religious operations. From the very beginning of alchemy right up to the fourteenth century, it was a general adage among alchemists that *bodies must be made incorporeal*.

A whole class of alchemical enquiries drew their theoretical significance from this distinction. The task was to discover which parts of a material substance corresponded to its 'spirit', and which to its 'body', and then to master the processes by which they could be combined, separated and recombined again. On this side, the alchemists got off to a promising start; for it was soon evident that some parts of the substances they handled were highly volatile, while others were stable and earthy. Furthermore, when an object with a well-defined form – for instance, a tree-trunk – was destroyed in the fire, a volatile vapour was commonly driven off, leaving behind only a shapeless pile of ashes. This familiar fact seemed to justify their fundamental analogy, and confirmed the Stoic idea that the *form* of an object came from a tenuous, breath-like ingredient which escaped to the heavens at 'death'. As one text put it, a material stuff when burnt loses its soul – the cinders being the *caput mortuum* or 'dead head'; but

these cinders will become green again through a rebirth, as with all new-made beings – animals, plants and trees. Dye-stuffs equally make use of spirits, when heated on a gentle fire and transformed into spiritual cinders. This spirit derives benefit from the fire and air, just as the head of an animal inspires the spirits from the air. In both cases, fire and air act in the same way.

The secrets of death and rebirth, destruction and regeneration, seemed accordingly to lie in the art of separating and reuniting the volatile 'spirits' with the earthy 'bodies'.

This emphasis on the role of 'spirits' in chemical processes helps to explain why the alchemists placed such importance on distillation. For, by distillation, one could drive off the 'spiritual' part of a body and collect it separately in a pure form. In this way, the ancient techniques of the perfumiers acquired a new theoretical significance. The oils and perfumes driven off when rose-petals were boiled in a closed vessel appeared to embody the very soul (or essence or attar) of the original plant. This is in fact how phrases like 'essential oils' and 'vanilla essence' originated.

But metals remained the alchemists' chief concern. Bright, glittering, cohesive, springy: they seemed in their own way alive, whereas the calces (oxides) from which they were manufactured crumbled to dust and looked like cinders. Theory at once suggested a natural analogy. The metal was formed from the calx by the incorporation of a pneuma or spirit; and this theory of metal-formation long remained in favour, being revived around 1700 as the 'phlogiston' theory. The central problem about metals was to identify the volatile constituents which combined with calces to form the finished metal. For a long time, the status of quicksilver was ambiguous. It is, after all, very unlike all other metals known to the ancients, resembling much more the volatile reagents which corrode metallic surfaces: mercury, in fact, forms an amalgam with other metals, and is even capable of dissolving gold itself. So the *Alchemy* attributed to Avicenna classed mercury as a 'spirit' rather than a 'body':

In the entrails of the earth, by reason of their mineralizing virtue, are engendered the *spirits* and the *bodies*. There are four spirits – mercury, sulphur, arsenic [i.e. yellow arsenic] and sal-ammoniac – and six bodies: gold, silver, copper, tin, lead, iron. The first two bodies are pure, the others impure. . . .

The spirits are engendered by the four elements and the four qualities, associated in unequal proportions. Sulphur and mercury, according to their relative proportions, purity and colour, engender in turn the six metals.

Before long, mercury and sulphur came to be regarded as essential constituents of all metals. Metals showed their 'mercurial' character by liquefying when heated – turning to a molten mass similar in appearance to quicksilver. They displayed their 'sulphurous' character in the reddish colour of the ores from which they can be smelted. So quicksilver was supposed to be not so much a fully-formed metal as the essential ingredient responsible for all metals being liquefiable – in fact, 'the principle of liquidity'.

As to mercury [writes one Islamic alchemist] we have already mentioned it in speaking of Bodies [i.e. metals]. It must be classified among them, because it is the First of them – from it they derive and draw their fundamental principles. But it must be classified also among the Spirits, because it volatilizes under the action of fire and is not fixed: that is the reason for adding it to them.

For the term 'body' covers things which are liquefied by fire without disappearing, while 'spirits' volatilize by fire and do not stay fixed. The term 'body' applies most exactly to metals because they are heavy [gravitate], while spirits are light [levitate] – bodies return to their [terrestrial] principle, spirits fly off to their [celestial] world.

The term 'principle', as used in the phrase 'principle of liquidity', had a long future ahead of it: even Lavoisier was to use it in defining *oxygen* as the 'principle of acidity'. Behind the phrase lay the belief that substances get their properties from the corresponding ingredients, one for one – in the way that common salt makes things *salt*. (Common salt might indeed be called 'the principle of salinity'.) The term continues in use even today in pharmacy, where the drug digitalin is referred to as 'the toxic principle' of the foxglove plant *Digitalis* – i.e. the ingredient in its tissues which renders them poisonous. The alchemical problem of converting base metals to gold could therefore be restated in another way: what 'principle' can offer on other substances the essential properties of gold? To discover an ingredient which would confer on another substance the colour, ductility, and other characteristics of gold, would be – in effect – to discover the Philosophers' Stone.

The Wider Influences of Alchemy

'*Spirits*' *are celestial*, '*bodies*' *are terrestrial.* This maxim provided a link between alchemical theory and the traditional cosmology. And we soon find men looking for parallels between geological processes and the movements of the heavenly bodies. Stephanos of Byzantium (seventh century A.D.) is quoted as saying:

The passage of the seven planets across the twelve signs [of the Zodiac] governs the mutation of the four elements, causing them to change and permitting their prediction.

An understanding of chemical change was in this way bound up with an understanding of the entire universe. Correspondingly, the practical alchemist was thought of as re-enacting the Divine Creation. In ancient Egyptian myth, the Creator-God gave birth to the world in the form of an egg; and the history of the universe was the life-cycle of the creature into which this egg developed. The glass womb into which the alchemist sealed his raw materials was a more or less conscious imitation of this original egg – an artificial 'microcosm' – so one can understand why many Christian theologians regarded alchemy with a jaundiced eye. Attempts to discover and exploit the secrets of the Creation struck them as grossly presumptuous, not to say impious, and this taint spread from alchemy to all the chemical arts: as late as 1530, an official decree in Venice made it a capital offence to practise them.

From A.D. 500 on, the main tradition in alchemy, as in astronomy, moved eastwards. For a few years the last relics of Hellenistic science – including alchemy – survived under the protection of the Temple of Isis at Philae (the modern Aswan) far to the south of Alexandria. But, with the rise of Islamic culture first round Damascus and later at Baghdad, the centre of gravity had moved decisively. In Islam new elements entered alchemical thought. According to tradition alchemy was introduced to the Islamic world by an Umayyad Prince of Damascus, Khalid Ibn Yazid, towards the end of the seventh century, but the flowering of Islamic alchemy came at Baghdad more than a century later, being associated particularly with the teacher Jabir Ibn Hayyan.

Jabir became a hero-figure: by now it is impossible to disentangle authentic facts about him from the legends of later generations. We do know that his chief patron was Jafar the Barmecide, vizier to Harun al-Rashid – the Khalif of Baghdad famous from *The Thousand and One Nights* – and that he was a member of the Shi'ite sect, whose intellectual traditions were most sympathetic to Alexandrian neo-Platonism. Nor can one separate the books Jabir wrote himself from those which were fathered on him, first by his followers among the Brethren of Purity (who flourished around Basra about A.D. 900) and later in Europe by the medieval Western alchemists, who knew him as 'Geber'.

However, by digging down through later accretions, scholars have discovered something of Jabir's original ideas. Here in a new environment, only a few miles from the site of ancient Babylon, we see the Alexandrian theories branching out in a new direction. Jabir set out to build alchemical ideas into a mathematical theory, which would explain the observable properties of substances in terms of a numerical structure. The theory owes something to the mathematical tradition of earlier Babylonia: particularly the 'magic squares' already associated at Babylon with the seven planets and the seven metals. In Jabir's writings one finds the relations between the different metals analysed in the terms of a series of numbers: 1, 3, 5, 8, 17, and 28. This series of

Alchemical diagram from Libavius, *Alchymia* (1606), illustrating the persistent influence of Babylonian symbolism

numbers is derived from a simple, nine-celled magic square composed of the first nine digits:

4	9	2
3	5	7
8	1	6

This square can be divided into a four-celled square and a 'gnomon': Jabir's number-series then comprises the figures in the four-celled square – 1, 3, 5, 8 – together with their total (17), and the total of the figures in the gnomon (28). Every metal possessed a particular numerical constitution, having an 'inner' and 'outer' nature represented by different numerals. The secret of transmutation lay in 'balancing up' this numerical constitution so as to yield the 'perfect number' (28) associated with gold.

Alchemy remained, however, a compromise between technology and religion, and was unable to turn itself into theoretical
chemistry. For a fruitful science must always be both speculative
and *critical*; and the religious associations of alchemy tended to
stultify the critical powers of the theorist. This is not to say that
alchemists were more muddle-headed or credulous than they
should have been: too often their hesitation to reject a theory or
recipe sprang from the best of reasons. If they were to succeed in
their work four separate conditions had to be fulfilled: the right
materials must be used, the right procedures must be exactly followed, the right time of day and year must be chosen – as in
farming – and, finally, the operator himself must be in a state of
spiritual purity. Where success depended on so many factors, it is
no wonder that repeated failures did not shake the theories. For
the attitude of the alchemists was like the attitude we ourselves
adopt towards (say) the recipes in Escoffier. If an attempt at *Sole
Véronique* does not come off, we blame our own clumsiness rather
than Escoffier: the fact that we are unable to make a recipe work
is not by itself sufficient reason to condemn the recipe. But science has to start from a study of processes whose outcome does
not depend upon the time of day or year, let alone the spiritual
condition of the observer; for the scientist hopes to state the
general principles underlying the changes he studies. If he is to
explain the success or failure of a technical process, it is not
enough to refer only to the skill or personal character of the
craftsman. So, in one respect, the intellectual methods of alchemy represented a step backwards from the level of rationality
achieved by the Greeks.

All the same, there was an element of scientific nobility about
the original alchemical ambition and something of the disinterested spirit of science in the manner of its pursuit. The medieval
picture of the avaricious fool and the modern portrait of the in-
troverted mystic are equally caricatures. We should not forget
how much the sciences of matter owed to the alchemists, for their
apparatus and techniques as well as for their ideas. This debt was
clearly recognized by the Dutch chemist Boerhaave, writing at the
beginning of the eighteenth century:

We are nevertheless exceedingly obliged to them for the immense
pains they have been at, in discovering, and handing to us, so many

difficult physical truths. . . . Credulity is hurtful, so is incredulity: the business therefore of a wise man is to try all things [and not to] assign bounds to Nature.

The unforgivable sin of alchemy, as of scholastic philosophy, was that it lasted too long, so that nowadays men recall only the figure of fun it became in its senility. History can be very unjust; and the verdict which it passes on ideas which outlive their time is frequently merciless.

NOTE: CHEMICAL RECIPES FROM THE ALCHEMICAL PERIOD

(a) *To make Artificial Gold and Silver*

The foundation of this art was a cheap alloy which was capable of taking on a gold or silver sheen. This alloy commonly had a tin or copper base. For instance, one could smelt six parts of tin, and stir into it one part of white clay and two parts of mercury, so obtaining a tin amalgam with the beginnings of a silvery appearance. The following alternative recipe, for a gilt-tinged bronze with a lead base, comes from a tenth-century Latin source:

Take 2 parts of pyrites [still known as Fools' Gold] and one part of good-quality lead. Melt the pyrites, until it flows like water; then add the lead, and keep the mixture on the furnace until they are perfectly mixed. Now take 3 parts of this mixture and 1 part of chalcite [a copper ore] and heat them together until the mixture turns yellow. Melt a quantity of purified brass, and add the mixture to it, as your judgement dictates. In this way you will obtain gold.

(b) *To prepare Mercury*

Mercury was obtained from the mineral, cinnabar (HgS). This was heated slowly from above: the sulphur formed sulphur dioxide and was driven off, while the mercury dripped into receivers below. The following recipe is taken from a Chinese text, dating at least from the ninth century A.D.: similar procedures were in use in medieval Europe from about the same period.

From 16 oz. of high-grade cinnabar, 14 oz. of mercury can be extracted. The method is to make a pipe from bamboo, which is cut so as to leave three joints. In the middle diaphragm, perforations are made the size of a pellet, or small holes about the size of the thick end of a chopstick, so that the mercury may flow downwards. To begin with, two layers of wax paper are placed over the middle diaphragm. Then the cinnabar is finely ground and introduced into it. The pipe

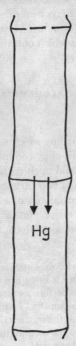

Hg

Use of bamboo stem in early China for preparation of mercury by sublimation*

is now wrapped around with hemp cloth and steamed for one day before being plastered over with yellow mud to a thickness of about three inches. It is buried underground so that its upper end comes level with the ground. The pipe must be tightly sealed all round to prevent leakage. Firewood is then piled up on top and burned for a day and a night, until the heat has penetrated the upper section. Mercury will flow into the lower section without any loss.

Cinnabar, which occurs widely in Nature, played a much larger part in the early history of mercury than did the red calx of mercury (HgO). However, an early reference to the process of calcining mercury – causing its red calx to form on the surface, by

*See article by Joseph Needham in *Ambix* VII, No. 2, 1959

heating it very slowly in an enclosed vessel – appears in the treatise on alchemy attributed to Avicenna: 'When mercury is heated in a closed vessel', he tells us, 'it loses its liquidity, acquires a fiery character and turns vermilion.'

(c) To make a Tribikos (Three-beaked Distillation Column)

Here is Zosimos' description of the *tribikos*, as devised at the very beginning of the alchemical period – probably between 100 B.C. and A.D. 100.

I will describe the *tribikos* to you. (This is the name of the copper apparatus traditionally attributed to Maria.) Her instructions are as follows: 'Make three tubes from thin copper sheeting, of a thickness similar to that of baking-tin, and one-and-a-half cubits in length. Three such tubes are required, and also another having a diameter of about one palm whose aperture will fit into the copper head. The apertures of the three tubes fit into the necks of small receptacles, one of which is keyed on to the front down-tube, while the other two tubes are fitted at either side. Near the bottom of the copper head are three orifices, which are carefully adjusted so as to fit on to the tubes. Solder the tubes at an angle to the upper recipient, which receives the volatile distillate. Place the copper head on top of an earthenware matrass [distilling column] containing the sulphur [for the reaction in question]. Having sealed all the joins with flour paste, fit large glass receptacles at the lower ends of the tubes: these must be strong enough not to crack under the heat of the distilled liquor.'

(d) To prepare Alcohol

Although Aristotle knew that wine gave off 'a light exhalation', and that this was why it could burn, recipes for preparing alcohol (*aqua ardens*) appear only in the Middle Ages. The following comes from Mark the Greek (twelfth or thirteenth century) in his *Book of Fires*:

Take old wine of good quality, and of any colour. Distil it in a cucurbit and an alembic [pieces of alchemical equipment related to Maria's *tribikos*] over a gentle fire, having sealed the joints carefully. The distillate is called *aqua ardens* [burning water].

It has this characteristic virtue and property – soak a linen rag in it, and then set fire to the cloth: it will burn with a great flame, yet after the flame goes out the cloth will remain intact, just as it was before. Dip your finger into this liquid and then set light to it: it will burn like a candle, yet will not injure you. Plunge a lighted candle in the liquid and it will not be extinguished.

Notice that the part of the liquid which distils off first is the most active and inflammable; while the later distillate is useful medically. One can use it to make an excellent salve for spots and inflammation of the eyes.

FURTHER READING AND REFERENCES

On the general background to Alexandrian life and thought, see:

M. I. Rostovtsev, *The Social and Economic History of the Hellenistic World*, Clarendon Press, 1941

F. Cumont, *Les Religions orientales dans le paganisme romain*, Paris, 1906

A. J. Festugière, *La Révélation d'Hermès Trismégiste*, Paris, 1949–54

On scientific thought in the Hellenistic world, see:

S. Sambursky, *The Physical World of Late Antiquity*, Routledge & Kegan Paul, 1962

On the craft background to alchemy, see particularly:

R. J. Forbes, *Metallurgy in Antiquity*, E. J. Brill, 1950

The essential references on alchemical texts and ideas are the numerous works of M. Berthelot, together with:

A. J. Hopkins, *Alchemy, Child of Greek Philosophy*, Columbia University Press, 1934

There are three recent general introductions to the subject:

F. Sherwood Taylor, *The Alchemists*, Heinemann, 1952

E. J. Holmyard, *Alchemy*, Penguin Books, 1957

J. M. Stillman, *The Story of Alchemy and Early Chemistry*, D. Appleton, 1924

For special topics, the volumes of *Ambix* should be consulted, particularly the articles on Chinese alchemy by J. S. Needham and on Islamic alchemy by M. Plessner and P. Kraus. Kraus has also written the only detailed analysis of Jabir's mathematical theory of matter in his book *Jābir ibn Hayyān* (published in two volumes by the French Archaeological Institute at Cairo in 1942–3).

On the psychological aspects of alchemy, see:

C. G. Jung, *Psychology and Alchemy*, Routledge & Kegan Paul, 1953

7

The Debate Reopens

In the years following A.D. 1500, European scholars and scientists took up the ideas about matter first fashioned in Greece and Alexandria without fundamental alteration. During the intervening centuries men had not been idle, but their work had been only a series of variations on themes stated by ancient philosophers and craftsmen. As a result, Renaissance Europe inherited a number of rival visions of the material world: the crucial steps, which transformed these into competing scientific theories, had yet to be taken. For all that, the classical inheritance was indispensable.

So the new scientific movements of the sixteenth and seventeenth centuries did not originate in an intellectual vacuum. The founders of the Royal Society abjured all authority in science – claiming to reject any doctrine which they had not probed for themselves, no matter how revered and distinguished its origins. But however sceptical and critical a scientist may be he must approach Nature with *some* questions in mind; and the very framing of these questions inevitably shows the intellectual tradition within which he stands. For at the heart of any 'system of Nature' lies an attitude of mind – a definite intellectual stance, which determines the general limits within which a man is prepared to theorize and the questions which appear to him relevant or urgent.

Looked at from this point of view, the new scientists were 'natural philosophers' quite as much as their predecessors. They were as passionately curious about the mechanisms of natural things as the Ionians had been about their ingredients, or Galen about their functions. But though the years between A.D. 1500 and 1700 saw a swing away from medieval orthodoxy, with its Christian amalgam of ideas from Aristotle, Galen, Ptolemy, and the Scriptures, the new 'mechanical philosophy' had by 1700 produced few positive chemical and physiological discoveries.

151

These were to come later. Where at the beginning of the period men had posed their questions in terms of 'spirits' or 'potentialities', many of them spoke now of 'corpuscles' and 'attractions' instead; but – astronomy apart – they did so with scarcely more scientific justification.

This may seem a surprising verdict to pass on the period of the 'scientific revolution'. But it does no good to assume that the new seventeenth-century perspectives which transformed dynamics and astronomy, *must* have borne immediate fruit in other branches of science; nor should we read back into the hopes and manifestos of the late 1600s the new discoveries and the clearer vision of the years between 1780 and 1850. The seventeenth century was a time of great activity in physics and chemistry, anatomy and physiology alike; in matter-theory, independent thrusts forward were made on several different fronts, each from a base within one of the earlier philosophical traditions; but these attacks failed to link up. A coherent system of chemical theory was still a century off, and the union of physiology with physics and chemistry had much longer to wait.

In retrospect, we can see the salient points round which chemistry was later to grow, but throughout the seventeenth century men were in no position to recognize these for what they were. For the basic categories of matter-theory were still confused: an intellectual fog lay over the whole field of study, obscuring from view things which later became fundamental intellectual landmarks. To understand the tasks facing those men who – a hundred years later – dispelled these obscurities and established chemistry as a science in its own right, we must first reconstruct the positions from which the seventeenth-century debate began and locate the obstacles which stood in the way of knowledge.

The Inheritance from Antiquity

In logic, mechanics, and astronomy, radical new conceptions were discussed throughout the high Middle Ages: in matter-theory there was little but embroidery on antique positions. How are we to explain this contrast? This question is one about the *pace* of scientific development, rather than about its *direction*, and we shall be returning to it in a later volume; for it obliges one to look, above all, at the inducements for original thought in medieval Europe. But social factors were not all: the very range of problems having a bearing on the nature of matter was itself significant. The channels by which Greek and Islamic ideas reached the West in this case operated selectively. They favoured some of the classical traditions and largely ignored others; and, as a result, it was a long time before the classical debates – between Aristotelians, Stoics, and Platonists, alchemists and atomists – could once again be joined.

Since medieval learning was carried on under the patronage of the Church, intellectual and abstract studies were encouraged at the expense of practical ones. (Even in mechanics, the mathematical analysis of motion reached a high level of sophistication without stimulating any experimental work.) Yet others besides philosophers and theologians had an interest in matter – for instance, doctors and metallurgists; and each group of men, thumbing through the manuscripts which enshrined the learning of the ancients, extracted and elaborated on those aspects which they could best appreciate and understand. Before the sixteenth century, however, there was little serious debate between supporters of different classical systems. Aristotelians might argue with Aristotelians, alchemists with alchemists: but only after 1550 was battle joined at a level fundamental enough to stimulate deliberate experimentation.

The Scholastic Tradition

A certain air of orthodoxy attached to the doctrines taught in the cathedral schools and universities: these had, naturally enough, harmonized with the theological teachings of the medieval Church. In this rarefied atmosphere the teleological theories of Plato and Aristotle won most attention, while the alchemical tradition came off worst. From the fourth century A.D., when Aristotle was known only for his treatises on formal logic, Plato's theory of geometrical atomism was already available in Latin. But, with the recovery of Aristotle's scientific works from Greek and Arabic sources, a new phase began. By the end of the thirteenth century Aristotelian ideas had become orthodoxy and atomism had lost much of its earlier support; the high Middle Ages saw an intellectual synthesis of several traditions – scientific ideas drawn from Aristotle, medical ideas from Galen, and theological doctrines handed down from the Christian fathers.

In all matters of natural history, Aristotle came to be accepted as 'the master of them that know'. For the most part, the scholastics confined themselves to questions arising naturally out of Aristotle's own matter-theory and metaphysics. Thomas Aquinas, the dominant figure in medieval studies, discussed chemistry hardly at all: one of his few excursions into this area dealt with the question, in what sense the elementary forms of matter continue to 'exist' in a compound. (His problem can be paraphrased in terms of a modern example: 'When hydrogen and oxygen go to form water, does the hydrogen which seems to disappear retain some real existence in the compound? Has it been annihilated? Or, seeing that – although its original properties are no longer observable – it can always be recovered, should we attribute to it some intermediate kind of existence?') In answering this question, Aquinas defers to Aristotle:

Thus the substantial forms of the elements retain their powers in compounds. Accordingly, the forms of the elements are present in compounds potentially rather than actually; which is what Aristotle teaches in the first book of his *De Generatione*. 'Two elements entering into a compound do not retain their real existence, as *whiteness* and *body* do in a white body, yet they are neither of them destroyed or transmuted; for their potentialities are all preserved.'

In matter-theory, as in astronomy, the Church's commitment to Aristotle was in due course to prove an embarrassment. In both branches of science his speculative distinction between terrestrial and celestial matter was insecure from the very beginning. His own most loyal commentator, Alexander of Aphrodisias (*c.* A.D. 200), had already dreamt of a theory unifying all material things, and John Philoponos (*c.* A.D. 500) rejected the distinction between terrestrial and celestial matter outright. Nevertheless, it was still an axiom of scholasticism almost a thousand years later.

The Alchemical Tradition

Chemical theory, however, could make no progress without a solid basis of practical experience. The Aristotelian doctrines rested on a very limited acquaintance with metals, salts, and other minerals. The alchemists, on the other hand, knew a great deal about the properties of material substances and the techniques for handling them; so, on the practical side, alchemy did much to determine the questions of seventeenth-century matter-theory. But it was an influence which respectable scholars took care to deny. Throughout the high Middle Ages alchemy remained under a cloud for several reasons. Few of the scholars in the universities were drawn towards practical science. The claims of the alchemists appeared delusive, as Albertus Magnus (1206–1280) even tried to demonstrate experimentally:

> Alchemy cannot change species, but can only imitate them: tinting a metal yellow to resemble gold, white to resemble silver, and so on. I have tested alchemical gold: after being heated six or seven times it burned up and was reduced to faeces.

But the objection went further. From the very beginning of Christianity the chemical arts had been regarded as materialistic, magical, even sacrilegious, and many Christians believed that the human race had learned the crafts of metallurgy, dyeing, herbalism, and astrology from 'fallen angels' cast out of heaven. Tertullian, for instance, declared that these fallen angels

> betrayed the secrets of worldly pleasures – gold, silver and their products; instructed men in the art of dyeing fleeces ... laid bare the secrets of metals, the virtues of plants, the force of incantations and all the knowledge coveted by men, including even the art of reading the stars.

(He condemned even mathematicians as idolators, who should be expelled from any decent Christian community.) Cursed with a single breath by the early fathers, the practical arts remained suspect for centuries; and few medieval schoolmen could afford to be sympathetic towards alchemy. Those few – such as the Catalan, Ramon Lull of Majorca (1235–1315) – lived and worked outside the main centres of learning.

The alchemical arts appealed more to practically minded laymen, a typical figure being the physician Arnald of Villanova (1240–1311) – another Catalan. But these men became really influential only after 1500, with the active revival of secular learning. The noisy and unorthodox Swiss physician, Bombastus von Hohenheim of Basle (1493–1541), owed a lot to the alchemical tradition. 'Paracelsus', as he called himself, refused to confine himself to herbal remedies, and prepared metallic and chemical medicines. He was a busy experimenter, trying out the old techniques and apparently producing the anaesthetic we now call 'ether' – he named it 'stupefying vitriol salts'. His theory of matter, quite as much as his practical procedures, was rooted in alchemy. All material substances were composed from three fundamental elements, salt, sulphur, and mercury. (These elements were most concentrated in brine crystals, brimstone, and quicksilver – i.e. common salt, sulphur, and mercury – but, being theoretical 'principles' rather than everyday materials, they were not identical with them.) Paracelsus attributed the forms of organized bodies to the action of a specific immaterial agency, which he called the *Archeus*. This was present invisibly in the seed from which the body grew, and had the power to impose an organized form on the raw nutrients.

Finally, alchemy attracted a mixed bag of fools, quacks, and Fausts: these camp-followers were later to give the subject its evil reputation. To begin with, amateur alchemy was confined to 'top people', such as the Canon in Chaucer's *Canterbury Tales*. But by the end of the fifteenth century alchemical 'adepts' were to be found at every level of society – even 'masons and tinkers, tailors and glaziers'. The springs of human action are slow to change; and these men were moved, not by any disinterested desire to advance medicine or metallurgy, but by the hopes and dreams which would turn them today to betting or patent medicines. In all centuries advertisers have profited from quack remedies, rejuvenating cosmetics, and 'get-rich-quick' schemes, and the very nature of their trade compels them to be voluble, trashy, and uncandid. These amateur adepts provided a steady market for worthless rubbish, and by the seventeenth century alchemy was largely degenerate. Still, despite the enveloping mass of trash, a core of sound doctrine and practical recipes got through: serious workers (such as Newton) could tell the one from the other as readily as a modern scientist can distinguish pulp science-fiction from the *Proceedings of the Royal Society*. And certainly the alchemical tradition passed down to the seventeenth century two things which scientists at that time rightly respected and badly needed – an extensive body of empirical knowledge about the properties and treatment of different substances, and the habit of handling chemical substances and studying them experimentally for oneself (see Plate 2).

The Humanist Movement

Separate again from both Aristotelian orthodoxy and alchemical heterodoxy, the men of the Renaissance inherited some knowledge of Plato, Archimedes, the Stoics, and the atomists. Only Archimedes had much to offer a utilitarian age; and the theory underlying his hydrostatic balance was taken up by Western mathematicians and developed into the medieval science of weights. Other ancient authors attracted none but the disinterested and curious, for their systems brought little grist to the mills of theology, and they could teach nothing to the budding physicians and engineers. An active revival of interest in alternative aspects of matter-theory came only in the sixteenth century, with the rise of the humanist movement in Italy.

Looking back to the intellectual debates of the sixteenth and seventeenth centuries, one can easily over-simplify the loyalties dividing the men of that time. From our distance it is natural enough to accept Francis Bacon's assessment of the situation, contrasting a ramshackle medieval tradition built from Aristotelian bricks with a modern scientific construction rooted securely in the *terra firma* of experience. Yet the truth was more complicated. The first generations of Renaissance scholars called themselves 'humanists' rather than 'scientists': they attacked the scholastic traditions of the medieval universities, not with a vision of what science might become in the future, but rather with their eyes fixed on a more remote past – on the *genuine* ideas of antiquity. Many Greek texts had been reaching Western Europe from Constantinople during the fifteenth century, and they stimulated a fashion for studying the classical philosophers in their original tongue. Comparing the originals with the medieval Latin versions, the humanists felt as though they were reading the classics for the first time: so they conceived a new mission – to 'purify the springs of Hellas'. As a result, the first attempts to overthrow medieval scholasticism did not aim at erecting some brand-new system of thought: instead, they hoped to restore the original authority of the classical philosophers themselves. The effect of this humanist movement was, on the whole, to turn men's attentions away from the study of science towards literature, poetry, drama, aesthetics, philology, and history and, after a winter of a thousand years, the literary and imaginative studies we know as 'the humanities' flowered again in Renaissance Italy. If one looks back through history for the origin of that division between Science and the Humanities, which still plagues us today, perhaps this is the point at which it should be located.

Still, the achievements of the humanist movement were not without incidental advantages for science. Scholars became familiar with a much wider range of classical texts, and Plato once again acquired an authority comparable to that of Aristotle. (His geometrical attitude to Nature was to be a stimulus to both Galileo and Descartes.) The pneuma-theory of the Stoics was revived by Marsilio Ficino, and became influential far beyond the limits of Galenic medicine and alchemical theory. The ideas of the neo-Platonists were the starting-point from which Kepler began his speculations about the forces responsible for planetary motion. (This was quite apart from his adoption of Plato's five regular solids as the key to his theory of planetary distances.) The mathematical works of Archimedes, which had been little studied since their original translation in the thirteenth century, were now re-edited, and stimulated a new wave of mathematical research. Finally, toppling the remaining idols of the Middle Ages, the men of the Renaissance adopted Hippokrates and Celsus as their medical guides in place of the later (and so, presumably, more corrupt) Galen; and guided by Lucretius, whose poem had been recovered complete only in 1417, they took a new interest in the hitherto-despised theories of the atomists.

So, towards the end of the sixteenth century, a number of intellectual traditions existed alongside one another within the field of matter-theory, each concerned with a separate group of problems, and each having its own body of theory. Faced with this diversity, a student was in the position of Socrates. Which tradition should he follow? Were there, indeed, any rational criteria which would enable him to make a choice? No single tradition had proved its unique superiority in open competition with the others, nor were there any agreed terms of compromise for dividing the sciences of matter into different 'spheres of influence'. In practice, therefore, the choice became, if not a matter of taste or distaste (since atomism was still suspected of being anti-religious), then at any rate one of preoccupation.

For the moment, a man beginning a course of scientific study could do only one thing. He had to select a starting-point within one tradition or another, read as his interests dictated, and work forward from that point in the hope that his position would be justified thereafter. So let us begin by looking at three men who made important contributions to matter-theory during the first half of the seventeenth century, but who approached the subject from very different directions. William Harvey, J. B. van Helmont, and René Descartes all helped to lay foundations for the science of the future; yet each of them had one foot in the past, and a different aspect of the past in each case. Harvey was a devout admirer of Aristotle and Galen, appealing like a true humanist to the original works of the masters themselves; van Helmont was 'an alchymistical philosopher', with a passionate and influential belief in the importance of experimental chemistry; while Descartes shared Plato's commitment to geometrical ideas and arguments on account of their rational clarity. Each man found something vital in one of the ancient traditions and passed it on to the new era of science. None of them was a die-hard supporter of any established intellectual authority. Yet the advances which they made were entirely separate, and at their deaths – which all occurred within a few years of 1650 – the traditions within which they worked were as distinct as ever.

Three Transitional Figures: William Harvey

It has become the fashion to depict William Harvey as an iconoclast: the man who exposed the blunders of Galen, denounced medieval teachers for placing more faith in verbal authority than they did in the evidence of their own eyes, and introduced the experimental method into physiology. The contrast between this image and the truth is so extreme as to be laughable, and Harvey himself would have been horrified. True, he was a masterly anatomist, skilled with his hands and ingenious in devising demonstrations; but the *arguments* which these demonstrations reinforced were even more brilliant. And, for all his shrewd exploitation of anatomical evidence, he was in his ideas very far from being a modern. He was in fact, as firmly rooted in Galen and Aristotle as Copernicus had been in Ptolemy. Though he might 'learn and teach anatomy not from books but from dissection, not from the tenets of the philosophers but from the fabric of Nature', both his questions and his interpretations were in the classical tradition, and he was profoundly loyal to the masters from whom he had learned. He quoted three men above all with respect and admiration: Aristotle, Galen, and Fabricius, his own teacher. On most points his own observations appeared to confirm the accuracy of their teachings, and he rejected their conclusions only when his dissections absolutely compelled him to do so. As for his famous work on the anatomy of the blood-vessels: Harvey's prime achievement, in method and doctrine alike, was to complete and clarify Galen's tentative analysis. If he toppled any idols, these were the medieval professors who – with their 'Galenic' doctrines about the ebb and flow of the blood – had so misrepresented the work of the revered physiologist.

Harvey trained as a doctor at the University of Padua, which was at that time a great international centre of learning. Being located in the territories of the Venetian Republic, it was free of direct Church control, and little affected by the repressive intellectual measures with which the Papacy reacted to the heresies of the Reformation. In Harvey's time – which was also Galileo's – Padua combined a lively school of humanist scholarship with opportunities for original scientific research, and attracted many foreign students, from countries as far apart as Ireland and Armenia. Many others besides Harvey came to learn from Fabricius and to follow the public dissections conducted in the university's new anatomy theatre. (This theatre is still visible at Padua today, and is one of the most impressive monuments of Renaissance culture: see Plate 4.) After completing his doctorate, Harvey returned to England and spent the greater part of his career in London, at the Royal College of Physicians and St Bartholomew's Hospital.

In all his works, Harvey's commitment to the basic Aristotelian principles was clearly stated and consistently maintained. Coming from a humanist university he had more respect for the original texts of Aristotle and Galen than for the usual medieval commentaries and abstracts. For the point will bear repeating. Medicine in medieval Europe was taught largely from the encylopadias of the great Islamic physicians; the few known works of Galen were in Latin translation, and fully furnished with editorial notes. Harvey, by contrast, had studied the scientific works of Aristotle and Galen at first hand, and was particularly well qualified to understand them. Indeed, some authorities believe that he was the first man since Theophrastos to appreciate fully the principles of Aristotle's biology.

For Harvey, as for Aristotle, the central fact of Nature was *organic development*, while the key to an understanding of this process lay, as ever, in its pre-ordained destination:

The Concocting and Immutative, the Nutritive and Augmenting Faculties ... do operate with as much artifice, and as much to a designed end, as the Formative faculty, which he [Fabricius] affirms to possess the knowledge and fore-sight of the future action and use of every particular part and organ. . . .

All things are full of deity: so also in the little edifice of a chicken, and all its actions and operations, the Finger of God or the God of Nature doth reveal himself.

About the atomists, Harvey was very scornful. Once again his objections were those of Aristotle and the Stoics – that you cannot account for organic development and function wholly by the jamming and separation of independent corpuscles:

Nor are they lesse deceived who make all things out of Atomes, as Democritus, or out of the elements, as Empedocles. As if (forsooth) Generation were nothing in the world, but a meer separation, or Collection, or Order of things. I do not indeed deny that to the Production of one thing out of another, these forementioned things are requisite, but Generation herself is a thing quite distinct from them all. . . .

They that argue thus assigning only a material cause, deducing the causes of Natural things from an involuntary or casual concurrence of the Elements, or from the several disposition or contriving of Atomes; they doe not reach that which is chiefly concerned in the operations of nature, and in the Generation and Nutrition of animals, namely the Divine Agent, and God of Nature, whose operations are guided with the highest Artifice, Providence, and Wisdome, and doe all tend to some certaine end, and are all produced, for some certaine good.

It does not follow from this that Harvey questioned the applicability of mechanical principles to the human frame. On the contrary: he treated the blood-vessels as an hydraulic system without the slightest hesitation, and many of his enquiries were designed to unravel the mechanical operations involved in bodily functioning. But in the last instance the understanding of structure was always to be subordinated to an understanding of function and design. So, at the very end of his treatise on the blood-circulation (*De Motu Cordis*, 1628), Harvey makes it clear that his fundamental concern is with the *usefulness* of different organs. Having relied on mechanical and hydraulic principles to demonstrate for the first time the whole course of the circulation, he concluded:

Thus Nature, perfect and divine, making nothing in vain, has neither added a heart unnecessarily to any animal nor created a heart before it had a function to fulfil, but by the same steps in the formation of every animal . . . she secures perfection in the individuals.

Fabricus had studied the one-way action of the valves in the veins, and (in Harvey's words) 'after having dealt carefully and learnedly in a special treatise with almost all the parts of animals left only the heart untouched'. So Harvey made the heart the subject of his first detailed excursion into anatomy. The result is often referred to as Harvey's 'discovery of the circulation'; but this description makes his achievement sound too easy – as though he needed only to use his eyes, where his predecessors had been blind. In fact, like all scientific investigations, his enquiries were complex, methodical, and only partly successful. If we are to see their relevance to our general theme, it is important to acknowledge just what he could achieve, and what problems he was in no position to solve. Whatever could be established about the anatomy and hydraulics of the blood-vessels without the use of the microscope, Harvey did establish; but about the wider functions of the heart and lungs, the 'vital spirits' in the blood-stream, and the chemical processes in which they all took part, he was – inevitably – as much in the dark as his predecessors.

His anatomical results need to be stated here only briefly:

though fascinating, they are less relevant than the biochemical obstacles that defeated him. His main novelty was this: instead of regarding the blood-vessels which join the heart to the lungs (the pulmonary circulation) as independent of the more extensive network going from the heart to the rest of the body (the systemic circulation), he argued that the two systems constitute together a single hydraulic unit with the form of a figure of eight. The heart acts as a double pump, simultaneously driving the bright red blood out to the tissues and the dark blood back to the lungs. As not every part of this circulation could be seen with the naked eye, he was obliged to postulate a network of invisibly small passages (as Galen had done), joining the smallest arteries to the smallest veins. These 'invisible narrow connections' or 'capillaries' were observed for the first time four years after Harvey's death, when Malpighi, using the newly-invented microscope, saw them in the wing-membranes of a bat. At the same time, Harvey denied one central feature of Galen's account: the additional set of invisible capillaries or 'pores' by which 'the thinnest portion of the blood' was supposed to leak across the dividing-wall or septum from one side of the heart to the other. On the figure-of-eight hypothesis these pores were unnecessary, and there were moreover solid reasons for doubting their existence. These reasons were drawn from the texture of the septum, from the hydraulics of the supposed blood-leakage, and from the existence of the hole in the foetal heart (the *foramen ovale*). His observations confirmed what these arguments demanded: 'Damme, there are no pores and it is not possible to show such'. By itself, however, the evidence of observation could not be conclusive, for in that case Harvey would have been forced to dismiss *all* invisible capillaries alike.

When Harvey turned to questions of biochemical function, he was unable to make any real progress – and through no fault of his own. With the main categories of chemistry still undefined, he could know less than nothing about the biochemistry of growth and respiration; and on this front he was faced by three groups of problems – digestion, respiration, and temperature-control – all of which had to wait a full two hundred years for their solution. It was one thing to unravel the precise path along which the blood circulated: but it was another to determine its material composition at each stage of its circulation. However, one does find in Harvey's writings a wonderful sensitivity to the focal points of difficulty – a controlled, though fruitless, groping through an intellectual fog which he had not the means to dispel.

The physiologists of the seventeenth century were standing on the threshold of a new age, which they did not live to see. The vital and animal spirits common to all their systems were before long to lose their place in our thought. Chemists were to convert the vital pneuma of Galen and the Stoics (the animating World-Soul which we literally 'inspire') into a simple, inorganic gas; and, as a result, all the relations between chemistry and physiology were to be transformed. In the 1620s, however, physiology could still not dispense with the idea of 'spirits', even though the term had to be handled with extreme discretion. One puzzle about the vital spirits had always been their mode of transportation: did they enter into the substance of the blood-fluid, or did they travel along the arteries as separate bubbles? But this process remained wrapped in the cotton-wool of ambiguity. Sometimes Harvey wrote as though the vital spirits in the blood were little more than loosely dissolved gases – like the oxygen in oxyhaemoglobin. Yet at other times the idea of spirits retained for him all its wider associations. In his notes *On Animal Locomotion* (1627) he referred to the motive spirit in animals as 'the first principle of spontaneous activity' and 'the medium between soul and body'. In later years he became more and more aware of the problems which by now the term 'spirit' was disguising, and in his essays *On the Circulation of Blood* (1649) he returned to the topic:

With regard to ... spirits, there are many and opposing views as to which these are, and what is their state in the body, and their consistence, and whether they are separate and distinct from blood and the solid parts, or mixed with these. So it is not surprising that these spirits, with their nature thus left in doubt, serve as a common subterfuge of ignorance. For smatterers, not knowing what causes to assign to a happening, promptly say that the spirits are responsible and introduce them as general *factota*. And, like bad poets, they call this *deus ex machina* on to their stage to explain their plot and catastrophe. ... Some make the spirits corporeal, others incorporeal, and those who want them corporeal sometimes make the blood, or its thinnest portion, the link with the psyche. Sometimes they conceive of the spirits as contained in the blood (like flame in the aroma of cooking) and sustained by its continuous flow; sometimes of the spirits as distinct from the blood. Those who declare the spirits incorporeal have no ground to stand on, but they also recognize capacities as spirits (such as the digestive, chyle-forming, and procreative spirits) and admit as many spirits as they admit faculties or parts.

But the schoolmen also enumerate spirits of fortitude, prudence, patience and the virtues as a whole, and the most sacred spirit of wisdom, and all divine gifts. Moreover, they suspect that there are bad and good spirits helping, possessing, leaving and wandering round.

We might conclude from this argument that the whole category of spirits should be dismissed outright. But Harvey himself could not do this: he could only try to distinguish the one sense of the term which was legitimate, and explain the exact association between the blood and the vital spirits.

What, however, is specially relevant to my theme after all other meanings have been omitted from consideration as being tedious, is that the spirits escaping through the veins or arteries are no more separate from the blood than is a flame from its inflammable vapour. But in their different ways blood and spirit, like a generous wine and its bouquet, mean one and the same thing. For as wine with all its bouquet gone is no longer wine but a flat vinegary fluid, so also is blood without spirit no longer blood but the equivocal gore. As a stone hand or a hand that is dead is no longer a hand, so blood without the spirit of life is no longer blood, but is to be regarded as spoiled immediately it has been deprived of spirit. Thus the spirit, which is specially present in the arteries and arterial blood, is either the product of such blood, like wine's bouquet in wine, and the spirit in brandy; or like a small flame kindled in spirit of wine and keeping itself alive on such a diet.

All seventeenth-century scientists who grappled with the fundamental problems of matter-theory faced the same dilemma. The air obviously played a crucial part in maintaining life, and it was a natural assumption that it must itself contain a 'vitall form' or 'divine treasure of life', by which the blood was 'soulified': in fact they were entitled to go on believing this, until the opposite was clearly demonstrated. Yet how could this belief be disproved? With seventeenth-century ideas and techniques alone, one could never unravel the chemical processes involved in respiration, and in this direction physiology had to wait for advances in chemical theory and experiment. The chemists of the eighteenth century provided material not only for a revolution in their own subject, but also for one in physiology; and 'vital spirits' were to be among the first casualties.

J. B. van Helmont

The second of our representative figures, the Flemish physician J. B. van Helmont (1577–1644), was a very different character from Harvey: ready to plunge much more deeply into the quagmires of Paracelsan physiology and alchemical theory, and content to pay the price.

Aristotle and the alchemists share one doctrine which completely cuts them off from the chemists of the eighteenth and nineteenth centuries. Between 1725 and 1900 it was widely taken for granted that the basic ingredients of material things had fixed natures – which had been established at the beginning of time, and would continue unchanged until the Last Trump: but before 1650 this view was not widely held, and it took a century and more to displace the developmental view of inanimate substances.

The change-over from a developmental to a static conception of matter was as profound as the change from a geocentric to a heliocentric astronomy, and its effects were as far-reaching. Moreover, it was a step which could never have been justified by appeal to logical principles and experimental evidence alone. For how could the weakness of the developmental view be proved beyond question? It has been well said that 'old theories never die, they just fade away'; and at no time in the seventeenth and eighteenth centuries was the developmental view directly faced and decisively refuted. (Indeed, in the twentieth century it has shown signs of reviving.) Rather, for a variety of reasons more or less relevant, the balance between the two views shifted slowly from generation to generation, until the static view of unchangeable elementary substances, each with atoms of a distinctive shape, finally became dominant.

J. B. van Helmont helped to initiate this transition, but he did so inadvertently. He was himself a supporter of the developmental view: his positive ideas about the nature of matter were the seventeenth-century offspring of a family-tree which leads back through Paracelsus and the alchemists to Aristotle. Yet his approach to the problems of chemistry was above all a practical one: he laid great stress on the familiarity with material substances that comes from handling and observing them.

Certainly I could wish, that in so short a space of life, the Spring of young men, might not be hereafter seasoned with such trifles, and no longer with lying Sophistry. Indeed they should learn ... Arithmetick, the Science Mathematical, the Elements of Euclide, and then Geographic. ... And then, let them come to the Study of Nature, let them learn to know and separate the first Beginnings of Bodies. I say, by working, to have known their fixedness, volatility or swiftness, with their separations, life, death, interchangeable course, defects, alteration, weakness, corruption, transplanting, solution, coagulation or co-thickning, resolving. Let the History of extractions, dividings, conjoynings, ripenesses, promotions, hinderances, consequences, lastly, of losse and profit, be added. Let them also be taught, the Beginnings of Seeds, Ferments, Spirits and Tinctures, with every flowing, digesting, changing, motion, and disturbance of things to be altered.

The most lasting part of van Helmont's work was the demonstration that there are many distinct kinds of 'elastic fluid' – or 'gases', as he christened them. This was the first of the stepping-stones by which the pneuma-theory of the Stoics turned into the 'pneumatic chemistry' of the eighteenth century; but, by one of the ironies of intellectual history, the labours of the pneumatic chemists very soon resulted in the rejection of van Helmont's entire theoretical system. Few scientists have done so much to forge the instruments with which their own ideas were struck down.

Val Helmont followed out the implications of the developmental view resolutely and consistently. His basic problem was that of Aristotle and the Stoics: to explain how organized beings acquire their *forms*. In his opinion, the 'hot air' theory of the pneuma had been pure guesswork, and he criticized savagely Aristotle's doctrine – the starting-point of the whole pneuma-theory – that the formative ingredient in the semen is 'a spirit or breath in the froathy body of the Seed [whose] Nature ... answereth in proportion to the Element of the Stars'. For hot air, or quintessence, or any other substance, could be no more than *the material by which* the formative agent acted: it could never *be* that agent.

He therefore that looks on heat, for every Instrument of nature, and accounts this very Instrument for the seminal and vitall nature: he supposeth one of the King's Guard, to be the King, or the File to be the Workman. Yea heat, as heat, is not indeed the Instrument proper to nature: but a common adjacent, concomitant, and accidental thing produced in hot things onely: but the knowledge of nature, and essence, is not taken from improper, adjacent, and accidental effects: but from the knowing of Principles, which hitherto (even as it plainly appears) the Schoole of the *Peripateticks* [Aristotelians] hath been ignorant of.

In place of the pneuma-theory, van Helmont offered a positive counter-theory of his own. Development occurs he replied, because there is in the seed an active but immaterial agent, which must be distinguished from the passive material on which it works. This agent he sometimes referred to as the 'Governour' or (borrowing Paracelsus' word) the *Archeus*; sometimes, using a symbolism reminiscent of the alchemists, as its 'Vulcan'. Thus at death,

the *Vulcan* or Master-Workman forsaking the body, the flesh, heart, veins, etc. do begin to putrifie, for that they are now deprived of the vital Balsam their leader.

What is this Archeus or Vulcan? It is, he says, 'a certain vitall Air'. This might seem like one more reincarnation of the Breath of Life, if it were not for one thing: that van Helmont refuses to identify it with *any* familiar inanimate substance. On the contrary, he insists, every different object contains in its seed an Archeus characteristic of its species, which turns it into (say) a beech-tree, a mackerel, an eagle, a man, or a lump of quartz; and under suitable circumstances, when the organic form is deliberately destroyed, the Archeus can be released. With this doctrine as his foundation, he goes on to draw an unexpected conclusion: namely, that the world contains many distinct kinds of *gases*.

To see the connexion between van Helmont's central doctrine and his conclusion about gases, we must consider his account of the life-cycle of an organism. Like Thales and the author of *Genesis*, he started with a belief that the undifferentiated, characterless raw material of all things is water; and, being a good Protestant, he derived much satisfaction from this coincidence between scriptural teaching and his own scientific views:

After that the Firmament did separate the waters from the waters, the Eternall gathered together the sublunary ones, and their Collection, he called Sea. From the opposition of a Diameter, the dry Land appeared, which he named Earth; and both these framed one Globe.

Repeating a demonstration devised by Nicolas of Cusa, he showed experimentally how great a part water plays in the growth of plants. Interestingly enough, his conclusion relied on an appeal to the conservation of weight:

I have learned by this handicraft-operation, that all Vegetables do immediately, and materially proceed out of the Element of water onely. For I took an Earthen Vessel, in which I put 200 pounds of Earth that had been dried in a Furnace, which I moystened with Rain-water, and I implanted therein the Trunk or Stem of a Willow Tree, weighing five pounds; and at length, five years being finished, the Tree sprung from thence, did weight 169 pounds, and about three ounces: But I moystened the Earthen Vessel with Rain-water or distilled water (always when there was need) and it was large, and implanted into the Earth, and least the dust that flew about should be co-mingled with the Earth, I covered the lip or mouth of the Vessel, with an Iron-Plate covered with Tin, and easily passable with many holes. I computed not the weight of the leaves that fell off in the four Autumnes. At length, I again dried the Earth of the Vessel, and there were found the same 200 pounds, wanting about two ounces. Therefore 164 pounds of Wood, Barks, and Roots, arose out of water onely.

At this time, the processes of photosynthesis and transpiration were unsuspected; and the water poured on to the soil in which the tree was growing was its only visible link with the surroundings. So the conclusion – that the water was transformed into a fully-formed tree by the action of some agency present in the original seed – was reasonable enough.

This accounted for the constructive process – the creation of an organized being; but what about the other half of the story? Suppose you cut down a tree, and chop it into logs. You then have a fuel which, in its texture and form, preserves something of the tree from which it came. Set fire to the logs: they are destroyed and leave only formless ashes behind. And this always happens, on one condition. The logs must not be enclosed in too narrow a space: if we heat them in a sealed vessel we may succeed in baking them, but they will not catch fire or be consumed. We cite this fact nowadays as evidence that burning requires a continuing supply of oxygen, but van Helmont interpreted it differently: the wood can be turned to ash only if the 'formative spirit' within it is free to escape.

Moreover, every coal ... although it be roasted even to its last day in a bright burning Furnace, the vessel being shut ... nothing of it is wasted, it not being able to be consumed, through the hindering of its eflux. Therefore the live coal, and generally whatsoever bodies do not immediately depart into water, nor yet are fixed, do necessarily belch forth a *wild spirit* or breath. Suppose now, that of sixty-two pounds of Oaken coal, one pound of ashes is composed: Therefore the sixty-one remaining pounds, are the *wild spirit*, which also being fired, cannot depart, the vessel being shut.

And at this point, we are introduced to the brand-new word for the 'wild spirit' associated with the Archeus:

I call this Spirit, unknown hitherto, by the new name of *Gas*, which can neither be contained by Vessels, nor reduced into a visible body, unless the seed being first extinguished, But Bodies do contain this Spirit, and do sometimes wholly depart into such a Spirit, not indeed, because it is actually in those very Bodies (but truly it could not be detained, yea the whole composed Body should flie away at once) but it is a Spirit grown together, coagulated after the manner of a Body, and is stirred up by an attained ferment, as in Wine, the juyce of unripe Grapes, bread, hydromel or water and honey, etc.

In a gas the universal water is sub-divided so finely as to be less visible even than steam. This finely divided water is associated with the formative agent – the Archeus – and escapes from organized bodies along with it, being the material instrument by which the Archeus operates. Different substances, when burnt, naturally release different formative agents; and these organize the basic water into specific gases. (Van Helmont himself distinguished at least four kinds of gas – including *gas carbonum*, two kinds of *gas sylvester*, and *gas pingue*: these roughly correspond to carbon monoxide, carbon dioxide, nitrous oxide and marsh gas.) To leave no ambiguity, van Helmont explained that the 'vital spirit' which maintains life has itself the character of a gas:

The Spirit of our life, since it is a Gas, is most mightily and swiftly affected by any other Gas, to wit, by reason of their immediate co-touchings. For neither therefore doth any thing thereupon, operate more swiftly on us, than a Gas: as appears in the Dog-vault, or that of the Sicilians, in the Plague, in burning Coals that are smothered, and in perfumes: for many and often times, men are straightway killed in the *Burrowes of Mineralls*; yea in Cellars, where strong *Ale* or *Beere* belcheth forth its Gas, an easie sudden death and choaking doth break forth. . . . For a Gas is more fully implanted, and odours do keep a more immediate co-touching with the vitall Spirits, than Liquors.

(Nowadays we speak of alcoholic liquors as 'spirituous', but of the soul as 'spiritual': for van Helmont these ideas were still one and the same. This long-standing view survives as a linguistic fossil in most European languages today: the Italian word *spirito*, for example, means both 'methylated spirit' and 'soul'.)

The instrument by which the soul operates on the body is the vital spirit, and like alcohol and ether this is highly volatile: indeed, alcohol acts swiftly on us just because of its similarity to the vital spirit, into which it may even be transformed.

Wherefore, they who for some good while, do undergo the beating of the Heart, although they shall then drink abundantly, and that, much of the more pure Wine, yet they are not easily made Drunk; Because that by reason of an urgent necessity, the Spirit of the Wine is most speedily attracted into the Heart, and Arteries, which are scanty in Spirits, and is suddenly formed into vital Spirit.

But the full contrast between van Helmont's developmental approach and that of later chemistry appears when we study the implications of his theory for inanimate things. Minerals, for instance, were formed by the same process as living things. If flesh, bone, and plant-tissue take shape through the action of 'seeds' on water, so too do rocks and stones: petrification is a kind of embryological process. One finds this theory stated most clearly by one of van Helmont's disciples, the personal physician to King Charles II, Thomas Shirley:

The Hypothesis is this, viz. That stones, and all sublunary bodies, are made of water, condensed by the power of seeds, which with the assistance of their fermentive Odours, perform these Transmutations upon Matter.

The Seeds of Minerals, and Metals are invisible Beings; (as we have shewed, above, the true Seed of all other things are;) but to make themselves visible Bodies they do thus: Having gotten themselves suitable Matrices in the Earth, and Rocks (according to the appointment of God, and Nature) they begin to work upon, and Ferment the Water; which it first Transmutes into a Mineral-juice, call'd *Bur*, or *Gur*; from whence by degrees it formeth Metals. . . .

The Saxeous, or Rocky Seed, contained in these Waters, (which is so fine, and subtile a Vapour, that it is Invisible; as I have before shewed all true Seedes are,) doth penetrate those Bodies which come within the Sphere of its Activity; and by reason of its Subtility, passes through the pores of the Wood, or other Body, to be changed . . . So this Stonifying Seed, by its operating Ferment, doth transchange every particle of the matter it is joyned unto, into perfect Stone; according to its Idea or Image, Connatural with it self.

Van Helmont's belief in the embryological action of seeds and spirits displays the continuity between his ideas and those of the alchemists. (He even claimed privately to have witnessed with his own eyes the transmutation of base metals into gold.) And this background, far from being a handicap, proved a source of strength. For his lifelong struggle to put alchemical theory into a precise and scientific form led him to concentrate on the chemical properties of gases; and it was by just this study that the chemical tradition was ultimately transformed. Those of his contemporaries who belonged to the 'atomistic' school were for the most part concerned with *physical* properties – studying atmospheric pressure and the like. Though the theoretical verdict was eventually to go against him, it was van Helmont rather than the atomists who drew attention to the crucial role of gases in chemical reactions. So it is only justice that the word 'gas' has found a place in the dictionary, as his permanent contribution to our system of thought.

Van Helmont's ideas throw one curious sidelight on the history of philosophy. After his death his writings were prepared for publication by his son, Francis Mercury van Helmont, who was a close friend of the German philosopher, Leibniz. Now the heart of Leibniz' metaphysics was his *Monadology*: according to this theory, every creature in the world develops independently by the unfolding of its own inner capacities, and its perceptions represent – more or less obscurely, according to its grade in the scheme of things – the development of the whole world, as seen from its point of view. Historians of thought have often wondered where Leibniz found the material for his system: some have related it to aspects of Aristotle's formal logic, others have located its origin as far afield as China. Yet one source was perhaps nearer at hand. Take van Helmont's account of the development of living things, as the imposition by the Archeus of a scientific predetermined form, and recall that we humans too – like all sentient beings – conform to this same pattern. How then will the universe appear to us? And what perceptual interactions shall we have with the world? An 'Archeus-eye view' of the world will be very like that lying at the basis of Leibniz' monadology: it is as though van Helmont had been describing from the outside those very same activities that Leibniz, from the inside, presented as 'the perceptions of the monad'.

René Descartes

When we turn from the writings of van Helmont to those of René Descartes (1596–1650), we seem at first to have left the Middle Ages behind, and to have entered the world of modern science and philosophy. Descartes' style, his approach, above all the things he takes for granted, are familiar and congenial; and the intellectual fog which cuts us off from medieval discussions of the material world has been banished at a stroke. Yet, as we read on, this first impression is joined by a second: have we really moved on into the modern world, or have we rather been carried back to an earlier age – to the first flowering of natural philosophy in Ionia and Italy? He sweeps us along through his far-ranging and imaginative arguments, disposing in thrilling succession of the most varied collection of problems – the origin and mechanism of the solar system, the transmission of light, the ebb and flow of the sea; the nature of quicksilver and sulphur, nitre and charcoal; the powers in the magnet, the fire in the heart, and the sensations in the mind – and fitting all these jigsaw pieces together unhesitatingly to form a coherent picture of the cosmic mechanism. His account is as mechanical and mathematical as any twentieth-century scientist could ask. But where is the critical discipline by which the theoretical imagination must be matched? For all his clarity and imagination he seems to lack humility in the face of Nature. Like the pre-Socratics, he is giving us a consistent, even a plausible, picture of Nature; but he is not taking the trouble necessary to establish that his picture is also lifelike and correct.

Both these impressions of Descartes' science are just. The detailed explanations he gave have mostly failed and been forgotten, but his *Principia Philosophiae* (1644) remains nevertheless a landmark in scientific thought; for it represented the first comprehensive attempt since ancient times to account for *all* aspects of Nature in terms of a single system of mechanical principles. His revolt against older ideas was directed partly at appeals to authority, but above all at the introduction of 'mental' or 'spiritual' notions into science. He rejected these notions, not because of any prejudice in favour of brute inanimate matter, but for a deeper reason. He could admit 'animal spirits' into his physiology – so long as these behaved in an accountable and predictable way, like any other mechanical constituent of Nature. The objection to spiritual categories lay in the element of wilfulness and arbitrariness for which they were always an excuse. The motive spirit, said Harvey, 'is the medium between soul and body . . . the first principle of those phenomena which happen of their own accord'; but for Descartes it was inconceivable that natural phenomena should 'happen of their own accord'. One could use the name *spirits* for the operative agencies in the nerves, only so long as these too operated in a straightforward, mechanical manner.

So, rejecting authority and purposive explanations alike, Descartes reappraised the foundations of human understanding, and built up a comprehensive system of natural philosophy singlehanded. (His analysis of 'the theory of knowledge', though not our direct concern in this book, has become the accepted starting-point of modern philosophy.) His scientific system began from certain limiting principles, within which all the possible mechanisms of Nature must be confined. In his view, the fundamental ideas of natural philosophy should be perfectly clear, the truth of its principles should be self-evident, and its arguments should proceed in logical steps. These requirements led him, as they had led Plato two thousand years before, to see *geometry* as the basis of any satisfactory science. Descartes' aim, accordingly, was a double one: to demonstrate that all natural processes take place in a mechanical way, and to account for the laws of mechanics itself in terms of geometrical ideas – the shapes, sizes, and motions of the objects involved. What Plato had dreamt of doing for planetary kinematics, Descartes set out to do for the whole of physics and physiology.

How could one convince people that such a system of Nature was possible? The only satisfactory course was to go ahead and produce one, so Descartes had to work out an entire cosmology. The main features of this forgotten system can be summarized as follows: In the beginning there existed simply a boundless Euclidean universe, which God endowed with a certain quantity of motion in every direction. (This quantity of motion, being created by God and dependent on Him, was unchanging. It could be neither increased nor destroyed, but only exchanged between one body and another when they collided; and in every impact the total quantity of motion in any direction – measured by the bulk of each body, multiplied by its speed – remained the same.) Size and shape were the essential properties of any body, so every part of space – having a size and a shape – must represent a body of some kind, whose matter could be either heavy or tenuous: unlike the atomists, Descartes always denied the possibility of an absolute void. When God set the world moving, there was no emptiness for bodies to move into, so they at once began colliding, interacting and passing on their motion. In this way, complete *circles* of bodies were immediately set moving in unison, so that no part of space was in danger of being left empty: all motion in the universe accordingly took place in *vortices* or eddies, and these still continue, carrying (e.g.) a planet – round in a closed orbit. (See Descartes' diagram, page 176.)

At the boundaries between the eddies there were violent collisions: adjacent bodies ground against one another, wearing away or breaking up, and so creating a stock of 'subtle' or 'ethereal' matter of great tenuousness. When the brasion was complete there remained behind also a stock of spherical globules, worn so perfectly smooth as to be luminous: these in turn

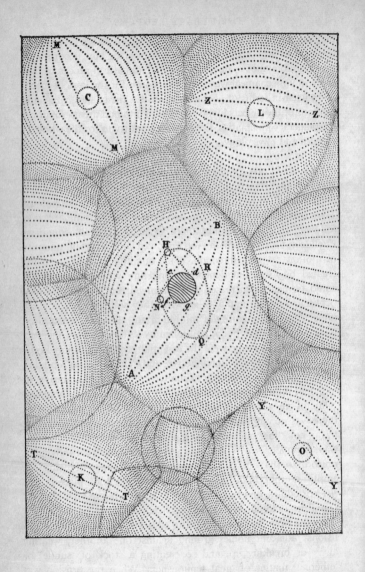

congregated at the centres of the vortices, adhering together to form larger aggregates – the familiar solid objects of the material world. Only those bodies which contained this third aggregated type of matter were subject to gravitation, and possessed an appreciable weight. No objects were composed *solely* of this most solid substance, or 'third matter', for they all had pores and spaces between the solid particles into which the more tenuous – ethereal and luminous – varieties could penetrate: in transparent objects, for instance, the luminous globules could pass right through. Two bodies of the same bulk might contain larger or smaller pores, and so different proportions of 'third matter': in that case their weights would be different. And this qualification was important. Since Descartes had identified 'body' with 'extension', the question was immediately asked: How can two bodies of the same extension have different weights? Descartes now replied: All bodies of a given volume contain the same bulk of matter, but only a fraction of this matter has any *weight*. (The Cartesians were, in fact, so confident about this reply that they attacked Newton's dynamics for gratuitously reintroducing 'quantity of matter' or 'mass' as a fundamental notion of physics, alongside and distinct from 'volume'.)

Basing himself on the principles of geometry, the vortices and the three kinds of matter, Descartes gave an account of Nature which contained room for physical processes of all sorts. True, he was obliged to introduce one fresh assumption after another, in order to accommodate all the new phenomena. Still, none of these assumptions was outrageously implausible, and the resulting picture of Nature, whether right or wrong, was always vivid and striking. Some of his explanations still carry conviction: others appear to us only quaint. Consider, for instance, how light from the sun warms solid bodies and causes them to expand. Descartes accounted for this as follows.)

All light-rays come from the Sun in the same direction, and act on the bodies which they meet only by exerting pressure on them in straight lines. Nevertheless, they produce a variety of motions in the particles of 'third matter' of which the surface region of the Earth is made up; for these particles, being moved also by other causes, present varying aspects to the rays. For instance, suppose AB is one of the particles of third matter, and rests on another marked C, while above it there are certain others (e.g. D, E. F): One can easily see that the Sun's rays, coming from GG, will be able to press on the extremity marked A with less hindrance from these other bodies than in the case of the end marked B, so that they must force A down; while at some subsequent time, when D, E, F have changed their position owing to the flow of celestial matter around them, they will happen to present

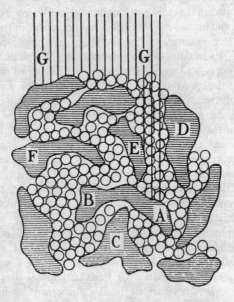

less obstacle to the sunlight pressing on B than in the case of A – which will give the earthy particle AB an entirely contrary movement. And the same for all the others: the result being that they will all be set in continual agitation by the sunlight.

Now it is just such an agitation in the minute parts of terrestrial bodies (whether excited by sunlight or by any other cause) that one calls their *heat*: particularly when this agitation is greater than usual, and so can stimulate in the nerves of our hands a movement sufficient to be felt. . . .

Finally, one must point out, this agitation of the minute particles of terrestrial bodies normally results in their occupying more volume than they do when they are entirely at rest, or at any rate less agitated. The explanation of this is that their irregular shapes can be lined up against one another better when they remain in the same positions than when their movement is leading to changes in their relative positions. So it comes about that heat rarefies nearly all terrestrial bodies, according to the shapes and arrangements of their parts.

This doctrine, that heat is a result of the random agitation of material particles, has held an established place in mathematical physics since the middle of the nineteenth century. But not all of Descartes' speculations were as 'far-sighted' and lucky. Consider again his theory of light. He associated all the heavenly bodies with intense vortices in the subtle matter of the heavens; the rotation of these vortices gave rise to centrifugal forces; and these forces drove streams of luminous globules outwards from the centre of the vortex in every direction. What we call 'light', Descartes taught, is in fact the pressure produced on the eye by these continuous streams of luminous globules. Each globule in a stream was in contact with the one in front, so any change of pressure at the centre must immediately make itself felt at the extremity : this gave the impression that the velocity of light was infinite. Thus, the motion of the solar vortex was the ultimate cause, which gave rise directly to an outward-streaming motion of luminous particles: the indirect effects of the motion were the pressure on our senses which we recognize as 'light', and the random agitation in terrestrial objects which we call 'heat'.

Sometimes Descartes reached the right answer for surprising reasons. For instance, he was one of the first men to recognize the 'law of refraction' often known as Snell's Law: the trigonometrical ratio connecting the angles at which a light-ray passes out of one transparent medium and into another. But he justified his formula by appeal to a purely mechanical analogy, comparing the light-globules to tennis balls: when the globules passed (say) out of air into water, the impact caused them to change their direction, and the results of this mechanical impact showed up as refraction.

Descartes' physiological theories were just as mechanistic as his physical ones. For instance: he accepted Harvey's anatomy of the blood-circulation, but regarded the heart as an ingenious steam-engine. In the beginning, Descartes said, God

kindled in the heart a non-luminous fire . . . exactly like that which causes damp hay to heat up when enclosed.

At every beat of the heart, quantities of blood entered from the lungs and the rest of the body. Once there, they

> rarefy and dilate, because of the heat which they find there. By this means, causing the whole heart to expand, they force home and close the five little doors [the valves] at the entrances of the two vessels from which they flow, so preventing any more blood from coming down into the heart. Becoming more and more rarefied, they push open the six doors in the entrances to the two other vessels through which they make their exit, so forcing all the branches of the arterial vein and of the great artery to expand almost as the same instant as the heart.
>
> Immediately afterwards the heart contracts, as do also the arteries, because the blood which has entered them has cooled; the six little doors close again, and the five doors of the *vena cava* and of the venous artery reopen, to make way for two more quantities of blood, which in turn cause the heart and the arteries to expand once more.

Having gone the rounds, the blood returned to the lungs, which acted as a kind of condenser:

> The true use of respiration is to carry sufficient fresh air into the lungs to cause the blood which reaches it from the right cavity of the heart – where it has been rarefied and (so to speak) vaporized – to thicken and be reconverted into normal blood, before passing down into the left cavity: without which process it would not be fit to serve as fuel for the fire in the heart.

This last example is a good illustration both of the strength and of the weakness of Descartes' approach. In detail, his account of the action of the heart will not survive testing: it implied – contrary to observation – that the blood vaporized in the heart, and travelled to the lungs in the form of blood-steam. For all that, its method was significant, in being so resolutely *mechanical*. As Descartes puts it himself:

> This motion [of the heart], which I have just explained, follows as necessarily from the very disposition of the organs [etc.] . . . as does the motion of a clock from the power, the situation and the form of its counterpoise and of its wheels.

Finally and most important: he was in fact well aware that all his theories were hypothetical, and said as much. For instance: if the globules from which bodies were made up were so minute, how had he found out anything about them? To this question he replied that all his conclusions were based on *suppositions*:

> First I considered in general terms, what were the simplest and most intelligible principles implanted in our understanding by nature [viz. those of geometry]. Next, I examined the chief ways in which invisibly-small bodies might differ in size, shape and situation, and how their mutual collisions could give rise to sensible effects. Lastly, when I found just such effects as these in the bodies perceived by our senses, it appeared to me that these might well have come about in precisely the way supposed.

This is a classic statement of the intellectual procedure still known as the *method of hypothesis* or 'Cartesian' method (commemorating the family name of des Cartes). In its logic, in fact, the modern scientific movement had two co-founders, Descartes and Francis Bacon (1561–1626), Lord Chancellor to King James I. The Englishman was anxious to guarantee that scientific theories should be based on a sufficient knowledge of the facts of Nature: in his method, the scientist collects, tabulates, and compares as many instances as possible of the effect under investigation, and only then can he justify any generalization about the effect. This is the *method of induction*. But according to Descartes there was an alternative procedure, without which the Baconian method could yield little theoretical fruit. For sometimes the scientist does better to proceed, not from previously collected facts to tentative generalizations, but the other way round – from some new conception or theory to the observations which will show its worth, or worthlessness. It is the merit of a good new theory that it brings a wide variety of natural happenings together into a coherent scheme of thought: provided it does that, it does not matter whether each step in its formulation was preceded by exhaustive Baconian fact-collecting. Thus the Cartesian procedure pays little attention to the manner in which we arrive at our hypotheses: it is their eventual performance that counts – and that is judged by deducing their implications, and matching these conclusions against Nature.

Descartes, in fact, went all the way. How you picked your hypotheses (he argued) was of no importance whatever. For instance, suppose that you had to decipher a message in code. If, when you experimented with certain substitutions, the words made consistent sense, you were entitled to conclude that this reading of the cipher was probably correct – especially in the case of a long message. This was a legitimate conclusion, however the trial substitutions were chosen – even if they were picked *at random*. Correspondingly in science, a hypothesis was to be judged by its fruits:

Consider how many different properties of the magnet, of fire, and of all other natural things, have been inferred with great clarity from the small number of causes which I set out at the beginning of this treatise. Even supposing that I had assumed these principles at random, without having had reason to be convinced of their soundness, there would still be as good reason to suppose them the true causes of all that I have inferred, as in the case of a code deciphered by guesswork.

Descartes' analogy between code-breaking and theory-making is excellent. The clues which Nature presents to the scientist – or which he extorts from her by shrewd interrogation – are like so many messages awaiting decipherment: a scientific theory is intended as a scheme of interpretation, which will make sense of all these messages. So the test of the scientist's success is like the cryptographer's: confidence comes when a novel interpretation makes consistent sense of more, and more varied, examples. Unfortunately, there are booby-traps, in science as well as in cryptography. One may well get a rough kind of sense out of the material, even using incorrect principles of interpretation; and, by making fresh assumptions *ad hoc*, to deal with every new example, one may continue to get apparent sense for a long time. The first scholars to interpret the 'Linear B' script used in Minoan Crete assumed that the language in question was Semitic; and the results they obtained in this way were not entirely meaningless. But only when Michael Ventris started from the alternative assumption, that the texts were in a primitive form of Greek, was there an interpretation which, without repeated assumptions, made consistent and convincing sense of new tests as they were discovered. This 'snowballing' effect is the crucial test.

As a logician Descartes was shrewd enough: as a scientist he was too indulgent to his own brain-children, accepting his scheme of explanations as 'morally certain', on the evidence of general, qualitative successes alone. He should have judged them by severer tests: calculating their implications in exact numerical terms, and testing them by deliberate observations and measurements. It was, in fact, left to Newton to compute the detailed implications of the vortex-theory for planetary astronomy, and the result demolished the foundations of Descartes' cosmology.

Still, Descartes' importance for science does not lie in the details of his cosmology. His decipherment of Nature might be crude, yet he had the courage to insist that mechanical sense could be made of the workings of Nature, throughout the realms of physics, chemistry, and even physiology. By reasserting the unity and rationality of Nature, he did as much as any man to put seventeenth-century scientists back on the intellectual road first trodden by the Greeks. Where Francis Bacon had provided the manifesto for experimental science, René Descartes now did the same for scientific theory. And though, in the three hundred years since 1650, there have been occasional conflicts between the Baconian and Cartesian tendencies in modern science, their opposition has been creative, and out of it have come many of our most profound insights.

The Implications of Mechanism

The 'new philosophy' took firm hold in the Protestant countries of northern Europe, and despite the forebodings of the Catholic Church it made headway also in France, Italy, and the Catholic parts of Germany. Yet this did not happen overnight. For its ideas were not merely mathematical and experimental but *mechanical*; and mechanical systems of Nature, as represented by the atomism of Epicurus, had long been suspect – so much so that Descartes emphasized the differences between his views and those of Demokritos, ending his *Principia* with an explicit submission to the Church.

At the same time, remembering my own insignificance, I make no positive affirmations, but submit all these opinions to the authority of the Catholic Church and to the judgement of wiser men; and I wish no one to believe anything I have written unless he is personally persuaded by the force and evidence of reason.

Before a mechanical system of natural philosophy could be made acceptable, either to the Church or to the ordinary believer, there had in fact to be a compromise; and the terms of this compromise have deeply influenced the subsequent development of science. Even today, their mark is evident in the structure of scientific ideas and institutions. For there were two topics which Descartes felt compelled to exempt from scientific enquiry: God and the human mind. Within a purely mechanical philosophy, these exemptions could be made only at a price: namely, an absolute division marking off theology and psychology from physics and physiology. And in the years that followed, most of his fellow-scientists have been prepared – though some more grudgingly than others – to accept the necessity for this division.

In practice, the price was considerable. Consider, first, its implications for our beliefs about the mind. Theories of Nature were to contain no mental or spiritual terms; and this rule applied not only to the motions of the planets, but equally to the activities of animals, and to bodily processes in the human frame. Yet in the case of human beings at least (for Descartes followed Catholic orthodoxy in denying souls to animals), one could not entirely rule out *all* references to mental activities and spiritual attributes. For theoretical purposes, the workings of the mind had somehow to be divorced from the bodily mechanism; and Descartes accepted this requirement. In his view, the world consisted of two fundamentally distinct 'substances' – mind and matter. Material things had locations in space and time, and were subject to change and decay; but the immaterial mind or soul had no dimensions in space, and was presumably immortal. These two substances interacted only in the case of human beings; and even there Descartes kept the mutual influence down to a minimum. Sensations, images, and passions could be aroused in the mind by bodily stimuli, and bodily motions could be initiated by the will; and these interactions took place at one point only in the human frame – possibly in the small organ at the base of the brain known as the pineal gland.

Throughout the eighteenth and nineteenth centuries, this absolute division between matter and mind (usually referred to as Descartes' 'dualism') set up far-reaching strains throughout both science and philosophy. For the division is more easily insisted on in the abstract than in practice: even the behaviour of animals does not fall obviously into two distinct categories – one 'material', the other 'mental'. So it is not surprising that other men soon carried the mechanistic approach further, and concluded that man, too, was in every respect a part of mechanical Nature. Julien de la Mettrie, in his essay *L'Homme Machine* (1747), declared that all mental activities, *thinking included*, were capable in principle of being explained mechanically.

The term 'soul' is therefore an empty one, to which nobody attaches any conception, and which an enlightened man should employ solely to refer to those parts of our bodies which do the thinking. Given only a source of motion, animated bodies will possess all they require in order to move, feel, think, repent – in brief, in order to *behave*, alike in the physical realm and in the moral realm which depends on it . . . Let us then conclude boldly that man is a machine, and that the whole universe consists only of a single substance [Matter] subjected to different modifications.

Most people found de la Mettrie's conclusion even less acceptable than Descartes' original dualism, and preferred the compromise by which scientists could theorize in mechanistic terms about all natural processes – with the solitary exception of mental activities. The expedient of throwing psychology to the wolves seemed a small price to pay in return for complete freedom of action in physics, chemistry, and physiology; and, before long, this limitation on the scope of science ceased to be any discomfort. (Those scientists who were preoccupied with the world of the inanimate could even afford to shut their eyes to it.) All the same, the compromise was not permanently satisfactory. It erected barriers between the 'natural sciences' – physics and physiology – and the 'mental and moral sciences' – psychology, sociology, and economics – higher and more impenetrable than experience warranted; and it created difficulties about the relations between mind and body which have perplexed philosophers ever since. Now in the twentieth century it has at last become clear that Descartes' dualism must be set aside in favour of a unified approach to the problems of psychology and physiology.

About the Divine Action, seventeenth-century scientists reached a similar temporary accommodation. Even for Harvey and van Helmont the creative activities of God were evident in the operations of Nature, and before physics and physiology could become entirely mechanistic some means had to be found of excluding Divine interventions, along with mental ones, from all the workings of the material world.

A way was soon found to mark off the sphere of natural science from that of theology, while preserving the scientist's freedom of action – at any rate, outside the sphere of human conduct. For men now concluded that it had been a mistake to suppose that God was for ever intervening in the course of Nature. The wonderful machine of the natural world operated perfectly without any 'miracles': the Divine Architect had designed it at the Creation so well that he was spared the necessity of any further intervention:

According to my opinion [wrote Leibniz], the same force and vigour remains always in the world, and only passes from one part of matter to another, agreeably to the laws of nature, and the beautiful pre-established order. And I hold that when God works miracles he does not do it in order to supply the wants of nature, but those of grace. Whoever thinks otherwise, must needs have a very mean notion of the wisdom and power of God.

So, from the seventeenth century on, the programme of science was dominated by the search for 'Laws of Nature'. The pattern of Divine Craftsmanship that Newton had revealed in the solar system presumably extended to the design of the whole universe; and the Creator's specification for the cosmos, as perpetuated in the Laws of Nature, must reveal itself to the devout and methodical enquirer.

The political analogy implied in the term 'laws' was not entirely idle: the Laws of Nature were regarded as expressions of the Almighty's sovereign will and design. The objects of the brute creation had not received the gift of free will, and had no option but to conform to these laws: their 'obedience' was automatic. But for the scientist this was a lucky dispensation, since it meant that he could infer the Divine Laws directly from the behaviour of natural things, without having first to ask whether they were obeying or rebelling against their Creator. The botanist John Ray saw himself as surveying *The Wisdom of God*, and eighteenth-century physicists and chemists saw the same Divine Wisdom manifested in the laws of gravitational attraction and chemical combination. And this fundamental conception, which divided off obedient Nature from the Creator by whose laws the world was governed, remained influential for two hundred and fifty years.

Yet this compromise between science and theology created difficulties for both sides. Once you denied the occurrence of miracles in the course of Nature, it was a short step to doubting whether they occurred at all – even in the sphere of human conduct. According to the 'Deists' the Almighty, having set the world going at the Creation according to fixed laws, was debarred from interfering in it thereafter in any way whatever. On the scientific side, too, the idea of a fixed order of Nature narrowed men's visions. Between 1650 and 1850 scientists came to believe, more dogmatically than ever before or since, that species of all kinds – animals, plants, and chemical substances equally – were fixed, distinct, and unalterable.

By the end of the seventeenth century Aristotle's programme for science had been quite abandoned, not only in mechanics and astronomy, where the new philosophy had led to substantial advances, but also in chemistry and physiology, where it had yet to bear fruit. The 'new philosophy' no longer accepted organic development as self-explanatory. Rather, it insisted on analysing all natural processes into fixed patterns of mechanical action and interaction. The bodies of animals, quite as much as inanimate objects, were to be regarded as configurations of material parts, moving and interacting like the pieces of a machine.

For the moment, this was only a vision for the future. Words are cheap; and it was not so simple a matter actually to build up a mechanistic science of physiology. One might perhaps show in simple cases how the general laws of physics applied – the valves of the heart, for instance, acting 'like the clacks of a pump'. But any understanding of biochemistry had to wait for improvements in chemistry proper. Meanwhile, men found it hard to possess their souls in patience. They could not accept promises of a mechanistic physiology on trust, and postpone all study of living things until physicists and chemists were ready for them. Around 1700, the sciences of matter, life, and mind reached a parting of the ways. Chemistry, physiology, and psychology went off in three separate directions. Hitherto, matter-theory had remained (so to speak) within call of medicine and physiology: with dynamics taking over the leading role, a novel situation was created. For the first time, men at large were agreed that matter was essentially passive, inert, uncreative, soulless, and static.

From this time on, the relations between matter, life, and mind became acutely, even insolubly, puzzling: the problem of life and the mind-body problem took central places in philosophical biology and psychology in a way they had never done before. For two hundred and fifty years the physical and chemical properties of matter, the activities of living things, and human thoughts and experiences, were cut off from one another and made the subjects of separate enquiries and theories. Only in the twentieth century have these intellectual barriers at last been seriously lowered. As a result one can study the development of ideas about matter and inanimate things since 1700 without needing to refer to contemporary ideas about life and living creatures and consider separately how the biological sciences – particularly physiology and biochemistry – came to terms with the new theories in the physical sciences. This is what we shall do here, following out first (in Part II) the changing conceptions of matter around which physics and chemistry have been built during the last two and a half centuries, and then returning (in Part III) to the growth of ideas about life and the structure of living things.

FURTHER READING AND REFERENCES

On the general development of science between 1300 and 1600, see:

A. C. Crombie, *Mediaeval and Early Modern Science* (2 vols), Doubleday, New York, 1959

A. R. Hall, *The Scientific Revolution*, Longmans, 1962

Marie Boas, *The Scientific Renaissance 1450–1630*, Collins, 1962

For the background to medieval science see:

R. W. Southern, *The Making of the Middle Ages*, Hutchinson's University Library, 1953

H. Pirenne, *Economic and Social History of Medieval Europe*, Kegan Paul, 1936

For the influence of alchemy, see the modern edition of E. J. Holmyard of *The Works of Geber*, tr. Richard Russell, 1678 (J. M. Dent, 1923), and also:

W. Pagel, *Paracelsus*, Interscience Publishers, 1958

William Harvey is best read in the original, preferably in the admirable editions of K. J. Franklin, who has translated both the *De Motu Cordis* and the *De Circulatione Sanguinis* (Dent, 1963). His notes on animal motion, *De Motu Locali Animalium*, have recently been edited and translated by Gweneth Whittridge (Cambridge University Press, 1959). On Harvey's anatomy, see the indispensable discussions by Donald Fleming in *Isis* (1955), and also F. J. Cole's *History of Comparative Anatomy* (Macmillan, 1944). J. S. Needham has a useful discussion of Harvey's biological ideas in his *History of Embryology* (Cambridge University Press, 1934).

Little has been published in recent years about van Helmont. The quotations in this chapter come from the *Oriatrike*, or *Physick Reviv'd*, the original translation of his *Ortus Medicinae*. The most detailed discussions available are those by J. R. Partington in *Annals of Science*, and in his *A Short History of Chemistry*, Vol. II, ch. 6 (Macmillan, 1937).

For the natural philosophy of Descartes, the most valuable modern discussion is to be found in:

Mary B. Hesse, *Forces and Fields*, ch. 5, Nelson, 1961.

A book on Descartes' science is in preparation by A. C. Crombie and Michael Hoskin. See also his original works, particularly the *Discourse on Method* and *Principia Philosophiae*. Scandalously, no complete English translation of the *Principia* is available: the standard edition by Haldane and Ross (Cambridge University Press, 1911, 1931, 1934) gives only section-headings for many of the most interesting scientific topics.

PART II

THE ACTIVITIES OF THE INANIMATE

8

Atomism Refurbish'd

HARVEY, Descartes, and van Helmont advanced our ideas about matter and material things, while still holding on to intellectual traditions established by Aristotle, Plato, and the alchemists respectively; but many of the natural philosophers involved in the scientific revival of the seventeenth century saw themselves rather as successors to Demokritos and Lucretius. In England these atomists included many of the founders of the Royal Society, and they referred to their system of mechanistic ideas as 'the corpuscular philosophy'. The name was well chosen. For the corpuscular theory started as a general *philosophy* of matter, barely distinguishable from the system of Lucretius, and it provided not so much knowledge of new facts as a framework for interpreting old ones. Still, a fresh flexibility of ideas was now tolerated. Consistency was no longer the supreme virtue in natural philosophy. Rationalists such as Descartes might be intent on pursuing a restricted and carefully defined system to its logical conclusions, but on the whole the new scientists were more anxious to bring their concepts into harmony with the observed processes of Nature – even at the price of added complexity, or eclecticism. And they were no longer content with a merely general, or qualitative, harmony: they were now beginning to demand that the implications of any new theory be worked out in detail – numerically – and tested by deliberate experimentation. So when, after a lifetime's experimental study of Nature, Isaac Newton subverted the very foundations of the traditional atomism and laid them down afresh in a brand-new pattern, only the French school of physicists – thoroughly drilled in Cartesian respect for action-by-contact, and for 'clear and distinct ideas' – protested at all vigorously and persistently.

The development of corpuscular philosophy in the seventeenth and eighteenth centuries had other curious features. In spite of the aspirations of the new scientists, the connexions between atomism and experience remained tenuous until 1803. Yet, when chemistry eventually provided solid experimental evidence for atomism, the confidence of the corpuscular philosophers did not increase in proportion. It could not do so, since from the start it had been complete. To a logician's eye this fact presents a paradox. He is accustomed to thinking of scientific theories as *products of* experimental enquiry – as being designed to expound and colligate results after the event, and to present us with a system of propositions which have where possible been verified. If that were the only legitimate point of view, our trust in a theory should certainly be related solely to the evidence supporting it – 'No scientific authority without experimental verification'. But theories have more than one function, and their merits are not entirely retrospective: they also direct the scientist's *approach to* his experimental enquiries, and present him with orderly sequences of new and unanswered questions. In a well-established science, of course, these two functions are inter-related: future investigations are all planned in the light of past discoveries. But at an earlier, more inchoate stage, when no system of ideas has extensive roots in Nature, one can lay bets and plan experiments only on the basis of promise.

That was the position in the sciences of matter at the beginning of the modern era. No theory had yet proved its worth. The only question was the old one: whether atomism or some other rival system provided the more promising approach. Galileo, Newton, and Lavoisier took one side; Leibniz, Diderot, and Lamarck the other. With the passage of time and the accumulation of experience – though only after amendments which would have horrified both Demokritos and Descartes – atomism made good its claims, leaving philosophy behind and achieving the status of an established scientific theory.

Atomism and the Spring of Air

In Italy and England the corpuscular system was already finding supporters before 1650. Galileo adopted atomism for general, philosophical reasons: it was the intellectual instrument by which he hoped to bring matter-theory within the fold of mathematics.

For, in his view, mathematics was capable of explaining all the processes of Nature.

Natural philosophy is written in a great Book, which holds itself at all times open before our eyes – I mean, the universe itself. But no one can understand it unless to begin with he sets himself to master the language, and recognize the characters, in which it is written. It is written in mathematical language, and the characters are triangles, circles and other geometrical figures.

The scientist's task, he taught, was to penetrate behind the surface appearances of things as they present themselves to our senses; for these were no safe guide to the underlying realities. His concern must be rather with the figures and motions of the constituent atoms of material things, since all sensory appearances were in fact produced by the action of these atoms on our sense-organs.

A truly scientific account of the behaviour of things should therefore refer only to shapes and motions – mathematically analysable properties, which Galileo called the 'primary' qualities of things. Characteristics such as colour and warmth, by contrast, had no place in scientific theory: such 'secondary' qualities were no more than by-products of the interaction between our bodies and the atoms of the outside world.

I find myself necessarily compelled, in conceiving a material or corporeal substance, to suppose thereby that it is marked out and de-limited by such-and-such a shape, that it is large or small as compared with other bodies, that it has this position (or some other) at this moment of time (or another), that it is either in motion or at rest, either in contact with another body or not. . . . By no effort of the imagination can I conceive it apart from these characteristics. But that it should be white or red, bitter or sweet, noisy or silent, fragrant or evil-smelling – I do not find myself in any way compelled to think of it as necessarily possessing any of these characteristics. On the contrary, if the senses had not distinguished these properties, neither the reason nor the imagination alone would perhaps have arrived at the idea of them.

I conclude that tastes, smells, colours and so on, regarded as the properties of objects, are mere names: their true location is, rather, in the sensitive body [of the observer] – so that, if every living thing was taken away, all these qualities would vanish and be destroyed.

This view was one that Demokritos had put forward long before, when he taught that objects are white or black, bitter or sweet, only 'by convention' or 'from our point of view'; and Galileo was happy to follow Demokritos in most respects, differing from him only in the central importance he attached to mathematics. He treated the atoms as the physical counterparts of the infinitesimal units of geometry: in this way, questions of embryological development or physiological function were swept aside, in favour of mathematical and mechanical questions. The agenda of science was then clear: one must start with geometry, next harness this to mechanics (the theory of primary qualities), and lastly relate the secondary properties of the bodies we can see and touch to the primary properties of their invisibly small atoms.

As a first practical step to advance his new mathematical science, Galileo and his pupils began to experiment on the physical properties of elastic (i.e. compressible or gaseous) fluids – notably, on the air of the atmosphere. This choice of starting-point was no accident. Atomism had always appeared most plausible when applied to the physics of gases, and Hero of Alexandria's treatise on the subject was familiar both to Galileo in Italy and, a generation later, to Robert Boyle in England. The first experiments simply carried further Hero's demonstrations of the material character of the air (see note at end of chapter): Galileo's pupils set out to measure atmospheric pressure, and in so doing produced the first true vacuum.

Craftsmen had long known that an ordinary suction-pump will lift water only up to a certain height – about thirty feet – and Galileo himself studied this phenomenon, though inconclusively. Torricelli, his secretary, was convinced that the key factor in the situation was the force exerted by the atmosphere: to test this idea, he suggested replacing the water by mercury, a liquid fourteen times as dense. In 1643, the experiment was performed by his colleague, Viviani. He took a long glass tube sealed at one end, filled it with mercury, and inverted it in a bath of the same liquid, leaving its open end under the surface. As Torricelli had foreseen, when the sealed end of the tube was lifted thirty inches or more above the surface of the mercury-bath, the column of mercury broke away from the seal, leaving a space above it: the pressure of the atmosphere on the mercury-bath was not sufficient, it seemed, to support a longer column.

This demonstration caused great excitement. News of it spread across Europe almost as quickly as Galileo's own *Starry Messenger* thirty-three years before. The Cartesians, of course, could not agree that the space at the top of the tube was a true void, empty of all matter: at most it was empty of 'third matter', and contained only the more ethereal kinds. And, certainly, Torricelli's vacuum was not entirely void of *all* physical influences: light, for instance, was transmitted across it. But for the moment the essential thing was to confirm that the height of the mercury column depended on the pressure of the atmosphere, and this was soon done. As Blaise Pascal argued, the column should in that case be shorter at the top of a mountain than at its base; and so it proved – a barometer carried up the Puy de Dôme in 1648 dropped markedly in the process.

Similar lines of research were followed up both in Germany and England, notably by Otto von Guericke and Robert Boyle. Using an air-pump designed by his assistant, Robert Hooke, Boyle embarked on a long series of experiments on 'the spring of air' (i.e. the pressure of the atmosphere) and the properties of the vacuum. Many of these experiments led to no result, but others were significant: he showed, for instance, that in a vacuum a flame cannot burn nor an animal breathe, while smoke falls instead of rising. In his most famous experiments, Boyle measured the volume taken up by a given quantity of atmospheric air as he varied its pressure. He at first offered the resulting table of measurements as it stood, without comment or interpretation; but, in response to criticisms, he extended his observations and stated the relation still known as Boyle's Law: 'The pressures and expansions' of any given quantity of atmospheric air are 'in reciprocal proportion' – so that, when the pressure exerted on an enclosed volume of air is (say) doubled, trebled, or quadrupled, the air shrinks to one-half, one-third, or one-quarter of its original volume.

Being a faithful disciple of Francis Bacon, Boyle had reached this conclusion as the result of a laborious sequence of measurements – enforcing it (one might say) by sheer weight of numbers. But the same result was achieved independently by Edme

Mariotte in France, using a method as Cartesian as Boyle's was Baconian. Whereas Boyle began by accumulating observations which were to be interpreted only later, Mariotte began from the other end – using his theory to pose a question. What Boyle established by 'induction', Mariotte established by the 'hypothetico-deductive' method. Supposing there *were* a 'reciprocal proportion' between pressures and expansions how could this relation be elegantly demonstrated? Mariotte devised a crucial test, and then needed only a few observations to satisfy himself of its correctness. (No single test can be crucial for a Baconian, since to him all events are on a par.)

Suppose that air must compress in proportion to the load which it bears: it necessarily follows that if, in the course of an experiment, the mercury [in a barometer] rises in the tube to a height of [only] 14 inches [instead of the normal 28 inches], the air enclosed in the rest of the tube [above the mercury] must be expanded to twice the volume it had before the experiment – provided that, at the same time, barometers empty of air support mercury to a height of 28 inches exactly.

Mariotte saw at once how one could check the relation between pressure and volume. One must construct a barometer-tube, in which an air-column at normal atmospheric pressure was enclosed by mercury. Then, if on inverting the tube into a mercury-bath, the length of this air-column was doubled and the 'reciprocal proportion' held, the pressure of the enclosed air must immediately be halved. The mercury in the tube would then be supported by an air pressure of only one-half atmospheric, and would be correspondingly shorter – 14–15 inches long instead of the normal 28–30 inches.

To check this conclusion, I made an experiment with the help of M. Hubin, who is very skilled at constructing barometers and thermometers of many kinds. We used a tube 40 inches long, which I had filled with mercury up to a height of $27\frac{1}{2}$ inches: so leaving $12\frac{1}{2}$ inches of air. If the tube was plunged one inch into the mercury-bath, leaving 39 inches above it, it should then contain 14 inches of mercury and 25 inches of air expanded to twice its [original] volume. My expectations were not mistaken. When the tube was reversed and its end plunged into the mercury of the bath, the mercury in the tube fell and, after oscillating, came to rest at a height of 14 inches; so that the

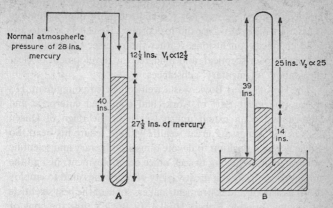

enclosed air then occupied 25 inches, and was expanded to twice the volume it had occupied when enclosed.

Experimental results such as these could be explained in atomistic terms, if one regarded changes in the volume of the air as corresponding to changes in the distances between its unobservable particles. But this was not the only possible interpretation. Mariotte himself shared Descartes' theoretical dislike of atomism, and found alternative ways of interpreting the spring of air. The basic appeal of atomism to seventeenth-century corpuscular philosophers remained general and philosophical: their experimental work on air did not, by itself, provide compelling evidence of the *truth* of the atomistic doctrines. It carried conviction only to the convinced.

Robert Boyle and Chemistry

Outside the physics of gases, 'corpuscular philosophy' provided material more for manifestos than for solid explanations. To see just how incapable it was of explaining chemical composition and reactions, we cannot do better than study the work and ideas of Robert Boyle. Boyle was both a practical chemist and a theoretical atomist, yet there was curiously little contact between these two aspects of his work. His chemical researches, though very fruitful, never brought to light any convincing support for atomism: this stage was not reached for more than a hundred years after his death. Nor did his corpuscular beliefs lead to any solid chemical conclusions. Rather the reverse: they made him somewhat over-sceptical, and hindered the development of clear ideas about 'elementary' substances.

The Hon. Robert Boyle was a well-connected young man. His father, the great Earl of Cork, had combined enterprise and shrewdness to an extent unusual even in the reign of Queen Elizabeth I, amassing great wealth without losing his head. So Boyle was in a position to devote himself to literary and scientific studies, without having to seek office or employment: he had the money to set in train a great variety of researches, and to employ as his assistants and instrument-makers some of the best scientists of the day, notably Robert Hooke. In Boyle's time the sons of the nobility were often educated privately: Boyle and his elder brother, however, spent four years at Eton, and were then sent to Geneva and Florence to complete their educaton. During his time abroad Boyle became a student of natural philosophy and made himself familiar with the 'ingenious books' containing 'the new paradoxes of the great star-gazer Galileo'. Returning to England he settled down on his estates to live the life of a country gentleman, so far as one could do during the Civil War. He at once began to experiment and write: producing the first of those literary compositions which today fill the bulky volumes of his *Collected Works*, and keeping in touch with all those correspondents and associates who were eventually to form the core of the new Royal Society.

From earthquakes and air-pumps to God and morality, all was grist to his mill. Being immensely curious, he took seriously many ideas which his more earnest nineteenth-century admirers regarded as superstitions: including those of the alchemists and the Jewish Cabala. His deepest admiration was reserved for Francis Bacon, and from the beginning he shared Bacon's conviction of 'the usefulness of natural philosophy'. So he was always prepared to investigate questions of a mechanical or (as we should now say) a 'technological' kind – recognizing how, 'by the help of Attention and Industry' in the study of Nature, we might 'do many things, some of them very strange, and more of them very Useful in humane life'. The demands of technology were not, however, overpowering: his fundamental aim was to advance the *theory* of matter, in the hope of bringing the practical knowledge of experience of chemical craftsmen into line with the insights of the natural philosophers. And, since his private income was quite sufficient, he was exempt from the financial lures of alchemy, concentrating (as he remarked in a letter to John Locke) on 'luciferous' instead of 'lucriferous' experiments. He was far from sceptical about the possibility of alchemical transmutation; but other experiments were more urgent, if matter-theory was ever to provide a true understanding of chemical processes.

From early on, Boyle was a firm supporter of the corpuscular philosophy, believing that all the properties and changes of material things could eventually be explained by the shapes, motions, and arrangements of their minute constituent particles. His views are set out most clearly in *The Origin of Forms and Qualities* (1666), a book which presented not a tentative set of conclusions supported by experimental evidence, but rather a corpuscular *pattern of thought*. Writing in the spirit of the Greek natural philosophers, Boyle argued that a coherent theory of matter could be built up only on corpuscular principles:

The doctrine I shall here attempt to establish, take as follows: (1) There is one universal matter, common to all bodies, an extended, divisible, and impenetrable substance. (2) This matter being in its own nature but one, the diversity in bodies must necessarily arise from somewhat else: and since there could be no change in matter at rest, there is a necessity of motion to discriminate it; and for that motion, also, to have various tendencies.

His arguments for the theory, like Galileo's, were chiefly philosophical – he was concerned to distinguish the essential (primary) properties of the 'universal matter' from its secondary effects:

These two principles, matter and motion, being established, it will follow, that matter must be actually divided into parts; and that each of the primitive fragments, or other distinct and entire masses, must have two attributes, its own magnitude or size, and its own figure or shape. And, since experience shows that this division of matter is frequently made into insensible particles, we may conclude that the minutest fragments, as well as the largest portions of the universal matter, have, likewise, their peculiar build and shape. For being a finite body its dimensions must be terminated, and measurable; and tho' it may change its figure, yet it will necessarily have some figure or other. We must, therefore, admit three essential properties of each entire part of matter, viz. magnitude, shape and either motion or rest: the two first of which may be called inseparable accidents; because matter being extended, and yet finite, it is physically impossible that it should be destitute of some bulk and determinate shape.

Colours, odours, and textures were to be explained by identifying the particular configurations of corpuscles responsible for them; and the different kinds of material substance – oil, fire, stone, and iron – represented so many different patterns or arrangements of the universal raw material. All natural change consisted in the alteration of these patterns, rather than in the creation or annihilation of matter:

When oil takes fire, the oil is not said to be altered but corrupted or destroy'd, and fire generated; [but] nothing substantial, either in this or any other kind of corruption is destroy'd, only that particular connection of the parts, or manner of their coexistence, upon account whereof the matter was term'd stone, or a metal, or belong'd to any other determinate species of bodies.

Nineteenth-century chemists could be excused for thinking that Boyle's theory of matter was the same as their own – immutable atoms moving, combining, and separating – for he foreshadowed the idea of molecules, formed by the stable association of smaller particles:

... such corpuscles, whether of a simple, compounded or decompounded nature, as have the particles they consist of so firmly united that they will not be totally disjoined, or dissipated, [even] by that degree of fire or heat, wherein the matter is said to be volatile.

But this was as far as his 'modernity' went. For one conviction is absolutely fundamental to all modern chemistry – the belief that matter is *not* infinitely transformable by chemical means, and that only certain specifiable reactions are possible. This conviction is the very opposite of Boyle's own belief. Whereas, for modern chemists, a given set of ingredients can be combined and transformed in only a limited number of ways, Boyle was convinced rather that the range of possible products was always *un*limited. If, for example, one planted a vine-cutting, which formed roots and drew in water from the soil, this liquid went through a remarkable sequence of changes:

Supposing then, this liquor, at its first entrance into the roots of the vine, to be common water; let us a little consider how many various substances may be obtained from it ... and first, this liquor being digested in the plant, and assimilated by the several parts of it, is turned into the wood, bark, pith, leaves, etc. of the vine; the same liquor may be further dried, and fashioned into vine-buds, and these a while after are advanced unto sowre grapes, which expressed yeeld verjuice, a liquor very differing in several qualities both from wine and other liquors obtainable from the vine: these sowre grapes, being by the heat of the sun concocted and ripened, turne to well-tasted grapes; these, if dried in the sun and distilled, afford a faetid oyle and a piercing empyreumatical spirit, but not a vinous spirit [etc., etc.].

Like van Helmont, Boyle concluded that these products were simply transformations of one single ingredient – water:

Into all these various schemes of matter, or differingly qualifyed bodies, besides divers others that I purposely forbear to mention, may the water, that is imbibed by the roots of the vine, be brought, partly by the formative power of the plant, and partly by supervenient agents or causes, *without the visible concurrence of any extraneous ingredients*.

In fact, he could see no justification for limiting the range of possible transformations in *any* way – e.g. by ruling out alchemical transformations:

I could not see any impossibility, in the nature of things, that one kind of metal should be transmuted into another; that being, in effect no more, than that one parcel of the universal matter, wherein all bodies agree, may have a texture produced in it, like the texture of some other parcel of matter common to them both.

One could even trim and reshape the very corpuscles themselves – a view which would have offended against the deepest principles of classical nineteenth-century chemistry. The shapes, sizes and arrangements of all atoms being capable of change, any material substance could change into any other.

The seeds of things ['seeds' in van Helmont's sense], the fire and the other agents are able to alter the minute parts of a body (either by breaking them into smaller ones of differing shapes, or by uniting together these fragments with the unbroken corpuscles, or such corpuscles among themselves), and the same agents *partly by altering the shape or thickness of the constituent corpuscles* of the body, partly by driving away some of them, partly by blending others with them, and partly by some new manner of connecting them, may give the whole portion of matter a new texture of its minute parts, and thereby make it deserve a new and distinct name; so that according as the small parts of matter recede from each other, or work upon each other, or are connected together after this or that determinate manner, a body of this or that denomination is produced, as some other body happens thereby to be altered or destroyed.

This unlimited transformability of Boyle's 'universal matter' had one immediate consequence. Instead of recognizing the existence of fixed chemical 'elements' (a step with which he is sometimes credited), *he was forced to rule these out*. That was the chief conclusion of his best-known book, *The Sceptical Chymist*. He quoted the traditional definition of 'elements' or 'principles':

Certain Primitive and Simple, or perfectly unmingled bodies; which not being made of any other bodies, or of one another, are the Ingredients of which all those call'd perfectly Mixt Bodies are immediately compounded, and into which they are ultimately resolved.

But he did so only to raise doubts about the existence of any such elements:

Now whether there be any one such body to be constantly met with in all, and each of those that are said to be Elemented bodies, *is a thing I now question*.

For he had shown what a vast range of transmutations occurs in Nature, and how inconclusive were all the received arguments for chemical elements – whether the four roots of Empedokles and Aristotle, or the *tria prima* of Paracelsus. Having demolished these ramshackle intellectual constructions, he concluded:

I see not why we must needs believe that there are any primogeneal and simple bodies, of which, as of pre-existent elements, nature is obliged to compound all others. Nor do I see why we may not conceive that she may produce the bodies accounted mixt out of one another by variously altering and contriving their minute parts, without resolving the matter into any such simple or homogeneous substances as are pretended.

Faced with this declaration, how can anyone say that Boyle introduced the modern idea of chemical elements? About corpuscles and their arrangements, he was confident enough; but the whole pursuit of material 'elements' was a chase after a will-o'-the-wisp. If there were any stable, homogeneous substances underlying all others, this had yet to be demonstrated; and one could certainly not do this unless chemical procedures and classification were first improved:

> The objections I made ... need not be opposed so much against the doctrines themselves ... as against the unaccurateness and the unconcludingness of the analytical experiments vulgarly relied on to demonstrate them.
> And therefore, if either of the two examined opinions, or any other theory of elements, shall upon rational and experimental grounds be clearly made out to me ... I shall not be so farr in love with my disquieting doubts, as not to be content to change them for undoubted proofs.

The immediate task was one requiring patience, industry, and method. Without improved techniques of investigation, theoretical speculation must remain a waste of breath. One must establish ways, both of reproducing any chosen chemical process, and of breaking down, building up and identifying chemical substances exactly and reliably. Only when this had been done would our chemical evidence be worth having. At this point Boyle the practical chemist took over, and Boyle the corpuscular philosopher retired to the background.

Boyle's atomism accordingly played only a negative part in the development of his chemical ideas: it served him as an antidote against *other* chemical theories. Eventually, it implied, chemistry must be taken over by physics, and provide explanations referring only to the shapes, sizes, motions, and arrangements of corpuscles. But this was a long-term programme: for the moment atomism gave him no help in his practical task – that of devising reliable, and preferably numerical procedures for analysing chemical constitutions and reactions.

The fundamental fact was that earlier chemists had classified material substances in a hurried and superficial way, paying too little attention to the *criteria* by which different classes of substance were to be distinguished. In the case of metals, the damage had not been serious, though there were some difficulties about mercury and certain alloys. But the class of 'salts' was a mixed one, and that of 'sulphurs' more heterogeneous still. The first pedestrian, but indispensable, step was to get these classifications better sorted out: then chemists would at any rate know what sorts of substances there were handling.

Nowadays, chemical analysis appears humdrum and unexciting. In Boyle's time it called for imagination and perception – anything but the repetition of a routine. For, without any established criteria, one had to unravel the constitutions of countless different material stuffs exactly as they occurred in Nature – few of them being pure, most of them being complex mixtures, many coming from animal or vegetable origins, and few of them having any obvious and distinctive characteristics. Two substances otherwise similar might differ in colour, solely because of minute impurities; yet the same colour difference might be highly significant – as with green, blue, and white vitriol (iron, copper, and zinc sulphates). So Robert Boyle, the practical chemist, was rightly preoccupied with identification tests. Through his careful work it became possible to identify substances of many other kinds with a reliability known hitherto only in the case of metals, and even to detect and distinguish impurities and adulterants. He introduced the 'flame test', in which even a minute fraction of a substance betrays its presence by the distinctive colour it gives to a flame. He extended Kepler's work on the geometrical forms of crystals, noting (for example) that saltpetre always formed 'long and hexaëdral' or 'prismatical' crystals. He also used specific gravity as a chemical test, so marrying physics and chemistry, and adding Archimedes' hydrostatic balance to the equipment of the up-to-date laboratory.

But a mere recital of these achievements gives one little of the flavour of Boyle's mind. For that one must dip more widely into the numerous books which were the outcome of all his researches. *The Sceptical Chymist* is unusually theoretical: more often, he would report *New Experiments and Observations touching Cold*, or raise *Suspicions about some Hidden Qualities of the Air*, enquire into *The Strange Subtilty, Great Efficacy and Determinate Nature of Effluviums*, or defend his position as a *Christian Virtuoso* – i.e. a religious, as well as a scientific, enthusiast.

His books display vast receptiveness and an open mind, omni-vorous reading and an inexhaustible appetite for new research. For experimental scientists the mid-seventeenth century was a Golden Age:

> Bliss was it in that dawn to be alive
> And to be young was very Heaven!

And Boyle was like the Elephant's Child: his curiosity was in-satiable, and he was always happy, provided that he had some novel phenomena to investigate or some new informants to cross-question. Suppose the problem was: what are the pressure and temperature deep down in the sea? He would question 'an ancient Sea-Commander that had many years frequented Africa and the Indies' and 'an Engineer of my Acquaintance, that had often been at Sea, and loved to try Conclusions' – who assured him that a brandy-flask sealed and lowered to forty fathoms was smashed by the water-pressure – while 'an inquisitive person of my acquaintance that made a long stay in the Northerne America (at about two or three and forty degrees of Latitude) and diverted himselfe with swimming under water' reported that the sea cooled rapidly as one went down, and below the two-fathom level was quite cold at all seasons.

Anything was worth recording, including much that Boyle could not explain, and all the time there was an endless stream of experiments on all subjects. Would organic matter placed in a vacuum putrefy as rapidly as usual?

A Piece of roasted Rabbet, being exactly clos'd up in an exhausted Receiver, the Sixth of *November*, was two months and some few days after taken out without appearing to be corrupted, or sensibly alter'd in Colour, Tast, or Smell.

(His experiments to answer this question remind one of Swift's Laputa.) So it went on: there was no limit to his assiduity or inventiveness. With his leisure and resources, he could undertake any enquiry his imagination suggested to him. Devoting to ex-periments the same energy that his father had expended on more worldly things, he set in train all the investigations one man could humanly handle. Long after we put his books aside the memory remains of this tireless man, endlessly contriving new trials, new tests, and new instruments; collecting, measuring, observing, describing, reporting; engaging the barest of his acquaintances with probing questions; hoping always to elicit fresh and accurate information about the behaviour of natural things. Boswell, one feels, could do no more for Samuel Johnson than Robert Boyle had already done for Nature.

The Newtonian Reformation

So by 1700 the fundamental debate in science was back at the level to which the Greeks had raised it. With the two important exceptions of dynamics and astronomy, seventeenth-century amendments to the classical concepts had been only marginal in their effects, and had not greatly increased the explanatory power of the older traditions. The really profound changes had taken place in men's minds – in their attitudes to Nature, and to natural science. For Nature, the Creation of God, had at last become as important as Revelation, and the study of Nature had acquired a new vigour and discipline. Looking at seventeenth-century science, we may miss the lucid clarity and imaginative sweep of Greek theory, but the critical concentration with which men now focused their minds on individual phenomena was soon to justify itself. Science found itself on a rising, not a falling, wave.

What was true of science in general was true also of atomism. All the current variants on the corpuscular theme – even the quasi-atomism of Descartes, from which the void was carefully excluded – were philosophical as much as scientific in their motives. Their ideas were general and indefinite, giving no indication of the actual sizes and shapes of any specific corpuscles; nor were they free from those deficiencies of traditional Greek atomism which the Stoics had countered with their pneuma-theory. And corpuscular philosophy could not hope to extend its scope beyond the limits of Demokritos' first theories, without drastically enlarging its vocabulary of concepts.

The pattern for the atomism of the future was sketched by Isaac Newton, and it took a form which in one fundamental respect ran counter to accepted ideas. Perhaps only a man of Newton's breadth of view could have imagined and elaborated the new theory: certainly only he could have got away with it. For the success of his theories of mechanics and gravitation gave him an intellectual fulcrum on which to bear; and the lever with which he proceeded to force an opening into the problems of matter-theory was his own concept of *attractions and repulsions*.

In astronomy and dynamics his predecessors had placed in his hands the material for a complete new 'system of the world'. His own achievement had been to construct a mathematical framework into which all these materials could be assembled – the resulting theory (presented in the *Principia*) rounded off one hundred and fifty years of cumulative enquiries, and so closed a chapter in physics. In matter-theory, he had no such inheritance of discoveries to build on, and his intellectual vision reached far beyond the facts then available. Consequently, he could express his ideas only in the form of 'Queries' – so opening doors for his successors, rather than closing them. His theory was first presented to the public in 1706, as an appendix to his treatise on *Opticks*. Throughout the eighteenth century its influence was even greater than that of the *Principia*; and a whole school of physical scientists, applying the new ideas in the most varied fields of enquiry, were proud to call themselves Newtonians. More widely still, the literature and even the poetry of Western Europe was stirred for many years by its reverberations.

Newton began from the same point as the Stoics: namely, from the inadequacy of a purely mechanical atomism. For solidity and cohesion were as much a problem as ever, which none of the existing theories did anything to solve:

The Parts of all homogeneal hard Bodies which fully touch one another, stick together very strongly. And for explaining how this may be, some have invented hooked Atoms, which is begging the Question; and others tell us that Bodies are glued together by rest [i.e. immobility], that is by an occult Quality, or rather by nothing; and others, that they stick together by conspiring Motions, that is, by relative rest among themselves.

(The monk, Michael the Scot, had taken advantage of this difficulty to save himself from the Devil. He agreed to be hanged, on one condition: that the Devil made the noose out of sand.) To remedy this deficiency, Newton introduced one radically new idea, which has since become so integral a part of our physics that we forget what a drastic novelty is represented. He had already demonstrated that certain physical forces – those of gravity, for instance – were capable of acting across great distances. The question now was: Might there not be similar short-range forces, which normally acted only at inter-atomic distances?

Have not the small Particles of Bodies certain Powers, Virtues, or Forces, by which they *act at a distance*, not only upon the Rays of Light [i.e. light-corpuscles] for reflecting, refracting and inflecting them, but also upon one another for producing a great Part of the Phaenomena of Nature? For it is well known that Bodies act one upon another by the Attractions of Gravity, Magnetism, and Electricity; and these Instances show the Tenor and Course of Nature, and make it not improbable but that there may be more attractive Powers than these. . . .

The Attractions of Gravity, Magnetism and Electricity, reach to very sensible distances, and so have been observed by vulgar Eyes, and there may be others which reach to so small distances as hitherto escape Observation; and perhaps electrical Attraction may reach to such small distances, even without being excited by Friction.

The idea of inter-atomic forces had great attractions for Newton, for it promised to unify into a single system the theory of the heavens and the theory of the minutest atoms:

And thus Nature will be very comformable to her self [i.e. uniform] and very simple, performing all the great Motions of the heavenly Bodies by the Attraction of Gravity which intercedes those Bodies, and almost all the small ones of their Particles by some other attractive and repelling Powers which intercede the Particles.

For the moment he was content to leave aside all questions about the *mechanism* of this inter-atomic action. As with gravitation earlier, the first thing was to prove that the attractions existed: there would be time enough later to study the mechanism.

How these Attractions may be perform'd, I do not here consider. What I call Attraction may be perform'd by impulse, or by some other means unknown to me. I use that Word here to signify only in general any Force by which Bodies tend towards one another whatsoever be the Cause. For we must learn from the Phaenomena of Nature what Bodies attract one another, and what are the Laws and Properties of the Attraction, before we enquire the Cause by which the Attraction is perform'd.

With this introduction, Newton launched himself on seven thousand five hundred words of brilliant exposition ranging over his whole scientific experience, in the course of which he explored the intellectual possibilities of his suggestion. By assuming a mere handful of inter-atomic forces he saw hope of including in his picture of Nature an unexpected variety of natural processes. Why do chemical substances react as they do? What happens when animals breathe, and plants nourish themselves? How do solid bodies cohere? Why does water rise up between narrow sheets of glass? Why do gases expand? How is it possible for flies to walk on water? What causes thunder? All these questions, and more, took on a fresh and promising appearance when related to this novel scheme of ideas.

He began with examples from chemistry. These provided evidence of short-range attractions much stronger than those of gravity. Certain substances have the power to absorb water-vapour from the air, and deliquesce unless kept in closed containers: the more pronounced this tendency, the more strongly they must be heated in order to drive off the water. Is this not evidence, asked Newton – clearly expecting the answer, Yes – of an attractive force binding the particles of water-vapour to those of the substance? If so, a stronger attraction would naturally produce both a more rapid deliquescence and a tighter resulting bond between the salt and the water. Similar attractions might explain the violent reactions between acids and metals, and a dozen comparable processes. Nitric acid and thick vegetable oils, for instance,

grow so very hot in mixing, as presently to send up a burning Flame; does not this very great and sudden Heat argue that the two Liquors mix with violence, and that their parts in mixing run towards one another with an accelerated Motion, and clash with the greatest Force?

The idea of chemical binding-forces or 'elective attractions' was taken up and developed later in the eighteenth century, and provided a ready-made explanation of 'chemical displacement' – in which a substance C displaces B from the compound AB, on account of its greater 'affinity' for A, and so forms the new compound AC. Newton cited several dozen examples of this very process, many of them quite authentic. To quote one instance only: mercury can be extracted from cinnabar (mercuric sulphide) by the addition of quicklime, for this active substance 'by a stronger Attraction' detaches the sulphur from the cinnabar, and so 'lets go the Mercury'. In this idea Newton saw the germ of a general theory of chemical composition, applicable to substances of all kinds:

> Is it not from the mutual Attraction of the Ingredients that they stick together for compounding these Minerals?... And the same Question may be put concerning all, or almost all the gross Bodies in Nature. For all the Parts of Animals and Vegetables are composed of Substances volatile and fix'd, fluid and solid, as appears by their Analysis; and so are Salts and Minerals so far as Chymists have been hitherto able to examine their Composition.

But if these chemical binding-forces were authentic, they must – like any other forces – produce physical as well as chemical effects. And here, at long last, Newton saw a way of explaining the *cohesion* of solid bodies. Instead of supposing 'hooked Atoms' or 'conspiring Motions',

> I had rather infer from their Cohesion that their Particles attract one another by some Force, which in immediate Contact is exceeding strong, at small distances performs the chymical Operations abovemention'd, and reacheth not far from the Particles with any sensible Effect.

How strong were these cohesive forces? Very strong indeed: capable, in fact, of producing some observable effects even on full-scale material bodies. And to support this he went on to quote yet another, quite distinct, line of experimental evidence—the phenomenon of 'capillary attraction' – which converged neatly upon the same theoretical point:

> If two plain polish'd Plates of Glass (suppose two pieces of a polish'd Looking-glass) be laid together, so that their sides be parallel and at a very small distance from one another, and then their lower edges be dipped into Water, the Water will rise up between them. And the less the distance of the Glasses is, the greater will be the height to which the Water will rise. If the distance be about the hundreth part of an Inch, the Water will rise to the height of about an Inch [and so on].

By using his own optical experiments to estimate the thickness of water-films, he was able to estimate the absolute strength of the cohesive attractions: they were sufficient, he calculated, 'to hold up a Weight equal to that of a Cylinder of Water . . . two or three Furlongs [i.e. 1500 feet or more] in length'.

There are therefore Agents in Nature able to make the Particles of Bodies stick together by very strong Attractions. *And it is the Business of experimental Philosophy to find them out.*

Were all the inter-atomic forces attractions? There was evidence to suggest that, beyond the range of chemical and cohesive forces, there were also forces of repulsion. His chief illustration is significant, not only on account of its own intrinsic interest, but also for a historical reason, since it gave rise to a misconception about the structure of gases which persisted until the middle of the nineteenth century. For Newton now attempted to explain Boyle's Law in terms of certain inter-atomic repulsions. In the course of the *Principia* he had proved a mathematical theorem which appeared to account for the 'reciprocal relation' between pressure and volume as neatly as the theory of gravitation accounted for Kepler's laws of planetary motion.

If a fluid be composed of particles fleeing from each other, and the density be as [i.e. vary in direct proportion to] the compression, the centrifugal forces of the particles will be inversely proportional to the distances of their centres and, conversely, particles fleeing from each other, with forces that are inversely proportional to the distances of their centres, compose an elastic fluid, whose density is as the compression.

Suppose that a large number of small particles is enclosed in an empty container, and that each particle repels every other with a force which drops off in proportion to their distance apart: then, as Newton demonstrated mathematically, in the absence of other forces the particles taken together must behave like a gas and obey Boyle's Law. Conversely: if Boyle's 'spring of air' is a consequence of Newtonian forces acting between every pair of corpuscles, then these forces must (by the same mathematical proof) be forces of repulsion varying inversely as the separation.

Within the *Principia* Newton avoided making the next, more questionable step. He did not assert that this was the *true* explanation of Boyle's Law, or that actual gases were *in fact* collections of mutually-repelling particles: at that stage he left the suggestion entirely hypothetical. But twenty years later he was prepared to go further. Other explanations of Boyle's Law had been discussed in the meantime – which supposed (for instance) that the atoms of gases were coiled and elastic – but these were all highly unconvincing, and Newton could see no plausible alternative to his own explanation. So the very existence of air and vapours was for him evidence of 'a repulsive Virtue' acting between the particles of matter –

the Particles when they are shaken off from Bodies by Heat or Fermentation, so soon as they are beyond the reach of the Attraction of the Body, receding from it, and also from one another with great Strength, and keeping at a distance, so as sometimes to take up above a Million of Times more space than they did before in the form of a dense Body. Which vast Contraction and Expansion seems unintelligible, by feigning the Particles of Air to be springy and ramous, or rolled up like Hoops, or by any other means than a repulsive Power.

This suggestion still remained part of a query to be investigated, rather than an established conclusion. However, when mathematicians began to study the physics of gases again, towards the end of the eighteenth century, many of them took the correctness of Newton's speculation for granted; and this (as we shall see) temporarily diverted the theory of gases and heat into a blind alley.

For the moment Newton paused. This flood of varied examples was enough to demonstrate the intellectual possibilities of his new matter-theory – based on atoms and central forces. Yet there was one final step. Up to this point he had dealt solely with the *forces between* the particles of bodies: his ideas about the particles themselves had still to be made clear. Evidently they were outstandingly hard – much more so than the hardest of ordinary material bodies. But they were not just hard: they were *immutable*; and this immutability was our ultimate guarantee that the Order of Nature was stable. Where Boyle's corpuscles could be divided, trimmed and reshaped, Newton's primitive particles were truly 'atomic' – that is to say, uncuttable.

Newton's much-quoted paragraph on this subject was the

crowning conclusion of a long train of thought, and the point at which a dozen different lines of evidence converged. Looking back over his long survey of chemical, optical, meteorological and other phenomena, he offered, not a dogma, nor a certainty, but a tentative general hypothesis:

All these things being consider'd, it seems probable to me, that God in the Beginning form'd Matter in solid, massy, hard, impenetrable, moveable Particles of such sizes and Figures, and with such other Properties, and in such Proportion to Space, as most conduced to the End for which he form'd them; and these primitive Particles being Solids, are incomparably harder than any porous Bodies compounded of them; even so very hard, as never to wear or break in pieces; no ordinary Power being able to divide what God Himself made one in the first Creation.

While the Particles continue entire, they may compose Bodies of one and the same Nature and Texture in all Ages: but should they wear away, or break in pieces, the Nature of Things, depending on them, would be changed. Water and Earth composed of old worn Particles and Fragments of Particles, would not be of the same Nature and Texture now, with Water and Earth composed of entire Particles in the Beginning.

And therefore, *that Nature may be lasting*, the Changes of corporeal Things are to be placed only in the various Separations and new Associations and Motions of these permanent Particles; compound Bodies being apt to break, not in the midst of solid Particles, but where those Particles are laid together, and only touch in a few points.

For nearly two hundred years the immutability of atoms – with its chemical counterpart, the stability of elements – remained an unquestioned presupposition of Newtonian science; and a great proportion of physical scientists during this time were sincere Newtonians. Yet the evidence cited by Newton supported this particular doctrine only weakly. No doubt it simplified one's picture of material change to consider only the arrangement and motions of the primitive atoms, instead of having to allow for changes of shape and size as well; and, in any case, if changes such as Boyle had envisaged did in fact occur, some further theory would be needed to explain them in turn. Rather than admit this additional complication, Newton preferred to start with immutable primary particles, and imagine them organized in more and more complicated architectural patterns:

The smallest Particles of Matter may cohere by the Strongest Attraction, and compose bigger Particles of weaker Virtue; and many of these may cohere and compose bigger Particles whose Virtue is still weaker, and so on for divers Successions until the Progression end in the biggest Particles on which the Operations in Chymistry, and the Colours of natural Bodies depend, and which by cohering compose Bodies of a sensible Magnitude.

(These 'biggest Particles' he estimated, from optical measurements, to be $\frac{1}{1000}$ to $\frac{1}{500}$ of an inch in diameter.)

The assumptions involved in Newton's position were in fact large ones. Was it so certain that Nature *is* lasting, or that the atoms do 'compose Bodies of one and the same Nature and Texture in all Ages'? Was there at the time – indeed, has there ever been – evidence enough to justify a conviction that atoms and material substances are of *fixed species*? This conclusion might have appeared much less secure if it had not had the additional support of Newton's theology. For, according to Newton, in the beginning God performed three actions, all of which were required if the world was to be scientifically intelligible. First, He arranged the planetary system, and set it moving according to laws of His own choosing. Secondly, He devised the human body, whose symmetry and ingenuity could be 'the effect of nothing else than the Wisdom and Skill of a powerful ever-living Agent'. And, finally, He completed the Order of Nature by making the imperishable atoms, and binding them together with interatomic forces or 'active Principles'. Once it had been set going, Nature was sustained by laws and principles which scientists could discover, but the original Creation must have been the work of a Divine Architect and Craftsman:

Now by the help of these Principles, all material Things seem to have been composed of the hard and solid Particles above-mention'd, variously associated in the first Creation by the Counsel of an intelligent Agent. For it became him who created them to set them in order. And if he did so, it's unphilosophical to seek for any other Origin of the World, or to pretend that it might arise out of a Chaos by the mere Laws of Nature; though being once form'd, it may continue by those Laws for many Ages.

Newton and the Aether

With his conception of 'Power, Virtues or Forces' acting at a distance between invisible particles, Newton remedied the most serious deficiencies of the corpuscular philosophy, and the perennial argument between Atomists and Stoics took a new turn. He had demonstrated clearly – in a scientific, as well as a philosophical way – that a comprehensive theory of matter required more than a random jostling of corpuscles. But his new system, built around the ideas of Atoms and Central Forces, did more than patch up an older theory: it was a brand-new one, and broke completely with earlier systems based on Atoms and the Void. (It is significant that Newton did not refer to himself as an atomist.) Philosophically, it was an eclectic system, combining the atoms of Demokritos into a coherent order by tensions or forces like those of the Stoics. And once again – as in the case of the pneuma – the question arose by what mechanism or medium these forces were transmitted.

In 1706 when Newton first revealed the picture of Nature which had guided his researches, he deferred all questions about this mechanism. As he knew, 'action at a distance' was anathema to up-to-date philosophers, and his new 'heresies' were liable to be denounced as reactionary – reviving a belief in the hidden powers and occult qualities which the new philosophy had aimed at discrediting. Just as earlier he had been on the defensive over gravity, so now he took care to present the inter-atomic forces

not as occult Qualities, supposed to result from the specific Forms of Things, but as general Laws of Nature by which the Things themselves are form'd; their Truth appearing to us by Phaenomena though their Causes be not yet discover'd.

Seven years later he wrote a short postscript to be added to the second edition of the *Principia* (1713), from which it is clear that the problem was still preoccupying him. (It is from this passage that the parallels between his ideas and those of the Stoics become most clearly apparent.)

And now we might add something concerning a certain most subtle spirit which pervades and lies hid in all gross bodies; by the force and action of which spirit the particles of bodies attract one another at near distance, and cohere . . . and all sensation is excited, and the members of animal bodies move at the command of the will, namely, by the vibrations of this spirit, mutually propagated along the solid filaments of the nerves, from the outward organs of sense to the brain, and from the brain into the muscles. But these are things that cannot be explained in a few words, nor are we furnished with that sufficiency of experiments which is required to an accurate determination and demonstration of the laws by which this electric and elastic spirit operates.

Finally in 1717, after the death of his old adversary Leibniz, Newton filled out these hints by publishing his speculations about the transmission of gravity and other forces. These took the form of further Queries, added to a new edition of the *Opticks*. The central feature was no longer a 'subtle spirit' but a tenuous medium, filling all space, which he called the 'aether'.

And is not this Medium exceedingly more rare and subtile than the Air, and exceedingly more elastick and active? And doth it not readily pervade all Bodies? And is it not (by its elastick force) expanded through all the Heavens?

The aether had a number of powers. It conveyed radiant heat through a vacuum, and played an essential part in the reflection and refraction of light. It transmitted the 'vibrations' or 'pulses' associated with the passage of light-corpuscles, and was accordingly of extreme elasticity (weight for weight, he computed, more than 490,000,000,000 times as elastic as air!). Furthermore, by supposing it to be denser in empty space than in the vicinity of massive bodies, one could provide a mechanism for gravitational attraction: the earth then moved towards the sun under the pressure of the aether, like a cork rising from the depths of the sea.

In point of theory, then, Newton's aether and the Stoic pneuma had a common function: to 'carry' the forces of cohesion and repulsion by which matter was maintained in ordered systems. This being so, one might have expected Newton to treat the aether as unquestionably *continuous*: how else could it support and transmit pressures and tensions at every point? To suppose – instead – that the aether itself was corpuscular threatened to launch one on the infinite regress that engulfed Lucretius' 'mind-stuff'. For if the aether had an atomic structure, and its medieval texts on alchemy, and even repeated some of the experiments and procedures for himself. Some people have interpreted this as evidence of a 'dark and hidden side' to his character. Yet not everyone who reads *Das Kapital* is on that account a Marxist, and Newton had the best of reasons for being interested in alchemical texts. What else should he have read? The works of 'respectable' atomists would have given him little beyond the physics of gases and the principles of hydraulics. As chemists, the neo-Platonists were fanciful, Aristotle and Aquinas simply irrelevant. Only the alchemists and metallurgists, with their Renaissance successors, passed on to the seventeenth century any serious body of chemical knowledge and experience.

Nevertheless, in the realm of practical chemistry Newton could go no further than Boyle, and he was far from being a nineteenth-century atomist. His basic atoms were immutable, but it was unclear what known substances – if any – were composed of these ultimate units. So he could see no conclusive argument against the transmutation of metals, nor any sharp distinction between organic and inorganic processes:

All Bodies have Particles which do mutually attract one another: the Summs of the least of which may be called Particles of the *first Composition*, and the Collections or Aggregates arising from the Primary Summs; or the Summs of these Summs may be call'd Particles of the *second Composition*, etc.

Mercury and Aqua Regis can pervade those pores of Gold or Tin, which lie between the Particles of *its last Composition*; but they can't get any further into it; for if any Menstruum [solvent] could do that or if the Particles of the first, or perhaps of the second Composition of Gold could be separated; that Metal might be made to become a Fluid, or at least more soft. And if Gold could be brought once to ferment and putrefie, it might be turn'd into any other Body whatsoever.

And so of Tin, or any other Bodies; as common Nourishment is turn'd into the Bodies of Animals and Vegetables.

So long as there was no clearer connexion with the substances of practical chemistry, the new system of atoms and central forces thus remained stuck at the level of general *theory*: in the event, it took Newton's successors more than a century to establish numerically and in detail the relations between atoms and elements, forces and bonds, which he had sketched in outline.

THE ACTIVITIES OF THE INANIMATE

NOTE: HERO ON AIR AND THE VACUUM

The most important document to survive from classical times on the subject of atomism and the properties of the air is Hero of Alexandria's treatise, the *Pneumatika*. The date of this treatise is one of the outstanding problems about Greek science, for we have no personal information about Hero. Different scholars have placed him as much as four hundred years apart – anywhere from 150 B.C. to A.D. 250 – but recent estimates have been converging on to the period around A.D. 60.

The greater part of the *Pneumatika* described useful or amusing gadgets driven by air, steam, or water power, but in his introduction Hero set out the general principles underlying their construction. In the course of this discussion he reported some simple experiments designed to demonstrate that air was corporeal:

Vessels which most men regard as empty are not empty, as they suppose, but full of air. Now this air, as physicists agree, is composed of particles which are minute, light and mostly invisible: so, if we pour water into a vessel which is apparently empty, air will leave it in direct proportion to the water entering it.

This may be seen from the following demonstration. Let the seemingly-empty vessel be inverted and pressed down into water, while being kept carefully upright, The water will not enter it even if it is entirely immersed. Evidently, since the air is corporeal and itself occupies the whole volume of the vessel, it does not permit the water to enter. If we now bore a hole through the base of the vessel, the water will enter through its mouth, the air escaping through the hole. On the other hand, if we lift the vessel vertically before perforating its base and turn it upright again, we shall find that its inner surface is entirely dry, exactly as it was before immersion.

Atmospheric air differed from other material substances in one respect only: this he explained in atomistic terms. Its corpuscles, instead of being jammed together, touched only at a few points and were elsewhere separated by a void:

The particles of the air are in contact with each other; yet they do not fit closely in every part, but void spaces are left between them, as between the grains of sand on a seashore. (These grains must be imagined to correspond to the particles of air, and the air between the grains of sand to the void spaces between the particles of air.) Hence, when any force is applied to it, the air is compressed and – contrary to its nature – is forced into the vacant spaces by the pressure exerted on its particles. When the force is withdrawn, however, the air returns again to its former position on account of the elasticity of its particles: in this, it resembles horn shavings and sponge which, if compressed and then released, return to their original position and volume.

Much of his discussion was devoted to arguing for the possibility of a void. In this connexion he described experiments in which he used 'cupping-glasses' and similar vessels to produce a temporary vacuum:

If you take a light vessel having a narrow mouth and apply it to your lips, then suck the air out and discharge it, the vessel will hang from your lips – the vacuum drawing the flesh into it, so as to fill up the exhausted space. It is evident from this that there is a continuous vacuum in the vessel. The same may be shown using the egg-shaped cups used by physicians, which are made of glass and have narrow mouths. To fill one with liquid, physicians suck out the air inside, place a finger over the vessel's mouth and invert it into the liquid; when the finger is withdrawn, water is drawn up into the exhausted space, even though this upward motion is against its nature.

It was no longer reasonable, Hero concluded, to maintain in the face of all the evidence that a vacuum was impossible.

Those who assert that there is absolutely no vacuum are at liberty to invent arguments on this subject, and their doctrines may be apparently convincing, although they offer no tangible proof. But if one can show, by appeal to observable phenomena, that a continuous vacuum actually exists – even though artificially produced – and also that a vacuum exists in Nature, not continuously but scattered in minute portions, bodies filling up these scattered vacua when compressed; those who rely only on plausible counter arguments will no longer be able to establish their case.

FURTHER READING AND REFERENCES

For purposes of convenient reference, useful discussions of these topics will be found in:

H. T. Pledge, *Science since 1500*, London, 1939

A. Wolf (and D. McKie), *A History of Science, Technology, and Philosophy in the Sixteenth and Seventeenth Centuries*, Allen & Unwin, 1935

On the revival of atomism generally, see the relevant chapters of:

A. G. van Melsen, *From Atomos to Atom*, Harper, 1960

Robert Boyle's *The Sceptical Chymist* is widely available, but his more typical works can mostly be studied only in early editions. However, Boyle is the subject of an admirable recent study:

Marie Boas, *Robert Boyle and Seventeenth-Century Chemistry*, Cambridge University Press, 1958

Newton's *Opticks* can be bought in paper backs (Dover Books, 1963): the book is both a bargain and an intellectual treat. His writings on a variety of topics related to our present theme are to be found in two recent collections:

H. S. Thayer, *Newton's Philosophy of Nature*, Hafner, 1953

I. B. Cohen, *Isaac Newton's Papers and Letters on Natural Philosophy*, Cambridge University Press, 1958

His private papers on chemistry are now in course of publication (for the first time!) and up to now one volume has been published, under the editorship of A. R. and M. B. Hall (Paris, 1958). For critical discussions of Newton's matter-theory, and its influence on the science of the eighteenth century, consult:

I. B. Cohen, *Franklin and Newton*, Philadelphia, 1956

Hélène Metzger, *Newton, Stahl, Boerhaave et la Doctrine Chimique*, Paris, 1930

Mary B. Hesse, *Forces and Fields*, Nelson, 1961

For the wider repercussions of the *Opticks*, especially on eighteenth-century literature, see:

Marjorie Nicolson, *Newton Demands the Muse*, Princeton University Press, 1946

1. Chinese 'rainbow vessel', used in the first century A.D. for preparation of mercury from cinnabar.

2. Medieval assay laboratory, from the *Treatise on Ores and Assaying* by Lazarus Ercker. Notice the similarity of the apparatus to earlier alchemical equipment.

3. Dürer's engraving 'Melancholia'. Notice the magic square in the top right-hand corner.

4. The Renaissance anatomy theatre built for Fabricius at the University of Padua.

5. Wright of Derby's painting, 'The philosopher demonstrating the air pump'. This picture illustrates eighteenth-century interest in pneumatic experiments. The bird in the globe is unable to fly because the air has been pumped out.

6. William Blake's satirical painting 'Newton'. Blake depicts Newton as an earthbound mathematician turning away from the wonders of Nature.

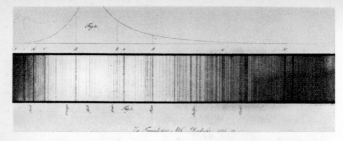

7. Fraunhofer's original map (1814) of the Solar Spectrum showing the sharp absorption lines. (Lent to Science Museum, London, by the Royal Society)

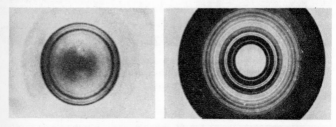

8. Diffraction photographs: X-rays and electrons. A beam of X-rays (left) and a beam of electrons (right) diffracted through similar crystals produce strikingly similar diffraction patterns.

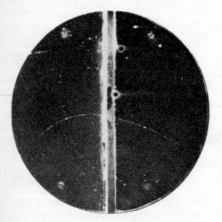

9. Cloud chamber track of the positive electron or 'positron'. The particle is slowed up by a lead sheet and the change of curvature in its path shows that it must be travelling from right to left: a negative electron would leave a track curving the other way.

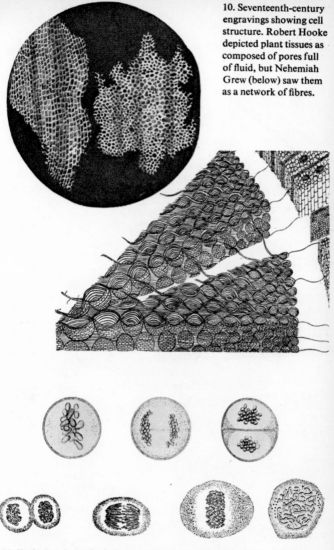

10. Seventeenth-century engravings showing cell structure. Robert Hooke depicted plant tissues as composed of pores full of fluid, but Nehemiah Grew (below) saw them as a network of fibres.

11. Early drawings of cell division. Hofmeister (1848) could already see some of the internal structures within the nucleus (above) and by the 1880s Flemming was depicting the chromosomes clearly (below).

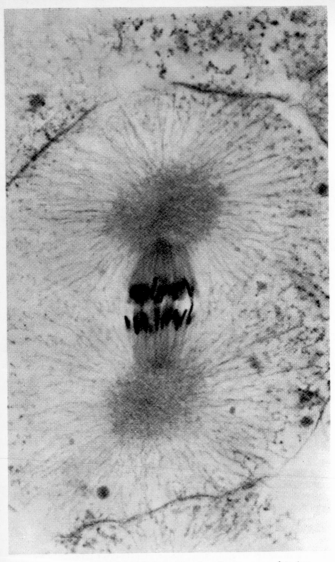

12. Electron micrograph of cell division showing chromosomes drawing apart. Compare this modern photograph with Plate 11.
(**Magnification** × 4,000)

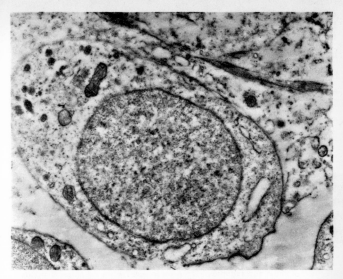

13. Electron micrograph of cell nucleus from bone marrow.
(Magnification × 11,000)

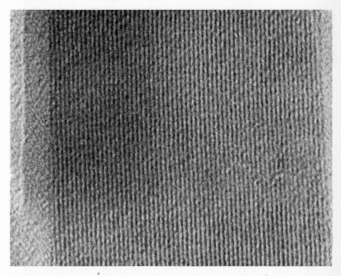

14. Electron micrograph of atoms forming the lattice of a platinum crystal.
(Magnification × 1,500,000)

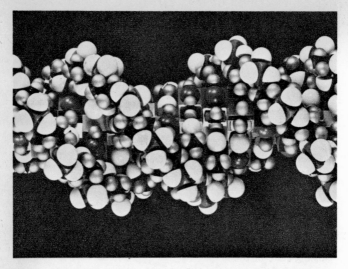

15. Part of conjectural model of DNA molecule. Notice the spiral structure in which the two main strands of atoms (represented by the larger balls) are intertwined.

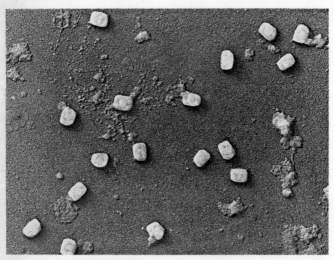

16. Electron micrograph of smallpox vaccine virus. In this picture the virus particles stand out against a neutral metallic background. (Magnification × 40,000)

9

The Problem of Incorporeals

IN the next century and a half, matter-theory was to be transformed from a branch of philosophy into a fully-fledged natural science. The transition was gradual and difficult, involving both new theoretical insights and new experimental techniques. Obviously enough, changes in theory could be justified only by appeal to the relevant facts – which often required to be established by experiment. But, equally significantly, one could design experiments and interpret their results only within limits set by the existing state of theoretical ideas. Confusion and ignorance fed upon each other, and neither of them could be attacked separately.

One obstacle above all others delayed the union of theory and experience – the problem of 'incorporeals'. For centuries men had possessed a working acquaintance with solids and liquids, but all less tangible agencies had remained shrouded in confusion and ambiguity. In 1700 men were not merely uninformed about them: they were positively *incoherent*, scarcely even knowing what questions to ask. But by 1790 they were hammering out the first indispensable distinctions, and by 1860 the problems were so completely resolved that the initial difficulties had been forgotten.

The problem is absolutely fundamental. Any theory of matter must draw a distinction between those things which are genuine *bodies*, and those which are not – between 'material substances' and 'immaterial agents', 'corporeals' and 'incorporeals'. Far from agreeing on definite lists of corporeals and incorporeals, men in 1700 did not even agree on the *meaning* of this distinction; and the intellectual contortions which resulted from the ambiguity were responsible for many of the birth-pangs of chemistry.

Solids and liquids presented no problem: everyone agreed that they were corporeal. Once you took a single step beyond them, all was chaos. At least three rival criteria were used for distinguishing 'matter' from other things. (a) At one extreme you could classify as 'corporeal' all agencies *capable of producing physical effects*. This had been the practice of the Stoics and Epicureans in the ancient world; and they were followed in the seventeenth century by Descartes, and by atomists such as Gassendi, for whom heat, cold, and magnetism were evidence of 'calorifick', 'frigorific', and 'magnetick' corpuscles. But this first criterion got rid of 'incorporeal agencies' by a linguistic sleight-of-hand: it made the phrase a contradiction in terms, so that you were obliged to accept (say) a magnetic field as corporeal even though it weighed nothing and you could walk through it. (b) An alternative procedure was to class as 'corporeal' only those objects which were *impenetrable*, or – allowing for vapours such as steam – could be made so when condensed and solidified. (c) Thirdly, one could choose to admit as 'corporeal' only those things which were subject to gravity, and so had both mass and weight. This meant identifying the corporeal with the *ponderable*, and ruling out all possibility of 'imponderable matter'.

This last criterion was, of course, a highly theoretical one, for in 1700 Newton's ideas about mass and gravitation were still new and contentious. At first it found few consistent supporters, and for a long time 'imponderable matter' seemed as legitimate an idea as 'incorporeal agencies': Newton himself, with his light corpuscles and aether-particles, would have hesitated to rule out all possibility of imponderable bodies. The crucial importance of mass, though clear enough in dynamics and astronomy, was not established in chemistry for nearly a century; and the very word 'imponderable' is recorded by the *Oxford Dictionary* only from 1794. It was in fact the middle of the nineteenth century before men were in a position to draw our 'common-sense' distinctions between (i) genuine chemical substances, which are both ponderable and capable of acting physically – and so 'material' in both senses; (ii) spiritual things, which are neither ponderable nor physical in their direct effects – and so doubly 'immaterial'; and (iii) the intermediate class, consisting of physical agencies such as heat and magnetism – which appear to be devoid of mass, even though their physical effects are unquestionable.

In 1700 there were no distinctions, only problems. Men disagreed about the very air of our atmosphere. Some evidence existed that it was corporeal – for instance, the first rough experiments done in antiquity by Hero of Alexandria. (See the note at the end of chapter 8.) Boyle's own demonstration, that smoke released into a vacuum lost its normal tendency to rise, suggested that air was at any rate denser than smoke. But more direct evidence was required for a fully convincing demonstration; and this was not easily come by, since no satisfactory techniques were yet in use for collecting and handling gases and vapours.

Similar difficulties arose over fire and flame, heat, cold, and light. Were any of these things 'material' – if so, which? It arose more acutely over 'effluvia' – a category embracing both rainbows and magnetic influences; over force-fields, and over force itself. And with so much obscurity lasting on even within physics, the situation in chemistry and physiology could hardly be better. What about the 'principles' which gave metals and combustibles their characteristic properties – were they corporeal? And the 'seeds' or 'formative powers' which (according to van Helmont and Boyle alike) were 'able to alter the minute parts of a body' and 'give the whole portion of matter a new texture' – were these corporeal? And what about 'spirits', in every sense of that slippery term? And life itself? And the mind? And the soul? If the answers to these questions seem for one moment obvious, one need only turn back the pages of history to the end of the seventeenth century: for at that time no one could answer these questions clearly and consistently, still less prove his answers.

The Weighing of Fire

Among all the symptoms of the confusion about incorporeals, none seems quainter to the twentieth-century mind than the belief that fire has weight. Newton was almost alone in rejecting this idea outright:

Is not Fire a Body, heated so hot as to emit Light copiously? For what else is a red hot Iron than Fire? And what else is a burning Coal than red hot Wood?

Is not Flame a Vapour, Fume or Exhalation heated red hot, that is so hot as to shine? For Bodies do not flame without emitting a copious Fume, and this Fume burns in the Flame.

But his own most devoted successors, Boerhaave and Lavoisier, retained a place in their theories for *matter of heat* and *matter of fire*; and Robert Boyle, who was fifteen years older than Newton, remained thoroughly in the toils.

Since so many kinds of particles were ponderable, Boyle felt that 'calorifick and frigorifick' atoms might have a detectable weight also, and set about devising experiments to detect their presence with the balance. His experiments 'to make Fire and Flame Stable and Ponderable' eventually gave a positive result, and he concluded that he had actually *weighed* the sharp and piercing corpuscles of fire.

His methods were exact and scrupulous. Eight ounces of tin were carefully weighed out and put into a glass flask, which was then hermetically sealed. (This was done to prevent fumes from the fire creeping into the flask and adulterating the contents.) Next, the flask was heated strongly over the fire:

The Metal was kept in fusion for an hour and a quarter as (being hinder'd by a Company of strangers from being there myself) the Laborant affirm'd. Being unwilling to venture the Glass any longer, it was taken from the fire, and when 'twas grown cold, the seal'd end was broken off; but before I would have the bottom cut out . . . the metal Lump and Calx together were weigh'd in the same Scales carefully, and we found the weight to have increas'd twenty-three Grains and better, though all the *Calx* we could easily separate, being weigh'd by itself amounted not to four Scruples or eighty Grains.

The metal had increased in weight by twenty-three grains. Where could this extra weight have come from? Nothing had apparently been done to the flask, apart from heating it, so where else could Boyle look for the source of the extra weight except in the fire? The 'particles of fire' must have penetrated through the glass vessel and lodged themselves in the metal:

It is no wonder, that being wedged into the pores, or being brought to adhere very fast to the little parts of the bodies exposed to their action, the accession of so many little bodies, that want not gravity, should, because of their multitudes, be considerable upon a balance.

This is one of the most tantalizing moments in the development of our ideas about matter. Boyle's experiments to prove that fire has weight were so very like those by which, a century later,

Lavoisier was to prove the exact opposite. Both men studied the same phenomenon: namely, the increase in weight which occurs when a metal is converted to a calx by heat. Both men asked the same question: namely, 'Where does this extra weight come from?' Yet they looked for different things, and interpreted their results against different theoretical backgrounds. As a result, they were able to quote similar evidence as support for contradictory conclusions.

So long as Boyle weighed the metal and calx in his flask *after* breaking the sealed neck, he could have no reason to reject his conclusion. Yet if only it had occurred to him to weigh the flask with its contents, first on sealing it, and then again *before* breaking the seal, might he not – one wonders – have recognized the fact which later gave Lavoisier his clue? For he would then have found that *no* change of weight takes place *during the heating*: it does so only when extra air enters the flask through the broken seal. So, as Lavoisier concluded, the extra weight must have come from something already within the flask. Yet it is a significant fact that Boyle never made these additional observations. For the business of experiments is to answer questions, and his questions were all about fire – not about the air within the flask. Even if he *had* made these further measurements, he would scarcely have known what to make of the results. He was in no position to give Lavoisier's answers, since he could not yet formulate Lavoisier's questions.

The historical situation is in fact even more piquant. As early as 1630, Jean Rey of Montpellier had published a series of *Essays* (recently re-edited by D. McKie), reporting observations very similar to Boyle's and interpreting them on lines similar to Lavoisier's:

This increase in weight comes from the air, which in the vessel has been rendered denser, heavier and in some measure adhesive, by the vehement and long-continued heat of the furnace: which air mixes with the calx (frequent agitation aiding) and becomes attached to its most minute particles.

But an explanation can become established only when there is a systematic body of theory into which it can fit, and Jean Rey's account of calcination found no place to lodge in the matter-theory of his time. It was revived only at a later period, when questions about the chemical properties of the air had acquired a new significance and urgency.

For the time being, questions about the weight of fire were as significant and important as questions about the weight of any 'substance'. So the picture we have of Voltaire in his laboratory, trying to devise a means of determining this weight unambiguously, is not that of a literary dilettante, but that of a genuine scientist struggling with a problem which – in the context of his own time – was real and inescapable.

10

Chemistry Comes of Age

GREAT improvements in scientific theory sometimes spring from over-simplifications. In order to establish clear and distinct ideas, we have to shut our eyes for the time being to the full complexity of Nature, concentrate our attention on some simple and (we hope) representative phenomenon, and draw with absolute sharpness the distinctions which this simple example suggests. Later on we may discover that our original distinctions were in fact *too* sharp, and can safely be blurred: thus our initial axioms turn first into working assumptions, and finally into mere approximations. This procedure may look abritrary and yet be none the less necessary and fruitful.

The cycle from axioms to approximations is sometimes completed within a single argument – as with Newton's assumption that the space between the planets is completely empty. But on other occasions it can take whole centuries. So here: in the years following 1725, chemists achieved an intellectual break-through by accepting as axiomatic two doctrines that twentieth-century science has put in doubt. One of these was Newton's thesis: that the ultimate particles of matter possess forms fixed at the first Creation, and that all material changes result from the motion, combination, and separation of these particles. The other may be called the 'criterion of ponderability' – the conviction that substances which are truly 'material' differ absolutely from all other things in the fact that they, and they alone, can be weighed.

At the beginning of the eighteenth century chemistry still lacked a method of its own. It remained uncertainly poised, somewhere between physics and physiology. The interest of chemical questions was still primarily medical; the terminology of the subject was largely functional; while 'corpuscular' explanations, though fashionable in some circles, were entirely speculative. By the end of the century an independent science of chemistry had been developed, and Lavoisier had formulated the basic distinc-

231

tions between elements, compounds, and mixtures which chemists have worked with ever since. Much of the intellectual fog which surrounded chemical change in Newton's time had been dispelled, and the foundations had been laid for the 'classical' physics and chemistry of the nineteenth century.

The Natural History of the Inanimate

The Queries at the end of Newton's *Opticks* displayed his unique capacity to view the facts of Nature in an all-embracing way, and to grasp the common patterns behind them. But the intellectual blank cheques which he issued could be redeemed only after a sufficient fund of factual knowledge – notably about gases, heat, and chemical affinities – had been accumulated by his successors.

Airs and Gases

Appropriately enough, the work began with Newton's own formal blessing. In February 1727, at the age of eighty-four, he officiated for the last time as President of the Royal Society, and on this occasion one of his duties was to give his formal *imprimatur* to a book by one of the Fellows – an Anglican clergyman called Stephen Hales. The book, *Vegetable Staticks*, had as its chief subject the Air: its nature, properties, and physiological functions.

Stephen Hales' book reported 124 ingenious experiments on the airs and fluids given out and taken in by animal, vegetable, and mineral substances, either naturally or when heated. (They included demonstrations which are repeated to this day in school botany classes: e.g. on transpiration from leaves, and the pressure of the rising sap.) Hales found, not surprisingly, that the chemical and physiological properties of the airs he collected varied from case to case, but the fact that they all obeyed Boyle's Law convinced him that they consisted for the most part of a common material, which existed normally in two alternative physical states – 'elastick' and 'fixt'. This he christened 'true permanent air'. Though Hales did not himself recognize that airs (or gases) were chemically as various as solids or liquids, his researches set off the train of experimental studies which were soon to lead to this conclusion. And he bequeathed to his successors one novel and indispensable piece of apparatus, with which gases could be collected in isolation from one another, and so studied separately.

In his experiments Hales kept running up against one snag. To begin with, he collected his airs by leading the tube from his retort directly into a container which was already partly full of air. The resulting mixture was apparently unstable, losing volume if left standing for several days: this he put down to the presence of impurities ('acid sulphureous fumes') which had come over from the retort with the air and were converting it from the elastic to the fixed state. So he looked for some means of eliminating these fumes, and began to collect his gases instead, by bubbling them up into a flask full of water.

The device worked: 'a good part of the acid spirits and sulphureous fumes were by this means intercepted and retained in the Water; the consequence of which was that the newly-generated air continued in a more permanently elastick state, very little of it losing its elasticity'. But we value the apparatus for its other, even greater, advantage. For now: if one started with the receiver entirely full of water, the airs from any source could be collected in a pure form and retained for subsequent study. So the 'wild spirits' or 'gases' of van Helmont's theory had finally been caged. This 'pneumatic trough' became a standard part of the chemist's equipment, and when the airs to be studied proved to be soluble in water, the receiver could be filled with mercury instead. From now on, it was possible to handle gases – and identify them – with little more difficulty than solids and liquids. (See Plate 5.)

After this it was only a matter of time before men recognized that different varieties of gas could not only be differentiated in practice, but were chemically quite distinct. In 1753, Joseph Black demonstrated that Hales' 'fixt air' had quite different chemical properties from atmospheric air, and in doing so brought to light many of the leading characteristics of the substance now known as 'carbon dioxide'. It was, as he recognized, the same gas that van Helmont had already studied under the name of *gas silvestris*, being given off during alcoholic fermentation and the burning of charcoal. The study of gases now proceeded rapidly. The next thirty years saw the recognition of all the common gases familiar to us today: inflammable air (hydrogen) by Henry Cavendish;

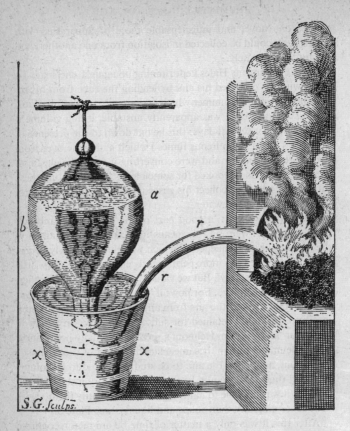

vitiated air (nitrogen), nitrous air (NO), and dephlogisticated nitrous air (NO_2) by Joseph Priestley; and most important the gas known variously as vital, dephlogisticated and eminently respirable air, discovered by Priestley, Scheele and Lavoisier – who gave it the name 'oxygen gas'.

By 1780 this class of incorporeals at any rate had been pretty well mastered: few scientists doubted any longer that 'elastic aeriform fluids' were so many different material substances with distinct properties, and took part in chemical reactions on the same footing as liquids and solids. It was now a simple matter to distinguish 'gases' from those other 'incorporeals' which –

obviously – could never be bubbled through water and bottled neat: gravity, aether, and (above all) the human soul. A wedge had been driven also between the different 'spirits' of Galen's physiology: whereas the vital spirits or vivifying principle of the air turned into a simple gas – i.e. the 'eminently respirable' variety of air, oxygen – the animal spirits were evidently different in kind. Perception and muscular action were so swift that they could hardly be due to gases going up and down the nerves.

Heat

Meanwhile Joseph Black was hammering out the fundamental distinctions required for an understanding of another class of incorporeals – heat, fire, and the rest. Starting from scratch he created the methods of *calorimetry*, with which schoolboys still begin their practical work in physics. He distinguished clearly between the degree of sensible warmth or 'temperature' of a body and the 'quantity of heat' which it contains, and showed that bodies of different sizes, states, and materials exchanged heat according to definite, numerical rules. These rules took the form of simple proportionalities, like those of Aristotle's dynamics. For instance: if he took two bodies of the same material in the same physical state, one twice as heavy as the other, the quantities of heat required to raise their temperatures by the same amount were also in the ratio two to one. However, if the bodies were of the same weight but composed of different substances, the quantities of heat required were *not* the same: every substance had its own 'specific capacity for heat'. Similar definite proportions applied when the material changed its state. Ice placed in warm water took up a definite quantity of heat from the water and progressively melted, its temperature remaining constant: the temperature of the water meanwhile dropped in exact proportion to the weight of ice melted. Even though part of the heat exchanged remained 'latent' rather than 'sensible', and could not be detected with a thermometer, his numerical proportionalities continued to apply with the same precision.

These investigations were a foundation for all subsequent study of heat. Yet, by themselves, they could not provide an answer to the central question about heat which divided eighteenth-century scientists: whether or not it was a form of matter. One party followed Newton and regarded it as no more than a species of motion – a 'vibrating motion' of the particles of a body; others, including Boerhaave, considered it a distinct species of material substance.

If heat were a material substance, then (as Boerhaave admitted) some of its characteristics were very extraordinary. It had the power to penetrate everywhere, even into the 'most empty vacuum of an air-pump', and there was no hope of isolating it in a separate container: yet, unlike the 'cause of gravity and power of magnetism' which made their presence felt instantaneously, heat required 'some space of time before it can penetrate the densest bodies' – the time needed, presumably, for the 'atoms of fire' to insinuate themselves into the material. So the particles of fire must be particularly 'subtile', perfectly 'smooth, even and polished', devoid of hooks, or points, or any thing downy and woolly', and without 'eminences or sinkings in any point of their whole circumference'. Fire must be, in fact, a substance almost as curious and exceptional as Lucretius' 'stuff of the mind'.

Though Black's results were consistent with both theories of heat, they tended on the whole to support the material theory. For, in giving the study of heat a numerical basis, he had demonstrated that the 'quantity of heat' is *conserved* from one body to another. If heat were indeed composed of immutable, indestructible particles, which could be passed from body to body, this conservation was readily intelligible; but if, on the other hand, the warmth of a body were only a sensible quality, or a kind of motion which might eventually be dissipated, its conservation would be less readily understood.

Affinities

Boerhaave and Black also helped to bring order into the description of chemical reactions by an intelligent application of Newtonian ideas about 'attraction': Black, for instance, explained the effervescence of common magnesia (magnesium carbonate) when dissolved in an acid by supposing that the 'fixt air' in the magnesia 'is expelled by the superior attraction of the acid'. This analogy with physics gave chemists a vivid terminology for describing the observed facts of chemical combination and separation; yet, as an explanation of the mechanisms involved, the theory of attractions turned out in time to have some real weaknesses. It was natural to assume that there were fixed and definite binding-forces between atoms of any two chemically combining substances – the so-called 'elective attractions'. But Black soon found that at certain important points this assumption ran counter to experience. Some reactions were *reversible*. At one temperature substance C replaced substance B in the compound AB, at another B displaced C: which substance, then, had 'the superior attraction' for A ? The principles governing the rates and directions of chemical reactions (chemical kinetics) were in fact far more complicated than one could have supposed from the account in Newton's *Opticks*, and little progress was made in this field before 1800.

But at this stage it did not really matter how one spoke about chemical bonds – whether as 'attractions' or 'affinities', or mere *rapports*. The important tasks were still those emphasized by Robert Boyle: to discover precise criteria for classifying chemical substances, to identify their leading properties and to see if any general rules governed the combination of substances of different kinds. The task of classification was one which Linnaeus was already undertaking for plants and animals – and indeed the worlds of the animate and the inanimate were in his eyes simply two parts of a single, larger scheme – the grand and all-inclusive *System of Nature*. (See figure, page 238.)

Phlogiston

Hales, Boerhaave, and Black were all Newtonians, and so atomists: their long-term vision was a union of chemistry and physics through the application of Newton's ideas about forces. But, as we have seen, atomism at this stage was only one of several separate traditions in matter-theory – and one which had yet to provide any very solid explanations in the chemical field. So practical chemists were justified in turning to the other traditions for their ideas, especially when these in fact had a greater explanatory power. And for many years after Newton's ideas had been firmly established within physics, their relevance to chemistry was quite uncertain. This was true even of his central concept – namely, *mass*.

The most convincing and detailed explanations of chemical

constitution and change available in the first half of the eighteenth century were those given by the *phlogiston* theory. This was formulated around 1700 by the German chemist Stahl, who developed and improved the alchemical theories about sulphureous (inflammable) and mercurial (metallizing) principles. The

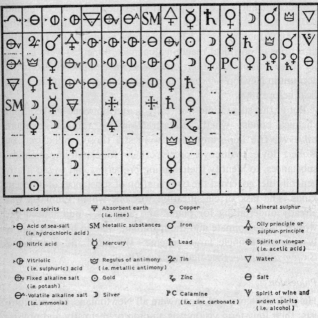

Acid spirits	Absorbent earth (i.e. lime)	Copper	Mineral sulphur
Acid of sea-salt (i.e. hydrochloric acid)	SM Metallic substances	Iron	Oily principle or sulphur-principle
Nitric acid	Mercury	Lead	Spirit of vinegar (i.e. acetic acid)
Vitriolic (i.e. sulphuric) acid	Regulus of antimony (i.e. metallic antimony)	Tin	Water
Fixed alkaline salt (i.e. potash)	Gold	Zinc	Salt
Volatile alkaline salt (i.e. ammonia)	Silver	PC Calamine (i.e. zinc carbonate)	Spirit of wine and ardent spirits (i.e. alcohol)

Geoffroy l'Aîné's Table of Chemical Affinities (1718)

theory started from a familiar observation: that the conversion of a metal to a calx closely paralleled the burning of an ordinary fuel to an ash. Many of the alchemists had taught that the first process (calcination) represented the loss of the material principle 'mercury', whose presence in metals conferred on them their characteristic cohesion and brilliance ; whereas the second process (combustion) involved the loss of another principle 'sulphur', whose presence in wood and coal conferred on them their solidity and combustibility. Stahl now concluded that there were, after all, not two distinct principles but only one – the agency which he christened 'phlogiston'; this was at one and the same time the 'principle of inflammability' and the 'metallizing principle'. When a metal rusted away or a fuel burned, the phlogiston departed from it and it crumbled to dust: conversely, an ash could be 're-vived' and recover its inflammability, or an earthy ore be smelted to form a metal, by causing it to take up phlogiston – either from the surrounding environment or from charcoal, which was rich in this principle and could be used to accelerate the process.

The doctrine of phlogiston did not take one very much further than we have already followed it, but even so it helped more than any other available theory to link the known facts about com-bustion, calcination, and respiration into a reasonable pattern. So it found wide support, notably in France and Germany, where Newton's ideas had been slow to catch on. Of course, the doctrine had its problems, especially for those scientists who, from 1760 on, were beginning to worry about incorporeals. For the physical status of phlogiston was highly ambiguous. Some chemists treated it as a genuine material substance which one could collect and weigh – and so as clearly corporeal; others denied that it had or could have any weight and regarded it rather as an incorporeal agency. Cavendish took the former view, and for a while went so far as to identify phlogiston with his own 'inflammable air', hydrogen. But the facts about calcination told against this view: since a metal gained weight on turning into a calx, while in theory 'losing phlogiston', one would be forced in that case to infer that phlogiston actually had a *negative* weight.

This conclusion was unacceptable to anyone who had accepted the Newtonian analysis of gravitation, and it was positively em-braced by only a few French chemists and Cartesians, who could still contemplate the possibility of a substance which possessed 'levity' rather than 'gravity'. Most chemists preferred to set the problem of weight on one side: it seemed to be one more sign that 'weight' and 'mass' were concepts for physics rather than chemistry, and so presumably irrelevant to questions about chemical constitution and change. The strongest argument of all was, perhaps, that of Richard Watson in his *Chemical Essays* (1781). He protested against the demand that phlogiston should be positively 'bottled' – as though it were a material substance like air.

You do not surely expect that chemistry should be able to present you with a handful of phlogiston, separated from an inflammable body; you may just as reasonably demand a handful of magnetism, gravity or electricity to be extracted from a magnetic, weighty or electric body; there are powers in Nature, which cannot otherwise become the objects of sense, than by the effects they produce, and of this kind is phlogiston.

Since this was just the type of argument by which Newton had defended his 'force of gravity' against the attacks of Leibniz, Watson's position could scarcely be dismissed out of hand.

Finally, there were those chemists who went further, and denied outright the relevance of Newtonian physics. Venel, for instance, in an influential article on 'Chemistry' in Diderot's *Encyclopaedia*, challenged Newton's explanations of fire and colour:

A glowing coal is no more identical with fire than a sponge saturated with water [is identical with water]; for the chemist can just as well remove from the coal and demonstrate separately the Principle of Inflammability (i.e. the Fire) as squeeze the water from a sponge and catch it in a vessel.

Colour in a coloured body is, for the physicist, a certain tendency in the surface which leads it to reflect such-and-such light-rays; but for the chemist, the green of a plant is inherent in a certain green resinous body, which he knows how to separate; the colour of jasper, which appears so perfectly united with that substance, can none the less be taken from it and collected, according to Becher's well-known experiment.... [Thus the chemist knows] a body, a physical entity, a particular substance which he can identify as the subject or cause of colour.

As a practical chemist Venel was, understandably, interested in 'know-how' rather than abstract theory, and he had as little patience with Newtonian analogies as Hippokrates had had with the speculations of the Ionians. So far as he was concerned, the *constitution* of a substance meant nothing so remote as atoms or invisible particles: it meant simply the pigments and essences which he could extract from it in his laboratory, or the ingredients from which he could make it up. The chemist's job was to know what properties were carried by each of the different ingredients and extracts, and to master the arts of mixing and combining these 'principles' (like a pharmacist) so as to produce substances with any prescribed combinations of properties.

The majority of the qualities in bodies which physics regards as *modes* are in fact real *substances*, which the chemist knows how to separate out, and either restore or incorporate in other bodies.

Despite – or because of – its alchemical ancestry, the idea of 'principles' was an eminently practical idea. Common salt made things salt, for it represented the principle of salinity. Bitters made them bitter, through containing an acrid principle. The same pattern demonstrably held for the pigments which gave plants their colour, and the essential oils which gave them their fragrance; and presumably it could be extended more widely still. If the physicists thought their ideas could throw light on the practical procedures of chemistry, it was up to them to prove it. As things stood, Venel and his colleagues were sceptical.

Lavoisier's New System

That is the background against which we must study the work of Antoine Laurent Lavoisier (1743–94). Throughout the ensuing scene the intellectual stage contained one large piece of fixed scenery, which was clearly visible in the wings but played little part in the action: namely, Newton's theory of atoms and forces. The supporting characters included all the familiar solid and liquid substances; but the centre of the stage was now occupied by *gases*, whose corporeal status was no longer in doubt, and by *matter of heat*, whose ultimate fate was still uncertain. Two tasks remained: to get the cast properly disposed on set, and to expose them to dramatic situations of a sort that would demonstrate their fundamental characters. These were the salient points of Lavoisier's achievement.

Lavoisier was a professional man of liberal mind and politics, who played a minor part in public life during the last years of the traditional French monarchy. He had inherited a modest fortune and used it to buy his way into the *Ferme Générale* – the financial syndicate which, in return for a guaranteed payment to the king, purchased the right to collect the taxes: from 1775 he also held an administrative post at the arsenal, where he was responsible for supervising the manufacture of gunpowder, saltpetre, and other explosives. In this position he could build and equip his own laboratory, which soon became one of the chief centres of scientific discussion. He corresponded with the most noted scientists of the day on both sides of the Atlantic, and collaborated with Benjamin Franklin in an official enquiry into the authenticity of hypnosis and 'animal magnetism'. In the French Revolution of 1789 his natural sympathies were on the side of reform, and until the Terror he was able to keep his position at the arsenal. But, once the revolution moved from its liberal into its extremist phase, wealthy moderates with aristocratic connexions were in peril. Tax-farmers were especially hated and despised and he went to the guillotine.

The most delicate problem in natural philosophy is to indulge one's proper passion for intellectual order without sacrificing fidelity to Nature. To re-order a whole science demands not only a sufficient practical understanding but also intellectual clarity and penetration of a high order. Taken by itself, neither the Baconian approach to science – the patient accumulation of natural facts – nor the Cartesian approach – the formulation of clear and distinct concepts – can get one very far: the major advances in scientific thought have all resulted from a happy alternation of the two methods. Just as the Baconian industry of Robert Boyle had required the theoretical insight of Isaac Newton for its fulfilment, so now the energy and enthusiasm of men such as Priestley, Scheele, and Cavendish were turning up a mass of new facts which cried out for some simplifying reinterpretation.

Lavoisier was particularly well equipped for the task which history presented to him. In his sympathies he was a Newtonian, and therefore a physicist; and throughout his work he continually brought the methods of physics to bear on the problems of chemistry. At the same time he was a practical chemist and a Frenchman, and so an heir to the traditions of Venel and the French school of practical chemistry. But, whereas Venel had regarded the theory of principles and the theory of atoms as opposed, Lavoisier thought they could be reconciled – by showing how the chemist's practical experience of substances and reactions could be explained, at a more fundamental level, in terms of physical principles and ideas. Yet this ambition was a long-term one. Meanwhile one must put first things first: before chemistry would be ready for a union with physics, it first needed the attentions of a Linnaeus. This was the point from which Lavoisier began.

His problem can be stated briefly. Practical chemists had been discovering and studying such a wealth of materials and processes that they found themselves with a positive *embarras de richesses*: chemical theorists, on the other hand, had not kept pace with the discoveries, and saw the riches of the laboratory rather as an embarrassing chaos of unrelated facts. The unsystematic character of the subject showed itself even in its nomenclature. The terminology of the new 'factitious airs' – with its 'lambent inflammable air', its 'dephlogisticated nitrous air' and so on – was comparatively revealing and enlightened. Most other substances however went by fanciful and confusing names like pompholix, colcothar and powder of algaroth; butter of arsenic, flowers of zinc, and martial ethops; which revealed nothing about their compositions and relationships, and were in many cases quite misleading. ('Butter of arsenic' was a violent poison!) Worse; there were still no satisfactory criteria for recognizing genuine material substances as such, or telling simple, indivisible substances from compounds or mixtures.

So Lavoisier embarked (in collaboration with Berthollet, Fourcroy, and Guyton de Morveau) on the task of producing a *New System of Chemical Nomenclature*. Fortunately he was well grounded in law and philosophy as well as in scientific subjects, for their project had a deliberately philosophical intention. The aim was to reform the vocabulary of chemical terms in such a way as to put Thought in accordance with Things; and the motto of the work was taken from Lavoisier's hero, the 'linguistic philosopher' Condillac:

We think only through the medium of words. Languages are true analytical methods. Algebra, which is adapted to its purpose in every species of expression, in the most simple, most exact, and best manner possible, is at the same time a language and an analytical method. *The art of reasoning is nothing more than a language well arranged.*

But, as Lavoisier worked, he found the task widening. One could reform the terminology of chemistry only at the cost of reforming its theory also. Any new nomenclature must rest on a new and improved classification; and this could be built up only if one first settled on more satisfactory criteria for recognizing 'substances' and 'elements'. So before the project of a new nomenclature could be realized in full, he found himself obliged to rethink the theories behind all his chemical ideas:

While I proposed to myself nothing more than to improve the chemical language, my work transformed itself by degrees, without my being able to prevent it, into a treatise on the Elements of Chemistry.

Lavoisier embarked on his reconstruction of chemistry with two intellectual commitments. The first of these was the *physical* axiom, that 'in natural and artificial processes alike, nothing is lost and nothing is created'. The second was the taxonomic principle that chemical substances conform to a natural order, similar to the natural order of living things. These two commitments guided his reform of chemical nomenclature and chemical theory alike.

The general idea of 'conservation' had, of course, appealed to scientists ever since Ionian days. (Anaxagoras declared that both creation-out-of-nothing and utter destruction were illusions: in reality, there is only 'mingling or separating of things that are'.) But so far no one had succeeded in applying this doctrine to a quantitative and consistent account of physical and chemical change. The reason was simple. It was still quite unclear exactly what, if anything, was conserved in chemical reactions; and, without some definite measure and criterion, the phrase 'quantity of matter' remained an abstraction. How should one measure this quantity? By volume? Surely not: for two enormous volumes of gas combined to form only a few drops of water. By weight? For Newtonians and Cartesians alike, the heaviness of bodies was a secondary phenomenon. By mass? That was a concept whose relevance to chemistry had yet to be demonstrated. In any case, how could one check that matter was *in fact* conserved, unless one could identify 'matter' in the first place? At this point the problem of incorporeals proved an obstacle. For the question arose whether, in balancing up the ingredients entering into any change against the products coming from it, one had to take into account heat, light, electricity, spirits, and airs, as well as solids and liquids, and this question was still unresolved. As the heirs of Lavoisier and Dalton, we find no difficulty in answering it: *mass* is what matters! But our predecessors were caught in a vicious circle. The obscurity about incorporeals reinforced the obscurity about the measure of matter, and vice versa. In the 1770s it was hard to see just where the circle could be broken.

Lavoisier cut through this Gordian knot. It was all very well being a Newtonian in one's sympathies, but one must also be practical. Instead of worrying too much about theoretical definitions, one must begin by accepting as a material substance anything which proved *in practice* to be conserved. Provided we had evidence of conservation from laboratory analyses, that was enough to be going on with. The conservation of matter thus became for Lavoisier an axiom, a criterion: whatever showed itself to be conserved, in ways which were physically observable and measurable, was to be taken as 'material'. As a physicist, of course, his first impulse was to regard continuity of *mass* as the best evidence of conservation; but one could not do this in every case. Heat, for instance, though apparently lacking in mass, was demonstrably conserved, and it must accordingly be accepted for the time being as a genuine form of matter – *caloric*, as he christened it – along with more massive substances.

In the case of 'simple substances' (our 'elements') Lavoisier employed a similar, practical criterion. It was tempting to speculate in general terms about the 'simple and indivisible atoms of which matter is composed', but hitherto chemical experience had not brought one within range of these ultimate units of matter: on the contrary, he declared, 'it is extremely probable we know nothing at all about them'. To base one's very classification of chemical substances on hypotheses about their atoms would be sheerly premature. One must proceed more modestly, and accept as 'simple' any substance which scientists had found no way of subdividing in the laboratory. For such substances

act with regard to us as simple substances, and we ought never to suppose them compounded until experiment and observation has proved them to be so.

Applying this criterion, Lavoisier compiled a first list of simple substances, which included – among others – the seven traditional metals, sulphur and bismuth, caloric and light.

The newly-discovered *gases*, however, had all to be classified as compound substances. Quite apart from the fact that some of them could be broken down chemically into more than one massive constituent, the very fact of their being gases at all was evidence for him of their compound nature. For a solid turned to a liquid, and a liquid to a gas, as a result of caloric (the matter of heat) becoming bound or *combined* with another material base. Thus what we call oxygen Lavoisier always called oxygen gas; and he took care to explain that this was a compound of latent caloric together with the oxygenic 'principle' or 'base'. His list of *simple* substances therefore included, not the gases we now call oxygen, hydrogen, etc., but the *bases* which – when combined with caloric – gave rise to these gases. One of the chapters of his *Traité Elémentaire de Chimie* in fact bears a title which reads strangely to twentieth-century eyes: 'On the Decomposition of Oxygen Gas'.

Once he had framed working definitions of 'substances' and 'elements', Lavoisier could embark on his central task, of re-ordering the classification of chemical substances on systematic principles. At this point he showed himself a true eighteenth-century taxonomist. In both botany and zoology, scientists had been attempting for some years to establish a 'natural' classification. Natural divisions would be based not on human interests – like the division into 'fruits', 'flowers', and 'vegetables', which reflects only the uses we make of different plants – but rather on the true constitutions and relationships of living things. Lavoisier was convinced that material substances would lend themselves to classification on similar principles, and he further assumed that the different simple substances entering into their composition would provide us with the necessary distinctions. We could mark off each 'genus' and 'species' of substances by reference to the elements of which they were composed, and this constitution would manifest itself also in their observed properties.

This assumption had one incidental consequence: it perpetuated into Lavoisier's new system the traditional vocabulary of 'principles'. For the simple substances by which he defined his genera and species were the material 'bearers' of the properties by which these classes were recognized in practice. Consider, for example, the account he gave of the constitution of acids:

The acids ... are compounded of two substances, of the order of those which we consider as simple; the one *constitutes acidity*, and is common to all acids, and, from this substance, the name of the class or the genus ought to be taken; the other is peculiar to each acid, and distinguishes it from the rest, and from this substance is to be taken the name of the species.

The generic ingredient which he thought was common to all acids he christened 'the acidifying principle' (or *oxy-gen*, for short): the specific acidifiable principle (carbon or sulphur, say) varied from acid to acid. (Not until well into the nineteenth century did Humphry Davy show for certain that 'muriatic acid', which we know today by the name of 'hydrochloric acid' in fact contained no oxygen in its composition; and by that time chemical theory was so firmly established that it could dispense with this particular assumption.)

Having laid down these principles, Lavoisier was in a position to carry through the programme which he had set himself. He proceeded to survey the whole range of subtances then known to chemistry, analysing, synthesizing, distinguishing, comparing – and, most important, identifying the constituent principles of which they were all permutations and combinations – the acidifying (oxygenic), acidifiable, salifying, salifiable, hydrogenic, and caloric principles, and so on. In this way he was confident that he had identified the chemical elements, and at the same time provided the basis for a satisfactory nomenclature: for now at last one could replace the older catalogue of fanciful and misleading names by systematic and revealing ones. A name such as 'carbonic acid', for instance, was a *good* name, just because it reflected the fundamental elements making up the substance: oxygen the acidifier, and carbon the base. On the same principles, fixed air became 'carbonic acid gas', Homberg's sedative salt became 'boracic acid', martial ethiops became 'black oxide of iron', and orpiment (the alchemist's golden pigment) became 'sulphuret of arsenic'.

But along with material substances, Lavoisier had clarified

ideas about the *processes* of chemistry also. Simple substances were those materials that were conserved during physical and chemical changes, and which we had no means of subdividing; compound substances were those materials which were formed from the union of simple substances by the operations of art or Nature, and which could subsequently be dissociated to yield their original ingredients. In the formation and dissociation of compound substances, both the quantity of matter (which Newton had christened 'mass') and the quantity of heat (which Lavoisier now named 'caloric') were unaltered; and to analyse the true nature of any process one must display the nature of the ingredient simple substances (including heat) and demonstrate that they *were* conserved throughout the process. Natural processes accordingly were of three kinds: (i) purely physical changes: in the shapes, sizes, and motions of solids, the pressures of gases and so on; (ii) purely chemical reactions: involving the combination and separation of massive substances, to form fresh substances with different properties; and (iii) changes of state: between the solid, liquid and gaseous conditions, which resulted from the quasi-chemical combination of caloric with a material base. In due course, when the material theory of heat was abandoned, these distinctions were to be sharpened up even further, but that was to happen only in the middle of the nineteenth century. For the moment, nothing in Lavoisier's principles compelled him to distinguish sharply between substances which could be weighed (and whose atoms were presumably massive), and those more 'subtle' substances, such as heat, whose conservation manifested itself in other ways.

Oxygen versus Phlogiston

As the first result of Lavoisier's work, chemical thought and vocabulary thus acquired a brand-new order and method, and one that wholly justified his second motto from Condillac:

The sciences have made progress, because philosophers have applied themselves with more attention to observe, and have communicated to their language that precision and accuracy which they have employed in their observations: *in correcting their language they reason better.*

But it was one thing to devise a new classification and nomenclature: it was another to demonstrate its merits. By itself, a vocabulary is neither 'true' nor 'false': at best, it can give us the means of saying clearly and precisely things which may be true – and may be false. Lavoisier's system certainly introduced a new clarity and crispness into ideas about material change; but before his colleagues could accept it they had to be convinced also that these 'clear and distinct ideas' accurately matched the possibilities of the natural world. The opportunity for testing this arose at once.

During the experimental studies on which the new classification was founded Lavoisier had paid attention to one group of processes in particular – combustion, calcination, and respiration. The explanation of these changes had been a matter for debate ever since the early 1600s, and it was crucial for the phlogiston theory. As Lavoisier went on he found, somewhat to his surprise, that his ideas on the subject (based on the accepted doctrines of phlogiston) would have to be completely revised before these processes could find a secure place within his new theoretical system. And, during the twenty years which followed the publication of his ideas, the decision of other chemists whether to adopt or reject the new nomenclature depended, first of all, on whether they accepted Lavoisier's novel analysis of combustion and calcination or whether they stood by the older explanations.

To recapitulate: Stahl's explanation had assumed that phlogiston was a constituent principle of all metals and combustible materials, which was driven off when they were heated to a point at which they ignited or calcined. Combustion and calcination thus involved a loss of phlogiston, and would normally continue for just so long as there was phlogiston left in the body; however, when the process took place in a closed container, it came to a stop sooner – apparently because the phlogiston which had already escaped 'saturated' the air in the container and rendered it 'incapable of supporting further combustion'. After going along with the phlogiston theory for a number of years Lavoisier performed some experiments on the 'eminently-respirable' form of air (i.e. oxygen gas) which Priestley and Scheele had recently discovered. The results of these experiments led him to replace

Stahl's analysis by another of his own, in which the *loss* of phlogiston was reinterpreted as a *gain* of oxygen.

The experiment which most impressed him was a refinement on one which Priestley had described to him when on a visit to Paris. He took a flask with an S-shaped neck and placed it on a furnace; the mouth of the flask opened into a bell-jar, which was supported in a bath of quicksilver. He put four ounces of pure

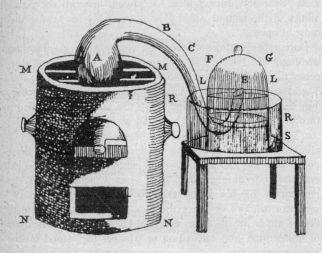

mercury into the flask, and computed the total volume of air in the flask and bell-jar as fifty cubic inches:

Having accurately noted the height of the thermometer and barometer, I lighted a fire in the furnace, which I kept up almost continuously during twelve days, so as to keep the quicksilver always almost at its boiling point.... On the second day, small red particles began to appear on the surface of the mercury, which, during the four or five following days, gradually increased in size and number; after which they ceased to increase in either respect. At the end of twelve days, seeing that the calcination of the mercury did not at all increase, I extinguished the fire, and allowed the vessels to cool.

Two things had happened, and these were presumably related: the 'red particles' had formed on the mercury, and at the same time the air in the container had shrunk. Collecting the particles from off the mercury, he confirmed what Priestley had told him – that they consisted of the red calx of mercury – and when he weighed them on a delicate balance they amounted to forty-five grains. Meanwhile, having allowed for changes in the atmospheric pressure and temperature, he calculated that in the course of the experiment, the air had lost about one-sixth of its volume: furthermore, the air remaining in the bell-jar was 'azotic' or 'mephitic' –

no longer fit either for respiration or combustion; animals being introduced into it were suffocated in a few seconds, and when a taper was plunged into it, it was extinguished as if it had been immersed into water.

The effect on the air of converting part of the mercury into red calx was precisely the same familiar effect as was produced by enclosing a burning candle or a living animal in a bell-jar: once the air in the bell-jar had lost about one-sixth of its volume, the flame, or animal, was stifled.

He now continued the experiment, heating the red grains from the mercury to a much higher temperature, at which the process was reversed:

I took the 45 grains of red matter formed during this experiment, which I put into a small retort, having a proper apparatus for receiving such liquid, or gaseous product, as might be extracted. . . . When the retort was almost red hot, the red matter began gradually to decrease in bulk, and in a few minutes after it disappeared altogether; at the same time $41\frac{1}{2}$ grains of running Mercury were collected in the recipient, and 7 or 8 cubical inches of elastic fluid . . . were collected in the bell-glass.

On investigation he found that the gas given off when the red calx turned back to mercury was 'greatly more capable of supporting both respiration and combustion than atmospherical air' and in every observable respect it appeared identical with the 'factitious air' which Scheele and Priestley had previously been studying under other names.

At this point, Lavoisier – bearing in mind the conservation of mass – stated the two conclusions to which the double experiment drove him. First: the conversion of the grains of calx to mercury was accompanied by the release of respirable air in just such a quantity (8 cubic inches) as matched the loss of volume when the mercury originally turned to calx. So the calx (45 gr.) had presumably formed as a result of mercury (41½ gr.) taking up and uniting with respirable air (3½ gr.) from the bell-jar – not from its *losing* phlogiston or anything else. Secondly: the calcination evidently stopped when it did only because all the respirable portion of the air in the bell-jar had been used up, leaving behind a different gas with chemically distinct properties. From this second conclusion, he drew a further inference which has since entered our stock of common knowledge:

Atmospheric air is composed of two elastic fluids of different and opposite qualities. As a proof of this important truth, if we recombine these two elastic fluids, which we have separately obtained in the above experiment, viz. the 42 cubical inches of mephitis [nitrogen], with the 8 cubical inches of respirable air [oxygen], we reproduce an air precisely similar to that in the atmosphere, and possessing nearly the same power of supporting combustion and respiration, and of contributing to the calcination of metals.

The two portions of the air (respirable and mephitic) were not, as Priestley had supposed, alternative states of a simple atmospheric air – the one saturated with phlogiston ('phlogisticated'), the other deprived of phlogiston ('dephlogisticated'). They were quite distinct substances; and the respirable part in particular was a specific gas, having a chemically simple base (oxygen), whose participation was indispensable for combustion, respiration, and calcination.

This conclusion represents a minor milestone in our understanding of Nature. Earlier workers had considered two possible theories of the atmosphere: either, that common air was composed of one single agency or substance, subject at most to physical modifications – this was the view of Newton, Hales, and Priestley; or else, that it was a highly-complex mixture – as Robert Boyle put it,

a Confus'd Aggregate of Effluviums from such differing Bodies, that ... perhaps there is scarce a more heterogenous Body in the world.

Lavoisier now produced striking, and novel, evidence that neither of these views was sound. Inspired by Hales' work and using Hales' methods, he had shown that the predominant ingredients of the atmosphere were neither one, nor many, but *two*, clearly distinct gases. And these same gases played a demonstrable part also in the other chemical processes he had studied: effervescence and calcination to begin with, and later respiration and combustion also.

As we read Lavoisier's account of this double demonstration, we are liable to be greatly impressed. To modern ideas, indeed, it has sometimes apeared as though this experiment destroys single-handed the whole basis of the phlogiston theory. First, the calx produced from mercury, and the air loses one-sixth of its volume; then, mercury is recovered from the calx, and a corresponding volume of respirable air appears. As we watch the volumes of gas changing we seem to see irresistible proof that the calx is a compound – that it is first produced from the metal, by imbibing respirable air, and afterwards converted back to the metal by releasing it – the evidence of the scales only confirming what our sight has already told us. But all perception involves interpretation. What we 'see' happening is read into the experiment by our theoretical hindsight. And though Lavoisier's immediate colleagues at once accepted his way of looking at it, other eighteenth-century chemists, watching the experiment for the first time, 'saw' it very differently.

Joseph Priestley, for instance, admitted that Lavoisier's arguments were attractive, and for a time he was 'much inclined to adopt them'. But he had second thoughts, and returned to the phlogiston theory, remaining faithful to it until his death in 1804. Why was he never convinced? Was he just an old fogey, past the age when he could bring himself to change a lifetime's habits of thought? Not at all: he was a good scientist – not merely obstinate – and he offered arguments for his position. In 1783, for instance, he devised a rival experiment which appeared to support his theory even more strongly than the mercury demonstration supported Lavoisier's. (See figure, page 254.)

I put upon a piece of broken crucible (which could yield no air) a quantity of minium [lead calx], out of which all air had been extracted; and, placing it upon a convenient stand, introduced it into a large receiver, filled with inflammable air [hydrogen], confined by water. [Next, he heated it with a burning-glass.] As soon as the minium was dry, by means of the heat thrown upon it, I observed that it became black, and then ran in the form of perfect lead, at the same time that the [inflammable] air diminished at a great rate, the water ascending within the receiver. . . .

Seeing the metal to be actually revived and that in a considerable quantity, at the same time that the air was diminished, *I could not doubt but that the calx was actually imbibing something from the air*; and from its effects in making the calx into metal, it could be no other than that to which chemists had unanimously given the name of *phlogiston.*

In point of logic, it is hard to find fault with Priestley's conclusion. In point of vividness, his demonstration was (if anything) *more* convincing than Lavoisier's. For the air in Lavoisier's bell-jar lost only *one-sixth* of its volume when the metallic mer-

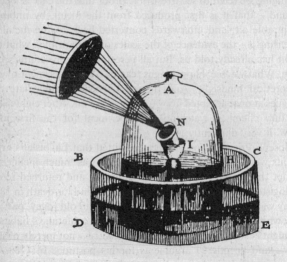

cury turned to red calx, whereas in Priestley's counter-demonstration, when the lead calx turned to metallic lead, *all* the hydrogen in a container disappeared.

How unfortunate – we may be tempted to reply – that Priestley enclosed his hydrogen over *water*. As we now interpret it, the heated calx gave off oxygen, which combined with the hydrogen in the jar to form a minute extra quantity of water: thus the illusion was produced that the calx and the hydrogen (evidently rich in phlogiston) had combined to form lead. If Priestley had noticed the extra water, could he have drawn the conclusion he did? He could, and he did: two years later he was still persisting in his fundamental view, even though he now acknowledged the formation of this extra water. The water, he argued, was only a by-product of the reaction: the basic phenomenon was still the union of the calx with phlogiston from the hydrogen to form the metal.

On the basis of the rival demonstrations alone, Priestley was entitled to hold his ground. For where we nowadays 'see' oxygen being evolved from heated mercury calx, Priestley 'saw' – even more vividly – hydrogen being imbibed by heated lead calx. And the true lesson to be learned from comparing their demonstrations is, in fact, this: that an overall reordering of chemical theory such as Lavoisier had proposed *could not* stand or fall by a single observation, or depend for its justification on any one 'crucial experiment'. For, in the last resort, the difference between Priestley and Lavoisier lay not in the vividness of their rival demonstrations, but in the merits of their respective interpretations. You cannot check chemical formulae by just *looking*: it was the *systematic* character of Lavoisier's theory – its power to embrace more and more chemical reactions, with the minimum of arbitrary assumptions – that ultimately carried weight with his colleagues. The phlogiston theory, by contrast, remained arbitrary and unsystematic, having to be trimmed and adjusted afresh to meet the demands of each new phenomenon, and this was a good sign that something was amiss with its principles. Indeed, Lavoisier's main complaint against the phlogiston theory was not that it *mis*represented Nature, but rather that it failed to give any clear representation of Nature at all. Its central notions were too vague. It permitted one to explain not too little, but too much. The term phlogiston (he grumbled) was a concertina, which was arbitrarily extended to embrace wider and wider phenomena, until its effective explanatory power was *nil*:

Chemists have made a vague principle of phlogiston which is not strictly defined, and which in consequence accommodates itself to every explanation into which it is pressed. Sometimes this principle is heavy and sometimes it is not; sometimes it is free fire, and sometimes it is fire combined with the earthy element; sometimes it passes through the pores of vessels and sometimes they are impenetrable to it. It explains at once causticity and non-causticity, transparency and opacity, colours and the absence of colours. It is a veritable Proteus which changes its form every minute.

What mattered in the long run was the *cumulative* success of Lavoisier's new system, in providing chemists both with the means of deciphering chemical constitutions and reactions and with the vocabulary for describing them. In this respect, the particular experiments which he himself described could do no more than provide sample demonstrations of its capabilities, and his lasting achievements thus lay as much in his intellectual method as in his immediate discoveries. For it was Lavoisier who put questions of physics at the very heart of chemistry, by demonstrating that the Newtonian idea of *mass* – as the measure of quantity of matter – could have the same fundamental importance for chemical theory as it already had for astronomy and dynamics. And, within a single generation, a great new theoretical structure was being erected on his foundations when, over the protests of a few last dissenters, his scientific successors – notably John Dalton (1766–1844) – finally succeeded in turning Newton's atomism into a theory of chemical composition.

Atomism becomes Scientific

The transition from Lavoisier's chemistry of principles to Dalton's chemistry of atoms was not entirely plain sailing. For Lavoisier himself had carried his theoretical revolution only part way: quite apart from his material theory of heat, he had based his system on assumption about 'generic and specific characters' which had led him to a faulty theory of acids. In the event his immediate successors, notably Claude-Louis Berthollet, left aside the whole question of heat and concentrated on the *weights* of substances entering into, and resulting from, any chemical reaction. Berthollet had collaborated in the work on chemical nomenclature, and after Lavoisier's death he developed the new system into an instrument for the exact analysis of chemical reactions. But in certain respects his ideas of chemical change were almost too sophisticated for the men of his time. The immediate need was to discover which of the known substances were true elements, and to decipher the constitution of compounds and mixtures; but Berthollet overleapt this problem, and launched straight into a study of rates of chemical change, and the laws governing 'mass action'. The result was a polemical debate with his contemporary, Joseph Louis Proust. Proust emerged from this debate the seeming victor, and his empirical discoveries were the foundation for Dalton's atomic theory.

The question at issue was: are composite chemical substances always formed from fixed proportions of their constituent elements, or can these proportions vary? For example: must the sodium and chlorine in common salt always be associated in the same ratio by weight, or could the ratio be different in different samples of salt? On this point Lavoisier had not finally committed himself. Berthollet was convinced that two elements such as sodium and chlorine could combine in an *indefinite* range of proportions to form composites of different properties; Proust, on the other hand, was equally convinced that true chemical compounds contained only *fixed* proportions of their elements, and that any pair of elements normally combined only in one or two (or in rare cases, three) definite proportions. Berthollet's evidence came from experiments on substances in solution, Proust's from the analysis of solid substances – he showed in 1799, for instance, that copper carbonate contained carbon and copper in the same proportion, whether it was found in Nature or prepared artificially.

Looking back, we can see that the nineteenth century was unjust in returning a firm verdict against Berthollet, since the point at issue was partly a verbal one. Proust used his results to justify an absolute distinction between true 'compounds' and mere 'mixtures': on this terminology, iron and sulphur combined to form only two genuine 'compounds' – iron sulphide and iron sulphate. Yet, as we know now, it is easier to state this distinction in theory than it is to apply it in practice. When chemical compounds are dissolved in water the distinction becomes especially tricky; for they exist in solution only in a partly dissociated form – the degree of dissociation depending both on the temperature of the solution and on its concentration. Proust's 'true compounds' were accordingly distinguishable only in the ideal case – when they were solid and perfectly dry. The result of dissolving iron sulphate crystals in water was a liquid conveniently called 'iron sulphate solution', but it was in reality one which comprised variable amounts of iron, sulphur, iron sulphide, and iron sulphate. (More recently, a similar ambiguous condition has been found even in the case of solids: certain substances – such as vanadium – can form a stable crystalline lattice, into whose interstices smaller atoms – such as those of carbon – can creep in varying proportions. The composite substances so produced form the kind of continuum for whose existence Berthollet argued: they have been christened 'interstitial compounds' or 'solid solutions', and allotted chemical formulae – such as $V_2C_{0.74}$ – that Proust and Dalton would have found meaningless. Such are the reversals of scientific fortune.)

Nevertheless, in a great many cases at least, it was clear that different elements did combine in definite and fixed proportions: that much Proust had certainly demonstrated. And the question immediately arose: What lay behind these definite proportionalities? Between 1799 and 1803 Dalton took Proust's results a stage further, by showing that the proportions were not only fixed, but related in a simple, numerical manner, and went on to explain these numerical ratios on the best Newtonian principles. For here at last (he showed) was positive evidence that the ultimate units of each chemical element were identical simple atoms, and those of any true compound were composite particles, or molecules, formed from a small number of atoms in a fixed arrangement.

Dalton had come to chemistry by way of meteorology and physics. He was especially puzzled by the structure of the atmosphere: as its different component gases – oxygen, nitrogen, and water-vapour – all had different densities, why did they remain mixed up together, instead of settling out into layers? (The problem had not arisen for Newton, since he had not known that common air is a mixture.) Dalton tried to account for this fact by extending the Newtonian idea of repulsions, supposing that in a mixture of gases the atoms of each gas repelled one another selectively, and had no effect on the atoms of the other gases. But the hypothesis was arbitrary: it could be accepted only if it was confirmed by direct laboratory study. And this, as he wrote in his *New System of Chemical Philosophy* (1808), was the starting-point of 'a train of investigation ... for determining the *number* and *weight* of all chemical elementary principles which would enter into any sort of combination one with another'.

The results of his investigations were significant, not just for meteorology, but for matter-theory generally. He began by analysing the gases formed when carbon combines with hydrogen and with oxygen. Leaving aside the ubiquitous caloric, ethylene and methane both consisted of carbon and hydrogen alone; but, on analysis, Dalton obtained twice as much hydrogen from methane, for any given quantity of carbon, as he did from ethylene. Similarly with carbonic oxide and carbonic acid: these two gases were composed of carbon and oxygen alone, but the proportion of oxygen to carbon turned out to be twice as great in carbonic acid (carbon dioxide) as it was in carbonic oxide (carbon monoxide). Evidently, the proportions in which elementary substances combined were not just fixed and *definite*, but were in many cases simple *multiples* of one another. He studied a great many instances in which two or more different compounds were formed from the same elementary substances, and he obtained consistently similar results. Given any chosen quantity of any one element common to two compounds, the weights of the other elements involved were always (so far as he could measure) in simple numerical proportions – e.g. 2:1, 3:1, or 3:2.

This was just the kind of discovery for which a good Newtonian was intellectually prepared. It fitted beautifully into the scheme of ideas outlined at the end of the *Opticks*, and it enabled one at long last to quote *chemical* measurements as direct evidence of *atomic* constitutions. Dalton was now in a position to do something which Lavoisier had hesitated to do: he could equate the fundamental material units of the chemical elements with Newton's 'hard, massy, impenetrable particles', and identify the molecules of compound substances with the 'particles of the first composition' formed by the simple combination of these elementary particles.

For Dalton, as for Plato, atomism was essentially a theory about the composition of *homogeneous* substances:

Whether the ultimate particles of a body such as water are all alike, that is, have the same figure, weight, etc., is a question of some importance. For what is known, we have no reason to apprehend a diversity of these particulars; if it does exist in water, it must equally exist in the elements constituting water, namely hydrogen and oxygen.

Though it is scarcely possible to conceive how the aggregates of dissimilar particles could be so uniformly the same if some of the particles of water were heavier than others, if a particle of the liquid on any occasion were constituted principally as these heavier particles, it must be supposed to affect the specific gravity of the mass, a circumstance not known. Similar observations may be made on other substances.

Thus we may conclude that the ultimate particles of all homogeneous bodies are perfectly alike in weight, figure, etc. In other words, every particle of water is like every other particle of water; every particle of hydrogen is like every other particle of hydrogen, etc.

With this assumption clearly stated, he could present his central conclusion. His argument was one of almost childish simplicity; but, at this moment in the development of our ideas, the simplicity of children proved more valuable than the subtleties of the mature:

If there are two bodies, A and B, which are disposed to combine, the following is the order in which the combinations may take place, beginning with the most simple, namely:

1 atom of A + 1 atom of B = 1 atom of C, binary
1 atom of A + 2 atoms of B = 1 atom of D, ternary
2 atoms of A + 1 atom of B = 1 atom of E, ternary
1 atom of A + 3 atoms of B = 1 atom of F, quaternary
3 atoms of A + 1 atom of B = 1 atom of G, quaternary, etc., etc.

The following general rules may be adopted as guides in all our investigations respecting chemical synthesis:
1st. When only one combination [i.e. compound] of two bodies [elements] can be obtained, it must be presumed to be a *binary* one, unless some cause appear to the contrary.
2nd. When two combinations are observed, they must be presumed to be a *binary* and a *ternary* [and so on].

Up to this point he had simply been *legislating*: now he had to show that his permutations and combinations had some relevance to the facts. (Oddly enough, his very first example involved an error, and the resulting confusion about atomic weights was finally cleared up only in the 1850s.)

From the application of these rules, to the chemical facts already well ascertained, we deduced the following conclusions:

1st. That water is a binary compound of hydrogen and oxygen [HO], and the relative weight of the two elementary atoms are as 1:7, nearly;

2nd. That ammonia is a binary compound of hydrogen and nitrogen [HN], and the relative weights of the two atoms are as 1:5, nearly [and so on]. . . .

That carbonic oxide is a binary compound, consisting of one atom of charcoal, and one of oxygen, together weighing nearly 12; that carbonic acid is a ternary compound, (but sometimes binary) consisting of one atom of charcoal, and two of oxygen, weighing 19 [etc., etc.] . . . In all these cases the weights are expressed in atoms of hydrogen, each of which is denoted by unity.

For the first time atoms were now being *weighed* – not absolutely, it is true; but at any rate comparatively. Dalton reasoned as follows: He knew of only one compound which was composed of hydrogen and oxygen alone – namely water. Applying his first rule, he assumed that it was a binary compound, in which every molecule contained one atom of each element. He found that, when he split water into its elements, the oxygen he obtained weighed seven times as much as the hydrogen. Since the atoms were combining one-to-one, their relative weights too (he concluded) must be in the same ratio, one to seven. He could no more observe the atoms directly than Newton or Lavoisier, but he had found a way of *inferring* their properties directly from large-scale measurements.

Dalton's principles soon established themselves. They supplemented and completed the work of Lavoisier, giving it not only a numerical precision but also the beginnings of a physical mechanism. From 1810 the preoccupation with *functions* characteristic of earlier chemical theories gave way entirely to considerations of *structure*. The problem of chemical composition became a problem about molecular architecture; and though a number of chemists hesitated to take Newton's ideas about atoms quite as literally as Dalton, his theories of molecular constitution soon became an essential instrument for chemical thought. The diagrams which he prepared for the Manchester Literary and Philosophical Society, to illustrate the composition and relative sizes of different molecules – with their radial shading to represent

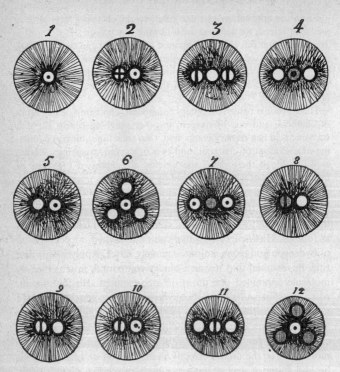

Some of Dalton's first diagrams of molecular structure. (Notice that the atoms are shown surrounded by shading representing 'atmospheres of caloric'.)

'combined caloric' or 'atmospheres of heat' – were no doubt very simple. But, simple though they may be, they are the direct ancestors of all subsequent molecular specifications, including those of our contemporary biochemical giants; the spiral models of the nucleic acid molecules – RNA and DNA.

The Persistent Sceptics

No branch of science ever came into its own more decisively than did chemistry in the half-century following 1775. During this time it moved from mere disordered gropings to maturity; and, although in 1825 some ambiguities remained about the relative weights of the different elementary atoms (and, indeed, about their ultimate reality), the main principles of chemical atomism and molecular structure were by then firmly established. It is scarcely surprising that chemistry became an object of enthusiasm and profound intellectual excitement; and Netwon's hint, that the raw materials of Nature might consist of hard, massy, impenetrable – and immutable – particles, was soon accepted by many chemists as absolute truth. If men had been ideally rational they would perhaps have clung to the shadow of a reservation, however dramatic the success of their theories; but after Dalton's numerical vindication of chemical atomism, chemists can be pardoned for having been only *humanly* rational. Forgetting the obligation to suspend final judgement, they shut their ears to the scruples of the few obstinate sceptics, and threw themselves into their researches with redoubled enthusiasm.

Yet even at the time there were a few sceptics, who never brought themselves to accept the claims of the new approach, and some of them rejected the new doctrines and methods as absolutely as the majority of chemists embraced them. These radical sceptics objected not just to Dalton's atomism or Lavoisier's oxygenic principle; they regarded the whole of pneumatic chemistry as one vast irrelevancy, and called down a plague on oxygenists and phlogistonians alike. They were the last of the Aristotelians, protesting against the conversion of chemistry into a science of the *inanimate*, their own eyes being fixed nostalgically on older and more physiological horizons. They included some of the most brilliant and enlightened men of the age, so it would be an error of historical judgement to pass them by without a glance: not only Venel, but also Diderot, Goethe and Lamarck, and in England the poet and painter, William Blake. (See Plate 6.)

Though they differed among themselves on many points, these men all objected to the new matter-theory for the same fundamental reason. Like Aristotle attacking Plato, they criticized it for being abstract and mathematical, so driving the life, colour, and activity out of Nature. As they rightly saw, the new approach was above all quantitative. Hales, Black, Lavoisier, and Dalton all made a point of measuring the substances and processes they were studying, and they ended, as we have seen, by restricting chemistry to a study of those entities which *could* be so measured. And this, the sceptics replied, was far from being the secret of success – rather, it meant shutting one's eyes to the real problems.

> The object of chemistry [wrote Lamarck] is the general and particular understanding, not of the *masses* of bodies, nor of facts connected with those masses, but rather of the very nature of these bodies, the properties connected with them, and also their interrelations, both closer and most distant.

Put a man on a weighing-machine, and it will tell you his weight – and that is all. Nothing follows from this about his character, intelligence, or likely behaviour. And why should it be any different with metals, airs, salts – or even atoms? Measuring only weights and volumes left questions about qualities and activities, colour, texture, and life entirely unanswered. So the price to be paid for converting chemistry into a branch of physics was too great.

The objections, like Aristotle's, may have been too sweeping, yet they had some genuine foundation. Throughout the nineteenth century, chemists accepted as arbitrary facts almost everything which Diderot, Goethe, and Lamarck were most anxious to have explained. By careful measurement, they produced evidence that oxygen atoms weighed sixteen times as much as hydrogen atoms, and those of iron fifty-six times as much; but that was all. Yet why should a substance of atomic weight 16 form a colourless gas and support combustion, while one of atomic weight 56 formed a dark, shining solid, which conducted electricity? While perfecting their knowledge of atomic weights (which they regarded as the crucial properties of the chemical elements), nineteenth-century chemists side-tracked these deeper questions. Once the ninety-odd elements were taken for granted, clever work with balance and gauge could unravel their molecular permutations, but the patterns of qualities characteristic of different elements could not be further explained: they had simply to be acknowledged. They were basic features of the universe, established unalterably at the Creation, but not (it seemed) otherwise intelligible; and this limitation was accepted by most nineteenth-century chemists with a quite surprising complacency.

However, though the sceptics had some grounds for their reservations, their own theories and methods were scarcely a satisfactory alternative, and their positive ideas and programmes proved unhelpful. According to Venel, the scale and the balance were worse than useless: they were positively misleading. Chemists must develop the craftsman's 'feel' for the materials they handled and understand them, not theoretically, but by direct familiarity – as a doctor does his patients. Chemical changes, too, were still at bottom *physiological* in character – either embryological changes in the womb of the earth or fermentations in the laboratory retort.

If Venel perpetuated ideas from Aristotle and the alchemists, Diderot and Lamarck were latter-day Stoics. For Diderot, the problems of matter were concerned with *interactions*: thermal and electrical influences, exhalations, nutrition, organization. Instead of assuming separate immutable atoms, which interacted across the void only by physical 'attractions', he started with a system of standing-waves – with 'universal elasticity' – and treated 'material objects' as stationary points or 'nodes' in those wave-patterns. Lamarck carried the counter-attack even further. First and foremost, he rejected Newton's belief that the fundamental atoms were immutable, and that molecules had simple, unchanging patterns. On the contrary, everything was in flux: molecules, like organisms, were caught up in a universal process of development, whose chief agent was fire in all its forms. (The electric and magnetic fluids, free and combined heat, 'acidifying' and 'carbonic' agencies, were all classified in his system as forms of fire.) The primary units of this universal evolution were individual animals and plants, and through their activities rocks and minerals, liquids and vapours were also bound up in the process. It was in fact twenty years before Lamarck extended the idea to include whole *species* of organisms, and began the work on palaeontology for which we remember him.

As for Goethe: he treasured above all the richness of the individual event, the unhampered pageant of Nature. True understanding (he thought) could never come from interfering with this wonderful procession, and to experiment was necessarily to falsify. So he ridiculed the methods of Newton's *Opticks*. If you wanted to understand *white* light, it was crazy to start off by sending it through a prism, and so turning it into *coloured* light:

> Friends! Avoid the darkened prisons,
> Where they pinch and tweak the light.

And it was not only ridiculous: it was wrong-headed. In this way you destroyed your objects of study as surely as did those physiologists who, in looking for the secret of life, first killed the creatures they studied; and the botanists who, faced by the dynamic form and growth of plants dug them up, pressed them, and preserved their faded corpses in the glass cases of a herbarium. To understand the nature of white light, one should study only white light; to understand life, one should make oneself patiently familiar with living creatures; to understand plants, one should live with them and tend them until their growth was seen as the natural unfolding of their inner directedness. Only by sympathetic observation could one hope to fathom the mysteries of natural change: the 'germs and productive powers' in things, and 'the inmost force, which binds the world and guides its course'.

Looking back from the twentieth century, we can understand the reservations of the sceptics; for only in recent years have we found ways of answering some of the questions about *qualities* which the nineteenth century ignored. Yet this small progress has not come about through scientists following the advice of Goethe and Diderot, and rejecting the mathematical approach. Rather, we have had to press further along the roads opened up by Lavoisier and Dalton and follow out all the new problems as they arose, until finally a picture has been built up whose grain and detail are finer than any that the nineteenth century knew. For Goethe and Diderot had misunderstood the aims of measurement and abstraction. Certainly you cannot find out everything about a living organism by killing it and cutting it up; or about a piece of metal by weighing it; or about a light-ray by spreading it into a spectrum. But few scientists ever assumed that you could. The fallacy of which Goethe accused them – of substituting the dead for the living, the part for the whole, and the single, measurable aspect for the qualitative totality – was one which they rarely committed. They were simply trying to proceed in a modest and methodical way: studying first the simpler and more manageable aspects of things, and working systematically towards more complicated and perplexing systems. Though they might often dissect out and scrutinize parts, their hope was always that in this way they would come to understand better the workings of wholes. And if they analysed weights and measures, their long-term ambition was also a larger one: to unravel eventually the whole complex of processes, whose interweaving makes up the unfolding of the cosmos.

FURTHER READING AND REFERENCES

Lavoisier has commanded the sympathy and interest of scholars to such an extent that he has thrown a shadow over most of his predecessors and contemporaries. Hales, Boerhaave, and Black have all suffered as a result. But useful material on matter-theory in the period between Newton and Lavoisier can be found in:

I. B. Cohen, *Franklin and Newton*, Philadelphia, 1956

Hélène Metzger, *Newton, Stahl, Boerhaave*, Paris, 1930

J. H. White, *The Phlogiston Theory*, E. Arnold, 1932

The current English biography of Lavoisier is that by D. McKie (Gollancz, 1935). His works and those of his school have been scrutinized in detail by McKie and his colleagues in *Annals of Science* and *Ambix*; also by Guerlac, Daumas, Duveen, and Klickstein. One recent book is of particular importance for an understanding of Lavoisier's debt to Stephen Hales, and of the development of his ideas:

H. Guerlac, *Lavoisier, The crucial year*, Cornell University Press, 1961

But there is no substitute for reading his original works, particularly the *Traité Elémentaire de Chimie*: the original English translation (1791) is now available in paper covers, and is another bargain. The most penetrating summary of his basic ideas about matter remains the brief monograph:

Hélène Metzger, *La Philosophie de la matière chez Lavoisier*, Paris, 1935

Priestley's rearguard action in defence of phlogiston is analysed in the paper by Stephen Toulmin 'Crucial Experiments: Priestley v. Lavoisier' (*Journal for History of Ideas*, 1957, reprinted in the collection, *Roots of Scientific Thought*). See also *Foresight and Understanding*, chs. 4 and 5 (Hutchinson, 1961), for the transition from physiological to physical modes of thought in chemistry. For the transition from Lavoisier to Dalton, and the rival traditions of Lamarck, Diderot, and Goethe, consult:

THE ACTIVITIES OF THE INANIMATE

C. C. Gillispie, *The Edge of Objectivity*, Princeton University Press, 1960, and 'Lamarck and Darwin' in the book *Forerunners of Darwin*, Oxford University Press, 1959

Agnes Arber, *The Natural Philosophy of Plant Form*, Cambridge University Press, 1950

11

The Classical Synthesis

A NEW system of physical theory (as Descartes had remarked) resembles a new *decipherment* of Nature; in each case, the surest sign that our principles are sound is the sudden 'snowballing' by which successful interpretations begin to accumulate. Indeed, a point is sometimes reached at which even the most puzzling and mysterious data come all at once to appear entirely straightforward. The age of profound new insights seems to be past: industry and ingenuity alone will suffice to extend without limit the reach of our understanding.

In the physical sciences, the middle decades of the nineteenth century were a phase of this kind. During this period the sciences of inanimate matter enjoyed an almost unchecked advance, and for a while it looked as though their success had been complete and final – as though the whole cryptogram of Nature had been resolved for good. As men now saw it, two distinct classes of beings exhausted the population of the physical universe, and the last fog surrounding the 'incorporeals' was dissipated. Matter in motion was the first great principle of Nature: atoms and molecules, which moved according to the laws of Newtonian mechanics, colliding and interacting by 'central forces'. The void between these particles of matter was spanned by beings of the other kind: the many varieties of radiant energy, which moved with the speed of light in the form of electromagnetic waves.

A detailed account of the tumultuous growth of the physical sciences during the nineteenth century could easily fill several volumes of history. But the very pace of their growth was possible only because certain general principles of interpretation were throughout widely agreed. So, even at the cost of making the story seem like an uninterrupted sequence of simple discoveries, we must concentrate our attention here on the central arguments by which the new system of ideas was first justified, and later called in doubt.

For this 'classical' system, as it is still called (the very adjective is significant), had a life-story curiously like that of the British Empire. From the first precipitate expansion came a system of theory on which – or so it seemed – 'the sun never set'. During the hey-day of classical physics many scientists really believed that the whole spectacle of Nature was comprised within the twin categories of atoms and radiation: and that their intellectual empire, being so comprehensive and broadly based, must look forward to a life of many centuries. Yet this hey-day – like that of the British Empire – proved surprisingly short. The same enterprise and independence of mind which had originally created the two systems led quite soon to their dismantlement. For the men responsible wished to establish neither a political nor an ideological tyranny; and when the time came they refused to shut their eyes to the necessity for fundamental change. The categories of classical nineteenth-century science may still provide today the bread-and-butter for introductory courses at school. But, at a more advanced level, the hard-and-fast intellectual boundaries of 1875 have faded – like the colonial frontiers of the Imperial Era – into dotted lines on an out-of-date map; while at the same time some more ancient dividing-lines, which classical physics and chemistry contrived to do without, are once again becoming visible and convenient.

The Units of Matter

As the classical picture of Nature took shape, Newton's ultimate particles of matter acquired precise and detailed properties. By 1860, it was generally agreed that the units of matter had *mass*, and so *weight*; they occurred in definite *numbers* – though it remained something of a scandal that the actual numbers of atoms in any object could be estimated only very roughly; they were *distinct*, each different chemical element having atoms of its own specific size, shape, and mass; they could be *electrified*; and finally they were perfectly elastic and engaged in a continual agitated *motion* – oscillating in solids about fixed positions, or colliding and rebounding in gases to form a disordered Lucretian chaos. The evidence for these conclusions, which came from a wide variety of phenomena, was in every case solid experimental observation, rather than unsupported speculation. This evidence we must now survey.

The Weights of Atoms

We have already examined the evidence by which the weights of atoms were inferred, but there is one thing we must emphasize. For the purposes of Dalton's theory their absolute sizes and weights were irrelevant. It was not necessary to know (e.g.) how many atoms there are in a gram of hydrogen, so long as one could assume that this number was very large indeed. For all one could infer by the application of Dalton's 'General Rules' were the *relative* weights of atoms and molecules of different substances. One could establish that each oxygen atom weighed 4/3 times as much as each carbon atom – but there was no way of knowing whether they weighed respectively 4 and 3 millionths, or 4 and 3 billionths, or 4 and 3 trillionths of a gram. The 'atomic' weights and 'molecular weights' of chemistry have always been expressed as multiples of an arbitrary unit – the weight of one hydrogen or carbon or oxygen atom being fixed *by definition* as '1' or '12' or '16'.

Since the absolute sizes of the hypothetical atoms could not be known, chemical atomism could legitimately be interpreted in either of two ways – 'realist' or 'phenomenalist'. One could read it as committing one to an outright *assertion*, that matter *is in reality* made up of minute corpuscles; or, alternatively, one could interpret it more cautiously as an intellectual *construction*, in which matter was depicted *as if it were* made up of minute corpuscles. It made no immediate difference to chemistry which way one took it, and as late as 1900 a minority of scientists still took the more cautious view – including one winner of the Nobel Prize for Chemistry.

Relative though they might be, their weights were, nevertheless, the crucial properties of the atoms. Every elementary substance had its own proper atomic weight, and every homogeneous compound a molecular weight equal to the sum of its constituent atomic weights – for carbon monoxide 28 (i.e. $12 + 16$), for carbon dioxide 44 ($12 + 2 \times 16$). As time went on, measurements of atomic and molecular weights gave results fitting more and more consistently with Dalton's rules of chemical construction. Complete success was not achieved until the 1850s, chiefly because Dalton had assumed that water was a 'binary compound' of hydrogen and oxygen. But once the true constitution of the water molecule had been recognized – two atoms of hydrogen to each one of oxygen – everything else fell rapidly into place.

The Numbers of Atoms

The first tangles about atomic weights were unravelled only when chemists generally began to consider the *numbers* of atoms in any piece of matter, following a clue put forward by Count Avogadro as early as 1811. Whereas Dalton attacked the problem of chemical combination by comparing the weights of different substances entering into a compound and, to explain his results, had put forward an hypothesis about the relative weights of the individual atoms, Avogadro focused his attention on the volumes of gaseous substances entering into compounds (studied experimentally by Gay-Lussac) and put forward another hypothesis – about the *relative numbers* of atoms. To stick to the crucial example: when hydrogen and oxygen (at the same temperature and pressure) combine chemically to form water, the volume of hydrogen consumed is exactly *twice* the volume of oxygen consumed. When, reversing the reaction, water is dissociated into its elements (e.g. by passing an electric current through it), the hydrogen and oxygen given off again fill volumes in the same proportion of two to one. And there was nothing in Dalton's theory to account for this volume-relationship.

Avogadro pointed out that these ratios could be explained quite simply, on one assumption – if one supposed that, at any given temperature and pressure, *all* gases *always* contained the same number of unit-particles as each other, whether these were atoms or molecules. At the time this hypothesis attracted little attention: his contemporaries seem to have considered it too wild and arbitrary to be true, for what could possibly lie behind this unforeseen equality? Besides, at several points the implications of the hypothesis seemed to contradict the accepted consequences of Dalton's newly-minted theory:

For the ratios of the masses of the molecules will then be the same as those of the *densities* of the different gases at equal temperature and pressure. . . . For instance: since, taking the density of atmospheric air as unity, the densities of the two gases hydrogen and oxygen are expressed by the numbers 0·07321 and 1·10359 respectively (the ratio of these two numbers representing the ratio between the masses of equal volumes of the two gases) this ratio will also represent on our hypothesis the relative masses of their molecules. *So the mass of the oxygen molecule will be about* 15 × *that of the hydrogen molecule* [cf. Dalton's 7]: or more exactly 15·074:1. Since we know that the ratio by volume of hydrogen and oxygen going to form water is 2:1, it follows that *water results from the union of each molecule of oxygen with two molecules of hydrogen* [cf. Dalton's HO].

For forty years Avogadro's hypothesis lay dormant, since men hesitated to abandon Dalton's newly-won victories. The theoretical niche for the idea appeared only after 1850, with the development of the new 'dynamical theory of gases' by Clausius and Maxwell.

The Distinctness of Atoms

In 1815 another hypothesis was put forward which was equally sweeping, equally daring, and even longer in justifying itself. This theory, which many classical chemists were to dismiss as entirely fanciful, was suggested by William Prout and has been rehabilitated, largely through historical good fortune, in the twentieth century. For, seventy-five years before any solid evidence had come to light, Prout guessed that the Daltonian atoms might have a common sub-atomic structure.

In the early days of Daltonian chemistry, the techniques of chemical measurement were not very precise, so atomic weights could be estimated only roughly. During this phase, accordingly, men felt free to look in the tables of measured atomic weights for numerical regularities which were not there to be found. Just as Kepler and Bode had scrutinized the planetary orbits with the conviction that the distances of the planets from the sun must be related by some simple formula, so William Prout was convinced that the atomic weights of the different elements had a similar arithmetical basis – that they were all *whole numbers* – and he took it for granted that, with improved techniques of measurement, this truth would become progressively more evident. Relying on this 'experimental evidence', he took a great intellectual leap: if the atomic weights of the chemical elements were exactly 12, 16, 40 (and so on) times the unit-weight of hydrogen, then perhaps the hydrogen atom was not merely the fundamental *arithmetical* unit for the chemical scale of weights but also the actual *physical* building-block of which all matter was ultimately composed. In that case (Prout concluded), all other atoms would be composed of the appropriate number of hydrogen atoms, held together by an attractive force far stronger than the molecular bond; and the atomic weight of each substance indicated simply the number of hydrogen atoms in each of its own atoms.

However, Prout's evidence proved insubstantial and his conclusion therefore seemed unfounded. As chemical measurement became more accurate, his doctrine that all atomic weights are whole numbers became less and less plausible. By the late 1830s, it had in fact become incredible: by then, the best available figure for chlorine (for instance) was 35·45, and to 'correct' this figure to 35 or 36 meant supposing an experimental error of worse than one per cent. So the general nineteenth-century verdict went against Prout. Historians such as Ernst von Meyer (1888) were very severe:

Seldom has it happened that an idea from which such weighty conceptions sprang, originated in such a faulty manner. [Prout's work] materially depreciated the atomic doctrine in the eyes of many eminent investigators. This idea, so lightly thrown out ... possessed both then and at various later periods a great charm for many distinguished chemists.

Von Meyer even congratulated J. J. Berzelius for resisting Prout's seductive voice:

Firm, and not led away by the alluring simplicity of Prout's hypothesis, he held fast to his aim – the accurate, purely experimental determination of the atomic weights, and he firmly established by his masterly work the then unsteady edifice of the atomic doctrine.

For the time being Berzelius and his followers sealed the fate of Prout's hypothesis. Scientists became highly suspicious of all attempts to discover regularities linking together the properties of different chemical elements; still more of theories which attributed a common matter or substructure to all the elements. Atoms of any one substance were absolutely *alike*: atoms of different substances were absolutely *distinct*. Thus, John Newlands noticed that, when the different elements were listed in order of their atomic weights, certain patterns of chemical properties recurred at regular intervals, potassium being followed by calcium just as sodium was by magnesium; but when in 1854 he proposed a 'law of octaves' to explain these analogies he was met with scoffing and ridicule. By that time the various elements were considered to be so completely *unique* that his suggestion was dismissed as quite visionary; one might as well, he was told, classify the elements by the first letters of their names.

In fact, Newlands' insight was entirely authentic, and five years later the Russian chemist Mendeleev followed it out in detail. The result was the Periodic Table; and the 'periodicity' in the properties of the chemical elements has acquired a new significance in the twentieth century, being explained by the electron theory of sub-atomic structure. Yet the very violence of Newlands' critics does something to show just how powerfully nineteenth-century chemistry had been canalized by Dalton's theory. Having accepted the axiom that every element has unique, invariable, and distinct atoms, chemists were able to disregard questions about the internal cohesion of atoms, and about possible analogies between different elements, so as to concentrate single-mindedly on the more immediate – and more easily soluble – problems of molecular architecture and composition. And until positive evidence of sub-atomic structure began to appear towards the end of the century their attention remained, very profitably, focused on this level.

Atoms and Electricity

Very early on, the atoms were found to have one other important property: they could be electrified. Indeed, when Berzelius stated his 'electrochemical theory' in 1812, he actually assumed that all atomic particles were permanently charged. Once again, the evidence was indirect, but it was quite forcible, and some of it even antedated Dalton's theory. Throughout the eighteenth century natural philosophers had been studying the electric properties of material bodies, in a series of researches which we cannot analyse here: by the end of the century, Franklin, Cavendish, and Galvani had established the basic facts of electrification and,

PERIODIC TABLE OF ELEMENTS ACCORDING TO MENDELEEV

Series	GROUP I R_2O	GROUP II RO	GROUP III R_2O_3	GROUP IV RH_4 RO_2	GROUP V RH_3 R_2O_5	GROUP VI RH_2 RO_3	GROUP VII RH R_2O_7	GROUP VIII RO_4
1	H 1							
2	Li 7	Be 9.4	B 11	C 12	N 14	O 16	F 19	
3	Na 23	Mg 24	Al 27.3	Si 28	P 31	S 32	—	
4	K 39	Ca 40	— 44	Ti 48	V 51	Cr 52	Mn 55	Fe 56, Co 59, Ni 59, Cu 63
5	(Cu 63)	Zn 65	— 68	— 72	As 75	Se 78	Br 80	
6	Rb 85	Sr 87	?Yt 88	Zr 90	Nb 94	Mo 96	—100	Ru 104, Rh 104, Pd 106, Ag 108
7	(Ag 108)	Cd 112	In 113	Sn 118	Sb 122	Te 125	?I 127	
8	Cs 133	Ba 137	?Di 138	?Ce 140	—	—	—	—
9	(—)	—	—	—	—	—	—	—
10	(—)	—	?Er 178	?La 180	Ta 182	W 184	—	Os 195, Ir 197, Pt 198, Au 199
11	(Au 199)	Hg 200	Tl 204	Pb 207	Bi 208	—	—	—
12	(—)	—	—	Th 231	—	U 240	—	—

in particular, the existence of two distinct kinds of electric charge, positive and negative. In 1800 Nicholson and Carlisle showed that, using an electric current, one could decompose water into its constituent elements: the natural interpretation of this fact was that hydrogen and oxygen had intrinsic and opposite electric charges, which bound them together in the form of water, and which could be overpowered by the action of an electric battery.

With the introduction of the atomic theory, the next step was even more natural. Berzelius inferred that the *individual atoms* of oxygen (like those of chlorine and many other substances) carried a negative electric charge, while the atoms of hydrogen (like those of metals and other substances) carried a positive one. The effect of an electric current was to tear the electrified atoms apart, and to drive them (in the form of *ions* or 'travellers') towards the oppositely charged plate.

For a while, these electric properties promised to answer completely the most serious theoretical question of Dalton's chemistry: namely, *by what force* are individual atoms held together to form molecules? For, as it soon appeared, many molecules consisted of two substances with intrinsic charges of opposite sign – e.g. 'positive' sodium with 'negative' chlorine and 'positive' hydrogen with 'negative' oxygen. Yet, as so often, the tempting answer did not tell the whole story. As time went on, more and more exceptions were discovered. It became evident, for instance, that two hydrogen atoms, instead of violently repelling each other, combined to form the normal hydrogen molecule, H_2. If such 'diatomic' molecules as H_2 and O_2 were to exist at all, chemical binding-forces could not be explained in terms of straightforward electrical analogies.

One particular electrochemical discovery was to have great significance for the twentieth century. Michael Faraday, working in Humphry Davy's laboratory, showed that a given quantity of electric charge produced precisely equivalent chemical effects on all chemical substances whatever. In every case, the passage of the electricity released an identical quantity of hydrogen or (as one went from reaction to reaction) an equivalent quantity of oxygen, chlorine, or any other substance. The conclusion which Maxwell drew from this observation had a significance he could not possibly appreciate.

To explain the phenomenon, we ought to show why the charge thus produced on each molecule is of a fixed amount, and why, when a molecule of chlorine is combined with a molecule of zinc, the molecular charges are the same as when a molecule of chlorine is combined with a molecule of copper. . . .

Suppose, however, that we leap over this difficulty by simply asserting the fact of the constant value of the molecular charge, and that we call this constant molecular charge, for convenience in description, *one molecule of electricity.*

This phrase, gross as it is, and out of harmony with the rest of the treatise [*On Electricity and Magnetism*], will enable us at least to state clearly what is known about electrolysis [the production of chemical changes by the passage of electric currents], and to appreciate the outstanding difficulties. . . .

It is extremely improbable however that when we come to understand the true nature of electrolysis we shall retain in any form the theory of molecular charges, for then we shall have obtained a secure basis on which to form a true theory of electric currents, and so become independent of these provisional theories.

The idea that electricity (which was regarded as a quality of matter) could have its own units or 'molecules' was undoubtedly out of harmony with the rest of classical physics. However, far from dispensing with 'the theory of molecular charges' (as Maxwell predicted), physicists since his day have made 'particles of electricity' the very foundation of their matter-theory.

The Movement of Atoms

The final step which, more than any other, established the atomic theory as the cornerstone of nineteenth-century science, came in the late 1850s. Up to that time the atomic theory had been entirely a *chemical* theory, and the evidence supporting it had come solely from the study of chemical compositions and reactions. Within the wider field of physics, however, the theory had made little progress beyond the brilliant guesswork of Newton's *Opticks*. As a result of Clausius's and Maxwell's new theory of heat and gases, physics at last caught up with chemistry.

On this theory, one supposed that the molecules of all substances were perfectly elastic, and were engaged in a continuous, agitated movement conforming to Newton's Laws of Motion. In two bodies having the same temperature, the average mechanical energy of the molecules was the same: when the bodies were brought into contact, the collisions between their surface molecules transferred on balance no energy in either direction. But, if one body were hotter than the other, its molecules were moving more violently, and would lose energy to the slower-moving molecules of the colder body – and this transfer of energy would manifest itself as a 'transfer of heat'. The 'spring of air' could also be accounted for by the same agitation of the molecules, the pressure of the air directly reflecting the number and violence of the collisions between its molecules and the containing vessel.

This theory was not entirely new. In outline, its mathematical foundations had been worked out by Daniel Bernoulli as early as the 1730s. Bernoulli demonstrated that random agitation of the atoms of air would explain Boyle's Law just as well as Newton's theory of repulsive forces; but although John Herapath immediately extended this explanation into a dynamical theory of heat it remained the minority view, being quite overshadowed by Boerhaave's and Lavoisier's *material* theory. Around 1800, it is true, a few scientists were positively sceptical about caloric. For instance, Benjamin Thompson (Count Rumford) observed that friction would generate unlimited quantities of heat, even when there was no obvious source of supply for the supposed 'matter of heat'; though to say (as Einstein and Infeld have done) that Rumford's experiments 'dealt a death-blow to the substance theory of heat' is a complete mistake, as the material theory retained the allegiance of leading scientists for another half-century.

Why was Maxwell's theory taken seriously in the 1850s, when Bernoulli's ideas had been neglected for so long? Once again, we must examine the wider theoretical frameworks into which the two suggestions fitted. Between Bernoulli and Maxwell, the scope and generality of Newton's dynamics had been continuously extending into fresh fields. Euler, d'Alembert, Lagrange, and Hamilton expounded the theory in more and more general forms, until at last *all* processes of a mechanical kind were seen as conforming to two basic mathematical principles – the Principle of the Conservation of Energy, and the Principle of Least Action. This mathematical drive towards a completely general theory of dynamics continued, overflowing beyond the bounds of mechanics into other branches of physics. If mechanical energy remained at a constant level throughout all purely mechanical processes, might not the conservation principle be extended so as to embrace, also, processes involving non-mechanical factors: heat, electricity, vitality, and chemical change? Enquiries soon focused on a single question: Can one find consistent ways of enlarging the concept of 'energy', so that the total amount of energy in *all* forms will be conserved – even in processes involving an overall gain or loss of ordinary mechanical energy? During the 1840s, several scientists independently took the final step, and asserted the conservation of energy as a completely general principle – something which held good in all physical processes whatever. The most comprehensive exposition was given in 1847 by Hermann von Helmholtz, though some residual confusion remained for another ten years or so, springing chiefly from the fact that one word was generally used for both 'force' and 'energy'.

It was implicit in the general principle of energy-conservation that different forms of energy could be converted into each other at 'rates of exchange' fixed by Nature. Newton's theory of motion and force could be extended to cover thermal, electrical, and even physiological phenomena, provided that these 'rates of exchange' could be determined experimentally. In 1848, J. P. Joule succeeded in doing just that: whether he produced heat by the passage of an electric current, or by mechanical effort, the conversion took place at fixed, measurable rates. And when he estimated the amount of mechanical work needed to produce a given quantity of heat, using four different experimental procedures, he got (within the limits of his experiments) identical results in every case.

Given this numerical correspondence between mechanical energy and heat-energy, it was natural to look again for an explanation of heat in mechanical terms. Perhaps the production of heat by friction merely transferred mechanical energy from a visible level to an invisible one – the level of the molecules – the increased motion of the molecules displaying itself as heat. Clausius and Maxwell turned this view of heat from an attractive possibility into a fully-developed branch of mathematics. (This was achieved in the years from 1857 to 1866.) By the time they had finished, heat-theory had been united into the general theory of 'matter in motion' – having as its special concern the random agitation of vast numbers of invisibly-small particles.

The resulting analysis of heat-exchange and gas-structure was so exact and detailed that the old disputes simply faded away, and the very name of 'caloric' went out of use. But most important of all: the properties of Maxwell's *physical* atoms and molecules matched perfectly with those of Dalton's *chemical* atoms. This happy conjunction greatly strengthened the arguments for the atomic theory in both fields of study. Before long it even became possible to estimate Avogadro's Number (a constant in chemical theory) on the basis of physical evidence, and so calculate at last the absolute numbers, sizes, and weights of individual atoms and molecules.

From Dalton in 1803 to Maxwell in 1866, the atomic picture of matter had progressively taken on shape and detail: by Maxwell's time it had crystallized into a definitive form, and lay at the heart of the classical system. Scientists now declared, with absolute confidence, that all matter was composed of ponderable atoms and, with the 'death' of caloric, the division between corporeals and incorporeals became absolutely sharp. The known incorporeal agencies – radiant heat, light, magnetism, and electricity – had to be dealt with in terms of other concepts.

Radiation and Fields of Force

By 1800 the existence of those incorporeal agencies was well attested; and it was clear that some of them, at least, were capable of carrying energy and so of playing a significant part in the economy of the physical world. In 1800 they still appeared distinct and unrelated, but by 1875 they had all, with the solitary exception of gravitation, been gathered under the wings of a common theory of radiation and force-fields.

Radiant Heat

If the caloric theory was so long a-dying, there were in fact good reasons for this. The problems posed by heat-transfer and heat-exchange had never been simple, and the task of formulating a theory which fitted all the phenomena equally well had never been plain sailing. Despite its attractions, the idea that heat consisted entirely in the vibration of material atoms could not be the whole story: for, if it had been, one inescapable consequence would have followed – namely, that *no heat can travel across a vacuum*. But this conclusion was directly contrary to certain plain facts. If you place a small bell in a glass jar, and gradually pump out the air, the sound of the bell dies away until it becomes quite inaudible. But replace the bell by a source of heat (or a thermometer) and you will get a very different result: however completely the jar is evacuated, the most you can do is to reduce somewhat the amount of heat passing across the vacuum. And if one accepted Newton's conclusion, that inter-planetary space is empty, there was yet more dramatic evidence that heat (as well as light) must travel through empty space: otherwise the sun would be powerless to warm the earth across a hundred million miles of void.

The phenomena of radiant heat are, of course, quite authentic and distinct from those of bodily warmth, and Maxwell's theory of molecular agitations could cover only the latter. Though scientists took some time to reconcile themselves to the fact, the quest for a single all-inclusive theory of heat was bound in the end to suffer shipwreck. Long before 1800, in fact, radiant heat had already been shown to have properties parallel to those of light itself. Concave mirrors had been used to focus heat and cold on to a thermometer, and the 'rays' of heat and cold were reflected at the mirror according to the usual laws of light-reflection. Then, in 1800, William Herschel showed that the analogy with light was even closer. When he formed a light-spectrum with a prism, radiant heat was detected with a thermometer in the dark ('infra-red') region beyond the red end of the visible spectrum, and soon radiant heat had been shown to share all the typical properties of light. (One could not only reflect it and refract it, but also produce diffraction and interference patterns, and even polarize it.) It was clear that there were not *two* separate physical problems, one about the nature of light and the other about radiant heat; rather there was a single problem, viz. the nature of that universal radiation which when visible we call 'light', and whose invisible parts include radiant heat and ultra-violet radiation.

Light

The full morals of the work on radiant heat were drawn only in the twentieth century, and will carry us beyond the scope of classical physics. For the moment we must remain at the beginning of the nineteenth century, and see first how thermal and optical rays were shown to consist of *waves*, and secondly how these waves themselves were interpreted in terms of *electromagnetic* concepts.

Newton's account of the phenomena of light had had three distinct aspects, all of which had survived in one form or another right down to the year 1800. In the first place he had regarded light as a *substance*, which could enter into chemical combination with other forms of matter; in the second place this substance was composed (like any other) of corpuscles, which were extremely hard and had a very pronounced shape; while finally these 'rays' – or atoms – of light were accompanied by waves in the aether, which acted upon the faces of the light-atoms and so directed their paths.

The idea of light as a chemical substance survived into Lavoisier's system, as an offshoot of the caloric theory. He drew attention to the 'affinity' which light appeared to have for oxygen, and explained the growth and colour of plants as due to the combination of light 'with certain parts of vegetables'. Whether or not light could enter into chemical compounds, most physicists in 1800 took the corpuscular view as established – even though, in Newton's own lifetime, Christian Huygens had used a most elegant wave-theory of light to explain 'double refraction'.

The wave-model for light started off with certain initial disadvantages. In all everyday situations, light appears to travel in precise straight lines, and shows none of that tendency to spread round corners which one commonly associates with waves. So, when Thomas Young took up again those wave aspects which had formed the third element in Newton's theory of light, he found himself very much in the minority. Yet within twenty years Young, Arago, and Fresnel were to show that the wave-model provided one with a conception of light quite as good as the corpuscular model, and in certain respects far better.

Initially, all the known properties of light could be accounted for on the accepted, corpuscular view – given sufficient mathematical ingenuity. But a critical test was at hand. In 1818 the French Academy of Sciences announced a competition for an essay on 'The Diffraction of Light'. The judges included the mathematician, Poisson, who criticized Fresnel's entry (defending the wave-theory) by pointing out that it entailed one fantastic

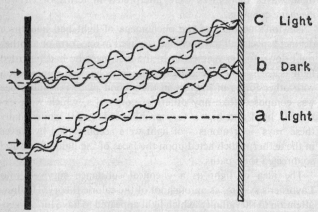

Young and Fresnel explained the light and dark lines in 'interference-fringes' as produced by the addition of wave-motions, which reinforced one another at 'a' and 'c', but cancelled each other out at 'b'.

consequence. If the wave-theory were correct, then at certain distances the shadow cast by a perfectly circular disc should have a bright spot of light at its very centre, at points where the waves, arriving in phase, would reinforce one another. (If light were simply a rain of particles, no such bright spots could possibly appear.) Fresnel took his chance, performed the experiment and was entirely vindicated; though the effect was apparent only if the light-source were sufficiently small and the obstacle exactly circular. And when, as a bonus, Foucault showed that light travels more slowly in water than in air, the triumph of wave-theory appeared complete. For it was an accepted consequence of the corpuscular view that the reverse would be true.

Still, the wave-theory of light was not without its difficulties.

Waves *of* what, men naturally asked, and waves *in* what? If one supposed the waves to be transmitted by some medium, this must have properties as extraordinary as those of the Stoic pneuma or Newton's aether – combining utter tenuousness with extreme

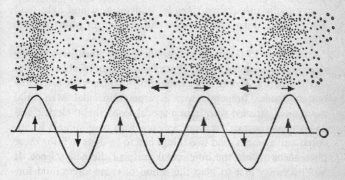

Sound-waves involve the longitudinal oscillation of air-molecules: light-waves involve transverse oscillation, and these can take place in either of two directions ('polarizations') at right-angles.

elasticity. So long as the waves had been thought of as longitudinal – like sound-waves – the problem had been bad enough; but if, as it now seemed, light-waves were *transverse* the difficulty was even more severe. One can normally produce such transverse waves only where there are *solid connexions* between adjacent parts, as in the waves travelling along a rope. And, if the luminiferous ether had now to be not only extremely tenuous and elastic but also *solid*, all the old difficulties would arise again. No known substance could combine these three characteristics in the required degree without gravely hampering the motion of the planets and other bodies.

Electricity and Magnetism

The answers to these questions came from an unforeseen – and totally unforeseeable – quarter. From time to time real life indulges in coincidences more gross than any novelist could afford to invent, and the clue from which the electromagnetic theory of light was developed represents just such a coincidence. Yet, by itself, coincidence does not give rise to a discovery, still less to such intellectual creativity as Maxwell showed in unifying the theories of electricity, magnetism, and light. Newton wove ideas from several sources into a comprehensive theory of motion and gravity, and Maxwell was now to create a new intellectual fabric from equally unexpected threads. Radiant heat and light were two of these threads. Electricity and magnetism were to be the others.

Ever since 1500 natural philosophers had been perplexed by electric and magnetic action. Since Descartes and Galileo had re-established the claims of a mechanistic physics, such ostensibly non-mechanical influences were a perpetual scandal. Men could not remain satisfied with barren speculations about 'electric and magnetic corpuscles' or 'vortices', nor with bare appeals to 'in-corporeal' agencies, and two things had to be done to bring these phenomena within the intellectual grasp of the new science. It was necessary first to map the action of these forces, and for-mulate in mathematical terms the laws by which they were governed; and secondly to devise some model or analogy by which electricity and magnetism could be reconciled with New-tonian mechanics. Throughout the eighteenth century steady progress was made in the first of these tasks, but the search for *mechanisms* became if anything more hopeless as time went on – especially after 1777, when Coulomb finally demonstrated that Descartes' vortex-theories were as unhelpful for magnetism as they had been for gravitation.

Real progress began only after 1820, when the first solid con-nexion was established between electrical and magnetic pheno-mena themselves. Certainly, some such connexion had long been suspected. The *Philosophical Transactions* for 1735 reported the extraordinary experience of a tradesman of Wakefield:

Having put up a great number of knives and forks in a large box, and having placed the box in the corner of a large room, there happen'd in July, 1731, a sudden storm of thunder, lightening, etc., by which the corner of the room was damaged, the Box split, and a good many knives and forks melted, the sheathes being untouched. The owner emptying the box upon a Counter where some Nails lay, the Persons who took up the knives, that lay upon the Nails, observed that the knives took up the Nails.

The mathematical laws governing the two kinds of action also turned out to be similar in form, and Poisson was able to expound them in a strictly parallel way. But in 1820 the Danish physicist, Oersted, chanced on the first clear and repeatable demonstration of the connexion. He had been searching for this for thirteen years: like most of his contemporaries, he had been preoccupied with Newton's idea of 'central forces', and had therefore supposed that, if an electric current in a wire exerted any force on a magnet, this must act *radially*, outwards or inwards. No such effect turned up; but, after demonstrating this negative result in a lecture, he happened to repeat the observation with the electric wire *parallel* to his magnetic needle. To his surprise, the needle at once displayed a marked deflection – it was clear that the magnetic force induced acted not radially but *tangentially*.

The first comprehensive study of the new phenomenon was made by Michael Faraday, Humphry Davy's assistant and successor at the Royal Institution in London. In personality and intellect alike, Faraday was exceptional among the great scientists of the last three centuries. He was largely self-educated: having trained as a bookbinder, he found his curiosity stimulated by the scientific volumes which passed through his hands. After attending some of Davy's lectures, Faraday showed him the notes he had made and described his own amateur experiments in electrochemistry. Shortly afterwards Davy appointed him his own assistant and Faraday remained at the institution for the rest of his career, becoming Director after Davy's death in 1829.

Faraday's background and unusual qualifications – or, as it seemed to his French contemporaries, his lack of qualifications – showed clearly both in his experimental enquiries and in his theoretical conceptions. For he lacked almost entirely that facility in mathematics which was already regarded as the foundation of a physicist's intellectual equipment; moreover, he paid little attention to abstract philosophical considerations, still less metaphysical ones. (In personal religion, he belonged to the eccentric and fundamentalist sect of Sandemanians.) Yet these intellectual blind spots – if one so judges them – were more than counterbalanced by two other characteristics. Having trained in a manual craft he was neat-fingered, inventive, and prolific in his experiments; and he had a highly developed capacity to organize his thoughts in visual, indeed *pictorial*, terms. Other physicists introduced order into their theories of electricity and magnetism by the use of mathematical equations. Faraday achieved this by a kind of imagery: when he looked at a magnet he visualized it as the focus of 'lines' or 'tubes' of magnetic force, which stretched out into space and closed back once more to form complete loops around it. And, with the help of this image, he was apparently able to master the phenomena quite as effectively as mathematicians did with their equations.

His experiments explored systematically both the electric effects of moving magnets and the magnetic effects of electric currents, and established, almost incidentally, the principles upon which electric motors and dynamos are built. The result was a comprehensive account of the manner in which these reciprocal effects take place, based on two fundamental insights. First, every current in a closed electric circuit is equivalent to a magnet, being surrounded by its own lines of force and exerting magnetic influences. Secondly – and this was to be fundamental to Maxwell's general theory – all *variations* in electric currents are accompanied by corresponding variations in the magnetic forces associated with them. And, however critical Faraday's mathematical contemporaries might be about his 'tubes' and 'lines' of force, these were the unquestionable starting-point for Maxwell.

Electromagnetic Fields and Waves

The contrast between the two men is an interesting one, for it demonstrates the particular importance – and unimportance – of mathematics in the physical sciences. Although one *can* make important discoveries about Nature without any assistance from formal mathematics, and even build up a general and detailed theory, it is impossible to unravel all the implications of one's theories without presenting one's arguments precisely and explicitly – which, in this case, meant mathematically. Though Maxwell developed a profound admiration for Faraday's *Experimental Researches*, he himself was the product of a very different background. His father was a Scottish landowner, and he himself was fully trained in the most rigorous schools of mathematics and natural science, first at Edinburgh and later at Cambridge. His professional career was entirely academic: he was in succession a Fellow of Trinity College, Cambridge, Professor of Physics at Aberdeen, Professor of Physics in London and first Director of the newly-founded Cavendish Laboratory. Although he sympathized with, and to some extend shared, Faraday's physical imagination, he combined this imagination with the analytic powers of a great mathematician, and from the very beginning of his career he set himself the task of giving mathematical expression to Faraday's intuitive explanations.

Maxwell saw the need for theories of two different kinds: on the one hand a formal system of equations, corresponding to those of Newton's *Principia* – which would state the basic axioms of electric and magnetic action and follow out all their mathematical implications – and on the other hand a convincing mechanical model, showing that these electro-magnetic effects were intelligible consequences of the structure and motion of the ether.

To begin with Maxwell was, if anything, more concerned about the explanatory model than he was about the mathematical equations. For physics (in Britain especially) was still fundamentally mechanical, and when Maxwell wrote his own popular account of 'the natural philosophy every educated man should know', he called it *Matter and Motion*. The title of the book gives a good idea of its scope: it did not occur to him to include a section on electricity and magnetism, since he did not think of these as separable from the movements of material particles – still less, as possibly more fundamental even than matter itself. He took it for granted that some mechanism must underlie *all* movements, those produced by electromagnetic influences quite as much as any other. The idea that electric and magnetic forces might be unsupported by any material medium was at first unthinkable. So, within the current mechanistic philosophy, the ether had ceased to be the speculative hypothesis it was for Newton, and had become a necessary – indeed, a compulsory – reality.

Maxwell visualized the ether as a maelstrom of invisible eddies, composing individual 'cells', which were separated by rolling layers of particles acting like ball-bearings. The effect of an electric force was to distort the ether-cells, so setting up stresses in the elastic substance of the imponderable medium. He showed that such a mechanical system would possess an energy of its own, taking two contrasted forms: one corresponding to the 'kinetic energy' (energy of motion) of the rotating cells, the other to the 'potential energy' of the ether-strains (like the energy stored in a watch-spring). Applying his mathematical genius to this elaborate analogy, he was able to make new sense of Faraday's results: the rotation of the ether-cells would explain magnetic effects, the strains in the ether would explain electric effects.

The mathematical analysis which Maxwell employed derived ultimately from the theories of Leonhard Euler, who had developed the first really systematic analysis of hydrodynamics.

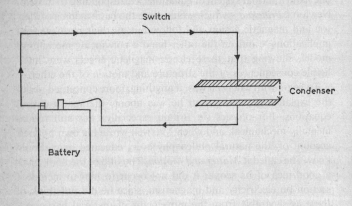

Euler's system was the first in which the motion of a continuous fluid had been explained by the action of a *field of force*, i.e. a motive agency which acted at every point in the fluid, and whose strength varied continuously from place to place. Maxwell now treated the ether as an 'incorporeal fluid', and presented the whole of Faraday's electromagnetic theory in equations similar to those of hydrodynamics – with one qualification. In order to perfect the symmetry of his presentation, he had to treat *all* electric currents (as well as all magnetic ether-rotations) as forming complete loops. This had one paradoxical consequence: one was sometimes forced to assume that an electric current was flowing, even though there was no apparent conductor for it to flow *in*: e.g. across the non-conducting space between the plates of a condenser. So far as the resulting electric and magnetic forces were concerned, it was exactly as though there were a 'ghost' current (the technical term is 'displacement current') travelling across the gap.

As a result, Maxwell seemed to some colleagues to be out on an exposed intellectual limb. His mechanical model of the ether was laboured, cumbrous, and artificial: well launched in the direction which Pierre Duhem (commenting on Oliver Lodge's treatise on electricity) was later to denounce.

> In it there are nothing but strings which move around pulleys, which roll around drums, which go through pearl beads, which carry weights: and tubes which pump water while others swirl and contract; toothed wheels which are geared to one another and engage hooks. We thought we were entering the tranquil and neatly-ordered abode of reason, but we find ourselves in a factory.

And worse: this mechanical model could be applied mathematically to electricity and magnetism only with the help of arbitrary assumptions. For all its merits, many of Maxwell's contemporaries were slow to accept his theory. William Thomson, Lord Kelvin, remained sceptical as late as 1904.

But there was an element of nostalgia about these objections. For the supreme merit of Maxwell's theory was its mathematical *elegance*, and as time went on he pushed all references to mechanical models further and further into the background, concentrating attention more and more on the formal mathematics. Forty years earlier, Poisson had shown that the equations of electric and magnetic action could be set out in strictly parallel forms. Maxwell had now cast the equations of electromagnetic interaction into an equally compact and symmetrical form – and what happened? *They turned out to be wave equations*, precisely parallel to those already in use to describe the varying intensity of light in a light-wave! The very least that one was entitled to conclude was surely this: that electric and magnetic influences were propagated in the form of transverse waves, similar to those already postulated in the case of light.

At this point, Maxwell appealed to one crucial 'coincidence'. In the wave-equations for light there was a *constant*, representing the velocity of light. At the equivalent point in Maxwell's electromagnetic equations, there was a corresponding constant, whose magnitude could be measured electrically, from simple laboratory observations. Repeating accepted procedures for measuring this 'electric constant', Maxwell found (as others had done before him) that its value was approximately thirty thousand million centimetres a second. This, within the limits of measurement, was *precisely the same* as the velocity of light, measured by Foucault and Fizeau. It was a fair conclusion that the equations of light and those of electromagnetism were not merely similar in form ('isomorphic', as mathematicians would say): they were alternative expressions of the same fundamental laws.

We can scarcely avoid the inference that light consists in the *transverse undulations of the same medium* which is the cause of electric and magnetic phenomena.

Throughout the history of physics, the claims of intellectual economy have always been accorded great weight. This is evident in the case of both Maxwell's theoretical simplifications. Having explained the thermal properties of material bodies as by-products of molecular agitation, he had no need to prove, in addition, the *non-existence* of caloric. And now the beautiful harmony between the mathematical theories of light and electromagnetism had an equally striking effect. Eighteenth-century scientists had recognized five distinct 'incorporeal agencies' (light, radiant heat, electricity, magnetism, and gravity), and nineteenth-century physicists had been faced with the prospect of several distinct aethers to support these incorporeals (luminiferous, electromagnetic, and gravitational). Now suddenly – gravity apart – all these separate agencies and aethers could apparently be rolled into one. The nature and structure of the underlying medium which transmitted both electromagnetic and optical waves might still be mysterious, but at any rate there was now only one mystery to be cleared up instead of several. And, although Maxwell's interpretation of light took time to win support, there was little real ground for continued scepticism after 1890. For by then Heinrich Hertz had succeeded in producing electromagnetic (or radio) waves artificially, and showing that they could be refracted, diffracted, and even polarized.

To be fair: such sceptics as remained were dubious less about Maxwell's formal mathematics than about the ether, which was still in the background. Kelvin may not have supposed that such laborious mechanical models as one could imagine for the ether had any necessary counterpart in Nature, but he still remained at heart a loyal Cartesian mechanist: 'I never satisfy myself', he said, 'until I can make a mechanical model of a thing. If I can make a mechanical model, I can understand it'. For Kelvin, mechanical explanation was absolutely primary, and in his view electromagnetic theory would become intelligible *only* when good mechanical sense had been made of the ether which 'carried' them. As things turned out, this was never done within the whole lifetime of classical physics: more recently, it has become doubtful whether it ever *could* be done – or would be desirable even if it were possible. After a tradition lasting from Galileo right up to Maxwell, the whole standing of mechanical explanation has now been called in question. For, in the twentieth century, scientists explain the mechanical properties of things as consequences of their electrical nature, rather than vice versa.

Energy and Entropy

Maxwell's electromagnetic theory had one additional merit. It brought the different forms of 'radiation' clearly within the scope of the conservation of energy. Light, radiant heat, and electromagnetic waves could be recognized as further incarnations of physical energy:

> The sun is the source of electromagnetic waves, and the earth is the scene of transformations of electric energy. A piece of coal burning in a grate has therefore a long electromagnetic history. It owed its origin to electromagnetic waves, and in burning it gives out again electromagnetic waves. . . . The continuance of all life on the earth is due to the electrical energy which we receive from the sun.

One could at last safely declare that 'Physics, in general, can be defined as that subject which treats of the transformations of energy'. The philosophical vision of Herakleitos and Empedokles, in which the kaleidoscope of natural happenings consisted in a continual cycle of changes and exchanges, had at last crystallized into a quantitative physical theory.

But this cyclical picture of Nature was, by itself, incomplete. For, as physicists clearly saw, there was a second, equally general and fundamental element in Nature – a *directional* one. This had first been formulated in the 1820s by the Mozart of physics, Sadi Carnot. Carnot's father had himself been a highly-competent mathematician: Sadi was a downright genius who, though dying at the age of thirty-six, left a body of work in which the theory of heat-exchanges was analysed mathematically with classic simplicity and elegance.

Carnot started with the question: What proportion of the heat in any system is 'available' as a means of producing mechanical energy? One might suppose that it could *all* be so used – just as all the mechanical energy of a body's motion (or all the electrical energy in a battery) can be used to produce heat. But, as Carnot demonstrated, this was not – and could not be – the case. Even a one-hundred-per-cent-efficient engine could exploit only a fraction of the heat supplied to it for producing mechanical energy. A 'super-efficient' machine, which would exploit *all* the heat supplied, would be (as Carnot's mathematics proved) a perpetual motion machine: by operating it round a complete cycle, one could get out of it more energy than was supplied in the first place.

This possibility Carnot dismissed as inconceivable. In a perfectly isolated system, which exchanged no energy with the surroundings, physical changes could at best be perfectly reversible: in normal cases they would result in the progressive loss or 'degradation' of mechanical energy by the production of unavailable heat. To characterize this one-way aspect of Nature, Clausius coined the word 'entropy'. In an isolated physical system, going through perfectly reversible changes, the entropy remained constant; when the change was imperfectly reversible the entropy increased; but the third possibility, of decreasing entropy, implied perpetual motion and had to be ruled out.

During the second half of the nineteenth century the concept of entropy was extended to embrace physical processes of all kinds. If the total conversion of heat into mechanical energy was impossible, so also was the total conversion of heat into any other form of energy. By the end of the century the combined theories of energy-conversion and entropy-increase, together with Maxwell's kinetic theory of matter, had given rise to the twin mathematical disciplines of statistical mechanics and thermodynamics. In the resulting mathematical system, the profit-and-loss account describing the cyclical transformation of energy became the First Law of Thermodynamics; while the directional principle of Carnot and Clausius (which gave precise expression to Newton's insight that 'motion is more easily lost than got, and is continually upon the decrease') became the Second Law of Thermodynamics.

The Empire of Classical Physics

The distinction which lay at the heart of the nineteenth-century world-picture appeared absolute. On the one hand, there was matter: on the other hand, radiation. Between them, these two concepts exhausted the realm of physics.

The stable enduring population of the physical world consisted of *atoms*: corporeal, massive, ponderable, immutable, and coming in ninety-odd distinct shapes and sizes. They were the starting-points for all physical speculation. The mathematician's motto might be 'God made the integers, Man made the rest'; that of the physicists was 'God made the atoms: we go on from there'.

It is a curious fact, to which we shall return in a later volume, that the idea of the *fixity of species* was becoming thoroughly discredited in zoology just at the moment when it achieved the status of an unquestioned axiom in physics and chemistry. Darwin's theory of organic evolution woke no echoes in the physical world, for there the tide of atomic theory was flowing strongly in the opposite direction. Though Mendeleev's Periodic Table certainly showed that the different chemical elements fell into seven or eight contrasted families, nothing was inferred from this beyond the comforting thought that the cosmos had a rational and intelligible structure.

In both chemistry and physics, the success of the atomic theory led to radical changes of method. Chemistry ceased to be the science of 'material principles', and was transformed into the science of 'molecular structure'. Before Dalton, there had been no way of labelling the constitutions of chemical substances, except by reference to their large-scale, observable properties. But now a new phase began: by paying close attention to their molecular weights and reactions, one could establish the underlying molecular structures of chemical substances directly. Minor checks apart, the resulting expansion of chemical science was an almost uninterrupted success-story. Before long, it became legitimate to represent molecular formulae not just by 'algebraical' expressions (such as H_2O), but by actual geometrical layouts:

And eventually the idea was extended still further to three dimensions – chemical formulae being treated as scale-models of the invisible molecules.

Despite its essentially *atomistic* nature, the classical world-picture involved one crucial advance on all earlier atomic systems. It was by now established beyond all doubt that the atoms could and did interact, not just by union, separation, and impact, but also by exerting forces on each other at a distance, and by exchanging energy in the form of radiation. Indeed, the deepest significance of Maxwell's electromagnetic theory lay in its capacity to unify men's ideas about the *non*-mechanical agencies of physics. Gravitation apart, these now formed one unlimited spectrum, of which the visible light-spectrum turned out to represent only a very small part.

In 1890 radiation still appeared to be something quite distinct from matter – and in the last resort, perhaps, not quite so fundamental to the economy of the universe. For light, magnetism, electricity, and radiant heat were all imponderable: one could not stop them, catch them, and weigh them. Their energy, instead of being localized within the moving atoms, seemed to be smudged out over the uncertain boundaries of the travelling-waves, and they had a seemingly transitory existence: indeed, even 'existence' might to be too strong a word for the presence – in space – of an electric or magnetic field. And it is no wonder that, for most of the century, scientists tended to think of 'electrifiability' and 'luminosity' as no more than passing affections of the solid, tangible, ponderable atoms which were the ultimate inhabitants of the physical world.

The classical system had tremendous practical and intellectual virtues. On the practical side, the scientists' theories of matter at long last began to make sense of, and even to supersede, the traditional *craft* techniques for processing, handling and fabricating material substances. Beginning in 1856, with Perkin's artificial 'mauve', the synthetic dye-stuffs industry became the first large-scale example of scientific technology, in which theoretical understanding was exploited for technological purposes. And the explosive growth of scientific technology during the hundred years since 1860 is a topic with exciting implications for social history, which has up to now been too little explored.

Intellectually, too, the revolution in matter-theory had some wider repercussions. The newly-discovered laws of physical and chemical change presumably applied not just in the laboratory, but throughout the whole cosmos. So the more precise and exact the ideas of physics and chemistry, the better men came to understand the geological history of the earth and the astronomical history of the solar system. Geology could at last discard its earlier embryological analogies: the history of the earth came to be interpreted, more and more, as the outcome of inorganic agencies and processes already familiar to us in our experience.

Applying similar arguments on the astronomical scale, however, gave rise to one serious difficulty, which the classical system never wholly resolved. The sun was manifestly losing heat, at a rate which – though vast – could be estimated mathematically; and on the best classical theories it seemed undeniable that, only a few million years ago, its temperature must have been so high that the surface of the earth would have been too hot to support life. This calculation delivered a body blow to Charles Darwin's new theory of the Origin of Species: natural selection could not have produced all the existing variety of organic species unless it had acted for all those millions of years and more. (Nowadays, the sun is believed to be generating heat continuously by thermonuclear fusion, and the whole astronomical time-sequence has been extended.) For the time being, scientists simply had to live with this difficulty. The basic assumption – that physico-chemical processes are similar throughout the universe – acquired more and more support; and, from the spectrum-lines to be observed in the light coming to us from the heavenly bodies, one could identify the very substances of which they were made, and the reactions going on within them. (See Plate 7.)

Some men were prepared to pursue still wider implications. The distinguished German chemist, Wilhelm Ostwald, erected a whole 'philosophy of values' on the theories of physics – particularly those of thermodynamics. Whereas Newton's omnipresent, eternal, unchanging Space had earlier seemed to possess many attributes of the Deity, now it was Energy whose universal, indestructible, and active character gave it the aspect of a pantheist divinity, while Entropy, by contrast, had more than a touch of the satanic. Science appeared to have replaced the Last Trump by an endlessly prolonged death by chilling, with the triumph of Entropy progressively destroying the creative works of Energy. (Men of the twentieth century have perhaps lost the ability to focus their emotions on an apocalypse so many million years away; especially since they have been doing their best to precipiate a premature, man-made apocalypse here on earth.)

Doubts and Reservations

Though the classical system of matter-theory appeared so tidy and complete, there were some things which it neither managed, nor even seriously attempted, to explain: for example, the reasons for those pervasive similarities between the different elements, and the source of the internal cohesion by which the atoms maintained their stable and immutable existence. A few scientists were uneasily aware that their theories had limitations, but those who were not in the top rank could afford to play down this fact. For a tremendous amount of consolidation remained to be done, extending the scope of the classical ideas to embrace ever-wider ranges of chemical compounds and hitherto-unexplored parts of the electromagnetic spectrum. Yet there were some among the foremost scientists who, at the peak of their phenomenal success, recognized that their theories were still only hypothetical. Before the century was out, two discoveries at least – the electron, and radio-active disintegration – were to come as a rude shock and surprise to most physicists and chemists; but there were a few who had already acknowledged the provisional character of their own theories, and faced the consequences.

Their reservations applied to both matter and radiation, but they were particularly articulate about the most fundamental postulate of the nineteenth-century system – namely, the atoms. These 'units of matter' were hypothetical twice over. Not only were they supposed to be invisibly small, so that their nature and actions could only be *inferred*: in addition, their basic properties (as laid down by Newton and Dalton) were not demonstrated, but *assumed* for the purposes of argument. So it is not surprising if some reflective chemists treated atomism in a 'phenomenalist' spirit, picturing matter *as if* made up of minute corpuscles, rather than risking the 'realist' assertion that matter *is in fact* made up of such corpuscles. When it came to visualizing fresh geometrical models for complex organic molecules, Kekulé was one of the most daring and imaginative of all chemists; but he took good care to guard himself against any extravagant assertions about the existence and fundamental nature of the atoms:

The question whether atoms exist or not has but little significance from a chemical point of view: its discussion belongs rather to metaphysics. In chemistry we have only to decide whether the assumption of atoms is an hypothesis adapted to the explanation of chemical phenomena. . . .

From a philosophical point of view, I do not believe in the actual existence of atoms, taking the word in its literal significance of in-indivisible particles of matter – I rather expect that we shall some day find for what we now call atoms a mathematico-mechanical explanation, which will render an account of atomic weight, of atomicity and of numerous other properties of the so-called atoms. As a chemist, however, I regard the assumption of atoms, not only as advisable, but as absolutely necessary in chemistry. I will even go further, and declare my belief that *chemical atoms exist*, provided the term be understood to denote those particles of matter which undergo no further division in chemical metamorphosis.

Should the progress of science lead to a theory of the constitution of chemical atoms – it would make but little alteration in chemistry itself. The chemical atoms will always remain the chemical unit; and for the specially chemical considerations we may always start from the constitution of atoms, and avail ourselves of the simplified expression thus obtained, that is to say, of the atomic hypothesis. We may, in fact, adopt the view of Dumas and of Faraday, that *whether matter be atomic or not, thus much is certain, that granting it to be atomic, it would appear as it now does.*

Kekulé's reference to Faraday is significant. For Newton's conception of the fundamental particles of matter as hard, massy, and impenetrable had not gone uncriticized, even among his most fervent admirers. The eighteenth-century mathematician, Boscovish, for instance, pointed out that any evidence for 'impenetrable solid atoms' of finite size could equally well serve as evidence for infinitesimal 'point-atoms' surrounded by a region of intense repulsive forces: from the physical point of view, indeed, the 'impenetrability' of a body simply meant its capacity to repel any object arriving at its 'surface'. And this view was taken seriously by both Priestley and Faraday. Joseph Priestley, in moments of philosophical reflection, would speak of all physical theories in a phenomenalist way – as 'artificial things contrived for the ease of our conception and memory'. Faraday, too, found the picture of atoms as geometrical points surrounded by fields of force thoroughly congenial. And Maxwell himself, whose kinetic theory did so much to reinforce the atomic model, demonstrated that the 'elasticity' and 'solidity' of the atoms in a gas could perfectly well result from sufficiently strong repulsions (varying inversely as the fifth power of the separation) driving the 'point-atoms' violently apart whenever they approached one another.

Yet the billiard-ball picture was simple, atttractive, and effective. After 1870 it became more eccentric to express serious scepticism about the reality of atoms: the agreement between Daltonian chemistry and Maxwell's theory of heat was so striking that practical doubts, at any rate, were set at rest. But at a deeper level there remained grounds for hesitation. As Ostwald repeatedly insisted, there was a vast logical gulf between the experience of practical chemistry and the inferences of the atomic theory. The chemist does not observe or study *atoms*: he discovers 'the simple and comprehensive laws to which the weight and volume-ratios of chemical compounds are subject'. And atoms are no more than 'a hypothetical conception which affords a very convenient picture' of matter – one of such 'great value for the purposes of instruction and investigation' that it 'has been made the basis of the language and modes of representation throughout the whole of chemistry'.

So far as we have treated them, the chemical processes occurred in such a way as if the substances were composed of atoms in the sense explained. At best there follows from this the *possibility* that they are in reality so; not, however, the *certainty*. For it is impossible to prove that the laws of chemical combination cannot be deduced with the same completeness by means of a quite different assumption.

One does not require, therefore, to give up the advantage of the atomic hypothesis if one bears in mind that it is an illustration of the actual relations in the form of a suitable and easily manipulated picture, but which may, on no account, be substituted for the actual relations. *One must always be prepared for the fact that sooner or later the reality will be different from that which the picture leads one to expect.*

Strictly speaking (Ostwald concluded) one should talk of 'combining weights' rather than 'atomic weights', and 'molar' rather than 'molecular' weights – these terms being more non-committal. Even Maxwell's kinetic theory related only the pressures and temperatures of bodies with the supposed *average* energy of their molecules, and the idea of single, individual processes taking place between two actual unit-atoms remained as speculative as ever. Meanwhile science was beset with dangers, as a result of the tendency to import into one branch of physics ideas developed and established in others:

Because the evolution of mechanics antedates that of the other branches of physics, mechanics has largely served as a model for the formal organization of the other physical sciences, just as geometry, which has been handed down to us from antiquity in the very elaborate form of Euclid, has largely been used as a model for scientific work in general. Such methods of analogy prove to be extremely useful at first because they can indicate how to get a grip on new sciences, in which all possibilities are still open. But later on such analogies are apt to be harmful. For each new science soon requires new methods, by reason of the peculiar manifoldness which it has to deal with, and the finding and the introduction of these new methods are easily delayed, and, as a matter of fact, often have been delayed, because scientists could not free themselves soon enough from the old analogy.

The impulse to look for analogies was first given by the extraordinary successes which mechanics has attained in the generalization and prediction of the *motions of heavenly bodies*. . . . These successes encourage the attempt to apply the mental instruments that were productive of such rich results to all other natural phenomena. An old theory, according to which all physical things are composed of the most minute solid particles of matter called *atoms*, supported these tendencies and invited the attempt to regard the little world of atoms as subject to the same laws as had been found to apply so successfully to the great world of the stars.

Thus we see how this mechanistic hypothesis, the assumption that all natural phenomena can be reduced to mechanical phenomena, appears at first sight self-evidently correct, and with its claim to be a profound interpretation of Nature it scarcely permits the question of its justification to be raised at all.

In fact, he declared, pressing mechanical modes of thought too far had 'not infrequently led scientific research into pseudo-problems . . . [which] are by their very nature insoluble, and constitute an inexhaustible source of differences of scientific opinion'.

But the most extreme doubts about the atomic theory were raised by Ernst Mach, the Austrian physicist and philosopher. Mach erected a complete philosophy of science on the basis of an absolute distinction between 'sense-observations' on the one hand, and 'theoretical conceptions' on the other – developing Priestley's description of theoretical notions as 'artificial things contrived for the ease of our conception and memory' into a metaphysical principle. For, in Mach's view, it was not merely statements about atoms and molecules which must be treated with reservation – as hypothetical contrivances – but *all* theoretical statements, at whatever level. Even statements about everyday material objects (such as tables and chairs) were hypothetical, when contrasted with direct sensory data (such as noises, smells, and patches of colour).

A man in Mach's position – where everything was so utterly hypothetical – could scarcely be impressed by *any* novel experimental evidence about atomic structure. But Ostwald was not so immovable. To his great credit, he was actually prepared to change his mind. Between 1900 and 1908 two new lines of evidence convinced him. One of these was J. J. Thomson's measurement of the unit electric-charge and discovery of the electron. The other came from the work of Jean Perrin on the phenomenon known as 'Brownian motion' (originally observed with pollen-grains by the botanist, Robert Brown): this is the random agitated motion which solid particles of extremely fine texture display when suspended in a liquid. Perrin argued that here, in the zigzag paths of the pollen-grains, one could at last observe the action of individual molecules. The changes of direction resulted from the impact on the grains of the fast-moving molecules of the liquid in which they were suspended. Not for the first nor the last time, the crucial scientific observation became possible only at the extreme limit of our senses, for the motions can be studied only with the help of the microscope, and with the most minute particles.

Once the mathematics of the process were fully developed by Albert Einstein, in a paper published in 1905, there was no longer any serious doubt – a way had been found of observing the effects of *individual* molecular interactions. Except that science is a perpetually optimistic activity, the situation would have had all the elements of tragedy. For by 1905 J. J. Thomson and Rutherford were rapidly undermining the structure of the classical system. The existence of atoms was finally accepted, just at the moment when they proved not to be 'atomic'.

FURTHER READING AND REFERENCES

The general background to the development of nineteenth-century thought can be studied usefully and enjoyably in the books on English Thought in the Nineteenth Century by D. C. Somervell, and by Elie Halévy. The indispensable general discussions of nineteenth-century science are to be found in the relevant sections of:

H. T. Pledge, *Science since 1500*, London, 1939

Mary B. Hesse, *Forces and Fields*, Nelson, 1961

Sir Edmund Whittaker, *History of the Theories of Aether and Electricity*, Nelson, 1951

Popular accounts of the development of classical physics (not invariably reliable) are given in:

A. Einstein and L. Infeld, *The Evolution of Physics*, Cambridge University Press, 1938

G. Gamow, *Biography of Physics*, Hutchinson, 1962

On chemical atomism, consult:

J. R. Partington, *A Short History of Chemistry*, Macmillan, 1937

A. J. Berry. *From Classical to Modern Chemistry*, Cambridge University Press, 1954

Modern Chemistry, Cambridge University Press, 1946

A Source Book in Chemistry (ed. H. M. Leicester and H. S. Klickstein), McGraw-Hill, 1952

On physical atomism, consult:

A. G. van Melsen, *From Atomos to Atom*, Harper, 1960

T. G. Cowling, *Molecules in Motion*, Hutchinson, 1950

A Sourcebook in Physics (ed. W. F. Magie), McGraw-Hill, 1935

Albert Einstein, *Investigations on the Theory of Brownian Movement*, Methuen, 1926

On electromagnetism and fields of force, Whittaker and Hesse are the most valuable references; but for the early development of electrical theory consult also:

A. Wolf, *A History of Science, Technology and Philosophy in the 18th Century* (ch. 10), Allen & Unwin, 1938

I. B. Cohen, *Franklin and Newton*, Philadelphia, 1956

while for Maxwell and Faraday one should read the original works of the two men, and also consult:

N. R. Campbell, *What is Science?*, Methuen, 1921

James Clerk Maxwell: A Commemoration Volume (Essays by J. J. Thomson and others), Cambridge University Press, 1931

J. Tyndall, *Faraday as a Discoverer*, Longmans, Green, 1868

(A new biography of Faraday is in preparation, by L. Pearce Williams.)

On the wave-theory of light, see:

Ernst Mach, *The Principles of Physical Optics*, Methuen, 1926

C. C. Gillispie, *The Edge of Objectivity* (ch. X), Princeton University Press, 1960

A. E. Bell, *Christian Huygens and the Development of Science in the 17th Century*, Edward Arnold, 1948

Henry Crew, *The Wave-Theory of Light* (including papers by Huygens, Young and Fresnel)

The volume

Critical Problems in the History of Science (ed. M. Clagett), University of Wisconsin Press, 1959

contains two useful essays on aspects of nineteenth-century physics by I. B. Cohen and T. S. Kuhn. (Note that, in Kuhn's view, the establishment of the Conservation of Energy had less to do with the generalization of dynamics than we ourselves believe.)

On entropy and the second law of thermodynamics, see Gillispie (ch. IX) and also:

W. F. Magie, *The Second Law of Thermodynamics* (including papers by Carnot, Clausius, and Thomson)

On the generalization of mechanics and forces, see:

N. R. Hanson, *Patterns of Discovery*, Cambridge University Press, 1958

Max Jammer, *Concepts of Force*, Harvard University Press, 1957

For the philosophical debates of the period 1890–1910, see:

P. Duhem, *The Aim and Structure of Physical Theory*, Princeton. University Press, 1954

E. Mach, *Populär-wissenschatfliche Vorlesungen*, Leipzig, 1896

K. Pearson, *The Grammar of Science*, A. & C. Black, 1900

H. Poincaré, *Science and Hypothesis*, Walter Scott, 1905

The debate is carried further in:

P. W. Bridgman, *The Logic of Modern Physics*, Macmillan, 1927

The philosophical implications of nineteenth-century physics are also discussed in:

S. E. Toulmin, *The Philosophy of Science* (ch. IV), Hutchinson's University Library, 1953, and 'Contemporary Scientific Mythology' (in *Metaphysical Beliefs*, ed. A. MacIntyre, S.C.M. Press, 1957)

On the rise of chemical technology, see:

A. and N. Clow, *The Chemical Revolution*, Batchworth Press, 1952

T. K. Derry and T. L. Williams, *A Short History of Technology*, Clarendon Press, 1960

12

Entering the Quantum World

BETWEEN 1890 and 1910 the foundations of the classical picture suddenly disintegrated. Instead of a grand and systematic account of all physical phenomena, natural scientists found themselves left with a fragmented collection of concepts and explanations, from which the principles of unity had been removed. All the axioms of nineteenth-century physics and chemistry now revealed themselves as no more than working assumptions, which were sound only if not pressed too hard. Yet, in their capacity as 'natural philosophers', scientists could never accept their fundamental notions uncritically, so the physicists of the 1890s deliberately began to exert pressure on the classical system at just those points where its weaknesses were becoming apparent.

Under this pressure, the firm crust of ideas with which the nineteenth century had spanned the void of our ignorance gave way like melting ice. Points of weakness turned into cracks, into fissures, into chasms; and scientists found themselves plunged at a dozen places into new and quite unsuspected depths. The result was an intellectual chain-reaction. Every nineteenth-century axiom turned into a twentieth-century problem; and these problems were the more acute just because the classical system had been so successful. The atoms of each chemical substance were not absolutely *immutable*: very well, then; why were they relatively so *stable*? They were not absolutely *indivisible* – why, then, were they relatively so *cohesive*? The old Stoic questions thus arose again, with no less urgency, at the new, sub-atomic level. Radiation, too, was not after all as pervasive and continuous as it had seemed: why then did it give, so often and so completely, the appearance of smooth waves? Even the fundamental barrier between material and immaterial agencies – between matter and energy – began to crumble: yet, if this distinction could no longer be maintained, why had its shortcomings taken so long to show themselves? These questions are among the most fundamental in physics, and they are not yet wholly answered.

We can conveniently divide the history of twentieth-century physics into three phases. During the first quarter of the century, the subject was in a transitional stage: the classical system of ideas was clearly breaking down, but the quantum synthesis had not yet taken shape – and as a result scientists, moving out from their old positions in the direction of the new, had to make certain compromises. Then, within ten years, between 1925 and 1935, a new system of 'quantum mechanics' suddenly crystallized, giving a consistent picture of processes at the sub-atomic level in terms which transformed the nineteenth century's absolute distinctions into differences of degree. Finally, since 1935, the physical sciences have been consolidating themselves on this new basis, with a vigour and excitement equalling that which accompanied the creation of the classical system a hundred years earlier. By the present time, one can even detect, among some physicists, the first symptoms of that 'hardening of the categories' which eventually overtook classical physics – an inclination to believe that quantum-mechanical categories have succeeded, where the classical concepts failed, in giving a final and complete picture of the fundamental architecture of the natural world, and to ignore the loose ends which hint at further intellectual revolutions to come.

The Flaws in the Classical System

From 1870 on, physical scientists were encountering problems and effects which we now recognize as being sub-atomic or quantum-mechanical in origin. At the time, their full significance could not be recognized, and until the year 1895 the need for fundamental and far-reaching reforms in physical theory was scarcely acknowledged at all. Once the gravity of the situation had been conceded, there turned out to be many clues pointing a road beyond the classical system to new levels of physical thought, and we must begin by looking at these clues. For, under closer scrutiny, both matter and radiation gave rise to perplexities. Neither was as simple as it had earlier seemed.

The Atom Disintegrates

The rays which pass between two electric terminal-plates within an evacuated tube, when an electric discharge is set up in it, were known as early as 1870, and C. F. Varley speculated at the start that these 'cathode rays' might consist of 'attenuated particles of matter'. But so long as the possibility remained that they were only one more form of electro-magnetic radiation, they made no deep impact on physical thought.

In the 1890s, however, J. J. Thomson and Jean Perrin proved beyond doubt that they were composed of minute particles, having a measurable weight (less than a thousandth of a single atom of hydrogen), and carrying a fixed charge of negative electricity. At first Thomson resisted strongly the conclusion to which he was eventually forced: that these were sub-atomic constituents – 'parts' of the hitherto uncuttable 'atoms' of chemistry. More: however he varied the glass of his discharge-tubes, and the gas within them, and the metal of the electrodes, the properties of the cathode rays were unaltered. Here was clear evidence that matter could exist in particles many times smaller than the basic units of Dalton's chemistry, and also that the sub-units had the same properties regardless of the chemical substances with which they were associated. Thomson's mind at once went back seventy-five years, to the neglected Prout:

The explanation which seems to me to account in the most simple and straightforward way for the facts is founded on a view of the chemical elements which has been favourably entertained by many chemists: this view is that the atoms of the different chemical elements are different aggregations of atoms of the same kind. In the form in which this hypothesis was enunciated by Prout, the atoms of the different elements were hydrogen atoms; in this precise form the hypothesis is not tenable, but if we substitute for hydrogen some unknown primordial substance X there is nothing known which is inconsistent with this hypothesis. . . .

Thus on this view we have in the cathode rays matter in a new state, a state in which the subdivision of matter is carried very much further than in the ordinary gaseous state: a state in which all matter – that is, matter derived from different sources such as hydrogen, oxygen, etc. – is one and the same kind; this matter being the substance from which all the chemical elements are built up.

Yet so directly did this discovery offend against all the presumptions of nineteenth-century science, that at first J. J. Thomson was scarcely taken seriously, and he was suspected of playing some kind of practical joke. Even when the seriousness of his evidence and his argument was established, so distinguished a scientist as Pierre Duhem was incautious enough to ridicule his conclusions. But his conclusions would not stay ridiculed. The existence of *electrons* (as the cathode-ray particles were christened) became established and accepted; and their minute weight could not be denied.

Equally important were the phenomena of X-rays and radioactivity, studied during these years by Röntgen, Becquerel, and Pierre and Marie Curie. Where Perrin and Thomson had established that the Daltonian atoms were not the *smallest* units of matter, the Curies now established that they were not *immutable* either. For they showed that the elements of highest atomic weight (such as uranium and radium), which give off penetrating beams of radiation, were changing their chemical natures and atomic weights in the process – disintegrating through a sequence of forms until they reached stable states, as lead. Three distinctive types of radiation (alpha-, beta-, and gamma-rays) were given off by these radioactive elements, and two were soon identified: the 'beta-rays' turned out to be composed of electrons, while the 'gamma-rays' consisted of electro-magnetic radiation with the highest frequnecy and penetrating power known – even greater than those of Röntgen's X-rays. The great pointer towards the future lay, however, in the 'alpha-rays'. These carried a positive electric charge, twice as great as the negative charge on a single electron, but they were very much heavier; and in 1902 Rutherford and Soddy identified them conclusively as helium ions – i.e. atoms of helium carrying a double positive charge. This discovery placed in position the first solid piece around which the jigsaw of twentieth-century atomic physics has been built.

Radiation is Atomized

If during the 1890s the simple atomic picture of matter was running into difficulties, so too was the simple wave-picture of radiation. The problem can be described, in general terms, as follows.

It was accepted that electromagnetic waves form a continuous spectrum, which stretches from radio-waves at the lowest frequency, through visible light, to gamma-rays at the highest. This being so, the question arose: Given a 'perfect radiator' or 'black body' – i.e. a body which could absorb and emit radiation with one hundred-per-cent efficiency – would there be some definite relation between the amounts of radiation of different frequencies which it would take in and give off at any set temperature? Suppose one heated this perfect radiator up to some definite temperature, what sorts of electromagnetic radiation would it give off – gamma-rays, ultra-violet light, or radio-waves? And, if it gave off a mixture of different waves, what proportion of the total radiation would be waves of any one kind? Boltzmann and Rayleigh showed that one could answer this question by a thermodynamic argument, comparable to Carnot's arguments about the 'perfect heat-engine'. The answer was that there must be a definite balance, at any given temperature, between the waves of different frequencies. And Rayleigh produced a formula, according to which the perfect radiator should give off waves of *all* kinds, but *predominantly* waves of the very highest frequencies.

This result was disconcerting for two reasons. For – quite apart from the fact that all known bodies radiated in quite another way – it implied a logical paradox. In practice all bodies, however efficiently they radiated, were found to have a 'heat spectrum' with a peak, and at normal temperatures this peak came somewhere in the infra-red region. (With a powerful furnace, this peak could be driven into the visible region, and as the balance shifted the body became first red-hot, then white-hot and finally even blue-hot; but by no known means could one get the bulk of the radiation to come off in or beyond the ultra-violet.) Putting these facts of experience side by side with Rayleigh's argument, theoretical physicists were at a loss to reconcile them. So long as one remained within the classical system of ideas, it proved impossible to justify any mathematical formula which provided for a peak of the observed kind. On the contrary, Rayleigh's graph continued to climb steeply and without limit, as one moved from lower frequencies to higher ones – so landing one in an 'Achilles and the tortoise' paradox. For, however high the frequency one considered, it followed from the theory that an infinitely greater proportion of the radiation should be given off at frequencies yet higher still.

Something must be wrong with Rayleigh's argument. Over a number of years, physicists attempted to eliminate this 'Scandal of the Ultra-Violet' without abandoning the classical principles, but in vain. Success came only on 14 December 1899, when Max Planck delivered the first paper on quantum theory, and so started physics along a new and revolutionary line of development. Once again a small amendment, introduced to meet a localized theoretical difficulty, was to have unforeseen consequences. As Planck pointed out, Rayleigh's argument had rested on one apparently innocent assumption: that a perfect radiator would emit and absorb radiation of all frequencies smoothly, in continuous streams – and could do so in quantities of any size, however small. On the classical theories, this was perfectly sound. But Planck now suggested replacing Rayleigh's assumption by a different one: namely that radiation could be given off or taken up only in quite definite minimum amounts (or 'quanta') – in gulps, not in streams – the size of the 'gulps' being dependent on the frequency, and getting larger as the frequency increased. With this one modification, Rayleigh's thermodynamic argument gave a very different formula: one which provided a peaked curve corresponding closely to the facts.

At first, Planck's device appeared an effective but arbitrary fudge. Physicists continued to think of electromagnetic waves as spread smoothly through space, but supposed that – for some unexplained reason – *interactions* between matter and radiation were discontinuous. But in 1905 Albert Einstein kicked open the theoretical door which Planck had unlocked and walked right through. Radiation, he argued, was not only *exchanged* in discontinuous packets: it actually *existed* in discontinuous packets. Certainly these energy-packets consisted of electromagnetic radiation, having a definite frequency, but the waves always travelled in bunches – or 'photons'. So a beam of light comprised not a smooth flood of electromagnetic energy, but a rain of separate wave-packets, each with its own individual quantum of energy and momentum. Photons were, in effect, a kind of *particle*; each of which would strike against a surface with a definite impact.

This, as Einstein showed, had other implications. When light strikes a metallic surface it can set up a current of electricity in the metal, provided that it has a sufficiently high frequency (this is the 'photo-electric' effect). The cut-off is extremely sharp: unlimited radiation at lower frequencies can be poured on to the surface without effect; but the moment the frequency reaches the critical limit for the metal in question, the photo-electric effect will begin – however feeble the light. This fact, Einstein argued, was really quite simple to explain. The photons could initiate a current only if, individually, each one brought enough energy to knock an electron free from an atom of the metal. Lower-frequency photons jolted the atoms without releasing the bound electrons, but a single photon of sufficient frequency (and therefore energy) could set an electron free.

With the arrival of Einstein's photons, physics was finally moving out of the last classical era, and an intellectual revolution began which was to last for a full twenty-five years, and carry the theories of matter and radiation to a new level of discrimination. From now on, the fundamental units were to be around one ten-million-millionth of a centimetre across, a hundred thousand times smaller than the atoms of Dalton's picture. So we find physicists and chemists in the 1900s hanging on to the classical theories of Dalton and Maxwell as providing by far the most comprehensive picture of Nature; but being increasingly aware, nevertheless, that something was gravely wrong with it.

Over the whole of physics, one last large question hung like the Sword of Damocles. As the ultimate foundation of physical thought, the laws of mechanics had – ever since the time of Galileo – taken second place only to the principles of geometry. Now there was a rising challenge from the theory of electricity. This was not only because J. J. Thomson had discovered electrical sub-atoms, smaller than the material atoms of chemistry, but because the mathematical *form* of Maxwell's electromagnetic equations was inconsistent with that of Newton's dynamical equations in certain crucial respects. Admittedly Einstein, with his Special Theory of Relativity, could bring them into line; but he did so only at the cost of treating light-signals, rather than any mechanical process, as the fundamental instrument for physical measurement. Newton's mechanics could no longer be the foundation of all else in physics, with electricity as a more or less incidental characteristic of matter. From now on electricity was going to occupy the centre of the theoretical stage, and matter itself would be reduced to a complex structure of fundamentally electrical units.

'Look First upon this Picture . . .'

The absolute distinction between smooth, continuous radiation and discontinuous, atomic matter had disappeared. Electromagnetic radiation in all its forms somehow combined the properties of corpuscles with the properties of waves. It was true that, in the case of visible light and radiation of lower frequencies, the wave aspects by far predominated, and that particulate or quantum effects became striking only at higher frequencies, in and beyond the region of the ultra-violet. Yet the double character of light could no longer be denied, and this discovery led some physicists, particularly Louis Prince de Broglie, to ask whether matter also might not have a similar, double character. After all, there were striking parallels between the mathematical principles of wave-optics and those of particle-mechanics, and these could easily be extended. If a photon of any given frequency (v) always carried a definite, proportionate quantity of energy ($E \propto v$), might it not turn out that – reversing the argument – a sub-atomic particle moving with the same energy (E) was associated with 'matter-waves' of the same frequency ($v \propto E$)?

This, suggestion, put forward by de Broglie in 1924, was of the greatest daring and simplicity. It would certainly have delighted Kepler and also, one suspects, Pythagoras; for de Broglie was treating *mathematical analogies* as the best evidence of the unity of Nature. The idea may have looked like the wildest guesswork, but it was soon fully justified. In 1927 Davisson and Germer reflected a beam of *electrons* from the surface of a nickel crystal, and produced diffraction patterns of exactly the same form as had previously been produced using X-rays of the equivalent energy. From that time on, the analogy between matter and radiation has been accepted as unquestionable. Quite apart from the success of wave-mechanics (which we shall consider in the next chapter) all subsequent experiments have confirmed that light and matter share the same dual sets of properties – even though matter-wave effects show up only in extreme conditions, and are never apparent in the course of our everyday experience. (See Plate 8.)

De Broglie's speculations helped to trigger off the theoretical revolution of 1925–35. But, long before this, experimental work had revealed a great deal about sub-atomic architecture; and in 1919 Rutherford had actually provoked the first artificial nuclear transformation.

Ernest Rutherford grew up in the New Zealand countryside and – as he liked to say – very nearly became a farmer. The firm practical reasoning of the experienced craftsman continued to display itself throughout his long career, as it had done in Faraday's case seventy years earlier. Rutherford owed his education to scholarships, first at the local secondary school, and later at Canterbury College, Christchurch: he was already doing original research on electromagnetism while still at college. In 1895 he was awarded a further scholarship, and took himself off to the Cavendish Laboratory as one of its first-generation 'research students'. He arrived in England at a time when J. J. Thomson (the Director of the Cavendish Laboratory) was in the middle of his work on electrons and X-rays. Rutherford quickly became Thomson's most brilliant associate, and eventually succeeded him as Cavendish Professor. Between 1895 and 1935, no one did more than these two men to unravel the sub-atomic architecture of matter, and under their leadership the Cavendish Laboratory remained the very spearhead of intellectual advance in physics.

Having identified the alpha-rays from radioactive substances, as streams of doubly charged helium ions flung out from the atoms of the disintegrating elements, Rutherford saw in them a possible 'probe', with which he might penetrate inside the boundaries of material atoms, and so bring to light something of their sub-structure. If the alpha-particles had come out of the atoms, presumably they would go back in. His chief question was: Is the massive material of an atom spread uniformly throughout its volume – with the electrons disposed within it like the currants in a bun – or is it more concentrated? He focused the alpha-rays from a naturally radioactive substance into a beam, and concentrated this beam on to a sheet or film of the substance whose atomic structure he wished to study. He then looked to see how the bombarding alpha-particles were scattered in passing through the film.

He found that the great majority of alpha-particles passed through the film without being appreciably deflected; a certain number were scattered on either side of the main beam, as though they had passed close to an area of positive charge; while a very small proportion were actually reflected back from the film, recoiling in the direction from which they had originally come. By analysing the results of such scattering-experiments, Rutherford was able to establish certain fundamental propositions about sub-atomic structure: e.g. that by far the greater part of the atomic mass was concentrated in a minute fraction of its volume, to form a positively charged central core or 'nucleus'. For the most part, his alpha-particles passed unaffected through the tenuous clouds of electrons which surrounded the positive nuclei. Only those which passed close to one of the nuclei would be deflected, while the few particles which had actually recoiled had evidently come into direct collision with a nucleus.

In this way, the common pattern underlying the structure of all the different elements was brought to light, and it was established that the really significant property of a chemical element was not after all, its atomic *weight*, but its atomic *number*. The numeral which had begun as a mere index-figure in the Periodic Table was now reinterpreted as representing the number of unit electric-charges carried by its nuclei – and so also the number of negative electrons associated with the nucleus, when the atom was in its normal, electrically neutral state.

How these associated electrons were arranged within the atom, Rutherford's experiments could do nothing to show. To answer that question it was no use probing forcibly into atoms: some way must be found of inducing them to speak for themselves. This was the achievement of Rutherford's pupil, the Danish physicist, Niels Bohr. For Bohr now drew attention to a second line of evidence which converged on Rutherford's, and provided a clue to the electronic structure. But, whereas Rutherford's results could be understood and explained quite easily in terms of orthodox electrical ideas, Bohr's argument had some novel and unforeseen features, and took physics beyond the limits of classical theory.

When any gas or vapour is excited by an electric discharge (as in a sodium lamp) it will emit light of certain, specific frequencies. Photographed through a spectroscope, the light given off by an excited gas shows up as a collection of sharp, bright lines – some of them in the visible part of the spectrum, others in the infra-red and ultra-violet. (Plate 7.) Hydrogen, in particular, gives off four visible lines and many more invisible ones. Now it had long been known that the frequencies of the four visible hydrogen lines formed part of a tidy mathematical series, though no reason was known for this regularity. Bohr took up this unexplained fact, and used it to provide evidence about the behaviour of the electrons within hydrogen atoms. On Planck's and Einstein's photon-theory of light, each of the sharp spectrum-lines must correspond to photons of a precise energy; and Bohr suggested that these photons were emitted or absorbed in a hydrogen atom because the electron had changed its distance from the nucleus. When an electron moved nearer to the nucleus it lost energy, which was emitted as a photon: it if absorbed a similar photon from outside it took over its energy and returned to the more distant – and more energetic – position. But if this interpretation was correct, it had one unexpected implication: the fact that atoms emitted and absorbed only radiation of specific frequencies – and not indis-

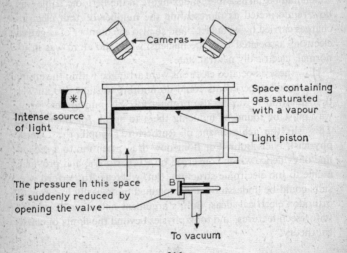

←— Cameras —→

Intense source of light

A

Space containing gas saturated with a vapour

Light piston

The pressure in this space is suddenly reduced by opening the valve

B

To vacuum

criminately – implied that the electrons could remain only at certain definite 'permitted' distances from the nucleus. This conclusion was inconsistent with classical ideas, and was to have far-reaching consequences.

In 1919 Rutherford finally succeeded in penetrating into the atomic nucleus. He focused an intense beam of helium nuclei (alpha-particles) on to a container filled with nitrogen, and found that hydrogen nuclei of high energy (protons) were thrown out from the nitrogen with surprising violence. What was happening? The proper interpretation took some time to establish, but it was greatly assisted by one ingenious new piece of apparatus – C. T. R. Wilson's 'cloud-chamber'. (This is a circular container with a glass top, containing water-vapour, whose pressure is suddenly reduced at the crucial moment. Any electrified particle moving across the chamber at that moment produces a vapour-trail, whose length and density vary from one kind of particle to another: in this way, individual nuclear changes can be made to leave a visible record of their occurrence and nature.) In due course, it became clear enough what was happening. About one in every fifty thousand of the bombarding alpha-particles ($^4_2$He, each of which possessed nuclear charge 2 and mass 4) was actually being captured by a nitrogen nucleus ($^{14}_7$N: charge 7, mass 14) to form a highly-unstable nucleus, chemically analogous to that of fluorine ($^{18}_9$F: charge 9, mass 18). This combination recovered its stability by forcibly throwing out one proton ($^1_1$H: charge 1, mass 1), and so turning into a nucleus with charge 8 and mass 17 – a rare 'isotope' of oxygen. The two steps in the process can be symbolized thus:

$$^{14}_7\text{N} + ^4_2\text{He} \rightarrow ^{18}_9\text{F}$$

$$^{18}_9\text{F} \rightarrow ^1_1\text{H} + ^{17}_8\text{O}$$

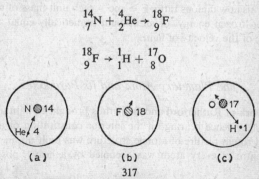

(a) (b) (c)

At every stage in this process, the total electric charge was conserved, and also – as far as round numbers went – the total mass. But the figures quoted here (14, 4, 18, 1, 17) represent in fact only *approximate* nuclear masses; and if you added together the *exact* mass of an alpha-particle and a nitrogen nucleus, the result did *not* exactly equal the mass of a proton plus one nucleus of oxygen-17. The same was true generally: whenever artificial transmutations were produced, the nuclear masses going into and coming out of the transformations never balanced quite exactly. Nor for that matter did the *energies* of the particles involved. Sometimes bombarding particles were swallowed up, energy and all, without the expected mechanical reaction, and at other times particles were flung out at the end of a process with a violence far greater than that of the incoming particles. What conclusion was one to draw? Had those twin axioms of physics and chemistry, the Conservation of Mass and the Conservation of Energy, suddenly broken down? The moment of near-disaster in fact turned into a moment of triumph. For the fractional loss (or gain) of mass in any transformation turned out always to balance the fractional gain (or loss) in the energy of the particles and nuclei. The marginal loss of mass in Rutherford's first artificial transmutation was thus balanced out by the violent energy with which the resultant protons were ejected. So it seemed that mass could be converted into energy, and vice versa – indeed, that mass itself *was* a kind of 'frozen energy'. Just as Einstein had foreseen in his theory of relativity, neither mass nor energy need be conserved *separately*: only the sum total of mass and energy was conserved. And every interconversion of mass and energy took place according to his now famous ratio, $E = mc^2$ – each unit-mass of matter storing 'frozen energy' of an amount numerically equal to the square of the velocity of light.

The Planetary Atom and its Paradoxes

The work of Rutherford and Bohr thus brought to light a great deal of evidence bearing on the interior constitution of atoms. A first rough picture of atomic structure was built up, in which the centre of every atom was occupied by a heavy, positively charged nucleus, and the associated electrons travelled around the nucleus like planets – moving in definite 'orbits' arranged in tidy 'shells', and from time to time 'jumping' precipitately from one orbit to another. This Rutherford-Bohr 'planetary atom' certainly provided a simple and attractive model, and to this day physical scientists can still use it, as a first approximation. Yet far from patching over the holes in the classical theories, it created new ones; and during the years between 1905 and 1925 physicists had to work with a compromise picture of matter – interpreting their experimental results by amending and adapting classical ideas as they went along. For certain of the assumptions on which the planetary model rested were arbitrary and paradoxical, and for serious theoretical purposes it has been quite superseded.

The chief feature of Bohr's theory was the system of *stable orbits*, in which the electrons alone in an atom were 'permitted' to travel around the nucleus; and this was also its most puzzling feature. By assuming that the possible orbits of electrons are limited in this way, one can do something to answer the first fundamental question of sub-atomic theory: namely, how is it that atoms are so highly stable? According to all classical ideas, a negatively charged particle travelling in an orbit around a positively charged nucleus should radiate its energy away in the form of electromagnetic waves, gradually approaching – and finally falling into – the nucleus at the centre of its orbit. Bohr amended classical ideas by supposing that this unstable behaviour occurred only when the electron was at a considerable distance from the nucleus. At close quarters, he supposed that the continuous range or possible distances gave way to a sequence of discrete orbits – the smallest of which represented the minimum distance at which an electron could travel around the nucleus. Photons absorbed by a piece of matter might either jolt electrons from one orbit to another, or even (given sufficient energy) knock them right out of the range of fixed orbits and into the region of continuous separations beyond. In the former case, the 'excited' electrons would eventually jump back into lower, less energetic orbits, emitting photons in the process. In the latter case, they were free to flow through the material in the form of an electric current, and the atoms from which they were released temporarily became 'ions' – retaining a positive charge until other electrons settled down into the empty orbits.

This theory involved all the difficulties characteristic of a compromise. They arose most acutely if one tried to envisage, *in mechanical terms*, how an electron made the transition from one of its 'permitted' orbits to another. For this transition (or 'quantum-jump') must take place either instantaneously or over a period of time, and both alternatives involved paradoxes. On the first alternative, one had to think of the electron as 'leaping' instantaneously from one orbit to another, without meanwhile occupying any definite location in the 'forbidden zone' between the two orbits. By comparison with astronomical distances, the atomic orbits might be extremely minute, yet the idea of an instantaneous and discontinuous change of orbit was no more intelligible when it was 'only a very little one'. Yet the alternative supposition, that the step was *not* absolutely instantaneous, also had curious implications, which Rutherford (commenting on Bohr's classic paper about hydrogen spectra) expressed in characteristically robust terms:

Your ideas ... are very ingenious and seem to work out well; but the mixture of Planck ideas with the old [classical] mechanics makes it very difficult to form a physical idea of what is the basis of it all. There appears to me one grave difficulty in your hypothesis ... namely, how does an electron decide what frequency it is going to vibrate at when it passes from one stationary state to the other? It seems to me that you would have to assume that the electron *knows beforehand where it is going to stop.*

Unlike the stability of atoms, the other fundamental question of sub-atomic theory – why atoms are so cohesive – did not find even a partial answer in the Rutherford-Bohr theory. In the classical picture the cohesion of solid bodies was explained as resulting from forces between their constituent atoms, while the internal cohesion of the atoms was simply taken for granted. Now the fundamental problem was again shifted one stage further back. If the mass of a solid object was entirely concentrated in its atoms, the mass of those atoms was largely concentrated in their nuclei; and the properties of these nuclei had now to be taken for granted – how they held together remaining, for the time being, a complete mystery.

Even so, the intellectual achievements of Bohr and Rutherford were considerable. Their planetary picture of the atom explained in detail not merely the structure of line-spectra, but also a great part of Mendeleev's chemical analogies. For these evidently resulted from similarities in the electronic structure of different elements. Helium, argon, and neon (for instance) were all alike chemically inactive gases, because the electrons in their atoms exactly filled one or more complete 'electron shells' – leaving no loose electrons, in outer orbits, available to interact with those of neighbouring atoms. Right up to 1925 this compromise theory of matter remained without a rival. Besides the planetary picture of the atom, it relied on two main axioms: (i) the belief that matter is built up from the two primary material units, the proton and the electron; and (ii) the dual character of radiation, which in some respects behaved like waves, in others like particles.

As to the first belief: J. J. Thomson had identified electrons as one essential constituent of all matter, and opened the way for a revival of Prout's original hypothesis of a 'universal matter' identifiable with hydrogen. Each atom of any particular substance (it seemed) contained within its nucleus a number of hydrogen nuclei (protons) equal to its nuclear mass, and this could be regarded as a whole number. (The chemical 'atomic weights' which had torpedoed Prout's theory were, after all, only *averages*: chlorine, for example, had two forms with nuclear masses 35 and 37, the former being three times as abundant as the latter.) Along with the proton in the nucleus went a smaller number of electrons, which cancelled out the surplus positive charge: thus, a helium nucleus had a mass of four units, but its charge was only two, so it must contain four protons together with two 'internal' electrons to cancel out the excess positive charges. This assumption that protons and electrons were the sole units of matter was at first only a working assumption, and Rutherford (for one) always took it with a pinch of salt. But after a time some physicists treated it with rather more confidence than was ever fully warranted. An authoritative textbook published in the mid 1930s could even say:

Up to the year 1932 [when the neutron and positron were discovered] it was reckoned as among the *incontrovertible facts* of physics that the positive charge is always associated with the mass of hydrogen, the negative with the mass of the electron, and that these two particles, protons and electrons, form the ultimate constituents of matter.

No similar confidence could be felt in the theory of radiation. And the provisional, indeed makeshift, character of early quantum theory is most evident in the attitude which physicists adopted to this theory. While recognizing that experience compelled them to acknowledge the dual character of radiation, they were unable to bring these two aspects into focus at the same time – let alone relate them into a single consistent theory. They were reduced (as W. H. Bragg put it) to thinking of light as waves on Mondays, Wednesdays, and Fridays, and as particles on Tuesdays, Thursdays, and Saturdays. To be more precise: when they were concerned with the *spatial pattern* in which radiation was propagated, the wave-aspect became of predominant importance; but when, instead, they studied the manner in which radiation exchanged *energy and momentum* with the material bodies on which it fell, the corpuscular view of radiation made much better sense. Somehow these two aspects had to be brought into harmony. There was certainly no possibility of dividing the spectrum of radiation into two halves, a high-frequency (corpuscular) region and a low-frequency (wave) region. Corpuscular effects showed up quite clearly in the case of visible and infra-red radiation, yet even with the much higher-frequency X-rays, you could still get striking wave-effects (e.g. diffraction-patterns: cf. Plate 8). For the moment, there seemed no choice except to operate with two different conceptions of radiation in parallel, applying the one or the other selectively, according to the nature of the problems under discussion.

During the years before 1925 this 'wave-particle duality' produced in physicists a kind of intellectual split-vision. When we look through a stereoscopic viewer at two complementary photographs, we often find it hard at first to unite the two scenes into a single picture. Bragg and his colleagues found themselves in an analogous position: they could focus in turn (as it were) through their two different conceptual lenses, but these had not as yet been assembled into a single theoretical instrument. With the advent of quantum mechanics in 1925–6, a consistent new set of ideas became available, by which the behaviour of Nature at the quantum level could be described directly – and in focus. But this new theoretical system was developed (as we shall see) only at a price: that of breaking the last threads of analogy which had linked the central notions of the first quantum theory back to the older ideas of classical physics and chemistry.

(For further reading and references, see the end of Chapter 13.)

13

Sharpening the Focus

IN January 1926 Rutherford received a letter from Niels Bohr telling him of the new recruit who was joining the team of physicists at Copenhagen. This was the young German mathematician, Werner Heisenberg – then barely twenty-five years of age. The letter held out the promise of exciting theoretical developments. As Bohr said, by Heisenberg's early work,

prospects have with a stroke been realized which, though only vaguely grasped, have for a long time been the centre of our wishes. We now see the possibility of developing a quantitiative theory of atomic structure.

With the arrival of Heisenberg in Copenhagen, one further link was added to that chain of intellectual affiliations – from Maxwell, through Rayleigh, J. J. Thomson and Rutherford, to Bohr – which has to its credit so many of the creative achievements in modern physical science. Each of these men made great and drastic changes in the theoretical tradition which he took over from his master, but in every case the occasion for the change was a problem *within* his master's own intellectual system. Now, with the work of Heisenberg and Schrödinger, the paradoxes of the first quantum theory were to be not so much resolved as transcended.

The Quantum-Mechanical Unification

Wilhelm Ostwald had (it seemed) spoken prophetically when he criticized as a source of pseudo-problems 'the attempt to regard the little world of atoms as subject to the same laws as the great world of the stars'. This was just the conclusion which had to be drawn from the new theories of quantum mechanics: the picture of the electron as a 'planet' moving steadily around the 'sun' of the nucleus was now thrown overboard, and the whole idea of 'quantum jumps' or 'transitions' re-interpreted.

It will be convenient to come to quantum mechanics by way of 'wave-mechanics'; and in any case one preliminary word of warning is needed. It is often said that the theory of quantum mechanics embodies a view of Nature whose intellectual essentials can be grasped only by mastering advanced mathematics – and this is presented as being somehow truer of quantum mechanics than of any previous system of physical ideas. If that point of view were absolutely sound we should be obliged, at the present stage of our argument, either to launch into mathematical symbolism or else to throw in our hands. Yet it is more just to see the contrast between quantum mechanics and previous systems as being, not absolute, but rather one of degree; for a parallel argument could – strictly speaking – be advanced about the classical ideas themselves. Nature offers us in everyday experience nothing corresponding exactly to Newton's hard, massy, impenetrable 'particles'; not any 'rigid bodies', 'pure substances', or 'inertial motions' along infinite Euclidean straight lines. Indeed, the laborious drill involved in mastering Newtonian mechanics consists chiefly in learning to restate real-life problems in terms of such idealized, abstract notions. As a result, introductory problems in dynamics are concerned with almost fictional 'projectiles', 'rigid pendulums', and so on – mathematical ideals, to which the behaviour of ordinary objects only lands one in something like a category-confusion: 'A perfectly smooth elephant of negligible weight is rolling down an inclined plane . . .'

The breach between physics and our everyday intuitive ideas is, accordingly, as old as Galileo. The real novelty of quantum mechanics was that it broke *also* with certain fundamental conceptions underlying the whole classical tradition in physics. Whereas Dalton, Maxwell, Rutherford, and even Bohr had all extended, exploited, and built upon intellectual foundations that Newton had laid down, Heisenberg and Schrödinger now revised and amended these very foundations themselves.

We remarked in passing how Louis de Broglie had speculated that moving particles of matter might display the same 'wave-particle duality' as was already familiar in the case of light. Even before this idea had been experimentally verified, it triggered off the long-awaited revolution in matter-theory. For, developing de

Broglie's idea of 'matter-waves', Schrödinger used it to give a new depth to Bohr's conception of atomic structure.

De Broglie himself had applied the wave-idea to 'free' material particles, such as the electrons in the beam of cathode-rays whose impact paints the picture on a television screen. These move, like the planets in Newton's theory, independently of other material objects and under the minimum of external forces. Such a beam of free electrons, de Broglie argued, should display analogies to a ray of light: the electrons or photons in such a beam or ray should both behave in certain ways like concentrated packets of electric charge or energy, in others like a system of plane travelling-waves. By subjecting electron beams to suitable electric or magnetic fields, one should be able to reflect, refract or focus them exactly like light-rays, and this is in fact done nowadays in the so-called 'electron microscopes'. Yet if one was to take this wave-aspect of matter seriously – Schrödinger argued – it was necessary to generalize de Broglie's theory further. What was true of electrons moving independently through space did not cease to be true just because they were trapped within a bar of metal or a crystal, or even within an atom. Naturally, a material particle restrained in an atom was no longer free to travel in a straight line, and so would no longer be associated with plane travelling-waves. But these were not the only kinds of wave-systems in which energy could be stored or carried. Ever since the Pythagoreans, natural philosophers had been familiar also with standing-waves, such as the sound-waves within the air-column of a flute and the wave-patterns on the surface of a drum-head, in which energy is concentrated and localized, instead of being propagated across space. So might there not be, in some circumstances, 'standing matter-waves' as well as travelling ones? This was the idea which Schrödinger and Heisenberg followed up with overwhelming success.

The key to the new 'wave-mechanical' picture of the atom can be explained briefly – in terms which recall not just the Pythagoreans but even more the Stoics, with their picture of material bodies held together in stable patterns corresponding to the different 'tones' of the all-penetrating pneuma. Suppose you have a resonant chamber full of air, which can be insulated from the surroundings, so that (unlike a bell) it does not lose energy by giving off sound. You can store energy in such a container by making it resonate at one of its natural frequencies and insulating it. Then, apart from the tendency (irrelevant to our analogy) for the sound-energy to be slowly changed into heat, it will continue to resonate indefinitely, the original supply of energy being 'trapped' within the container in the form of a standing sound-wave. Any particular container of this kind will have only certain frequencies at which it will naturally resonate, corresponding to the 'fundamental' and 'harmonics' at which a flute or clarinet will sound when blown, or over-blown. At any one of these natural frequencies, the wave-pattern builds up progressively and the incoming energy is stored away in standing-waves: at other ('un-natural') frequencies, the waves already in the system cancel out instead of reinforcing the incoming waves, and no standing-wave storage can take place. This is a general characteristic of *all* wave-systems: the ideas of 'resonance', 'standing-waves' and 'energy-storage' are all equally applicable, whether one is concerned with sound-waves, electromagnetic waves, or even the mechanical vibrations in a rope or a violin-string. In every case there are certain definite frequencies at which the resonant system will readily take up energy from its surroundings, while at other frequencies no energy is exchanged at all.

Now suppose one thought of the electrons around an atomic nucleus in the same way – as constituting a system of standing matter-waves – these waves should once again be capable of reinforcing themselves, and storing energy, only at certain definite frequencies; and each of these frequencies would correspond to a definite 'energy-level', in accordance with Planck's quantum relation, associating every wave-frequency with a corresponding quantum of energy. When a photon of suitable energy was absorbed by an atom, its effect would then be, not to make an electron 'jump' across space, but to change the pattern of matter-waves around the nucleus from one of its natural frequencies to a higher one; the increase in frequency (and energy) involved in this transition being equal to the frequency (and energy) of the incoming photon. Likewise in emission: when an atom relapsed from an excited (higher-frequency) state to a less excited one, the electronic wave-patterns in the atom would switch back from a higher to a lower level, releasing energy in the form of a photon.

Allowing for the differences between sound-waves and matter-waves, these changes would resemble those taking place in – say – a clarinet when it switches between its fundamental and upper, over-blown registers: no structural change takes place in the clarinet, no bits of it 'jump' from one end to the other; but the whole wave-pattern by which energy is stored in its air-column is altered.

This extension of de Broglie's ideas gave not just an elegant new picture of the atom but an exact mathematical *theory*. The limitations which Bohr had imposed on the 'permissible' states of atoms ceased to be arbitrary and found a highly convincing explanation. Furthermore, the paradoxes which had perplexed Rutherford, when he was first faced with Bohr's ideas, now no longer arose. For they turned out to be only 'pseudo-problems' – 'questions [in Ostwald's words] only in terms of the particular model, to which no actual reality can be shown to correspond'. So long as one thought of electrons as being minute 'planets', travelling round precisely delineated 'orbits' and occasionally 'jumping' from one orbit to another, the restrictions on the orbits remained a puzzle. But once the idea of an 'electron jump' was replaced by that of a change in standing-wave patterns, the problem ceased to exist. When an atom absorbed a photon it simply changed to a higher register. To put the point in Stoic terms: absorbing the photon changed the 'tone' of the atom, which thereby became (as physicists found themselves saying) 'excited'. In this way the explanatory image which the Stoics had first envisaged, of the various stable conditions of matter as corresponding to different standing-wave systems in a continuous intangible medium, has found a place in science as fundamental as that which the atoms of Demokritos have held since Dalton.

But this was not the end of the story. For Heisenberg was meanwhile developing his own 'quantum mechanics' on a completely fresh basis. In the same way that Maxwell's electromagnetic theory had thrown up the unanswerable question, 'What are electromagnetic waves, waves *in*?' Schrödinger's wave-mechanics now threw up the equally perplexing question, 'What are wave-mechanical waves, waves *of*?'; and, just as Maxwell found himself concentrating more and more on the mathematical formalism of electromagnetic theory (so ignoring the problems raised by the 'ether' model), so now Heisenberg as a matter of deliberate policy took the corresponding step. Some people continued to hope that Schrödinger's waves would turn out to have some tangible embodiment in the real world – perhaps variations in the density of a continuous electric 'cloud'. But this idea did not work out. In the end, the least misleading thing one could say about them – though even this was only half-intelligible – was that they were 'waves of probability'; since, given any point in space, the mathematical properties of the waves determined the likelihood of an electron being observed there. Heisenberg, however, considered the question 'What are matter-waves, waves of?' as much a pseudo-problem as Rutherford's question, 'How does the electron know where it is going to jump?' It was forced on you *only* if you still relied on analogies with classical physics. So instead of clinging on to the classical apron-strings, he concluded that it was better to start again from the beginning and base the theory of quantum mechanics directly on 'observables' – i.e. quantities measurable in a laboratory – instead of on theoretical models. In this way, the abstractions of the new theory would be referred *directly* to our experience of Nature, rather than applying to the world only at a remove – by way of analogous classical notions – as in the first quantum theory.

Heisenberg's system has proved to be mathematically equivalent to Schrödinger's in all its central features, while avoiding those last puzzling questions which result from taking the wave-model too literally. Yet his further step – which reminds one in some ways of Ostwald's 'phenomenalistic' reinterpretation of Dalton's atomism – was not one that all physicists could take immediately, or happily. The break with the past was too complete. Rutherford, for instance, found older ways of thought too hard to abandon. Mathematical physicists such as Heisenberg, he remarked – in words which are no less significant for being uttered jokingly – 'play games with their symbols, but we, in the Cavendish, turn out the real solid facts of Nature'. And to the end of his life he continued to find the intuitive ideas of wave-mechanics more manageable than the unvisualizable concepts of pure quantum mechanics;

I was brought up to look at the atom as a nice hard fellow, red or grey in colour, according to taste. In order to explain the facts, however, the atom cannot be regarded as a sphere of material, but rather as a sort of wave motion of a peculiar kind. The theory of wave-mechanics, however bizarre it may appear – and it is so in some respects – has the astonishing virtue that it works, and works in detail, so that it is now possible to understand and explain things which looked almost impossible in earlier days. . . . The new mechanics states the type of radiation emitted [from an atom] with correct numerical relations. When applied to the periodic table [of the chemical elements], a competent and laborious mathematician can predict the periodic law from first principles.

If Rutherford never felt absolutely at home with quantum mechanics, one other architect of the quantum theory was positively hostile to it: namely, Albert Einstein. For in Heisenberg's new generalized form, one of the axioms of quantum mechanics was the so-called 'principle of indeterminacy', and the effect of this principle was to place a theoretical limit on the accuracy with which certain pairs of variables could *simultaneously* be observed. The very act of measuring (say) the position of an electron with extreme precision entailed, according to Heisenberg, a corresponding indeterminacy in its momentum. And this fundamental restriction on our knowledge was too much for Einstein.

There is, indeed, still some dispute about the proper interpretation of Heisenberg's Principle. Does the 'indeterminacy' in question mean only that we are restricted in our powers to observe and measure quantities which nevertheless have, in reality, perfectly definite and determinate values? Or does it mean that the fundamental entities of matter-theory are like clouds or claps of thunder – things which, by their very nature, have vague, indefinite boundaries, so that there are no absolutely determinate physical properties to be measured? Or is it rather a question of meaning and definition – do the equations by which our concept of 'electrons' is intellectually constructed somehow imply that the idea of an absolutely exact simultaneous measurement is devoid of physical significance? Whether one regards Heisenberg's Principle as reflecting a limitation on our measurements, an essential property of material things, or a consequence of the meaning of our concepts, the practical effect of the principle is the same: though the theory explains the *overall statistical patterns* of events which occur in any physical situation, it obliges one to abandon all hope of predicting individual quantum events with complete accuracy. To give an example which goes back to the beginning of twentieth-century physics: when a radioactive material is throwing out alpha-particles, we can calculate with quantum mechanics the *proportion* of atoms which, over any period of time, will decay in this way; but we can never say (on Heisenberg's theory) exactly how long we must wait for the next decay of an atom, or precisely when any particular nucleus will give off its alphaparticle. Unlike most of his younger colleagues, Einstein could not reconcile himself to this feature of Heisenberg's new theory. He saw the 'abandonment of causality' as its fatal flaw, and in his eyes it was at best one more transitory step along the road to a more adequate system of physical ideas.

The Ramifications of Quantum Mechanics

Whatever one felt about indeterminacy, there was no denying the new mathematical grasp which quantum mechanics gave to theoretical physics. In the course of a few years, half a dozen classic papers by Heisenberg, Schrödinger, Dirac, and Jordan (among others) laid the foundation on which physics has built over the succeeding thirty-five years and right up to the present day. This phase in the history of our physical concepts has been as much a period of consolidation as the fifty years after John Dalton; and though, as we shall see, the very consolidation and elaboration of the theory has created fresh problems for physics the main principles of the theory remain very much as stated by Heisenberg and Schrödinger in 1926–7.

From the very beginning, the new quantum mechanics treated electrons, photons, and all other physical entities in a way which *drew no distinction* between their wave-properties and their particle-properties. The 'mental squint' in the first quantum theory was thereby eliminated. So one can speak if one likes of an electron or photon as a wave-packet or 'wavicle' – a reminder that, though its mass or energy is concentrated, it also has some properties and characteristics in common with wave-systems. By bringing both aspects into focus simultaneously, quantum mechanics introduced one great simplification as compared with the earlier quantum theory. In other respects, however, the picture of matter soon became far more complex. Up to 1932, no fundamental particles of matter had been identified other than protons and electrons. Then two fresh forms of particle were recognized in the course of a few months. Rutherford and his colleagues had been on the lookout for one of these since 1921, if not earlier. They had found it incredible that electrons should retain any kind of independent existence *inside* the nucleus of an atom (see page 321), and they supposed rather that the helium nucleus contained two protons, not four, with two uncharged particles of much the same mass as the proton. At last, in 1932, Rutherford's pupil Chadwick demonstrated that particles of just this sort (the *neutrons*) were given off when beryllium was bombarded with alpha-particles: an artificial transmutation resulted, alpha-particles being captured by the nuclei of the beryllium, which then turned into normal carbon nuclei, giving off neutrons in the process.

$$^{9}_{4}Be + ^{4}_{2}He \rightarrow ^{13}_{6}C$$

$$^{13}_{6}C \rightarrow ^{12}_{6}C + ^{1}_{0}n$$

The other new species of particle, the *positron*, had an even more curious discovery. When in 1928 the theoretical physicist, P. A. M. Dirac, amended the general equations of quantum mechanics so as to bring them into line with Einstein's Theory of Relativity, he could find no theoretical reason for distinguishing between the electrons which were already known and other – as yet hypothetical – particles, having the same mass but a *positive* electric charge. This was 'an originally unwelcome conclusion of an otherwise highly successful theory': and, to begin with, Dirac looked for ways of escaping the conclusion that Nature contained particles of this other hypothetical kind. For several years, indeed, no one thought seriously of looking for the 'positive electron': instead they went on trying to amend the theory, so as to remove this unwanted implication. Only in 1932 was Dirac reluctantly forced to believe that his theory actually required the existence of positive electrons. Then in the next year – without having read Dirac's papers – Anderson, an American experimental physicist, drew attention to the existence of certain particles among cosmic-ray tracks which he was studying: these behaved in every respect exactly like electrons, except that when they travelled freely through a magnetic field their tracks curved the opposite way. (See Plate 9.) These particles apparently had the same mass as the electron but the opposite charge. It was left to P. M. S. Blackett to bring Dirac's theory and Anderson's observations together, and demonstrate conclusively that the newly-observed particles were the very 'positrons' required by Dirac's theory.

Here for once three different elements in scientific discovery can be distinguished sharply: recognizing a theoretical possibility, recording a novel observation and demonstrating that this observation brings the theoretical possibility to life. In recent years it has become apparent that positron tracks had been appearing in published photographs for a number of years before 1932; but with the proton and electron apparently secure in their joint command, physicists had not given these anomalous tracks a second glance. Instead, they had brushed them aside as spurious, or as stray electrons moving through the cloud-chamber in the opposite direction.

Once the properties of positrons were investigated more closely, it was clear why they were so rarely observed. For, whenever a positron appeared among cosmic-ray tracks, its life was extremely short: as soon as it came within range of an electron, the two particles fell together and – as Dirac had foretold – destroyed each other in a clap of high-energy gamma radiation. This observation has incidentally undercut still further the older, absolute distinction between matter and energy. For now one can demonstrate the transformation of two *material* 'wavicles', each of them having a rest-mass – or 'frozen energy' – into a single *electromagnetic* 'wavicle' devoid of rest-mass, which disappears at the velocity of light, carrying off their combined energy in the form of a gamma-ray photon. (The reverse process of 'pair-creation' also occurs, converting electromagnetic photons into pairs of material particles.)

Just as quantum mechanics provided an explanation of the cohesion and stability of individual atoms, so too it explained how atoms are held together in molecules. Nineteenth-century chemists and physicists had been clear enough about the existence of 'molecule bonds', but how atoms remained so closely united in molecules was something the classical theories never satisfactorily explained. It could now be shown that the molecular bond resulted from the sharing of electrons. We may suppose (for example) that the two protons in a hydrogen molecule do not each retain exclusive possession of one electron, but have a common pattern of matter-waves around them; and this arrangement proves to be a very stable one, having a set of energy-levels or 'natural resonant frequencies' all its own. So it turns out that there is a good physical reason for hydrogen atoms to combine together in pairs; and, though the detailed calculations can become extremely complicated, the same general principle will explain much of what had previously been discovered by the experimental study of molecular combinations. It is as though the very stability of the combined state, in which the electrons are shared, creates a new kind of 'attraction' between the atoms which binds them together very strongly, and these novel attractions are nowadays referred to as 'exchange-forces'. All the same, in this particular case it is perhaps straining analogy somewhat to use the word 'force' at all. If two heavy cannon-balls are placed close to each other on yielding ground, they will tend to roll together into a common depression, for reasons of sheer mechanical stability; and they will do so *just as though* they were 'attracting' each other with a 'force' far stronger than their direct gravitational attraction. Two solitary hydrogen atoms in close proximity can likewise, by 'marrying' into a molecule, reach a state more stable than the separated one. So, given the occasion to unite, they have a strong tendency to do so.

The next step in the argument was to be one of those dramatic leaps of the mind, based entirely on mathematical analogies, which have contributed so much to the development of modern physics.

If the fact that atoms hold together in molecules had to be explained, so too did the fact that protons and neutrons hold together to form nuclei. Gravitational attraction is neither selective enough, nor nearly strong enough, to explain how (say) two protons and two neutrons hold together so firmly in a single alpha-particle, nor will electrical or magnetic forces explain this cohesion either – for the neutron does not respond to such forces. But (accepting the phrase for the moment) the recognition of molecular 'exchange-forces' opened up a new possibility – that nuclear cohesion also might be the result of comparable exchange-forces. To check this interpretation, it was necessary to match the appropriate mathematical equations against the facts of nuclear structure, and see what this combination would imply.

Once again, naïvety paid off handsomely. Supposing the nuclear bond, like the molecular bond, resulted from the protons and neutrons 'sharing' or 'exchanging' some lighter satellite, one had to ask: *What* do they exchange? This problem had all the simplicity of an item in a quiz: 'Atoms form molecules by exchanging electrons, so nucleons form nuclei by exchanging *what*?' Following out the mathematical analogy, the Japanese physicist Yukawa calculated that the intra-nuclear satellites must be entities of a new kind, viz. *mesons*: particles, or wavicles, having the same negative charge as the electron, but a mass some three hundred times as great. These mesons, like neutrons and positrons before them, turn up among the products of atomic disintegrations stimulated by the 'cosmic rays' – which are themselves believed to consist largely of high-energy protons and other nuclear debris reaching the earth from the sun. Along with Yukawa's mesons, however, there have turned up also a good two dozen other kinds of particle for which no such theoretical function was foreseen, and by now some thirty 'elementary particles' are recognized, Rutherford's electron, proton and neutron being only the most familiar and long-lived.

To complete the picture, a new speculative possibility has opened up in the last few years. For the theoretical arguments about electrons which forecast the discovery of positrons can be extended also to protons: if there is no theoretical objection to 'positive electrons', nor is there any to 'negative protons'. Of course: since a proton weighs one thousand eight hundred and forty-six times as much as an electron, it must have one thousand eight hundred and forty-six times as much energy 'frozen' into it – and so will require that much more energy to *create* it. But this implies only that negative protons will be rarer, and more difficult to produce, than positive electrons. (In fact, these new particles, too, have by now been added to the physicist's repertory.) But at this point, speculation can legitimately begin. What if a negative proton and a positive

335

electron avoided annihilation for long enough to come together: would they not then form a new kind of atom, with a negatively charged nucleus – what might be called 'anti-hydrogen'? And if anti-hydrogen were possible, why not also anti-helium, anti-carbon and even anti-uranium? In our own part of the world, no doubt, such *anti-matter* could occur only with extreme rarity: normally, anti-particles vanish very soon, combining with normal protons and electrons and turning to photons. But we can no longer deny that anti-matter, composed of positive electrons and negative protons, is a serious theoretical possibility, which could well be realized in a part of the universe sufficiently remote from our own. As Rutherford himself was already hinting in 1935:

May it not be that elsewhere in the Universe, or under circumstances different from those familiar to us . . . the *roles* of the positive and negative electrons may be reversed?

This possibility is not just an idle one. It has in fact already caught the attention of theoretical astronomers. For the different heavenly galaxies *are* extremely remote from one another; the light from a galaxy composed entirely of anti-matter would be no different from that of our own galaxy; and so long as two galaxies of opposite kinds did not encounter each other we should have no way of distinguishing them. Suppose, on the other hand, that two such galaxies – one of normal matter, one of anti-matter – *did* collide: corresponding particles would then annihilate each other in a vast burst of radiant energy. Can it be that something of the sort happens, in those rare celestial conflagrations astronomers call 'super-novas'? To go further – suppose that, at some earlier phase in cosmic history, there had existed a single enormous photon (representing a tremendous concentration of high-frequency radiant energy): might this not have been transformed into the raw material for two galaxies of opposite charge, by the very same process we ourselves observe producing electrons and positrons, or positive and negative protons? And might not these masses of raw material have been flung apart in opposite directions to form separate galaxies, remote from one another, composed of matter and anti-matter respectively?

Today we can only state these questions, without the certainty of ever answering them. Yet even the possibility of stating such questions illustrates the intellectual command achieved by the new physics. For, as at the very beginning of all science, ideas about the 'first principles' of matter are once again reacting immediately, and drastically, on ideas about the origin and character of the astronomical universe. So much for those logicians who suggest that 'natural philosophy' has been replaced by 'scientific theory' as a result of scientists moderating their ambitions, and substituting piecemeal enquiries for the overall questionings of the earlier philosophers: that is, at best, a half-truth. Through the marriage of relativity theory and quantum mechanics, of nuclear theory and cosmology, contemporary scientists are making their own distinctive and distinguished contributions to the great debate originally set in motion by the Ionians six centuries before Christ.

Shadows of the Future?

Before we leave the physical sciences and consider parallel developments in physiology since 1700, we should perhaps take one last, dispassionate look at the overall state of quantum mechanics today. The physicists and chemists who have been caught up in its development during the last thirty-five years are understandably impressed by its success – by the ways in which our intellectual grasp has been extended throughout the whole sub-atomic level, and a picture of matter provided whose 'grain' and discrimination are a hundred thousand times as fine as those of the classical system. So they are sometimes tempted to regard the intellectual stirrings of a few younger physicists as the iconoclasm of malcontents – the more so when the aspect of quantum mechanics held up for scrutiny is that indispensable axiom of the whole system, the principle of indeterminacy. They fear that a 'nostalgia for classical causality' may distract promising young men into theoretical blind-alleys, just when their energies should be being employed extending the scope of the quantum-mechanical system, and resolving the last theoretical difficulties which are at present delaying the completion of this work.

Tactically, this attitude may prove justified. Yet there is an alternative, strategic point of view. If we consider the creation of quantum mechanics as the latest major development in the evolution of matter-theory, we may properly ask: Have any signs appeared of the need for another similar increase in our intellectual discrimination? Historical parallels are notoriously fallible. Whether political, economic, or intellectual, situations rarely repeat themselves exactly, and even the most striking similarities are open to more than one interpretation. Still – with that initial qualification – we can fairly say this: that the present state of fundamental physics strikingly resembles the state of the classical system in the years around 1885. The resemblances can be summarized under three heads: arbitrary constants, unexplained analogies and mathematical divergencies.

(i) The atomism of Dalton and Maxwell began, as we saw, by taking the basic properties of the atoms as axiomatic, and actively debating only the ways in which these given units combined and interacted. The more that men discovered about the properties of the different atoms, the more numerous became the arbitrary features of the system. The gas oxygen was the eighth element in the Periodic Table, and had an atomic weight of 16. The silvery metal bismuth was eighty-third in the Periodic Table, and its atomic weight was 209. Such facts as these were 'brute facts' for classical physicists and chemists: they were explained only when men went beyond classical atomic theory to the finer-grained, sub-atomic picture.

Similarly, twentieth-century quantum theory has again accepted certain units as elementary and fundamental, and has deferred all questions about their own finer nature and structure. It has been a great achievement to discover how much was explained by the interaction and combinations of protons, electrons, neutrons, and the rest; but certain basic facts have again had to be accepted as ultimate and inexplicable features of the natural world – e.g. the fact that every proton weighs one thousand eight hundred and forty-six times as much as every electron. (Indeed, the attempts of Sir Arthur Eddington to find some more fundamental reason why Nature should have these arbitrary features were ridiculed, like the speculations of Prout and Newlands.) Yet, if in 1890 one could legitimately ask, 'Why does oxygen have atomic number 8 and atomic weight 16?', surely in the 1960s one may equally ask, 'How are the arbitrary constants of quantum physics to be explained?'

(ii) With the progress of chemistry during the nineteenth century, it became evident that different elements and atoms were not, after all, completely distinct and unique. On the contrary, they fell into well-defined families, substances with analogous properties recurring at regular intervals as one ran down the Periodic Table of the elements. This aspect of the natural world, also, could be explained only at the sub-atomic, or quantum, level. (As Rutherford put it: given the theory of wave-mechanics, 'a competent and laborious mathematician can predict the periodic law from first principles'.) But similar analogies have been turning up since 1946 between the different 'elementary' or 'fundamental' particles. The thirty distinguishable sub-atomic constituents are no more incomparable and unique than the elements in Mendeleev's Table. They too fall into natural families: leptons (electrons and positrons), nucleons (protons of both charges, and neutrons), mesons of several kinds – and most recently 'hyperons', nearly twice as heavy as the nucleons. Can the likenesses and differences between all these particles be explained without going behind the principles of quantum mechanics? Or will our experience with Mendeleev's Periodic Law be repeated – through a further penetration to a 'sub-elementary' or 'sub-fundamental' level?

(iii) The flaws in the classical system were not confined to the atomic theory: they turned up also in the theory of radiation. Rayleigh's formula for 'black-body radiation' led to a paradoxical conclusion: its implications were both formally unacceptable and physically unintelligible. This could perhaps have been circumvented by a mathematical fudge, but physics would have been poorer if it had. Instead, Planck and Einstein faced the problem squarely and quantum theory was the direct result. Once again, history seems – rightly or wrongly – to be repeating itself. The attempt to apply the principles of quantum mechanics to electrodynamics has been running up against similar difficulties: theoretical calculations which should lead to straightforward numerical results have once more been threatening to diverge without limit towards infinity. As an emergency measure, physicists have resorted to mathematical fudges of an arbitrary kind – carrying out the computations only up to a certain point, and simply ig..oring the later terms in their equations. If the only need was computation, 'Ptolemaic' measures of this kind might be legitimate as a stop-gap. But to accept them with any complacency, and call off the search for a more satisfactory physical explanation, would be going against the principles of strategy on which the whole scientific tradition has been built up. Perhaps these divergences will be circumvented without any serious amendment to accepted quantum mechanics. But we must keep our minds open to other possibilities, remembering that the trail which led to quantum theory itself began from just such an intractable mathematical divergence.

By themselves, these resemblances between present-day quantum mechanics and latter-day classical physics would be highly suggestive, and nothing more; but in the last few years there have been other signs which look like the first stirrings towards a change. Two such indications are worth mentioning here: one experimental, the other theoretical. The experiments are those for which Richard Hofstadter shared the 1961 Nobel Prize for physics. Before 1950, no one seriously questioned that the hydrogen nucleus, or proton, was rightly described as an 'elementary particle'. But, during the 1950s, the question had to be posed whether they were after all as simple as had been assumed. These doubts arose as a result of experiments similar in principle to Rutherford's original scattering experiments. Physicists at Stanford University shot high-energy beams of electrons into hydrogen gas, and looked to see how these were scattered as a result of colliding with the protons in the gas. As Hofstadter reported in a conversation:

In 1954 we found that there were deviations from the behaviour which we had expected from a very small particle or point – a geometrical point – and this was the first indication that the proton had any finite structure. If it had turned out to give a scattering behaviour like a geometrical point, then we would have said: 'Well, this is really an elementary thing, you see; and it can't be made of other things if it's clearly a point.' But it turned out to have quite a large – relatively speaking – radius. And this has encouraged us to see if we could find structure within this small dimension we are investigating.

By now it seems established that the proton is in fact anything but a point-concentration of matter and electric charge: instead, we must think of it as having an internal structure which differs only in scale from that of the atoms of which it is a part. On the present evidence, Hofstadter suggests, the proton has

a hard core similar to the consistency of a billiard ball, which thins out to a kind of cloud-like consistency reaching eventually to zero.

Similar experiments with deuterium gas (the isotope of hydrogen whose nuclei each contain a neutron as well as a proton) have suggested that the neutron has a similar internal complexity. At the very least, these experiments raise the question just *how* fundamental and elementary protons and neutrons are. Shall we perhaps find that molecules are composed of atoms, composed of nuclei, composed of nucleons, composed of 'clouds' surrounding 'hard cores' whose own composition is yet to be discovered?

Other recent lines of investigation, of a more theoretical kind, also point towards finer levels of discrimination. For, while orthodox supporters of quantum mechanics have accepted the principle of indeterminacy as irreducible, and dismissed the desire to predict every last click of the Geiger counter as Victorian nostalgia, some other physicists have continued to work towards a theory in which the principle was, at the very least, *not axiomatic*: one in which some reason would appear why, at the quantum level, events should display this special feature. Such a theory cannot be constructed simply by *modifying* the principles of quantum mechanics, for von Neumann has proved that indeterminacy is a mathematical keystone of the existing theory. Nothing less will do the job than a brand-new system of ideas as different from quantum mechanics as quantum mechanics itself was from the classical system.

Up to now, the most systematic attempt to develop such a theory has been made by Bohm and Vigier. They begin from the fields of force, whose modes of action have been established by experimental physicists, and which all (according to the quantum theory) have the same dual wave-particle character. Bohm and Vigier interpret this duality as an effect of a 'turbulence' at a finer sub-quantum level – like tidal bores in a river, or thunderclaps travelling through the air. Configurations of energy travel across the fields – being transmitted from point to point by the turbulent interactions at this finer level. What we have hitherto called elementary particles are on this view 'cloud-like', localized concentrations of energy which are continuously forming and dissolving in the turbulent substratum:

> Of course, if a particle in a certain place dissolves, it is very likely to re-form nearby. Thus, on the large-scale [quantum] level, the particle-like manifestation remains in a small region of space, following a fairly well-defined track, etc. On the other hand, at a lower [sub-quantum] level, the particle does not move as a permanently existing entity, but is formed in a random way by suitable concentrations of the field-energy.

On this interpretation, the statistical character of quantum mechanics is just what at first sight it appears to be: a consequence of the fact that, at the quantum level, we are dealing with the *average* outcome of a large number of individual events taking place on a much smaller scale.

Two things must be said about Bohm's and Vigier's ideas. Firstly, if their soundness were to be established, it would mean orthodox quantum physicists abandoning some of their firmest convictions. For the orthodox view is that events on the quantum scale have something *intrinsically* indeterminate about them; and Bohm's critics have expressed themselves sarcastically about his ambition to bring to light a world of more determinate sub-quantum events. On the other hand, a historian has reasons for treating Bohm and Vigier with some respect, if only as a pointer to what *may* be the next stage in 'natural philosophy'. Anyone who can produce some convincing system of ideas, which explains the arbitrary constants, unexplained analogies – and, above all, the mathematical divergences – at the heart of present-day quantum theory, may expect to be hailed by other physicists as the Planck or Einstein of our generation. If Bohm and Vigier could do this, they would inaugurate a theoretical revolution which others would hasten to exploit. On the other hand, if they cannot resolve any of the key difficulties of quantum theory, they will go on being treated like the unfortunate Prout – as stimulating but misguided heretics, who have allowed their imaginations to outrun their experience.

The Hierarchy of Forms

The future of sub-atomic physics is, then, as open as it has ever been. We do not know whether any of our fundamental particles will keep their elementary status until the year 2000, or whether by that time they will all have been reinterpreted as tidal waves in a sea of field-energy. Certainly, as the penetrating power of our cyclotrons, synchotrons, linear accelerators and the rest has grown greater and greater, it has at last brought us to a position from which we can envisage a world of substructure even within the boundaries of the nucleons, and this process will presumably continue.

Every increase in our penetrating powers brings with it a double reward. It gives us the ability to probe, and break tighter and closer bonds between the component parts of material things, and at the same time it provides us with evidence to build our conceptions of matter into pictures having an ever-finer grain and discrimination. Hitherto, finer and finer grain has always gone with stronger and stronger bonds. The weakest interaction between material things acts over the largest distances – namely, gravity. Electromagnetic forces, molecular exchange-forces, the bonds within the atom, and the exchange-forces within the nucleus itself – all these varieties of interaction become more and more powerful, while making their effects felt at shorter and shorter ranges; and it is natural to assume (though still an assumption) that this parallel will continue to hold for the immediate future, so that stepping up the power of our probes yet further will give us a picture of matter yet finer still.

Natural philosophers now work at dimensions of about one-ten-million-millionth of a centimetre. Their theories are – as ever – hypothetical. They suppose that certain conceptions apply to Nature, and they compare the implications of these ideas with Nature herself. In focusing more and more finely, they have increased the discrimination both of their intellectual and of their practical instruments: moving from visible to microscopic, from microscopic to molecular, from molecular to electronic dimensions. At each new level, a novel type of structure has turned up. On the everyday level, atomism and continuum theory began as

343

rivals; at the molecular level, they became partners with divided responsibilities; at the electronic level, they have become merged together into a single composite theory. Thus, the 'wavicles' of modern physics are today's heirs to the intellectual traditions both of Demokritos and of the Stoics. As men in many countries continue to probe, and speculate about, the finer structure of the inorganic world, we may well wonder what will turn up next. The only thing we cannot be sure of doing is – to foresee what they will discover. The greatest minds will be prepared for the most profound changes.

FURTHER READING AND REFERENCES

The general intellectual situation from which twentieth-century physics has developed is discussed in:

H. T. Pledge, *Science since 1500*, London, 1939

Mary B. Hesse, *Forces and Fields*, Nelson, 1961

Sir Edmund Whittaker, *History of the Theories of Aether and Electricity*, Nelson, 1951

There are many useful introductions to the problems and ideas of quantum theory, but two deserve special mention:

B. Hoffmann, *The Strange Story of the Quantum*, Constable, 1959

G. Gamow, *Biography of Physics*, Hutchinson, 1962

The biographies of Marie Curie, by Eve Curie (Heinemann, 1938), J. J. Thomson, by Lord Rayleigh (Cambridge Univeristy Press, 1942) and Rutherford, by A. S. Eve (Cambridge University Press, 1939) are well worth reading. Robert Jungk gives an interesting account of the Göttingen school of physics in the 1920s in his book *Brighter than 1000 Suns* (Gollancz & Hart-Davis, 1958; Penguin Books, 1960). Most of the leading figures in the story of twentieth-century physics have also written their own accounts of the issues involved, notably:

E. Rutherford, *The Newer Alchemy*, Cambridge University Press, 1937

L. de Broglie, *Physics and Microphysics*, Hutchinson, 1955

M. Planck, *A Scientific Autobiography*, William & Norgate, 1950

M. Born, *Physics in my Generation*, Pergamon Press, 1956

W. H. Bragg, *Concerning the Nature of Things*, G. Bell, 1925

W. Heisenberg, *Philosophic Problems of Nuclear Science*, Faber & Faber, 1952

A. S. Eddington, *The Nature of the Physical World*, Cambridge University Press, 1928

E. Schrödinger, *Science, Theory and Man* (chs. 3, 8 and 9), Allen & Unwin, 1958

A. Einstein and L. Infeld, *The Evolution of Physics*, Cambridge University Press, 1938

The logical and philosophical aspects of quantum theory are discussed with profound insight in:

W. H. Watson, *On Understanding Physics*, Cambridge University Press, 1938

N. R. Hanson, *Patterns of Discovery*, (chs. 5 and 6) and *The Concept of the Positron*, Cambridge University Press, 1963

On the debate about the principle of indeterminacy, see:

Albert Einstein, Philosopher-Scientist (ed. P. A. Schilpp), Cambridge University Press, 1950

D. Bohm, *Causality and Chance in Modern Physics*, Routledge & Kegan Paul, 1957

A. B. Pippard *et al.*, *Quanta and Reality*, Hutchinson, 1962

PART III
THE STRUCTURE OF LIFE

14

The Animal Machine

To understand your problems is the beginning of wisdom: this maxim applies in scientific as surely as in practical affairs. To analyse the difficulties facing you, stating them so clearly and unambiguously that systematic observations or experiments can begin, is more than half the battle. Once that is done, intellectual victory may take time, but it can be predicted with confidence: until then, one's problems remain not just difficulties but mysteries.

The intellectual complications attending the birth of modern physiology provide a good illustration of this pattern: both at the gross anatomical level (of organs, nerves, and tissues), and at the microscopic level (of cells and cell-structure). From the very beginning of natural philosophy, men had acknowledged the difference between uniform substances (such as iron and water), and those complex, highly differentiated objects we know as organisms – most notably, human beings. Yet in what terms the natural philosopher should account for these differences in his theories of Nature was for a long time quite unclear. The properties of organisms, as of everything else, were no doubt partly determined by the raw materials from which they were composed; and to that extent, as Plato put it, the demands of necessity were served. But one cannot learn architecture by studying bricks and mortar alone, and there was more to the animal frame than would be revealed by a study of its material elements. What this extra 'something' was, and how one should formulate questions about it, remained a matter for argument as much in A.D. 1700 as in 350 B.C.

The structure of living things was not only a mystery: it was also an admirable mystery. So men were tempted to short-circuit questions about their origin and make-up by seeing them solely as products of a Divine Craftsman, praising their functional efficiency as evidence of His wisdom of rationality.

At the outset [said Plato] the material elements were in disorder, and then God conferred on them every possible kind of measure and harmonious proportion. . . . Having first set these elements in order, from them He then frames the whole Cosmos, as a single organism comprising within itself all other living things – mortal and immortal.

And a similar reflection led Newton to ask:

Can it be by accident that all birds, beasts and men have their right side and left side alike shaped (except in their bowels); and just two eyes, and no more, on either side of the face; and just two ears on either side of the head; and a nose with two holes; and either two forelegs or two wings or two arms on the shoulders, and two legs on the hips, and no more? Whence arises this uniformity in all their outward shapes but from the counsel and contrivances of an Author? . . .

Did blind chance know that there was light and what was its refraction, and fit the eyes of all creatures after the most curious manner to make use of it? These and suchlike considerations always have and ever will prevail with mankind to believe that there is a Being who made all things and has all things in his power.

Still, however august their authorship and origin, it was evident that living things *did* function with great efficiency; and that their make-up must be such as to bring this about. Close attention to their structure should therefore throw much light on their functioning, and so we find a new interest in physiological questions forming part of the general scientific revival during the seventeenth century.

The point from which physiology began lay somewhere between medicine and theology. Michael Servet, for instance, had published his new account of the pulmonary circulation as part of a treatise on *The Restoration of Christianity*, teaching that the soul enters the body by way of the mouth and lungs, and has its seat in the blood. For such heresies as these, Calvin had him burnt at the stake in 1553; and it was to take a good three centuries before the special problems of scientific physiology were isolated, and their relation to problems of other kinds – physical, chemical, and medical – were properly understood.

THE ANIMAL MACHINE

Two Kinds of Mechanistic Physiology

The revival of the 'mechanical philosophy' in the seventeenth century created as many problems as it solved. Whereas Aristotle and the alchemists had accepted organic development as scarcely requiring explanation, the New Science emphasized the brute, static, mechanical aspects of matter. Whether the ultimate constituents of things were simple geometrical shapes or hard, massy, impenetrable particles, development, growth, feeling – in a word life – became more mysterious rather than less: so much so that (as we saw earlier) William Harvey dismissed atomism as irrelevant to physiology, and remained in outlook and method a good Aristotelian. And, though proclaiming as a manifesto that animals were nothing but machines, Descartes in fact did little to build up a mechanistic science of physiology. As things worked out, the crudities and ambiguities of his first theories had to be outgrown before the science could make systematic progress; and the first real appreciation of the special problems of physiology came only in the 1740s, through the work of Albrecht von Haller.

The ambiguities in Descartes' theories can be explained briefly in general terms, and then illustrated. Suppose one takes as an axiom the assertion: *Animals are Machines*. This axiom can be interpreted *either* as a general statement of doctrine *or* as a principle of intellectual enquiry. Taken in the first sense, the seventeenth-century physiologist would understand it to imply: 'Animals are merely unconscious automata; all the processes that take place within them are of kinds with which we are already familiar, from experience of (e.g.) pumps and levers, fire and steam. So we can build up a complete system of animal physiology, without going beyond the realm of purely mechanical factors'.

'Mechanism' of this sort was certainly one strand in Descartes' system of thought, and it made an absolute distinction between man and the lower animals not arbitrary but unavoidable. For though one could argue a case for thinking of other animals in this way – scaling the workings of their bodies down to the measure of familiar mechanical processes – the same could not be done in the case of human beings. For the fact of which

351

Descartes was more certain than any other, and which he felt he could not consistently deny, was the fact that he possessed 'consciousness'; and other men, he found, testified to similar convictions. Other bodily processes in humans might be just as mechanical as those in animals, but (Descartes argued) those involving 'consciousness' must be a function, not of matter alone, but also of the soul – an agency whose influence (in his view) was exerted in human beings alone.

Yet there was another possible sense to the doctrine that animals are machines. For, regarded as a *principle of method*, this could mean: 'Although animals differ from any known machine in their complexity, delicacy, and the self-regulating character of their activities, nevertheless these activities are perfectly natural; so that, in principle, machines of sufficient complexity could reproduce them all – even perhaps those involving "thought" or "consciousness". We shall understand fully the physiology of the animal frame, only when we recognize what mechanisms it must comprise, if it is to perform all its admirable – and unique – activities.'

This second interpretation permitted a much more flexible approach. One was then free to imagine an unlimited range of explanatory mechanisms, going far beyond those which the seventeenth century managed to build or conceive. A system developed according to this method would not cut animals down to the measure of known machines: instead, it would scale conceivable machines up to the point at which they would match the performances of animals. In the years before 1750, the distinction between these two interpretations was never clearly seen, and the only man who publicly took up the second position – Julien de la Mettrie – was forced to take refuge in Berlin with that patron of free-thinkers, Frederick the Great. For this second thesis had one implication which most other philosophers found embarrassing, but which de la Mettrie embraced gladly: Descartes' argument was entirely sound so far as it went, but it should be extended – Man, too, was a Machine.

The Vitality of the Muscles

This was a position which at that time even the most 'advanced' thinkers could scarcely maintain. But meanwhile physiology had been making a beginning, within the limits of the first, more restrictive, interpretation of the mechanical philosophy. The resulting theories had one notable feature. Whenever questions arose about the ultimate motive power, or directing agencies, in the physiological machine, they tended to appeal to the soul, or to the animal spirits. Just as most of the literal 'machines' of the seventeenth century were not prime movers, but devices for directing and exploiting external sources of power (such as horses or waterfalls), so also the metaphorical 'machine' of the body seemed, even to many of the new scientists, to depend ultimately on some *external* agency for its vitality and control. The great physiological insight of the 1740s was the recognition that all the tissues of the body possess, also, certain *inherent* vital activities, and that the first priority for physiology must be to study and characterize these activities. Questions about the mechanisms underlying them would come later.

The contrast between seventeenth-century mechanical philosophy and eighteenth-century physiology is most obvious in the case of the nerves and muscles. Ever since classical times it had been known that these organs were connected, and that their functions were interrelated. This degree of understanding was embodied in the theory of 'animal spirits', which transmitted the nervous influence from the sense-organs to the brain, and back from the brain to the muscles; and this theory was taken over by the new scientists without serious alteration. To begin with, indeed, one finds them operating with a somewhat naïve picture of nerves as simple hollow tubes along which the animal spirits travelled. As to the muscles: Borelli, in his treatise *On Motion in Animals* (1680), put the accepted view clearly.

The muscles are the organs and machines by which the motive faculty of the soul sets the joints and limbs of animals in motion. . . . In itself a muscle is an inert and dead machine, which is awakened from sleep and rest and put into action solely by the access of the motive faculty.

A muscle will display vitality only if 'the commands of the soul and motive faculty' are able to reach it from outside, by way of the motor nerves.

Arteries, veins and nerves all lead into the muscle, but the first two of these cannot perform this function [of stimulating muscular action] since, even when they have been cut through, the muscle will continue to move as though it were intact. When, however, the nerve leading to a muscle is cut or strongly ligatured, it ceases to move and becomes as inert as in a corpse.

So it is the nerve which transmits the motive faculty, and which communicates the commands of the appetites to the muscle, thereby stimulating its motion.

About the mechanism of nervous transmission – what he called 'the nervous juice' – Borelli kept an open mind: he would not commit himself as to 'whether what is transmitted through the nerve is an incorporeal force, a vapour, wind, humour, motion, impulse or something else'.

The effect of this first attempt to put physiology on a new, mechanical basis was, therefore, to banish the problems of vitality, activity, and sensation into the remote depths of the brain. Bones, muscle, intestines, blood-vessels, even the nerves and 'nervous juice' itself, acted in a purely-mechanical way, according to the same principles as familiar artificial machines. But, in the last resort, these mechanical organs were simply instruments, rather than prime movers. The effective origin of initiative and vitality still remained 'immaterial'.

The principle and the effective cause of animal motion is the Soul. Everyone knows that animals derive their vitality from the Soul, which causes them to move during their lifetime; while after death, when the Soul has left the body, the animal machine becomes inert and immobile.

This physiological alliance between mechanical principles and animism remained popular throughout the eighteenth century – achieving, in the medical schools of France, the status of a new orthodoxy.

But it soon began to become clear that mechanical principles must be applied to physiology with more care and discretion. The received analysis of the bodily frame – into solid and liquid parts (which were brute and inert), the more tenuous and fiery spirits (by which vitality was transmitted) and finally the incorporeal soul – could be only a tentative working-model. For these first crude analogies did not always stand up to examination. The mechanical theory of muscular tension, as resulting from the explosive pressure of animal spirits within the muscles, had already been countered when Borelli published it. For, in 1677, Francis Glisson reported a convincing experimental demonstration that, when under tension, the muscles do not distend, but actually decrease in volume. From this observation, he drew a radical conclusion:

> The fibres contract by reason of their *intrinsic vital activity*, and not because they expand (and so become shorter) on account of the flow of vital or animal spirits transmitting commands from the brain and causing such voluntary motions.
>
> This intrinsic property of muscle is similar to that of the gall bladder, which, though continually taking in bile, discharges it only at definite intervals. This is the property of being *irritable*, and that property of certain organs may be called *irritability*.

The 'intrinsic vital activity' of muscle-fibres had been recognized by William Harvey also, but for a century his observations were treated as curiosities, while Glisson was dismissed as a mere scholastic philosopher. Well into the eighteenth century mechanical philosophers continued to explain the tension of the muscles, either (like Borelli) as the result of an explosion, or (like Descartes) as a pneumatic effect – muscular tissues being inflated by animal spirits entering from the nerves.

The crucial step forward, which converted mechanistic physiology from a system of doctrine into a method of enquiry, was taken by two men, both of whom were former pupils of Hermann Boerhaave at Leiden, and both of whom prepared editions of their master's *Institutiones Rei Medicae* – Albrecht von Haller and Julien de la Mettrie. They were very different characters, and had very different aims. Haller's ambitions were detailed and narrowly scientific: he surveyed and analysed all the results of physiological experiment from the previous century and more, and established beyond doubt that the tissues of organisms do display intrinsic vital properties and activities: far from being the inert instruments of an incorporeal agency in the brain, they possessed autonomous powers of motion within themselves. So the continued beating of muscle-fibres dissected out from the heart was no mere curiosity: rather, it was characteristic of all living material.

Therefore the heart and the intestines containing the muscular fibre are by their very nature irritable; they are able to function by themselves alone without any influence reaching them from outside.

Some writers are inclined to call this the 'vital force', but such a term does not seem justified in my view, since it is possible to demonstrate effects caused by it even after life has departed. I prefer to call this the 'inherent or intrinsic force' of the muscles. We have seen that it comes into action through the application of various stimuli [hence the name 'irritability'], but the very interesting fact also comes out that a very small stimulus may provoke a movement of great intensity.

Accordingly, vital activities resulted from the interplay of two factors: the 'inherent force' of the tissues, and the 'nervous force' from the brain. In both cases there undoubtedly was an underlying mechanism, but Haller condemned premature assertions about its nature. Maybe the nervous force was transmitted by 'spirits' of some kind, but 'there are no proofs that these hypothetical spirits are of an alcoholic, acid, sulphurous, albuminoid or combustible nature'. As for the idea that they were 'ethereal and electrical', that was just a Newtonian fad:

During the present century the name 'aether' has become so fashionable that it is customary to credit the aether with causing everything whose mechanism is still unknown and cannot be established by factual demonstration – e.g. light, the force of gravity, and magnetism. Certain people accordingly assume that the spirits, or 'nervous fluids', are of an ethereal nature and composed of aether. I do not see that this idea is justified, nor that such agents should be credited with electrical properties.

What then can the nature of these spirits be? A 'spirit' must be an element having its own distinct and characteristic properties, so tenuous in nature that we cannot perceive it with our senses, but coarser than fire, aether or electric and magnetic effluvia since it can be contained within ducts, restrained by ligaturing, and produced and maintained by food. From all of this we may assume that, since light, fire and the magnetic substance all differ from each other, while air and aether are different yet again, what we call 'spirits' – in the case of the inherent, as well as the nervous force – may well be some special element peculiar to living organs and observable only in its effects.

The first and most urgent task for physiology was to observe these effects (the actual behaviour of living tissues) in as scrupulous a manner as possible. So, from 1750 on, the most fruitful work in experimental physiology was done by men who followed in Haller's footsteps, and stuck to description and observation – studying the individual functions of different tissues, and resisting the temptation to over-simplify what they observed in support of some favourite theory.

Man, the Thinking Machine

The wider implications of Haller's teachings were taken up by de la Mettrie with the greatest of enthusiasm. Indeed, his treatise *Man a Machine* (published anonymously in 1747) opened with a dedicatory epistle addressed to Haller, which the addressee repudiated with indignation. For, unlike Haller, de la Mettrie was prepared to pursue the new line of thought to its very limit. As he saw it, Haller's 'inherent forces' had removed the last need for introducing 'incorporeal principles' into physiological theory:

> So I reject the dominion of Stahl's *Anima*, of van Helmont's *Archeus* and of Wepfer's *Presiding Principle* . . . over all the activities of the human body.

Physiologists had invoked such non-material agencies only because of their first, and quite arbitrary, assumption that the basic material elements were *essentially inanimate* – incapable of combining on their own to form animated and thinking creatures.

If vitality had been manifested only by complete, intact organisms, this view might perhaps have had some plausibility; but in fact it was mistaken. De la Mettrie listed ten different pieces of evidence showing that vitality was a general property of organic materials, even of tissues separated from the rest of the living body. This evidence included one new physiological discovery, which had caught the imagination of the eighteenth-century public more than any other: namely, the quite remarkable power of regeneration possessed by the hydra (or polyp), as described by Abraham Trembley in 1744. Trembley had discovered that, when this extremely simple animal (which lives on the undersides of water-plants) was cut into small pieces, each of them would actually grow by itself until it had regenerated into a complete new organism. In de la Mettrie's view this was only an extreme illustration of a general principle: that 'every single fibre or part of an organized body has its own intrinsic principle of motion, whose action does not depend at all on the nerves as voluntary movements do'.

On what did these 'intrinsic principles' depend? They were, he argued, simply the consequences of the different make-up of the various organs. The eyelids, the pupils, the pores of the skin, the stomach and lungs – even the sexual organs – all displayed reflexes, movements and capacities corresponding to their structures. And if this was true of the other organs (he asked), why should it not also be true of the brain? Surely *thinking* came as naturally to an organ with the structure of the brain as beating to the heart, breathing to the lungs, and peristalsis to the gut. So long as one assumed dogmatically that ordinary matter was incapable – even potentially – of displaying vital and mental properties, this conclusion would of course be unacceptable. But that assumption was no more than a dogma. Everybody knew how closely feelings and sensations were bound up with bodily processes – when we recover from jaundice, for example, 'the soul having fresh eyes, will no longer see yellow'. So what ground could there be for denying that mentality, like vitality, was a characteristic property of organized matter?

Finally, by a sweeping generalization, de la Mettrie sketched the bold outlines of a new system of physiology: one in which the key concept was 'organization'.

Let it only be granted to me that organized Matter is endowed with a motive principle, which alone marks it off from unorganized [Matter] – and can one deny that most indisputable of observations? – and that in Animals everything depends on the diversity of this Organization, as I have shown: that is enough to solve the Riddle of the Substances [Mind and Matter] and that of Man. Only one [substance] is to be seen in the World, and Man is the most perfect [form] of it. He is to the Ape and to the most intelligent Animals what Huygens' Planetary Clock is to a Repeater-watch made by Julien le Roi. If more gadgets, more Cogwheels, more springs were needed to register the movements of the Planets than to register the Hours, or repeat them; if Vaucanson [a craftsman noted for his automata] needed more ingenuity to construct his *Flute-player* than for his *Duck* he would have needed still more to contruct a *Talker* – a Machine which can no longer be dismissed as impossible, particularly in the hands of a new Prometheus.

Likewise, Nature would require still more ingenuity and apparatus to construct and maintain a Machine, which was capable of registering for a whole century all the palpitations of the heart and the spirit; for, even if you cannot tell the time by the pulse, it is at least the Barometer of warmth and vivacity, by which one can judge the state of the Soul.

Vaucanson's Automata: the machinery
was built into the pedestals.

Like Descartes, de la Mettrie was putting forward a system of natural philosophy rather than a sober physiological theory; and like the natural philosophers of a much older tradition, he was as interested in advocating a novel attitude to life as in improving our understanding of the human body. He was, in fact, a conscious Epicurean, and his writings seemed to confirm and justify all the suspicions about materialism that had darkened the minds of preachers down the centuries. We should, he taught, not only recognize our status as creatures of Nature (who 'produces millions of Men with more ease and pleasure than a Clockmaker has trouble in making the most complex watch'): we should embrace that status gladly ('cherishing life, and scarcely understanding how [feelings of] disgust can taint the heart in this home of delight'). There was nothing vile and reprehensible either about matter or about our animal inheritance. Nature deserved more credit than she had been generally allowed, and the proper course of life would be found, not by turning our backs on our material and animal natures, but rather by enjoying with discrimination all the pleasures both of the mind and of the body. When, in 1751, de la Mettrie was struck down by some sudden digestive complication after eating pheasant *pâté* and died in a few days, a great sigh of relief went up from the devout. How fitting – they commented – that a materialist such as he should die through his own gluttony!

The scandal of Julien de la Mettrie's atheism and moral materialism distracted attention from the profundity of his physiological insight. Without having Albrecht von Haller's detailed command over the facts of physiology, he saw far more clearly and consistently the ultimate implications of Haller's work. The dedicatory preface to *Man a Machine* may have been mischievous in its effusiveness, but the admiration it expressed was quite sincere; and Haller could disown praise from so disreputable an author only at a price. For all the physiologists of the eighteenth century were in a genuine dilemma, from which de la Mettrie alone had escaped, and few people could bring themselves to follow him.

This dilemma sprang from a presupposition lying at the very heart of all matter-theory: namely, the presupposition that the raw materials of Nature must, intrinsically, be *either* animate *or* inanimate. If, on the one hand, matter was essentially brute, mechanical and insensible, the consequences were clear: no assemblage constructed solely out of matter could be anything but brute, mechanical, and insensible – as Descartes had declared animals to be. If that were so, the very idea of a *conscious machine* must be a contradiction in terms: nothing composed of matter alone would be capable of thinking or feeling, and mental capacities (perhaps vital properties also) must spring from some distinct, non-material ingredient. This in fact, was the very argument by which seventeenth-century mechanical philosophers such as

Borelli were compelled to reintroduce animistic factors into physiology.

At the time there appeared only one way of evading this conclusion: namely, to choose the other alternative and assert that – on the contrary – all matter equally was caught up in a process of life and development. As we saw in Chapter 10, this course was taken by many supporters of the French Enlightenment, and by the German Romantics who followed them. Diderot, Buffon, Lamarck, and Goethe alike rejected the whole of pneumatic chemistry and Newtonian matter-theory: chemistry itself, in their view, should be founded on physiological principles. For Buffon, the very units of matter were certain 'organic molecules', from which the lower organisms arose spontaneously; and Lamarck was convinced that chemical compounds themselves were formed by a physiological process.

All existing material compounds continually tend to destroy themselves; and no substance in Nature has in itself any direct tendency to enter or put itself into the compound state. . . . This tendency of all compounds to disintegrate is counterbalanced only by the vital principle. . . . Living things alone have the capacity to form compounds directly, by the functioning of their organs. . . .

All the compounds making up what are called *minerals* are, without exception. the material remains sloughed off by organic or living beings, and without these organisms Nature would nowhere present us with chalk, clay, gypsum, sulphur, lead, gold, etc. etc.

There was one way, and one way only, of escaping between the horns of this dilemma – namely, to reject the fundamental presupposition that matter must be essentially *either* animate *or* inanimate. This was the course taken by de la Mettrie. Matter was in itself neither organic nor inorganic, neither living nor dead, neither sensible nor insensible. The difference between these states or properties of material things sprang, not from the intrinsic natures of their raw materials, but from the different ways in which these materials were *organized*.

I consider *Thought* is so little incompatible with *organized matter*, as to be apparently one of its properties – along with *Electricity*, *Mobility*, *Impenetrability*, *Extension*, and so on. . . .

No: there is nothing base about Matter, except to those crude eyes which fail to recognize her [Nature] in her most brilliant Creations; and Nature is an Artist of unlimited capacities.

In the eighteenth century this vision of Nature remained the heresy of the small minority – highly speculative from a scientific point of view, and scandalous to the guardians of faith and morals. So far as *facts* went de la Mettrie had little more solid evidence for his point of view than (say) Robert Boyle had for his corpuscular ideas. Just what was 'organized', and how, and in what ways this 'organization' was maintained and transmitted from generation to generation: on these subjects he was necessarily silent. He had framed not a new physiological theory, but rather a new *form* which future physiological theories could take. And it is for his principles of method that history has justified him. Today, the idea of a *thinking machine* can no longer be dismissed as a contradiction in terms, and even begins to appear a practical possibility. It does so, just because the physiological discoveries of the intervening two hundred years have filled out and sharpened de la Mettrie's sketch-picture, and given a far more precise meaning to his vague notion of 'organization'.

The Two Worlds

De la Mettrie might outline a programme for future physiology: meanwhile the doctors and scientists of the eighteenth century had more immediate problems. Haller's example was fruitful and, by 1805, John Hunter and Xavier Bichat had effectively completed the task which he began. Their classic analyses and descriptions of the gross properties of organisms, their organs and tissues – growth and development, self-regulation and reproduction, irritability and sensibility – completed the first phase in modern physiology. But the better that men understood the character of vital powers and properties, the more urgently they began to ask how these were to be *explained*.

When they faced this deeper problem, physiologists found themselves pulled in two directions, by two different motives which were both – scientifically speaking – respectable and weighty. For, while all their biological experience convinced them that living things had unique properties, they had also to come to terms with the newly-established 'universal laws of Nature' which had been the glory of seventeenth-century science. This double knowledge produced an intellectual schizophrenia. For these two beliefs tended to conflict. Whenever they did there was a dispute, and the terms of armistice remained in debate until the 1860s at the earliest.

Throughout the resulting argument, two extreme positions were popular, though in the end neither proved tenable. At one pole there was a group of doctrinaire chemists, who were so insistent on the universality of physico-chemical laws that they were prepared to deny any distinctive character to the properties of living things. (Their most striking evidence was the analogy between respiration in animals and combustion in the inanimate world.) At the other pole was a party consisting chiefly of doctors and theologians anxious to maintain the uniqueness of living things, who denied at almost any cost that physico-chemical discoveries were relevant to physiology. (They were particularly impressed by the processes of growth and regeneration, and by the capacity of the higher animals to maintain a constant temperature regardless of change in the surroundings.) Few people before 1850 had the intellectual poise needed to keep these opposing motives in balance, and the French chemist Chaptal was exceptional in the 1790s for advocating a compromise:

The abuse which, at the beginning of the present [eighteenth] century were made of the applications of chemistry to medicine, have caused the natural and intimate relations of this science with the art of healing to be mistaken. . . .

In order to direct the application of chemistry to the human body with propriety, correct views must be adopted of the animal economy itself, together with accurate notions about chemistry. The results of the laboratory must be regarded as subordinate to physiological observations. It is in consequence of a departure from these principles that the human body has been considered as a lifeless, passive substance. . . .

In the mineral kingdom everything is subject to the invariable laws of affinity. No internal principle modifies the action of natural agents. . . . In the vegetable kingdom, the action of external agents is equally evident; but the internal organization modifies their effects. . . . In animals, functions are much less dependent on external causes, and Nature has concealed the principal organs in the internal parts of their bodies, as if to withdraw them from the influence of foreign powers. But, the more the functions of the individual are dependent on its organization, the less is the dominion of chemistry over them, and it becomes us to be cautious in applying the results of this science to all phenomena which depend essentially on the principles of life.

(But then, Chaptal had a foot in both camps. Though in chemistry he was a follower of Lavoisier, he taught at that stronghold of anti-mechanistic physiology, the University of Montpellier; so he was well able to judge the obstacles to be overcome before physical and chemical principles could be extended into the biological field.)

Chaptal formulated clearly the basic dilemma facing would-be biochemists. 'There is no function in the animal economy', he declared, 'upon which the science of chemistry cannot throw some light'. Yet nothing which chemistry taught us could abolish the differences between the living and the inert: the behaviour of living things 'presents to us phenomena which chemistry could never have known or predicted by paying attention only to the invariable laws observed in inanimate bodies'. At the very least biochemistry was chemistry 'carried out', to use Claude Bernard's later phrase, 'in the special field of life', and the immediate problem was to see just what that qualification implied.

About this, few people in 1800 had much doubt. They agreed with Chaptal that, within the bodies of living things, the actions of physical causes were in some way modified by an active or 'vital' principle. And these two themes – the contrast between 'internal functions' and 'external causes', and the action of 'the vital principle' – were to remain staple topics of physiological debate for another fifty years. They were connected with a certain general picture of Nature, which was widely taken for granted at this period by physiologists and others. The more that men thought about the special character of living things, the more it seemed clear to them that the vital world within the organism worked quite differently from the inanimate world outside it. Bodily processes were functional and directed; outside the body, all was causal and chaotic; and this contrast between the two worlds could be explained only by seeing the internal workings of the body as governed by some 'vital principle'.

The resulting picture of Nature, as divided into two distinct realms, represented (so to say) an after-image of Aristotle's cosmology, and it had a similar origin. Where eighteenth- and nineteenth-century scientists regarded all matter as essentially inorganic, Aristotle had thought the same about the four primary elements of the terrestrial world. Things composed only of terrestrial matter were condemned to decay and disintegration, and those which contained some portion of the 'quintessence' could alone preserve indefinitely an enduring form. So, in Aristotle's system, there was an absolute distinction between the unchanging world of the quintessence (comprising both the heavenly bodies and the hereditary pneuma) and the world of change and decay.

For some years after 1800, the contrast between organic and inorganic processes showed signs of hardening into an equally absolute opposition. Though Aristotle's division between the sub-lunary and super-lunary worlds had been swept away in the seventeenth-century astronomical reconstruction, the stability of inherited organic forms remained mysterious; and to many people the contrast between the stable, constructive world within the organism and the chaotic, destructive flux of the physico-chemical environment outside was the first and most significant fact of all physiology. The world of inanimate things, they concluded, was all the Epicureans had said: a world of inert, passive objects, held in the iron grip of physico-chemical laws and at the mercy of destructive causes which, left to themselves, would progressively efface all traces of organic form. This was a sad, disintegrating world, symbolized for the Italian poet Leopardi by the lava-scorched slopes of Vesuvius, on which the golden broom just managed to survive – a world whose motto should be: *Tout lasse, tout casse, tout passe.*

Inside living things, by contrast, one entered a world of form, order and cohesion: everything was modified by an active principle, which worked for constructive ends and prevented the physical forces of the external environment from making destructive inroads on the stable form of the living creature. There, to some extent at least, the rigid determinism of the inanimate world was relaxed; and the spontaneous vitality of the living creature remained possible, just so long as the vital principle maintained its influence. So far as the individual was concerned, this too was a world with an essentially tragic fate; for the governing principle of life was continually under siege from the environment and, at death, surrendered its authority over the body to the destructive causes of the physico-chemical world. Worse: the material substances taken into the body during life acted after death like a 'fifth column' – allying themselves with the external agencies in a common process of destruction. Yet, so long as life lasted, the vital principle kept its command over the processes within the body, organizing its material constituents into the stable organic pattern without which vitality could not be maintained.

Few people carried this particular line of argument quite to Lamarck's extreme, of giving the vital principle credit even for the forms of inorganic atoms and molecules. By 1800, almost everyone accepted chemical substances as having naturally stable and enduring forms, and the vital principle was called in only to create and maintain the organs and tissues of living creatures. Still, bare appeals to 'vitality' and 'active principles' did little to explain even the uniqueness and stability of living things. The physiological mode of action of the vital principle could no longer be left unexamined. The next question was: How does it act, and what is its nature?

Theories of Vitality

There are times in the development of a new science when advances can be made only by a painstaking process of elimination. Looking back, we may be exasperated to see how repeatedly our predecessors set off down theoretical blind alleys, before recognizing the way ahead. Yet in fact we owe them a debt. If an intellectual road has never been explored, it may be impossible to label it as a dead end, and we often come to recognize a sound method only in the light of earlier failures.

By the beginning of the nineteenth century Dalton was bringing a new order into the theory of chemical combination, which Berzelius was to extend before long to substances of organic origin. Electrical theory was still barely launched, while gravity and dynamics were irrelevant to most physiological questions. Meditating the unique characteristics of living things, physiologists naturally supposed that behaviour so striking must reflect internal processes of an equally unparalleled kind. The nature and action of the vital principle could be understood only if these unparalleled processes were discovered.

Four different kinds of theory were examined and rejected before the full complexity of the physiological problem was appreciated. At first, men spoke of the vital principle as an incorporeal constituent or agency, having the power to intervene in all organic processes. When immaterial agencies went out of favour, some physiologists explained the behaviour of living things as governed by 'laws of vitality', distinct from those obeyed by inert matter. Others saw vitality as evidence of special material constituents, distinct from the chemical substances of the inorganic realm. Others again regarded it as the effect of a unique force comparable with, but distinct from, the forces of impact, gravity, electricity, and chemical affinity. And, as men worked their way through these four hypotheses, they brought to light the material for a fifth and more fruitful theory.

Vital Agents

Van Helmont's *Archeus* and Stahl's *Anima* had been proposed as incorporeal *causes*, having direct and widespread effects throughout an animal's body; and this was the view of the vital principle which dominated medical thought in France for the whole of the eighteenth century. But, as the fog surrounding the incorporeals slowly lifted and chemistry took on a more systematic form, this conception gradually suffered a sea-change. The vital principle became less and less the *cause* of anything: rather, the name was used to label a certain *effect* – the phenomenon of vitality, whose existence was the justification for physiology, but whose ultimate causes remained hidden.

Around 1770 the anatomist John Hunter was still oscillating between the one interpretation and the other. He likened 'animal matter without life, to 'a bar of iron without magnetism'; yet this analogy did not help him greatly, since the theory of magnetism was itself still so unclear – 'Is this [magnetism] any substance added? Or is it a certain change which takes place in the arrangement of the particles of iron giving it this property?' And there was the same ambiguity about 'the vital power':

By the living principle I mean to express that principle which prevents matter from falling into dissolution – resisting heat, cold and putrefaction. . . . Life simply is the principle of preservation.

Animal and vegetable substances differ from common matter in having a power superadded totally different from any other known property of matter, out of which arise various new properties; it cannot arise out of any peculiar modification of matter, but appears to be something superadded. . . . Organization may arise out of living parts, and produce action; but life can never arise out of, and depend on, organization. . . . Organization and life are two different things.

But a few years later the change had gone further. J. F. Blumenbach spoke of organic development as evidence of a vital, formative power (the *nisus formativus*), but insisted quite explicitly that he was using this term only to describe manifest phenomena.

By this name I wish to designate, not so much the cause [of development] as some kind of perpetual and invariably consistent effect, deduced retrospectively from the very constancy and universality of [vital] phenomena. Exactly likewise, we use the name of 'attraction' or 'gravity' to refer to certain powers whose *causes* nevertheless still remain hidden in Cimmerian darkness.

His analogy between vitality and gravity caught on widely, and around 1800 the comparison recurred in the writings of physiologists like a refrain. They repeatedly protested that they were seeking only to apply to the science of life the methods of thought employed by the great Newton. If physicists were content to display the manifold effects of gravity as varied instances of the action of a common power, could not physiologists, too, justifiably point to the phenomena of life as the manifold effects of 'vitality' – and leave it at that?

Laws of Vitality

This change of attitude had important consequences. For, as Bichat pointed out in 1801, the phenomena of life were very varied, and could scarcely be manifestations of any *single* principle:

This principle, termed *vital* by Barthez, *Archaeus* by van Helmont, is an assumption as void of truth as to suppose one sole acting principle governing all the phenomena of physics.

Rather, one must recognize a multiplicity of vital properties, every tissue of the body having its own powers, whose operations were largely independent. And this new theory of vitality, as the harmonious alliance of many vital powers and properties, was crystallized in his famous definition of 'life' as 'the totality of processes which resist death'.

Bichat's approach had one great merit: it compelled scientists to study the structure and operation of all the bodily tissues separately and systematically. But it left open the question, what was *unique* about the vital powers. He himself was convinced that in one fundamental respect these powers were absolutely distinct from all the forces of physics and chemistry. In physical science the laws of nature had 'constant and invariable' effects and 'admit neither of diminution nor increase'. Vital properties, by contrast,

are at every instant undergoing some change in degree and kind; they are scarcely ever the same. In their phenomenon nothing can be foreseen, foretold nor calculated; we judge only of them by their analogies, and these are in the vast proportion of instances extremely uncertain. To apply the science of natural philosophy [physics] to physiology would be to explain the phenomena of living bodies by the laws of an inert body. Here is a false principle.

Since the laws of vitality were essentially variable, physiology would have to adopt a method of enquiry all its own:

One calculates the return of a comet, the speed of a projectile; but to calculate with Borelli the strength of a muscle, with Keill the speed of blood, with Lavoisier the quantity of air entering the lungs, is to build on shifting sand an edifice solid itself, but which soon falls for lack of an assured base. This instability of the vital forces marks all vital phenomena with an irregularity which distinguishes them from physical phenomena [which are] remarkable for their uniformity. It is easy to see that the science of organized bodies should be treated in a manner quite different from those [sciences] which have unorganized bodies for their object.

Yet this variability was not conclusive, for it could be interpreted in two different ways – either as evidence that living things can evade the laws of physics and chemistry, or alternatively as evidence of the extremely complex ways in which bodily processes interact. Bichat chose the first of these alternatives, and this choice was neither arbitrary nor without some foundation. For, at a certain level, living things *can* evade the laws of physics. Warm-blooded animals, for example, evade 'Newton's Law of Cooling': whereas lumps of rock and metal which have been heated cool off to the temperature of their surroundings in a regular and predictable way, the higher animals retain a constant temperature, despite the fluctuations going on around them. (For many years this phenomenon of 'animal heat' was an obstacle in the way of any mechanistic physiology.) Yet the autonomy of bodily processes could have a different explanation. As the chemist Justus Liebig pointed out in 1842, when we breathe we consume oxygen at a very variable rate; but this variation can be accounted for perfectly well if we take enough factors into consideration – how recently we last fed, took exercise, and so on. So there need be nothing *intrinsically* variable about such processes. And when, some twenty years later, Claude Bernard finally disentangled the mechanisms underlying the phenomenon of animal heat, these proved to involve a similar complexity: a delicate interaction between digestive, respiratory, and nervous processes, which conformed individually to the laws of physics and chemistry but reacted on each other continuously, so producing an illusion of irregularity.

As the nineteenth century went on, the burden of proof shifted decisively. In 1800 it had been up to physicists and chemists to show that their laws *did* apply to organisms; but by 1860 it was up to physiologists to show that they did *not*. By that time, Liebig had analysed the chemistry of digestion, and Helmholtz had demonstrated that the Conservation of Energy could be applied to organisms. Experience suggested more and more that, for all their complexity, organic processes – like any others – conformed to physico-chemical principles. If there remained an area of doubt it was the central nervous system. What Berzelius had said in 1813 was still largely justifiable:

The unknown cause of the phenomena of life is principally lodged in . . . the nervous system, the very operation of which it constitutes. Nothing of which chemistry has taught us hitherto has the smallest analogy to its operation, or affords us the least hint towards a knowledge of its hidden nature.

Still more astonishing are the operations of the brain. . . . Is it not probable that human understanding, which is capable of so much cultivation . . . may one day explore itself and its nature? I am convinced that it will not.

Vital Substances

Did the unique character of living things spring rather from their material constituents? Did they contain organic substances different in kind – even different in principle – from those of the inorganic world? This approach received some early set-backs; the ultimate triumph of biochemistry was long delayed and was several times announced prematurely.

In the early years of the New Science, few people questioned that living things contained within them certain remarkable, and probably unique, substances. (Descartes' 'animal spirits' and Borelli's 'nervous juice' are two obvious examples.) But with the transformation of chemistry during the eighteenth century, it was necessary to face directly the question whether animal, vegetable, and mineral substances were chemically specific and distinct. Almost at once the category of 'spirits' was discredited, and during the 1770s Scheele prepared from beer, milk, and other organic sources a whole range of novel 'organic acids' (such as formic and lactic acids) having the same generic properties as the familiar mineral acids. By 1814 Berzelius was showing that many true 'organic' substances, isolated from animal and vegetable tissues, conformed to the chemical laws of proportion and combination recently explained by Dalton. So if one was justified in thinking of iron rust, green vitriol and nitric acid as compounded out of certain elements, according to fixed molecular formulae, there was now an equally strong argument for thinking of organic substances in the same way. And the suspicion that organic substances were generally similar to inorganic ones was further confirmed in 1828, when Wöhler showed that urea (one of the products of the kidney) could be prepared in the laboratory using the normal procedures of inorganic chemistry.

Yet the wider implications of animal chemistry gave rise to much dispute. It is impossible to prove a negative, and it was too soon in 1828 to assert that living things contained *no* material substances with unique properties. Wöhler in due course acquired a posthumous but irrelevant glory, when his obituarist hailed his work on urea as the first solid proof that organic and inorganic substances are essentially of the same nature. Yet that is not at all how Wöhler's discovery appeared at the time it was made. At most, it suggested that the constituent materials of living things might differ from familiar mineral substances in their degree of complexity, rather than in kind. In any case, long before Wöhler's death the ambitions of biochemistry had run up against one serious obstacle.

This had to do with fermentation. The protagonists to the dispute were Liebig (for the chemists) and Louis Pasteur (for the microbiologists), and the result shows how far nineteenth-century chemists were from disproving the unique character of many biological processes. The argument dated from 1837, when Berzelius demonstrated the action of chemical 'catalysts' – those substances whose presence speeds up chemical reactions, although they themselves are not changed in the process. For Berzelius claimed that he had thereby discovered the key to many biochemical processes: 'Fermentation', he said, 'is similar to the decomposition of hydrogen peroxide in the presence of platinum, silver or fibrin – a catalytic action like any other'. He expressly denied that fermentation was due to the action of microscopic organisms.

Yet Louis Pasteur was not satisfied. He was convinced that there must be some process going on in organisms which had *no* counterpart in the inorganic world. Otherwise, what was there to exclude organisms being generated directly from inorganic substances? Since, above all, he was anxious to rule out such 'spontaneous generation', it was important to demonstrate some biochemical process for which the presence of microorganisms was indispensable. In his opinion, fermentation was the example he required, and he carried out a long series of researches to establish his point. In 1869 Liebig wrote a critical paper, claiming that Pasteur's central point was mistaken, and that fermentation had nothing especially 'biological' about it. An acrimonious exchange followed, in which Pasteur made good his claim, establishing by a classic sequence of experimental demonstration that microorganisms played an indispensable part in the process of fermentation.

Liebig declares that fermentation, like putrefaction, is a phenomenon similar (so to say) to death. . . . I maintain, on the other hand, that fermentation goes essentially with life: I think I have proved beyond question that a substance capable of stimulating fermentation never actually does so unless some continuous chemical reaction is going on by which its living cells multiply, assimilating into themselves part of the fermenting matter. . . .

I assert, for instance, that whenever wine turns to vinegar it does so by the action of the vinegar organism *Mycoderma aceti*, a film of which forms on its surface. Nowhere on earth is there a single drop of vinegar produced by wine souring on contact with air without a spore of the yeast *Mycoderma* having been present. This microscopic plant has the capacity to take in oxygen from the air, just as platinum black and the red blood-corpuscles do, and to fix it in the substances on which it forms.

Pasteur showed that in many biochemical reactions the role of the catalyst was played, not by any inorganic substance, but by living micro-organisms, the reaction continuing only so long as the organisms were free to grow and multiply. And since these micro-organisms consisted of one or more biological units or *cells*, comparable to those composing larger organisms, these researches not only threw doubt on spontaneous generation: they also put a new road-block in the way of biochemistry. So the union of chemistry and physiology had once again to be postponed. The chemical status of organic substances and processes could be finally determined only if chemical analysis was carried to an even finer level – the sub-microscopic chemistry within the cell itself.

Vital Forces

Liebig's own theory about the nature of vitality was a theory of the fourth kind. Many scientists between 1800 and 1860 (it is true) spoke of a 'vital force' very loosely, bringing it into their explanations without any solid preparatory analysis, and (as Harvey would have said) using it as 'a common subterfuge of ignorance'. But Liebig attempted to give the notion some theoretical precision, and even a numerical measure.

Although Liebig had denied (as against Pasteur) that living things were composed of special, distinct substances, he was quite ready to recognize the special character of certain organic *pro-*

cesses: notably, those of growth and regeneration. In these cases, he concluded, one was presented with matter in a new mode of combination, and – as a good Newtonian scientist – he accounted for this by the hypothesis of a new central force. Whereas the inorganic forces of cohesion and chemical affinity exhibited themselves in geometrical shapes, such as were found in crystals, the 'vital force' produced and maintained organic forms of very different shapes, only rarely bounded by straight lines. It seemed to be a physical force of a quite specific kind, strictly comparable to the forces of magnetism, electricity, gravity, and affinity, and capable at times of overcoming them:

> The vital force in living animal tissue appears as a cause of growth in the mass, and of resistance to those external agencies which tend to alter the form, structure and composition of the substance of the tissue in which the vital energy resides. . . .
>
> The vital force causes a decomposition of the constituents of food, and destroys the force of attraction which is continually exerted between their molecules; it alters the direction of the chemical forces in such wise, that the elements of the constituents of food arrange themselves in another form . . . it causes the new compounds to assume forms altogether different from those which are the result of the attraction of cohesion when acting freely, that is, without resistance. . . .
>
> The phenomenon of growth, or increase in the mass, presupposes that the acting vital force is more powerful than the resistance which the chemical force opposes to the decomposition or transformation of the elements of the food.

Here, Liebig claimed, was a hypothesis which combined the two necessary virtues: it conformed to the general principles of physics, but allowed for the particular properties of living things:

> There is nothing to prevent us from considering the vital force as a peculiar property, which is possessed by certain material bodies, and becomes sensible when their elementary particles are combined in a certain arrangement or form.
>
> This supposition takes from the vital phenomena nothing of their wonderful peculiarity . . . a living part acquires, on the above supposition, the capacity of offering and overcoming resistance, by the combination of its elementary particles in a certain form; and, as long as its form and composition are not destroyed by opposing forces, it must retain its energy uninterrupted and unimpaired.

The theory might even (he thought) be reconciled with the conservation of energy. When an animal exerted itself, the 'forces' within it were transformed: vital and chemical bonds being broken down, and mechanical energy being produced. (Like most other scientists of the 1840s, Liebig used one word for both *force* and *energy*, and telescoped the idea of the 'conservation of energy' with that of the 'equilibrium of forces'.)

For a certain amount of motion, for a certain proportion of vital force consumed as mechanical force, an equivalent of chemical force is manifested; that is, an equivalent of oxygen enters into combination with the substance of the organ which has lost the vital force; and a corresponding proportion of the substance of the organ is separated from the living tissue in the shape of an oxidized compound.

In all material transformations, the vital, chemical and other forces were never annihilated: they were merely transformed into each other. And, just as Joule was meanwhile measuring 'the mechanical equivalent of heat', so Liebig now tried to give mathematical expression to 'the mechanical equivalent of life'. He assumed that a healthy adult required seven hours' sleep in twenty-four, and compared the amounts of energy which, on his theory, would be expended mechanically, in physical exertion, and 'vitally'. i.e. in the maintenance of bodily structure:

	Force expended in mechanical effects	Force expended in formation of new parts
In the adult	17	7
In the infant	4	20
In the old man	20	4

Liebig's theory failed to arouse any serious interest, for it fell between two stools. On the one hand, his biochemical colleagues were galloping off in the opposite direction. Having shown how many of the processes within the living body consisted in straightforward chemical reactions, they were in no mood to distinguish between chemical bonds and vital ones unless they were compelled to. On the other hand, microbiologists like Louis Pasteur were unwilling to see anything done to weaken the distinction between vital processes and chemical reactions, for fear of reviving the heresy of spontaneous generation. So they could scarcely accept

Liebig's thesis that mechanical, chemical, and vital energies were equivalent and interconvertible. The theory would have carried conviction only if it had led to striking numerical results: supposing, for instance, Liebig could have explained in detail the mechanics of growth and regeneration. But this did not happen. The 'vital force' struck no roots in either physics or physiology, and the only faint echo which it raises in modern chemistry is the concept of the 'high-energy phosphate bond' – which plays an important part in the chemistry of respiration but has no counterpart in inorganic chemistry.

Claude Bernard's New Method

The phase in the development of physiology which began with René Descartes in the early seventeenth century was brought to a close in the mid-nineteenth century by another Frenchman, Claude Bernard. For Bernard not only succeeded in stating acceptable terms for reconciling physiology with physics and chemistry, but also demonstrated in his own experimental enquiries how this compromise worked out in practice.

Today Bernard is thought of as a scientist – as one of the founders of modern physiology – and so he was. But he spoke of his own work as 'experimental medicine', and the name is significant. For, throughout the two hundred years which separated him from Harvey and Descartes, the central problem had been to combine the natural philosopher's theoretical vision with the medical anatomist's fidelity to experience. (This was the problem Hippocrates dismissed as insoluble.) The secret of Bernard's success lay in his capacity to bring these two elements in physiology into a fruitful intellectual harmony. Both in his original researches and in his analysis of physiological method, Bernard treated the animal frame as a functioning whole. Though his experimental work was rigorously quantitative and chemical, he always saw the particular processes he was studying in their relation to the rest of the body; and this made him the natural successor to Harvey and Galen, as much as to Liebig and Descartes. As we shall see, it also made him less dependent than his predecessors on the hypothesis of a 'vital principle'. For he showed that the special characteristics of organisms could be explained as resulting from the *complexity* and *interconnectedness* of their bodily processes, without the need to introduce any uniquely 'vital' cause into one's account.

The era of the vital principle looks to us now like a period of vain groping after shadows. But the time had not been wasted, and its lessons were not lost on Bernard. For the successive failures all pointed in the same direction, and this gave him a lead when he came to re-analyse the central theoretical problem. The hypothesis of a single incorporeal agency had been displaced by the doctrine of *many* vital powers acting in harmony. The theory that organic substances were unique in kind was giving way to the idea that they were only more *complex* than inorganic ones. And Liebig's idea of a novel kind of vital force failed to establish itself for the same reasons. At all gross levels there was much positive evidence to show that bodily processes were multiple and interrelated; and no positive evidence at all of the action of uniquely 'vital' agencies or factors.

From his early work on the gastric juices, glycogen, and the function of the liver, Bernard knew just how necessary it was to recognize all the influences to which an organ was subject, before one could hope to identify and reproduce the chemical reactions going on within it. But he knew equally that, once this had been done, the reactions turned out to be explicable on normal chemical principles. Bichat had been right to insist that the bodily processes were highly variable and largely independent of the external environment, yet it now began to appear that these unusual features represented not breaches of physical and chemical law so much as the direct responses of the organ to physical and chemical conditions within it. Bernard declared:

I am one of those who think that the laws of physics and chemistry are not violated in the organism; but on the other hand, I believe that though chemical *laws* are unchanging, chemical *processes* are variable, and are able in some cases to show such individuality as to become special physiological processes.

This was the basis for his reconciliation of physiology and the physical sciences. The special character of physiological processes could be respected without subverting the principles of physics and chemistry, only if one could reconstruct the conditions within the organs concerned *in all their complexity and individuality*.

I should agree with the vitalists if they wished simply to recognize that living beings exhibit phenomena which are peculiar to themselves and unknown in inorganic nature.... [But], if vital phenomena do differ from those of inorganic bodies in complexity and appearance, this difference obtains only on account of determined, or determinable, conditions proper to themselves. So, if the science of life must differ from all others in [certain of its forms of] explanation and in [recognizing certain] special laws, the different sciences are nevertheless not set apart by [requiring different kinds of] scientific method.

Two groups of functions had always been especially mystifying, and had done most to make the idea of a vital principle plausible. These were the regulatory functions (by which, for instance, the temperature of warm-blooded animals is maintained constant) and the general class of developmental functions, including growth, regeneration, and reproduction. Now, development was – and still is – a more profound and complex problem for the physiologist than self-regulation, and Bernard made no progress with it. (It depends essentially on sub-cellular processes, which he was in no position to analyse.) But his work on the regulatory functions was highly successful, and put the general soundness of his theoretical analysis beyond doubt. Incidentally, it cleared up almost entirely the long-standing perplexities about animal heat.

The important thing about the body was not that the organs were responsive to a 'vital principle' but that they were *responsive to each other*. If animals were in so many ways independent of their environments, this simply testified to the efficacy of the *regulatory mechanisms*, which established a condition of equilibrium within the '*milieu intérieur*' of the body, and maintained it despite wide variations in the external conditions. For purposes of biochemistry this 'internal environment' was a world no less physico-chemical than the familiar environment outside: if the external environment seemed hostile and destructive, that was only because the regulatory mechanisms did not extend beyond the skin.

The regulatory mechanism which Bernard studied in most detail was the 'vaso-motor reaction'. This controls the temperature of the body by delicately balancing a number of interconnected processes in the nerves, the blood-vessels and the digestive organs. The essential thing which he established is this: that the vaso-motor reaction operated on the principle known to engineers nowadays as 'negative feed-back'. The ultimate source of bodily heat is the respiratory 'combustions' which go on in the cells, and these are sustained by oxygen carried to the cells by the blood-stream. If the rate of blood-flow to any part of the body alters, these processes are affected, and its temperature changes from normal: the vaso-motor response, as Bernard showed, controls the temperature by varying the flow of blood. For the tempera-ture of each limb or organ indirectly affects the sympathetic nerves in the walls of the arteries concerned. If it begins to rise, the nerves are so stimulated that the arteries contract and the flow of blood is reduced: if it drops below normal, the arteries are dilated and the flow of blood is increased. The 'negative feed-back' principle of modern engineering is simply a generalization of this mechanism: one controls the output of a mechanical or electrical process by establishing a linkage between the output and the input, so that, whenever the output deviates from the required level, this change is 'fed back' and reacts on to the input in such a way as to counteract the deviation.

After Bernard, the stability of organisms was no longer thought of as a static condition, maintained by the vital principle in defi-ance of physics and chemistry. It became, instead, a dynamic equilibrium between physiological processes of two kinds: some of them building up the bodily tissues, others breaking them down. The whole integrated system of processes was sustained by drawing in energy from the surroundings in the form of food, and the rates of all the different processes were delicately controlled by 'negative feed-back' mechanisms: in this way the conditions required for life were maintained within the body.

In his intellectual methods, therefore, Bernard was certainly a 'mechanistic' physiologist. But this is true only with one import-ant qualification. Descartes and Borelli, in the seventeenth cen-tury, had tried to explain the workings of the animal machine by comparing it with sixteenth-century, or even medieval, machines. Bernard, in the nineteenth century, explained the regulatory mechanisms on principles which have been fully exploited only in *twentieth-century* machines – the principles underlying thermostats, electronic controls, and servo-mechanisms. This contrast is crucial, and sets Bernard firmly in the tradition of Harvey and Galen. All three men accepted the functions of the organs as the primary given facts which had to be established with scrupulous clinical care, and explained their workings by imaginatively applying the best mechanical principles of their times. (If Bernard could go so much further than Harvey, that was because he had at his disposal intellectual tools forged by Lavoisier, Dalton, and Liebig.) In each case the facts of organic life came first, and the mechanistic imagination had to be stretched to the measure of these facts. In the comparison between animals and machines, the behaviour of the animals had to be taken as given, and the concept of 'machines' was the intellectual concertina which scientists expanded to cover this behaviour. The result was mechanistic physiology, not as Descartes had practised it, but as de la Mettrie had conceived it. By this same method, physiology has since advanced – as Bernard was convinced it could – far beyond the frontiers to which he himself took it.

Bernard and the Problem of Development

In the whole history of science there has been scarcely a man who saw and accepted in full all the implications of his own intellectual innovations: Galileo still clung to the ghost of circular motion, Descartes preserved the pineal gland as one last point of influence within the body for non-material causes, and Lavoisier kept caloric in his theory to serve as 'the matter of heat'. In his own generation, each man straddles the gap between old and new – one foot planted firmly on fresh intellectual soil, the other retaining a toehold in the ideas of his youth. Only succeeding generations can take full possession of the territory which he has won for them, and accept as commonplaces the ideas which for him are hard-won novelties.

Claude Bernard was no exception. Although he had explained in general terms how experimental medicine could work in harmony with physics and chemistry, and had applied this insight to good effect in the case of the regulatory mechanisms, one group of physiological functions continued to baffle him. He was not just at a loss to imagine physico-chemical mechanisms to explain them. Rather, his mind boggled at the idea of *any* physico-chemical systems being ingenious and complex enough to produce the effects in question. Faced with the facts of embryology and development, Bernard jibbed, and it is instructive to ask why this was so.

The relevant passage in his classic *Introduction to the Study of Experimental Medicine* reads as follows:

The primary essence of life is a developing organic force, the force which constituted the *mediating nature* of Hippocrates and the *Archeus Faber* of van Helmont. [He might have added also the *nisus formativus* of Blumenbach, and even the *vis vitae* of Liebig.] But whatever our idea of the nature of this force, it is always exhibited concurrently and in parallel with physico-chemical conditions proper to vital phenomena...

When a chicken develops in an egg, the formation of the animal body as a grouping of chemical elements is not what essentially distinguishes the vital force. This grouping takes place only according to laws which govern the chemico-physical properties of matter; but the *guiding idea* of the vital development belongs essentially to the domain of life, rather than to chemistry or physics or anything else.

In every living germ is a *creative idea* which unfolds and exhibits itself through organization. As long as a living being persists, it remains under the influence of this same creative vital force, and death comes when it can no longer express itself. Here, as everywhere, everything is derived from the *idea*, which alone creates and guides: physico-chemical means of expression are common to all natural phenomena, and remain mingled pell-mell like the letters of the alphabet in a box, until a force goes to fetch them to express the most varied thoughts and mechanisms. This same vital idea preserves beings, by reconstructing the living parts disorganized by exercise, or destroyed by accidents or diseases.

Reading these words in the 1960s, we are forcibly reminded of the boundaries which a hundred years ago confined the vision of the most enlightened physiologist living. Our first impulse is to protest: *surely* the general method which had elsewhere served him so well could have saved him from abandoning his principles at this very last moment? Having established so brilliantly that, in its capacity as a controlling agency, the 'vital principle' had a material counterpart in the 'regulatory mechanisms' of the body, why should he now despair of relating development and regeneration directly to the physico-chemical make-up and workings of the living tissues?

Today, indeed, one could actually rewrite Bernard's account of the 'creative idea' expressed in organic development, in such a way as to make it a description of the fundamental genetic material in the cell:

In every living cell is a 'genetic template', which unfolds and exhibits itself through the bodily organization. As long as a living being persists, its development remains under the influence of this template, and death comes when it can no longer express itself. . . . Physico-chemical raw materials are common to all natural phenomena, and remain mingled pell-mell like the letters of the alphabet in a box, until a particular form or 'code' is imposed upon them by the action of the template. This same template preserves living beings, by controlling the regeneration of parts disorganized by exercise or destroyed by accidents or diseases.

Yet this is just the step that Bernard could not take. For the full understanding of the developmental mechanisms involves three branches of biology which, at the time of his death, were still in their infancy: evolution, genetics, and sub-cellular chemistry. During the eighteenth century the providential framework of Galen's and Harvey's anatomy (in which every organ had been created fit for its purpose) had fallen away and been replaced by the idea of a static order of Nature (in which everything came into existence according to natural laws); and in Bernard's own lifetime, which stretched from 1813 to 1878, this static picture was being dismantled, in its turn, in favour of a dynamic, evolutionary perspective. But in the '50s and '60s, when Bernard was in his prime, this process was only just beginning, and Darwin's theory (as we shall see in a later volume) was slow to gain acceptance in France. Genetics was no further ahead. Gregor Mendel's classic paper appeared in print in 1865, but languished unread until 1900, when the subject as we know it was born. So Bernard's central physiological ideas were influenced neither by Darwin nor by Mendel.

There remains the cell-theory, which will be our topic in the next chapter. Bernard certainly knew of the existence of cells, and he had great hopes for their biochemical study. But he was never himself familiar with cells in the way he was with the organs and tissues of experimental medicine and the substances of chemistry.

He knew as much about them as the physicists of the 1870s knew about 'cathode rays'. And he could no more estimate the full potential significance of sub-cellular structure and chemistry than those physicists could estimate the ultimate significance of the cathode-ray particles – the 'electrons'.

FURTHER READING AND REFERENCES

The general period in physiology covered in this chapter is discussed in the relevant sections of E. Nordenskiold's *History of Biology*, Kegan Paul, 1929 (of variable merit), and H. T. Pledge's *Science since 1500*, (London, 1939), and in less detail in Charles Singer's *History of Biology* (H. K. Lewis, 1950). But, to a greater extent than in the physical sciences, one is obliged to read the original sources for oneself and form one's own interpretation. This is, of course, the best course to take in any event, and can usefully be started with the help of such introductory source-collections as:

T. S. Hall, *A Source-Book in Animal Biology*, McGraw-Hill, 1951

M. L. Gabriel and S. Fogel, *Great Experiments in Biology*, Prentice Hall, 1955

A. Pi Suñer, *Classics of Biology*, Pitman, 1955

See also the series of reprints under the general title *Les Maîtres de la Pensée Scientifique*. For Descartes, consult the references given in Chapter 7. On Abraham Trembley, see J. R. Baker's interesting biography, (Edward Arnold, 1952). The best recent discussion of Julien de la Mettrie, including his relations with Haller, is:

A. Vartanian, *La Mettrie's 'L'Homme Machine'*, Oxford University Press, 1960

For the period of 'vital principle', little historical analysis has yet been published. Admirable (and slightly sceptical) surveys were published at the time in:

J. C. Pritchard, *A Review of the Doctrine of the Vital Principle* (1829)

J. Bostock, *An Elementary System of Physiology* Baldwin & Cradock (esp. 3rd edition, 1876, pp. 402–5)

See also the commentary by J. Palmer in his edition of *The Works of John Hunter*, London, 1835–7

Recent discussion of the methodological issues culminating in the work of Bernard are:

G. J. Goodfield, *The Growth of Scientific Physiology*, Hutchinson, 1960

W. P. D. Wightman, *The Emergence of General Physiology*, M. Boyd, 1956

The physiological section (Part II) of Liebig's *Animal Chemistry* (London, 1842) is fascinating, though no modern edition exists. Fortunately, there is a modern paper-back edition of:

Claude Bernard, *An Introduction to the Study of Experimental Medicine*, Henry Schuman, 1949

On Claude Bernard, see also:

J. M. D. Olmsted, *François Magendie; Claude Bernard, Physiologist*, Cassell, 1939; and (with E. H. Olmsted) *Claude Bernard and the Experimental Method in Medicine*, Henry Schuman, 1962

Max Black, 'The Definition of Scientific Method' (in *Science and Civilization*, ed. R. C. Stauffer)

On Louis Pasteur, see the biography by René Dubos (Gollancz, 1951). The common exaggeration of Wöhler's work as fatal to traditional theories of vitality is exploded by D. McKie in his article, 'Wöhler's Synthetic Urea and the Rejection of Vitalism', *Nature*, Vol. 153 (1944), p. 609; but its ghost is unfortunately still abroad!

15

Living Units

DISCOVERY in science is a threefold process. If we simply observe objects of a novel kind, that is not a scientific discovery – though it may be the prelude to one. If we simply conceive some new idea, or envisage a theoretical possibility hitherto unrecognized, that is not a scientific discovery either – though once again it may be the first step towards one. In each case it is necessary to go beyond the first observation or idea to a point at which experience and theory are brought together. For it is their union which both justifies our ideas and shows the significance of our observations.

This triple step may take only two years to complete: the positron (as we saw) was conceived in 1929, observed in 1931, and recognized almost at once. It may take more than two thousand years: the idea of atoms, already in circulation by 400 B.C., found an established place in science only after A.D. 1800. In the case of the unit of living matter, it took two hundred years. The first cells were seen under the microscope, named and described in the 1660s. But it was only around 1860 that the relation of the cell to the living organism was properly understood, and it has taken another hundred years to reach the present standpoint, from which one can actually identify the individual chemical transactions over which the sub-cellular components preside.

Throughout these three centuries, our intellectual command over the fine structure of matter (whether living or non-living) has at every stage been limited by the tools at our disposal – both our laboratory instruments and our intellectual ones. It was the invention of the magnifying-glass in the seventeenth century that first drew men's attention to the presence of cellular structures in living beings; though at the time this observation could have no fundamental significance for physiology. By the time the general theory of matter had acquired a certain precision, it was time to improve the optical instruments also: Dalton's chemistry and the compound microscope were equally indispensable for the establishment of the cell-theory proper. The same twin advance, in laboratory tools and theoretical concepts, has once again been equally important in the last hundred years, during which cytologists, geneticists, and biochemists have carried their study of the cell right down to the molecular level. Thus the evolution of cell-theory has taken men twice in succession through the complete cycle of scientific discovery – from novel observations and ideas to deeper understanding.

The World of the Magnifying-Glass

In 1664, John Evelyn published his *Sylva*, and included a brief description by his colleague 'Mr Hook' of the microscopical appearance of petrified wood. This author was the same Robert Hooke that we have already met: Newton's irascible adversary and Boyle's ingenious assistant. In the following year, Hooke published a more elaborate account of his observations in his *Micrographia* (Plate 10a), and described the fine structure of cork and charcoal:

an infinite company of exceedingly-small, and very regular pores, so thick and so orderly set, and so close to one another, that they leave very little room or space between them to be fill'd with a solid body, for the apparent *interstitia*, or separating sides of these pores seem so thin in some places, that the texture of a Honey-comb cannot be more porous.

In these reports, we meet the first clear reference to the objects we call *cells*: for these 'pores or cells', which Hooke compared to the cells of a honeycomb, were indeed the empty husks of genuine plant-cells, separated (as is usual in vegetable matter) by permanent solid walls of 'cellulose'.

Hooke's microscopical observations were directed by no particular theoretical ideas, beyond a natural and proper curiosity about the minute world which his new instrument had opened to enquiry. Nor was there very much about this charcoal honeycomb to capture men's imaginations: they were much more diverted by the grotesque structure and antics of fleas. Samuel Pepys, for instance, bought from 'Reeves, the perspective glass-maker' one of his 'very excellent microscopes, which did discover a louse or a mite most perfectly and largely'. And from the 1660s on, the microscope became the wonder of the age and the plaything of drawing-rooms, as the telescope had been half a century earlier.

The world it revealed was even more surprising than the cosmos which Galileo had discovered beyond the confines of the heavenly vault. For what Galileo saw, lying between the visible stars, was at any rate *more stars* – heavenly bodies like those already visible to the naked eye, only fainter. But the world of the microscope was entirely new and unsuspected:

Little eels or worms [as Leeuwenhoek reported, in his description of protozoa] lying all huddled up together and wriggling; just as if you saw, with the naked eye, a whole tubful of very little eels and water, with the little eels a-squirming among one another: and the whole water seemed to be alive with these multifarious animalcules.

So, whereas Galileo could at once bring the evidence of the telescope to bear on fundamental questions of astronomical theory, the microscope only confused people, and there were as yet no serious questions on which its testimony could throw light. In short, men were intellectually unprepared for it, and there was little they could do but exclaim – either wonderingly or scornfully.

Edward Young found the world of the microscope admirable, even though mysterious:

> Glasses, (that revelation to the sight!)
> Have they not let us see in the disclose
> Of fine-spun Nature, exquisitely small,
> And though demonstrated, still ill-conceived?

Samuel Butler, on the other hand, laughed at the *virtuosi* of the Royal Society for their curiosity to know

> How many different Specieses
> Of Maggots breed in rotten Cheeses;
> And which are next of kin to those
> Ingender'd in a Chandler's nose;
> Or those not seen, but understood,
> That live in Vinegar and Wood.

Even Alexander Pope argued that man's proper task was to come to terms with the world at his own level –

> Thro' worlds unnumbered though the God be known
> 'Tis ours to trace Him only in our own.

If there had been any advantage to man in peering at the more minute details of the world, Providence would surely have equipped him with sense-organs of higher discrimination –

> Why has not Man a microscopic eye?
> For this plain reason, man is not a Fly.
> Say, what the use, were finer Optics giv'n
> To inspect a mite, not comprehend the heav'n?

The hardest thing of all was to keep the products of microscopic enquiry in a proper intellectual proportion, and see them in true relation to ourselves and the world in which we live. The inclination, rather, was to see down the microscope a kind of 'looking-glass world', differing from our own in nothing but scale, and having perhaps in its own interstices another, even more minute, sub-microscopic world. Jonathan Swift seized on the popular image as a simile for the hierarchy of poets and critics, each grade more petty and niggling than those above:

> So, Nat'ralists observe, a Flea,
> Hath smaller Fleas that on him prey,
> And these have smaller Fleas to bite 'em,
> And so proceed *ad infinitum*:
> Thus ev'ry Poet in his Kind,
> Is bit by him that comes behind.

And in *Gulliver's Travels* he contrived fables in which the worlds of the microscope and the telescope were brought to life. Men and women were shown living, at a different scale of dimension, lives which were recognizable slight caricatures of normal human lives.

For lack of any serious theoretical motive, the first enthusiasm for microscopical investigations soon flagged. In 1692, indeed, Hooke reported to the Royal Society that the art was 'now reduced almost to a single votary, which is Mr Leeuwenhoek; besides whom, I hear of none that make any other use of that instrument, but for diversion and pastime'. Almost alone amongst early eighteenth-century philosophers, one finds George Berkeley, the future bishop, trying in his student days to square the new 'differential calculus' with the revelations of the microscope. Like the positivists of a later age, he was convinced that we should admit into our theories only objects which could be perceived and propositions which could be verified by sense-observation: he would happily have forbidden mathematicians to speak about 'points' smaller than could be detected by the senses – 'therefore no Reasoning about Infinitesimals'. And this was where the microscope posed a problem. If living things (e.g. cheese-mites) existed even at the limits of vision, what fineness of discrimination must one suppose *their* senses to possess? And if one could not determine the 'minimum sensible distance' which was to serve as the smallest meaningful unit of length, what meaning could then be attached to the mathematicians' *point*? It was all very perplexing.

The Background to the Cell-Theory

In due course, 'cells' were to figure as largely in the physiologist's picture of living things as 'atoms' did in the classical chemist's picture of inert ones. But a cell-theory which was capable of serving physiology in this way took shape only slowly. For there were a number of independent aspects to the idea, which developed separately and had to be brought together. Cells, as we think of them today, are the 'units of life' in several senses. In the first place, they are the *visible* units, which enter into the structure of all living things: minute bodies having the consistency of jelly, composed largely of a translucent substance enclosed by a membrane, and – apart from the opaque spot or 'nucleus' – presenting a clearly apparent internal structure only under the electron microscope. (See Plate 13.) Secondly they are *working* units: capable of sustaining their own life independently, if dissected out undamaged and 'cultured' in a suitable broth, but normally acting within the body as the 'retorts', in which all the biochemical reactions involved in respiration and assimilation take place. Finally, they are the units of *growth*: living things develop by the self-multiplication of cells, which expand and divide, expand and divide, throughout their lives, in an unending rhythmical sequence.

Before the cell-theory could take anything like its current shape, all these different ideas had to be formulated and combined. Moreover they had to be harmonized not only among themselves, but also with ideas in other relevant branches of science: particularly the theories of the new chemistry. The critical years in this intellectual process were those around 1860. Before then, one finds skilful microscopic observations, fascinating theoretical debates and even (by 1840) doctrines which took men a good half-way towards the modern cell-theory. But the threads were finally drawn together only between 1857 and 1861, through the work of Remak, Leydig, and, above all, Virchow.

At the outset, the evidence of the magnifying-glass sent men off on a very different tack. Hooke and Grew began by observing plant-cells, and this fact did something to direct men's thoughts about living matter during the next century and a half. For plant-cells, like prison-cells and the cells of a honeycomb, are enclosed by *walls*; and for a long time men's attention was focused on these walls, rather than on what they contained. Yet, from a physiological point of view, not all true cells by any means possess such walls, and when cell-walls are formed they constitute only the anatomical husk of a living organism: the fibrous stems of umbelliferous plants, and the bony skeletons of animals, can preserve the shape of the living creature long after active cellular life – in fact, all trace of 'cells', in our sense of the term – has entirely disappeared. So, though Hooke might allude in passing to 'the natural or innate juices' which filled the honeycomb structure of living plants, he could not guess at the vital complexities concealed in this seemingly formless fluid.

Before 1700 there had been found the first traces of what we now recognize as authentic cell-structure in animals also. Malpighi not only saw for himself the hypothetical capillaries of Harvey's blood-circulation: he also watched the blood-corpuscles passing through them. Leeuwenhoek meanwhile discovered spermatozoa in the semen from several animal species, and Swammerdam apparently glimpsed the early stages of cleavage in the fertilized egg. But, for lack of any general physiological doctrine into which these observations would fit, no one could know what to make of them – still less put our interpretation on them. Eighteenth-century physiologists, indeed, tended more and more to employ a conception of living matter quite contrary to our own. Whereas Nathaniel Grew began by thinking of plant-cells as little 'bladders' full of fluid, he later changed his analogy for another, with very different implications – speaking of plant-structure as a fine fabric or tissue, like extremely minute lace (Plate 10b). This second analogy retained its intellectual power, and for many years men continued to regard the living flesh as – quite literally – an assemblage of 'tissues': a wonderful inter-weaving of 'fibres', cohering like a well-woven carpet in the form of the living body. This interpretation actually gained strength as time went on, since it fitted in so well with Haller's discoveries about muscle-fibres, and right up to the 1800s it kept alive a picture which survives now only in dead metaphors. Haller was quite forthright about fibres being the units of living matter: 'The *fibre*', he declared, 'is for the physiologist what the *line* is for the geometer'.

Against this background, microscopists might observe skilfully and scrupulously, but they could scarcely do so perceptively. In

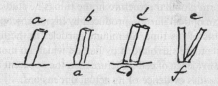

1765, for instance, Abraham Trembley drew the above sketch of the diatom *Synedra* dividing. He recognized the process as a form of reproduction, but he mistook these microscopic plants for animals and was unable to exploit the observation: he could not know that he had been the first man to depict the process of cell-division. In 1781, Fontana referred in passing to the 'minute spherical bodies' (apparently cell-nuclei) which he had observed in the skin of eels; but he was too intent on establishing that the ultimate fibres of the bodily tissues were certain 'primitive twisted cylinders' to reflect further on these observations. (Leeuwenhoek, too, had seen nuclei in the blood-corpuscles of fishes.) It was 1833 before Robert Brown, who was probably the first microscopist to equal Leeuwenhoek in accuracy of observation and perceptiveness, could establish the idea that the structural units of plants were *cells* containing *nuclei*. And this was as far as anyone could get, while using the simple magnifying glass alone.

Meanwhile, those who theorized about the structure of living organisms on the basis of what they saw down microscopes were at the mercy of their instruments. From 1824 on, Dutrochet was arguing that living matter is an agglomeration of globular, vesicular (bladder-like) corpuscles; and this 'globulist' doctrine looks at first like a brilliant anticipation of the cell-theory. But when one scrutinizes more carefully the evidence advanced for globulism, second thoughts are necessary. For Dutrochet relied heavily on the observations of the microscopist Milne-Edwards, and so over-reached himself: although some of the corpuscles or 'vesicles' which the two men acclaimed as elementary globules may well have been true cells, many of them certainly were not. The suspicious thing about Milne-Edwards's observations was the very *uniformity* in the sizes of the globules he described. All of them, he said, were spheres 1/300 of a millimetre in diameter, and this uniform globular structure in the things he studied was very possibly an optical illusion produced by his microscope. With the instruments of his time, all minute particles in the field of view were liable to be surrounded by haloes, which no more provided authentic evidence of cell-structure than the apparent diameter of a star provides evidence of its actual dimensions.

Microscopes being what they were around 1800, Bichat dismissed them as being of little use to physiologists and anatomists – 'since, when one gazes into the darkness, everyone sees in his own way and is affected accordingly'. Bichat's opinion was widely shared, and its effects were lasting: in 1829 his pupil, de Blainville, was still declaring:

The microscope teaches nothing new about the anatomical structure of cellular tissue. It creates the impression – in between the anatomical elements which make up this tissue, through all their junctions and their frequent openings – of parts so extremely minute ... that many observers took them for *globules*; and that, the more easily, because they liked to see globular shapes everywhere – being so preoccupied with the sort of false theories to which the microscope easily lends the support of its illusions.

In any case, Bichat and his followers had no theoretical motive for taking microscopy seriously. They continued to regard living matter as consisting primarily of fibres, as in those parts of the body which are still called 'fibrous connective tissues'; and, when they referred to the bodily tissues as 'cellular', they used that word in a way which looked back to Hooke and Grew, rather than ahead to Schwann and Virchow. The woven textile making up the human fabric was 'cellular' in the same way as the material of cellular blankets – it was an openwork fabric of fibres enclosing pores or cavities. Vitality lay for them (as for Haller) in the fibres: the contents of the cavities were of secondary interest.

While microscopes still could not display objects as small as most animal-cells, the debate about the 'units of life' had to be carried on largely at a theoretical level. During the eighteenth century this topic was treated by most scientists as part of a larger, more profound and ancient theoretical problem: that of generation and development. The argument turned chiefly on the question whether all the parts of an adult organism are predetermined already existing in miniature in the seed and the embryo (the doctrine of preformation), or whether they come into existence only as the embryo grows, one after another (the doctrine of epigenesis). Harvey had firmly held to the latter view, but the invention of the magnifying-glass caused many people to think again. With its help, Marcello Malpighi and Henry Power repeated Aristotle's classic studies on the development of the chick, and were struck by the variety of rudimentary organs which at once became visible. Power declared:

So admirable is every Organ of this Machine of ours framed, that every part within us is entirely made, when the whole Organ seems too little to have any parts at all.

Leeuwenhoek speculated that a human spermatozoon might be a man in miniature – a *homunculus*. As for Swammerdam, he carried this new idea right up to – and beyond – its logical conclusion, by comparing the chicken in an egg with the butterfly in a cocoon: the whole of living Nature consisted of eggs, within eggs, within eggs:

In nature there is no generation but only propagation, the growth of parts. Thus original sin is explained, for all men were contained in the organs of Adam and Eve. When their stock of eggs is finished, the human race will cease to be.

In the eighteenth century both parties to the resulting debate appealed to the evidence of the microscope in support of their views, and threw out speculations which were taken up again as the cell-theory developed. Trembley's friend, Charles Bonnet, did not assert dogmatically that all of an organism's parts were already *preformed* in the seed; but he did insist that the whole form of the adult creature must somehow be *predetermined* in the simpler embryo.

By the word *germ*, I understand in general any *preordination* or *preformation* of parts capable of determining the existence of a plant or animal. I will not assert that the swellings from which arise the buds of a branched polyp were themselves [already] miniature polyps concealed beneath the mother's skin; but I will assert that there exists in the mother's skin certain particles [as it were, *genes*] so organized beforehand that from their development there results a little polyp.

Meanwhile, the leading advocate of epigenesis, C. F. Wolff, put forward a theory of development echoing Grew's first idea, that plants are composed entirely of bladders or 'vesicles'. These vesicles multiplied like soap-bubbles, out of a primary homogeneous fluid: growth took place by the formation of further similar units in the form of spherical cavities, between and alongside existing bladders.

All the parts of a plant in its earliest stages consist of a glassy clear homogenous substance containing no trace of vesicles. . . . One can compress the vesicles without injuring them. One can open them, the liquid runs out, the bladders collapse and disappear. They are merely small cavities in the solid vegetable substance, joined together in different ways. One should better call them pores or cells. . . .
The firm, soft substance which fills the interstices between the bladders is dilated into a bladder by the liquid which it contains. Leaves grow by the interstitial development of new vesicles between the old ones, as well as by the expansion of the [existing] vesicles.

The eighteenth-century antithesis between preformation and epigenesis was in fact too sharp. Embryology profited by following up Wolff's ideas since, at and above the cellular level, embryos unquestionably get more complex as they develop. But this development is nevertheless largely pre-ordained. The fluid in Wolff's vesicles (or 'plant-cells') concealed within them the hereditary 'particles' of whose existence Bonnet was convinced on purely theoretical grounds. Yet the picture of organic structure as built up from certain primitive spherical bladders kept its influence, and was the ancestor at a remove of Schleiden's cell-theory. The intermediary was Lorenz Oken, who wrote (in 1805) that 'all higher animals must be made up out of constituent animalcules', similar to Leeuwenhoek's protozoa. He described these animalcules as multiplying out of an *Urschleim* (primary mucus):

The primitive mucous vesicle is called an *infusorium*. Every organism is a synthesis out of infusoria. Organic development consists of nothing but the accumulation of an unlimited number of mucous particles or infusoria. Thus, in the most minute of beings, organisms are not completely and in every respect prefigured: they are not preformed. It is merely that the infusorial vesicles behave differently when they are combined in different ways, and go to compose higher organisms.

So spontaneous generation was *possible*, though only at the fundamental level of the unit-infusoria themselves:

Consequently, no organism is ever *created* larger than a single infusorial particle: no organism is created or ever has been created which is other than microscopic. Everything larger has not been created, but is the product of development. Man has not been created but has developed.

Throughout the period from 1660 to 1830, the gulf between observations and theory remained unbridged. The point was never reached at which the results of microscopic study could be brought to bear *conclusively* on the theoretical questions that men were asking. For the full significance of even the most brilliant observations was not apparent until men came to them with the right questions; and the most far-sighted theoretical anticipations remained unconvincing, since the evidence to support them was either lacking or unrecognized.

The Emergence of the Cell-Theory

Between 1830 and 1860, the whole cellular picture of organic structure acquired a sharp focus. The process began with the work of the botanist, Robert Brown, even before satisfactory compound microscopes had come into general use. But, before any major intellectual advance was possible, it was essential to study the smaller cells of animals with the same exactness that Brown had brought to plant-cells.

Early attempts to increase the power of microscopes by using more than one lens had been frustrated chiefly by 'chromatic aberration': the refractive properties of the lenses employed varied so much from colour to colour that at high magnification the whole picture turned into an unintelligible blur of overlapping coloured fringes. The first compound microscopes to be tolerably 'achromatic' overcame this difficulty by using matched pairs of lenses made from different kinds of glass, whose aberrations – so far as possible – cancelled each other out. These achromatic microscopes first became available in the 1830s. These instruments were not markedly more discriminating than Leeuwenhoek's best single lenses, but they were much easier to use and were marketed in substantial numbers. The fresh wave of microscopic investigations which followed soon produced intellectual results.

Before the speculative theories of Oken and Dutrochet could be transformed into the fully-fledged cell-theory, three distinct steps were required. The existence of cells, as the material constituents of animals and vegetables alike, had to be asserted and demonstrated. The three essential components of cells – the membrane, the nucleus, and the intervening cytoplasm – had to be identified and recognized in a sufficiently wide range of instances. And the 'genealogy', or mode of production by which new cells were formed, had to be discovered. It was 1858 before all three steps had been taken.

The observations of Robert Brown in England and Turpin in France were generalized by the German botanist Schleiden, who asserted in 1838 that *all* plant-tissues were composed of 'nucleated cells', whose multiplication and development were responsible for growth and reproduction. His colleague Schwann at once extended the doctrine to animals: using the new compound microscope, he demonstrated very strikingly that nucleated cells are also to be found in the embryonic backbones of tadpoles and young fishes. Their structure and composition were, in fact, remarkably similar to those of plant-tissue, and Schwann felt that he could consequently 'prove the most intimate connexion of the two kingdoms of organic matter, from the similarity in the laws of development of [their] elementary parts'. From the spinal cord he turned his attention to cartilage, and from there to the tissues of other animal organs. In every case, he concluded, the basis of organic development was the proliferation of cells:

The foundation of all organic tissues, however different they may be, is a common principle of development – namely, the formation of *cells*. Nature never fits molecules together directly to form a fibre, a duct, and so on: rather, she forms always a spherical cell, and subsequently transforms this cell, if need be, into the different elementary formations such as one finds in the adult state.

There were accordingly two separate groups of questions: one was concerned with the processes by which cells were originally created (these he called 'plastic' phenomena); the other with the chemical processes within and around the cells, by which the life of the organism was maintained (for these he introduced the name of 'metabolic' phenomena). In this distinction, both the strength and the weakness of Schwann's point of view were enshrined. To his credit, he treated the cell, not just as an anatomical 'brick', but as a functioning unit whose internal processes were of central relevance to physiology. For instance, he located the respiratory 'combustion', by which animal heat was generated, squarely within the cell itself:

Oxygen, or carbonic acid, in a gaseous form or lightly confined, is essentially necessary to the metabolic phenomena of the cells. The oxygen disappears and carbonic acid is formed, or vice versa, carbonic acid disappears, and oxygen is formed. The universality of respiration is based entirely upon this fundamental condition to the metabolic phenomena of the cells.

Schwann's conception of *metabolism* has won an enduring place in physiology. On the other side of the ledger, his conclusions about cell-creation have had to be entirely rejected. When he spoke of Nature 'fitting molecules together' to form cells, which in turn 'form a fibre, a duct, and so on', this was no mere manner of speaking. He firmly believed that the unit-cells of organisms were formed directly from free molecules. Fresh cells proliferated like crystals in the surrounding medium, and attached themselves to the existing core of cells:

The process of formation of elementary cells takes place in broad outline according to the same laws in all tissues. The subsequent development and transformation of the cells differ between different tissues. The fundamental phenomenon involving cells is the following: to begin with, there exists a substance devoid of structure [cytoblastema], which can exist either within the cells already present, or outside them. In this substance are formed first cellular nuclei, i.e. corpuscles having a round or oval, spherical or flattened, shape and generally containing also one or two dark spots [nuclear corpuscles or *nucleoli*]. Cells take shape around these nuclei in such a way as initially to enclose them very tightly. The cells expand by growth, i.e. by drawing the surrounding substance into themselves, and this phenomenon also takes place often within the cellular nucleus for a certain time. When the cells have reached a certain degree of development, the nucleus generally disappears.

One law governs the place of formation of new cells within existing tissues: they always form in places where the nutrient liquid directly penetrates into the tissue. Accordingly, new cells form in the unorganized [parts of the] tissue solely where they are in contact with organized material. In completely organized tissues, having a complete blood distribution, this formation takes place throughout the thickness of the tissue.

Schwann pursued to great lengths the analogy between cell-formation and *crystallization*. He considered that, if only a mechanism could be found by which a crystalline structure might imbibe a fluid as it formed, the ordinary laws of physics and chemistry should then explain directly the generation of cells out of a cell-free fluid. And it is some indication of the difficulty of microscopy, at the cellular level, that Schleiden and Schwann not only continued to believe in 'free cell-formation', but were convinced that they had seen it taking place under their eyes, just as Schwann described it.

The truth of the matter took some time to establish, and it was curiously unlike what most physiologists at that time had expected. To begin with, the chief difference of opinion was between those who supposed that the nuclei of fresh cells formed like embryos within the fluid of existing 'mother' cells, and those who believed (with Schwann) that they formed in the liquid medium alongside and between the cells. Neither opinion was to prove of lasting value. The actual process of *cell-division*, by which an existing cell splits into two equal halves, was first fully described in 1841 by Remak, who followed the stages of division in the blood-corpuscles of a chick-embryo. Between 1841 and 1858 he continued his investigations with great persistence and care, and succeeded in demonstrating convincingly the typical stages by which one cell splits into two successor-cells of roughly equal size.

For all its merits, Schleiden's and Schwann's original cell-theory had one further weakness. Having originated in botany rather than zoology, it continued to place undue importance on the wall surrounding the cell. The nucleus was treated as a temporary feature, which had a part to play only during the formation of the cell-wall, and the theory effectively ignored the remaining (apparently fluid) contents of the cell – i.e. the cytoplasm. Yet the connexion between the cellulose fibres of a plant-stem and the living cells whose activity creates them is scarcely stronger than that between the wax hexagons of a honeycomb and the bees which manufacture them; and the *functional* units, in vegetable and animal organisms alike, are not the 'hexagons' but the 'bees'. In animal tissues, indeed, the membranes of adjoining cells commonly jostle against one another directly, or are actually shared, without there being any dividing-wall. So what unites animals and plants is not a common anatomical structure, but a common *physiological* unit: plant-cells resembling bees in a honeycomb, animal-cells bees in a swarm. And, until microscopists had shifted their attention from the 'comb' to the 'bees' (as it were), Schwann's original insight could not be properly followed up.

At this point the third outstanding question became important: what are the indispensable elements of cell-structure? Schwann had supposed that, as a general rule, the nucleus disappeared once the cell-wall had been properly formed. This may well happen in a plant-stem, where cellular activity is no longer required in order to maintain the structure. In animal-cells, too, the nucleus is more compact and clearly visible just before and after cell-division, and becomes more diffuse and hazy during the intervening, or resting, period. But, in the years after 1840, Remak showed that these appearances are misleading. The nucleus is a permanent feature of every live and functioning cell, and persists even through the process of division: indeed, the nucleus itself splits *before* the rest of the cell, division apparently beginning at the 'nucleoli' (the 'nuclear corpuscles' which Schwann had noticed) and spreading outwards through the rest of the nucleus into the surrounding cytoplasm, to affect the membrane around the cell last of all.

The second essential feature of the cell was – not the wall – but this enclosing membrane. To begin with, it had been overlooked – not surprisingly since, in plant cells, it cannot at first sight be distinguished from the cellulose wall. During the 1840s and '50s, however, those microscopists who were looking for the common structure linking plant and animals cells gradually turned away from the distracting wall: after all, there was nothing in animals corresponding to it, apart from the calcium deposit surrounding bone-cells. In its place they recognized the existence of a more flexible enclosing membrane which marked the true line of division between one cell and the next.

But what about the substance between the nucleus and the enclosing membrane? Here, Oken's ideas still remained influential. His speculations about a 'primary mucus', from which the constituent micro-organisms of living matter were formed, had survived in Schleiden's and Schwann's 'cytoblastema': 'that viscous fluid' (as von Mohl put it in 1845) which

precedes the first solid structures that indicate the future cells [and] furnishes the material from which the nucleus and the primordial [enclosing] sac are formed.

As a name for this fluid, von Mohl introduced the term 'protoplasma', and the word caught on. Remak used it in 1852 as a name for everything within the cell-membrane other than the nucleus – though without implying any support for Schwann's theory of cell-formation. Used in this non-committal way, the term was equivalent to our own current term 'cytoplasm'; but among the general public a more fanciful conception of *protoplasm* became popular. And the vision of a universal 'living jelly' retained an appeal for men at large long after its utility to physiology had been exhausted. Something about Schwann's picture of living things crystallizing out of a formless but dynamic life-fluid had captured the popular imagination. Here, it seemed, the microscope had revealed the common substance of all living things, and the material bond uniting all the offshoots of Darwin's evolutionary family tree. For those who cared to see it that way, it was as though the 'vital principle' had proved, after all, to be only a special kind of material substance. Through T. H. Huxley's famous lecture on *The Physical Basis of Life* (1868) the word 'protoplasm' became more than ever a popular catchword – finally achieving immortality in the libretto of Gilbert and Sullivan's *The Mikado*: 'I can trace my ancestry back', announced Pooh-Bah, 'to a protoplasmal primordial atomic globule'.

Meanwhile, the physiologists' own picture of the cell was rapidly taking final shape, and this picture dispensed with any primary mucus or cytoblastema. The crucial four years began in 1857. First Leydig gave his classic description of the structure of the cell, and this shows how much ground had been covered in the nineteen years since Schwann and Schleiden published their theories:

For the idea of a morphological [i.e. structural] cell one requires a more or less soft substance, primitively approaching a sphere in shape, and containing a central body called a kernel [nucleus]. The cell-substance often hardens to a more or less independent boundary-layer or membrane, and the cell then resolves itself, according to the terminology of scholars, into *membrane, cell-contents* and *kernel*.

In the next year, the German pathologist Rudolf Virchow published a treatise on cellular pathology which gained wide circulation. In this, he stated the fundamental doctrines of the cell-theory in the form which they have taken ever since, and showed the wide implication which these doctrines could have both for science and for medicine. Virchow was a man of great versatility – a pioneer anthropologist, a biochemist, and one of the leading liberal statesmen in Germany during the Bismarck régime. In

1845, during his pathological work, he discovered leukaemia – a cancerous condition in the cells of the bone-marrow – and from this time on he was more and more convinced that the chief seat of disease lay within the cells themselves. His intimate acquaintance with the condition of cells 'in sickness and in health' led him to the conclusion that pathology must be primarily a study of cell-changes.

According to Virchow, Schwann had been absolutely right to regard cells as the universal units of all living matter; but he had been equally mistaken in supposing that cells can form out of a structureless fluid. The process of division, as described by Remak, was the *only* process by which new cells were formed. The principal novelty in Virchow's account was his emphasis on this central doctrine, which he expressed in a Latin motto. Recalling William Harvey's embryological doctrine, *Omne Vivum ex Ovo* – 'Every living creature comes from an egg' – Virchow now declared: *Omnis Cellula e Cellula.* Cells were formed only by the division of pre-existing cells, and not from any more fundamental cell-free substance.

Virchow's doctrine was to become a fundamental axiom of cell-theory, and its statement ends the first half of our present story. It had important theoretical repercussions, and these we must consider briefly. For the fully-fledged cell-theory was a landmark in the development of matter-theory, in a very precise sense. It placed a sharp and definite boundary between the realms of the 'living' and 'non-living', just where the frontier between them had been most unclear.

The success of the theory was, in fact, due to this very sharp distinction. Virchow had finally equated the metabolic units of living matter with the developmental units revealed by Remak's work. He had shown that the organism could be regarded as 'a society of living cells', and that disease represented in most cases a disturbance in the metabolism of the cells.

What the astronomer achieves in universal space with his telescope, this and even more the biologist achieves in the restricted space of the organism with the help of his microscope. The cells are his stars, and I hope that the time will come when the discovery of a new kind of cell will seem just as important as a new addition to the great number of tiny planets – perhaps even more important.

Most significantly, he had insisted that the objects of the material world fell into two mutually-exclusive categories – cellular organisms, and non-cellular 'non-organisms'. Cellular organisms were never formed except by the division and multiplication of cells originating in *other* cellular organisms.

The point is worth emphasizing. As early as 1668 the Italian biologist Redi had reported experiments in which the traditional belief that insects generated 'spontaneously' in decaying flesh was refuted by placing dead snakes, fish and meat in two similar sets of jars, one of which was sealed and the other left open: maggots and flies appeared only in the open jars, where eggs could be laid. (Pasteur's own experiments to disprove the doctrine of spontaneous generation, using flasks of sterile broth, were simply a refinement on Redi's.) The trouble was that the doctrine would not stay refuted. So long as now more fundamental – and theoretical – reason appeared for ruling it out, the hope naturally kept reviving that *at some level or other* the creation of life would turn out to be a continuing process: primitive organisms of a sufficiently lowly grade coming into existence directly from inorganic raw material. Now at last the door could be closed. The experiments of Pasteur and Mitscherlisch on fermentation and putrefaction were given a secure theoretical foundation. If living things were built up out of cells, and cells were produced only by division of existing cells, then no organisms *of any kind* could be formed from inorganic materials, without the intervention of some other 'parent' organism. As Virchow put it, in 1895:

Thus was *generatio aequivoca* [i.e. spontaneous generation] eliminated from the interpretation of living things at the present time. I say expressly 'living things at the present time', for the question of the primal origin of organic beings in the developmental history of the earth has not been answered.

The deeper question, about the historical origin of life, remains unanswered today; though the evidence which will eventually help to establish an answer is beginning to accumulate. Still, even without facing that deeper question directly, the point which Virchow had established was sufficiently profound and important. So, by the 1870s, it was widely accepted among biologists that the rule *Omnis Cellula e Cellula* had held good for as far back as historical and zoological researches revealed, and that – whatever mechanism (or non-mechanical intervention) originally produced life on this earth – no such agency was still at work.

It followed that the biochemists' hopes of revealing the chemical basis of life had to be deferred yet again. So long as one could still imagine primitive infusoria or cell-walls taking shape directly out of inorganic nutrients, the boundary between homogeneous inorganic substances and organized beings remained indefinite – and one might still dream of explaining it away. But, so far as concerned events on the cellular level and all larger-scale processes, this dream was now finally shattered. From 1860 on, there was a new and imperative motive for studying the component parts and internal structures of cells. Since the hoped-for reunion of physiology and molecular chemistry had failed to take place at the point where Schwann had expected (the crystallizing-out of the cells), one must suppose that it would eventually take place at some far finer level – if at all. Once more the fundamental problems of biochemistry had disappeared into the minute recesses of the cell; and that is where scientists during the hundred years since Virchow's classic thesis have been obliged to pursue them.

For the moment, physiology and pathology have been provided with 'living atoms' of their own. And these new units, in Virchow's eyes, could redress the philosophical balance upset by the inert, immutable particles of Newton's physics and Dalton's chemistry. If Goethe and Schiller had been moved to protest at Newton's devitalization of the natural world, that (Virchow said) was understandable:

Should we fill the whole of nature with individuality? Have the sun, the planets, the air and the sea, have stones and crystals, a claim to individuality? Many a modern philosopher and many a living scientist would answer Yes. Antiquity was universally of the same view, and even filled the whole of nature with its gods.

In the wake of Newton's all-conquering theory of mechanics, this heart-warming picture of Nature had seemingly crumbled away. Schiller had recorded, in his poem *The Gods of Greece* (which Virchow now quoted), the sad contrast between the ancient vision of Nature and the lifeless mechanism of post-Newtonian cosmology:

> Where now, our scientists declare,
> Only a soul-less fireball spins,
> Helios formerly, in tranquil majesty
> Steered his golden chariot.

> All those heights were filled with oreads
>   [mountain nymphs]
> A dryad lived in every tree,
> Out of every vase of lovely naiads
> Gushed the silver-foaming stream.

> Ah! From all that warm and living vision,
> Only the shadow remains behind today. . . .
> Like the dead strokes of a pendulum-clock,
> Nature, bereft of all her Divinities,
> Slavishly serves the Law of Gravitation.

But physiology could now undo the damage to our world-picture earlier wrought by dynamics and astronomy. The discovery that all living individuals were composed of *cells* – units so contrary in all their properties to the lifeless chaotic atoms of Demokritos – could restore our deep faith that Nature was not essentially inert and mechanical, but had about her something creative, something fruitful.

If this were properly understood, Virchow argued, then one could see how needless Goethe's fears and suspicions about the analytic methods of science had been; and it is good to find the German physiologist answering so ably the doubts and scruples of the German poet.

It is not so easy for the investigator to grasp the unity [of the individual organism, for this] rests on the commonwealth of its parts. . . ` How long is the way and how many illusions it offers! We seek unity, and find multiplicity; the organic structure disintegrates and crumbles in our hands, and in the end only the atoms remain. Is this really the right path to an understanding of the individual? Can we seek for a science of life only where death is to be found? Is this wholly disintegrative science of nature nothing other than a will-o'-the-wisp, and is it not truly high time we turned aside to follow other paths?

If only there were others! But we have no choice! There is only one path of investigation, and that is the path of observation, dissection and analysis, whether carried out on bodies or on ideas. Admittedly, the scientific investigator can no more reassemble a plant or animal body, once he has taken it apart, than a boy can reconstruct a watch on which his youthful spirit of curiosity has exercised itself. But Nature is fruitful. Therefore let us go forward, for only from the parts can the Whole be understood!

FURTHER READING AND REFERENCES

In addition to the general references given at the end of chapter 14, there are interesting surveys of the development of the cell-theory by M. Klein in the Hermann series, 'Actualités Scientifiques et Industrielles', and by J. R. Baker in the *Quarterly Journal of Microscopical Science*, starting in 1948. (Klein's brief monograph stops at 1860: Baker's admirable series of articles – to our loss, still unfinished – will deal with all major aspects of the theory, up to and into the twentieth century.) An excellent recent account of the whole development, to which the reader can turn with confidence, is:

A. Hughes, *A History of Cytology*, Abelard-Schuman, 1959

The subject will also be covered in the general survey of nineteenth-century biology by E. Mendelssohn (in preparation).

On the seventeenth-century microscopists, and their wider influence, see:

Margaret 'Espinasse, *Robert Hooke*, Heinemann, 1956

C. Dobell, *Anthony van Leeuwenhoek and his Little Animals*, J. Bale, 1932

Dorothy Stimson, *Scientists and Amateurs*, Schuman, 1948

Marjorie Nicolson, *Science and Imagination*, Great Seal Books, 1956

There is great fascination to be had from the original works of the early microscopists themselves: Hooke's *Micrographia* (London, 1665), Grew's *Anatomy of Vegetables* (London, 1672), and *Anatomy of Plants* (London, 1682), and Swammerdam's *Biblia Naturae* (published in Leiden only after his death, in 1737–8).

John R. Baker's *Abraham Trembley* (Arnold, 1952) contains a useful brief discussion of Bonnet's views on pre-ordination and the polyp. On the whole Preformation *v.* Epigenesis dispute, see J. S. Needham's *History of Embryology* (Cambridge University Press, 1934). The standard biography of Schwann is still the nineteenth-century one by L.

LIVING UNITS

Fredericq. T. H. Huxley's article on 'The Physical Basis of Life' was printed in the *Fortnightly Review*, Vol. 5. On Virchow, see the original *Cellular Pathology* (London, 1860), and also:

E. H. Ackernecht, *Rudolf Virchow, Doctor, Statesman, Anthropologist*, University of Wisconsin Press, 1953

Disease, Life and Man (essays by Virchow, ed. Ratner)

16

Exploring the Interior

VIRCHOW can be thought of as the Dalton of physiology, so it is not surprising to find, after 1860, a burst of activity in the sciences of living matter similar to that in physics and chemistry earlier in the century. Once again, in fact, we are at a point beyond which we can pursue only those topics which throw particular light on general and fundamental issues in matter-theory. From this point on, it will not be possible to give a proper impression of the labour, heartbreak, ingenuity, and patience – not to mention the failures – which have gone into the process of discovery. (A single sentence, which can be read in a few seconds, may represent twenty years of hard labour.) All we can hope to do is to indicate something of the intellectual imagination that has transformed our conceptions of living matter.

During the century since 1860, the pace of advance in our understanding of cells, and of cellular processes, has been restricted by certain external limitations: some intellectual, others instrumental. These are not always what one might guess. For instance, the happy discovery was made only a few years back that the exposed edges of freshly-broken glass were even sharper than experience suggests: as used in the 'ultra-microtome', they will slice wafers of organic tissue one hundred times as thin as those cut with knife-blades for study under normal microscopes. (This discovery was important, since without it there was no way of exploiting the discrimination of the electron microscope for the study of cells.) In general terms, however, the factors limiting our undertsanding of cells have been similar in kind ever since 1660: first, the resolving-power of the microscopes with which we study, photograph, and now also film, structures and processes within living things; and, secondly, the refinement and scope of the physico-chemical ideas which we can use to interpret the results.

To deal briefly with the intellectual factors – at no stage in the last hundred years have relevant physico-chemical ideas and techniques languished for long before being applied to the problems of physiology. At times, indeed, biologists have found themselves treading on the heels of their colleagues in the physical sciences. This has been especially true in biochemistry; for the intellectual analysis of the cell-nucleus demands an understanding of some uniquely large and complex molecules, whose constitutions and chemical properties a new generation of 'molecular biologists' are having to decipher for themselves as they go along. To some extent, these men have taken over ideas and methods of analysis already worked out by physicists and chemists – e.g. the use of X-rays to provide clues to molecular structure, as developed by Bragg and von Laue in the study of inorganic crystals. But to a considerable extent they are being compelled, as their work develops, to improvise and invent new physico-chemical methods specially adapted to the problems of the subcellular world. For they are working in an intellectual borderland where the objects one encounters can be regarded *either* as the minutest recognizable biological units *or* as the vastest coherent chemical ones.

In the field of instruments, there have been two main decades of advance: the 1890s and the 1950s. Before 1890, microscopists continued to refine on the techniques of earlier decades. They used various stains, including the newly discovered synthetic dyes, in order to colour their specimens and so – they hoped – reveal the fine structures of tissues with more detail and contrast. (Sceptics alleged that some of the resulting discoveries were as spurious as the 'globules' of Milne-Edwards, being artefacts produced by the staining-technique itself. But this criticism was just only in a few cases, and staining has in fact led to important observations: *chromosomes*, for example, were first seen as loops of 'chromatin', the substance in the cell-nucleus which most readily takes up stain.) During the '70s and '80s, microscopists cut out further deficiencies in the optical performance of the compound microscope, notably by introducing drops of a suitably refracting liquid between the objective lens and the glass plate covering the specimen. But the first major advance came only after 1886, when Zeiss and Schott produced the 'apochromatic' microscope using lenses made of specially developed types of glass (the 'Jena' glasses), by which a further range of colour-defects was eliminated. This step forward was the instrumental counterpart to the intellectual step forward of the '80s and '90s, by which the cell-nucleus was further analysed into its individual chromosomes and other structures. And, for a full fifty years, the apochromatic light-microscope remained the most discriminating instrument available for the scrutiny of cell-structure.

Since the 1940s, further improvements have come with a rush. Through sheer ingenuity, rather than the application of fundamentally novel principles, the capacities of the light-microscope have been greatly multiplied. The traditional light-beam used to form the microscope-image was a chaotic mixture of radiation, coming originally from the sun or from an incandescent lamp-filament: this has been superseded by more revealing probes (light of a single wavelength, or of extra-short wavelengths – i.e. ultra-violet light – or light polarized in a single direction), and specimens are now made to display their own internal structure through exploiting their power to produce optical interference-patterns when suitably illuminated. More dramatically, though more expensively, the electron microscope is increasing the magnifications at our disposal to a point at which internal 'organs' even within the cytoplasm – which had for so long appeared to be a featureless fluid – can be studied in operation. Since one can use the electron microscope to form an image of the layout of individual atoms in a sheet of platinum (see Plate 14), molecular biologists are confident that they will be able to close the last gap between the *observed* organic structure of physiology and the *inferred* molecular structures of physics and chemistry. If they do so, that will complete the great scientific pincer-movement which began in the days of Leeuwenhoek and Newton.

Since Virchow's time, three lines of enquiry have contributed most to 'cytology' (the science of cells): direct microscopic scrutiny of cells and their parts, chemical analysis of substances obtained from them, and the statistics of inheritance-patterns. For many years, these enquiries went along in parallel: only in the last twenty years have their findings all come together, sometimes in unforeseen ways.

Remak's work on cell-division was clearly only a beginning. The whole process of cellular fission was obviously going to repay closer examination. Though the fine details of this process are still being elucidated today, careful microscopy soon made two things plain: first, that the nuclei of cells were themsslves highly complex objects and, secondly, that they had a genealogy of their own as continuous as that of cells. Just as cells were formed only by the division of pre-existing cells, so too nuclei were formed only in the presence of – even 'out of' – pre-existing nuclei; and by 1875 Strasburger could add to Virchow's motto the corollary: *Omnis Nucleus e Nucleo*. Yet between Virchow's doctrine and Strasburger's there was a subtle change in the meaning of the preposition 'out of'. At first, the reproduction of nuclei seemed to parallel that of cells exactly, but this turned out not to be so. More was involved in nuclear reduplication than simple growth and division: instead, a complex sequence of steps took place, in which the dark threads of chromatin (chromosomes) within the nucleus played an important part. (Compare Plates 11 and 12.)

For twenty years and more, the microscopic study of cells and cell-division proceeded largely empirically: the pairs of chromosomes, which had first been described by Balbiani in 1861, were studied with growing familiarity by Strasburger and by Flemming, who recognized nine distinct phases in the process of nuclear division. By 1881 Balbiani had even described, in the case of certain giant chromosomes, the dark bands which we now associate with 'genes'. But from 1883 on, the whole microscopic study of the cell was given a new purpose and direction by the work of August Weismann. It was as though one had put a magnet down on to a box full of iron filings: a novel and definite shape was imposed on the whole intellectual field.

Weismann's Vision . . .

Fate sometimes plays good turns in the most unlikely-looking ways. August Weismann first practised as a doctor, and later became a talented research-worker in microscopic biology, being appointed Professor of Zoology at Freiburg in 1866, at the age of thirty-two. But as he approached forty his eyesight became so bad that he could no longer work with the microscope himself, and his busy mind was diverted more and more into theoretical studies. He took up the major problem left unsolved in Darwin's

Origin of Species: the problem of variation – i.e. the mechanism underlying those slight changes of form and colouration which, in species that reproduce sexually, appear between every generation of living individuals and their offspring – and soon he moved on to the problem of inheritance in general. Yet all the time part of his mind remained on questions about cell-structure, and these two different concerns now cross-fertilized, with unusually fruitful results. In a series of closely argued papers, beginning around 1880 and culminating in 1892 with his book on *The Germ-Plasm*, he canvassed all the possible theories of heredity. He tested them, both against the established facts of breeding and inheritance, and against his own knowledge of cellular structure and reproduction. Where, a full century earlier, Charles Bonnet had inferred the existence, in each reproductive bud of a polyp, of 'particles' capable of pre-ordaining the form of another whole polyp, Weissmann was in a position to go much further. As a result he built up in his own mind a clear outline picture of the genetic mechanism involved in sexual reproduction. This picture has been tested in detail against experience, and given a much more definite interpretation in the mid-twentieth century.

As an intellectual phenomenon, the way in which Weismann conceived his vision of the germ-cells – as being definite molecular structures, which act as the material carriers of all inherited characters – has few parallels. It was a sustained feat of controlled theoretical imagination, resembling most nearly Newton's vision of a future atomic theory in the closing section of the *Opticks*. Both men drew together many separate intellectual threads whose interrelations had not hitherto been clearly recognized; and their achievement was in both cases to extrapolate the implications of all these ideas for as far ahead as could be envisaged. In the detailed working-out of their hypotheses both men can be criticized for having sometimes guessed wrong: Newton, in his explanation of Boyle's Law, Weismann in his interpretation of chromosome-division. But, like Newton's general conception of atoms and central forces, the general idea underlying Weismann's theories – that the stable patterns of inherited characters are transmitted from generation to generation by complex molecules – was to stand the test of time.

From the start Weismann approached the problem of variation

at a more profound level than Darwin. For Darwin – as we shall see elsewhere – unthinkingly took for granted what he called 'the strong principle of inheritance'. Instead of being surprised that inheritance took place at all, he let his mind play, in a way quite divorced from considerations of cell-structure or biochemistry, over conceivable mechanisms to explain the origin of variations. (Darwin was no microscopist.) Very possibly, he speculated, sexual union brought together in the fertilized egg separate contributions ('pangenes') from every limb and portion of the parents' bodies, which by their blending determined the individual character of their offspring. This theory, in Weismann's view, was both theoretically superficial and cytologically impracticable. There was no sign of any cellular mechanism by which the alleged pangenes could influence the genetic material in the sperm and the ovum. And, in any case, the really profound mystery was not the variations between generations but the extreme *smallness* of these variations – the unparalleled exactness with which each generation of organisms developed into a replica of the last. Even the minutest details of organic structure were preserved through all the many thousands of cell-divisions which occur between the adult parent and the adult offspring.

In this way, Weismann appealed behind Darwin's questions to those of Aristotle. Whatever the defects in the pneuma-theory of genetics, the fundamental problem had been evident to both Aristotle and the Stoics. Genetic inheritance involved a continuity and stability of organic form that cried out for some material 'carrier'. Once some convincing way had been seen of accounting for the stable features in genetic inheritance, the problem of variation could be dealt with as a corollary; but the crucial problem remained *stability*. The hereditary pneuma was the guesswork of men whose physics and chemistry did not measure up to the needs of their biology: now, in A.D. 1880, Weismann could raise the same questions with more hope of success.

His own conclusions were clear-cut. This is how he expressed them in 1885:

If it is impossible for the germ-cell to be, as it were, an extract of the whole body, and for all the cells of the organism to dispatch small particles to the germ-cells, from which the latter derive their power of heredity; then there remain, as it seems to me, only two other possible, physiologically-conceivable, theories as to the origin of germ-cells, manifesting such powers as we know they possess. Either the substance of the parent germ-cell is capable of undergoing a series of changes which, after the building-up of a new individual, leads back again to identical germ-cells; *or the germ-cells are not derived at all, as far as their essential and characteristic substance is concerned, from the body of the individual, but they are derived directly from the parent germ-cell.*

I believe that the latter view is the true one: I have expounded it for a number of years, and have attempted to defend it, and to work out its further details in various publications. I propose to call it the theory of 'The Continuity of the Germ-plasm', for it is founded upon the idea that heredity is brought about by the transference from one generation to another of a substance with a definite chemical, and above all molecular, constitution.

The great novelty of this theory lay in Weismann's suggestion that the germ-plasm in the sexual cells of each generation was derived *immediately* from the corresponding cells of the previous generation, rather than developing afresh during the life of the individual at some later point in the unfolding organization of the body. Only in this way could he account to himself for the degree of stability in inheritance actually observed.

The hypothesis had two immediate consequences – first, that the rudiments of the individual's reproductive cells must be formed at a very early stage in the growth of the embryo, and subsequently isolated; and secondly, that 'acquired characteristics', formed by factors peculiar to the parents' life and environment, could not appreciably influence the character of the germ-cells passed on to the offspring, or be transmitted to later generations as permanent variations in the hereditary material:

The nutrition and growth of the individual must exercise some influence upon its germ-cells; but ... this influence must be extremely slight, and ... it cannot act in the manner in which it is usually assumed that it takes place. A change of growth at the periphery of an organism [as in the case of bony calluses induced by pressure] can never cause such a change in the molecular structure of the germ-plasm as would augment the predisposition [to such calluses], so that the son would inherit an increased susceptibility of the bony tissue or even of the particular bone in question.

If this theory were sound, one could draw a sharp contrast between the general run of cells in the individual's body and those of the germ-plasm. Any range of variations in the structure of the body-cells (even of their nuclei) would be consistent with the facts of inheritance, provided only that the continuity of the germ-plasm were assured. It was almost as though, in the higher animals, the germ-cells were a separate race of beings to which the individual acted as host:

The germ-cells are no longer looked upon as the product of the parent's body, at least as far as their essential part – the specific germ-plasm – is concerned: they are rather considered as something which is to be placed in contrast with the *tout ensemble* of the cells which make up the parent's body; and the germ-cells of succeeding generations stand in a similar relation to one another as a series of generations of unicellular organisms, arising by a continued process of cell-division.

To leave no room for mistake, Weismann reiterated that his theory was – implicitly, if not explicitly – a *biochemical* one. The germ-plasm was

that part of the germ-cell of which the chemical and physical properties – including *the molecular structure* – enable the cell to become, under appropriate conditions, a new individual of the same species.

By this theory, one could fit all the available clues together to form an elegant and parsimonious system:

It seems to me [concluded Weismann] that this theory of continuity of the germ-plasm deserves at least to be examined in all its details, for it is the simplest theory upon the subject, and the one which is most obviously suggested by the facts of the case, and we shall not be justified in forsaking it for a more complex theory until proof is forthcoming that it can no longer be maintained.

Weismann's theory not only framed in outline mechanisms of inheritance which have in general terms found solid confirmation in the last twenty years: it also served as an immediate stimulus to research in microscopy and genetics. For observations which Strasburger had made – before and after fertilization – on the cells and nuclei in the pollen-grains and ovaries of flowering plants, now acquired a new significance. Whereas in the division of body-cells ('mitosis'), the separation of the nuclear chromosomes was always preceded by their duplication – so preserving the number of chromosomes in the cells from one cell-generation to the next – Weismann now argued that the formation of germ-cells must involve two successive divisions without an intervening duplication of the chromosomes. This would produce, in the ovum and the sperm (or pollen), cells possessing only half the normal number of chromosomes. The fusion of sperm and ovum at fertilization would then restore the chromosome number, in readiness for the subsequent development of the embryo. This conclusion was confirmed in 1888, when Boveri and Strasburger independently observed the special mode of division by which the germ-cells are formed, now known as 'meiosis' or 'reduction division'. So, by 1892, fresh microscopical evidence already gave Weismann the means to state his theory more precisely:

The complex mechanism for cell-division exists practically for the sole purpose of dividing the chromatin, and . . . thus the latter is without doubt the most important part of the nucleus.

Taken together with Wilhelm Roux's hypothesis, that the banded patterns arranged linearly along the length of the chromosomes were preserved intact in cell-division and transmitted to both successor-cells alike, Weismann's inferences have provided biologists with signposts for seventy years of intellectually profitable research.

. . . And its Fulfilment

Weismann had speculated about the cytological structure and mechanisms in the light of familiar facts about inheritance. Now the argument began to flow back again: knowledge of cell-structure suggested new lines of research into inheritance itself. If the germ-cells should by any chance be modified, would this not show up as a discontinuity or 'mutation' in the pattern of inheritance? And if the mechanisms of pollination or insemination responsible for inheritance were so precise, simple, and positive in their results, would not this fact too find some reflection in the inheritance-patterns? During the 1890s several men simultaneously attacked the problems of heredity from this new point of view, looking for recurrent patterns in the transmission of hereditary characteristics, and employing the new statistical methods which Galton was developing for the study of human inheritance. In the years 1899–1900, de Vries, Correns, and Tschermak all reached the same results and, looking back through the literature, they discovered to their surprise that they had been 'scooped'. Thirty years before, in 1865, the abbot of a Bohemian monastery, Gregor Mendel, had anticipated their conclusions.

Mendel's story is one of the minor tragedies of science. It is at worst a *minor* tragedy, since its victim allowed himself to be distracted quite readily away from his own profoundest insights and into intellectual dead-ends. (His acquaintance, the Munich botanist Nägeli, persuaded him to give up his studies on inheritance in cultivated varieties of pea, in favour of more difficult and unrewarding enquiries using wild species of hawkweed.) Yet in its own way the story has tragic elements in it: a man who works in complete isolation, however brilliant and penetrating his work, is condemned to be forgotten. If Mendel had made Weismann his regular correspondent instead of Nägeli – still better, if he had lived nearer Freiburg and talked with Weismann personally – what might science not have gained from the collaboration of their complementary intellects?

As things were to turn out, Mendel was fated to play one unquestioned role only in the historical development of genetical thought. All that he had proved was rediscovered before anyone read his work with understanding: so the only effect of this recognition was to avert any dispute over 'priority' between the three men who had independently reasserted his fundamental laws of inheritance. Nevertheless, his own investigations between 1859 and 1865 were a model of scientific method, which must have carried conviction if his paper had reached any colleague who could recognize the force of the questions he had tackled. But there existed, in fact, few men who could have understood; and Mendel was in touch with none of those few. His paper was delivered to the Natural History Society at Brunn (Brno), printed in the society's Proceedings, briefly noted in one encyclopedic survey of botany . . . and forgotten.

Still, the paper did have certain remarkable features. There had been isolated mathematical excursions into the study of heredity before. Early in the eighteenth century Maupertius had analysed the occurrence of congenital malformations in one Berlin family, many of whose members possessed an extra finger. But, with these rare exceptions, scientific work on inheritance before Mendel's time had been rough, general, and non-mathematical. This was particularly true of the experimental studies, which had been numerous – at any rate in botany. So Mendel was right when he said:

Among all the numerous experiments . . . not one has been carried out to such an extent and in such a way as to make it possible to determine the number of different forms under which the offspring of hybrids appear, or to arrange these forms with certainty according to their separate generations, or definitely to ascertain their statistical relations.

The novel and commendable feature of his own work was the way in which he set about remedying these deficiencies: starting with 'pure lines' of pea-plant, choosing to study simple, recognizable characters, controlling inter-breeding carefully in several successive generations, and recording the resulting distribution of forms with statistical precision.

The fact was this: even if earlier experimenters had *wanted* to proceed statistically they would not have known what statistics to measure and collect. They had come to think of a plant as having a complete specific nature, which was transmitted from one generation to the next *as a unit*. The characters of each individual could be considered as a blending or compromise between the unitary contributions of the two parents, but that was as far as their analysis could go. By contrast Mendel treated the 'nature' of his pea-plants not as a unit, but as an aggregate or 'mosaic' of *separate independent units*, each of which corresponded to some observable character. Dwarf or normal height, smooth or wrinkled pods, yellow or green seeds: each corresponded in the pea to one inheritable 'factor'. Mendel was (so to speak) the Lavoisier of botany, trying to unravel the genetic 'principles' responsible for 'carrying' the individual 'characters' of his plants – seeing each constituent 'factor' within the plant-seed as the counterpart of some character in the adult plant.

On this basis Mendel built up his famous theory of dominant and recessive characters; and showed how each of two pairs of independent characters will reappear, as the generations succeed one another, in fractions which can be predicted numerically. The statistics of his own experiments confirmed the predicted ratios – confirmed them (as Sir Ronald Fisher has shown) more exactly than, by rights, they should have done. Why was this? The Abbé Mendel could scarcely have fudged his results! Perhaps we can deduce two things from this discovery: first, that Mendel had worked out clearly *beforehand* what the theory of 'independently segregating factors' implied, and had planned his experiments to *check* this very hypothesis – not to *suggest* one. (Mendel was Cartesian rather than Baconian.) Secondly, it is probable that the assistants who worked his experimental garden came to know what result the good father was hoping for, and on occasion discarded or turned a blind eye to the odd, discrepant few individuals.

In any case, Mendel could do no more than hint that his 'hereditary factors' were material in Nature: he did not assert, like Weismann, that they took the form of *molecules* or anything else. And the true character of the material 'carriers' to which the Mendelian 'factors' corresponded was not really demonstrated until after 1930. Meanwhile, genetical research was to build up a picture of great refinement, in which the Mendelian factors – now rechristened 'genes' – were mapped in linear sequences in what were called 'linkage maps'. Some people interpreted these sequences ('realistically') as corresponding to a series of material particles located along the chromosome threads: others treated them ('phenomenalistically') purely as a theoretical convenience. But, even if one deferred problems about the material basis of the gene, the analysis of inheritance-patterns nevertheless went ahead rapidly, developing into the vigorous science of genetics, as the result of patient industry outdoing even that displayed by nineteenth-century 'higher critics' of the Bible. (Geneticists were fortunate to find a convenient subject for their experiments: the fruit-fly *Drosophila melanogaster* breeds very rapidly and has only four chromosomes in the nuclei of its cells.)

The genetic studies of these years had two chief leaders, Bateson, in England, supported the theory of evolution throughout his work, but questioned the suggested link between Mendel's factors and the microscopic chromosomes: T. H. Morgan, in New York, began by rejecting the theory of evolution, but was favourable throughout towards the chromosome hypothesis. Only when the two men at last met, in 1921, did Bateson come round to the chromosome theory; while Morgan too in due course became a convinced supporter of the Darwinian theory. (It was left to Sir Ronald Fisher to show, mathematically, just what extra strength Morgan's genetics could lend to Darwin's idea of natural selection.)

T. H. Morgan undoubtedly thought of his linkage-maps 'realistically', as reflecting some corresponding sequence of material carriers in the fruit-flies' chromosomes. In 1933 Painter began publishing photographs of cells from the salivary glands of the flies, in which the chromosomes are abnormally large, and he suggested that the genes on Morgan's linear series might be associated directly with successive dark bands along these giant chromosomes. Soon the opaque, or stained, parts of the chromosomes came to be dubbed 'genes' also. (Yet treating the gene in this way, as 'a unit of structure' and 'a unit of function' simultaneously, was something that involved serious, and at times misleading, implications. In recent years, a finer analysis had led to the earlier idea of the gene being refined almost out of existence. In the 'gene-complex' of contemporary theory, distinct genetic units with different functions have been given different names, and the various offices of the classical gene have been divided up between 'cistrons', 'mutons', and 'recons'.) As a result of the new microscopic studies inaugurated by Painter, Morgan's quasi-spatial 'maps' were all reinterpreted as presenting authentic spatial relations between adjacent portions of the hereditary chromosomes. Just as these chromosomes were duplicated before every cell-division, so now it was clear that the gene also must be physically duplicated. As a result, all the questions which Weismann had originally raised, about the *molecular constitution* of the germ-plasm, came alive once more in a new and critical form.

Cyto-Chemistry

These questions presented a new challenge to biochemists and biophysicists. Before 1870, the physiological chemist Miescher had already found a way of dissolving out cell-nuclei from pus-cells, and had studied their chemical composition. He identified one of the chief constituents as a strong organic acid, containing an unusual amount of phosphorus, and he gave this acid the name of 'nuclein'. Two years later he repeated the experiment – less distastefully – on sperm from the Rhine salmon, and obtained both a similar nuclein and another nitrogenous substance which he christened 'protamin'.

Miescher's nuclein was the first of the family of 'nucleic acids', which have now become the chief centre of interest among molecular biologists. Desoxyribonucleic acid, or DNA, proves to be the most striking constituent in all cell-nuclei; and its complementary substance, ribonucleic acid, or RNA, features prominently in the cytoplasm – particularly in the small dark bodies often called 'ribosomes'. (These appear in electron-micrographs as a scatter of opaque blobs, contrasting with the thinner background of the cytoplasm.) Miescher himself had hazarded a guess that nuclein might play a part in inheritance. He even hinted that its constituent atoms might lend themselves to alternative spatial arrangements, and provide a basis for hereditary variation by forming a number of different 'isomeres'. Yet it seemed improbable to his colleagues that this would leave scope for anything like the range of forms needed to explain heredity. Only in the last few years have scientists recognized the astronomical variety of isometric forms in which the nucleic acids may appear. Whatever other hurdles may stand in the way of identifying DNA as the sole material substance of genes, this one at any rate has been cleared out of the way.

The chemistry of the nucleic acids was gradually unravelled, but its relevance to genetics and microscopy was not established until the late 1930s. Then Caspersson and his school in Stockholm set about locating the precise position of the nucleic acid in the cell. They took photographs through the microscope, using ultra-violet light of wavelengths which were strongly absorbed by the nucleic acids concerned, and were able to localize the DNA and RNA exactly within the nucleus. In 1941 the connexion between the nucleic acids and the phenomena of genetic inheritance was clinched by the work of Hollaender and Emmons. This brought to light positive evidence to confirm the soundness of Weismann's original hunch: that the *biological* stability of inheritance-patterns was reflected in the *chemical* stability of the molecules of the germ-plasm. Evidently the molecules concerned were nucleic acid molecules. When fungus spores were irradiated with suitable ultra-violet light, one result (on the accepted physical principles) was to alter the patterns of molecular bonds within the acid-molecules: but, simultaneously, a striking biological result appeared – the rate of genetic mutations among the fungi rapidly increased. Finally, in 1944, the connexion was put beyond doubt by Avery, MacLeod, and McCarty. They collected DNA from a virulent strain of bacteria and added it to a non-virulent strain: some of the non-virulent bacteria absorbed the foreign DNA, and proceeded to breed virulent offspring. In the case of organisms as simple as bacteria, it appeared, the DNA molecules were capable of acting *by themselves* as a fertile genetic material. (The discovery that even bacteria share some genetic mechanisms with the higher forms of life, where the sexual character of reproduction is so much more evident, has given a great filip to experiments on the genetic action of specific chemical substances in cell-nuclei.) In their biological action, genes and DNA seemed thus to be equivalent. At this point biochemistry has come into its own, so that the general problem of cell-division now has at its heart a more specific biochemical problem. The question, 'How are the genes in the chromosome physically duplicated?' has been transformed into the question, 'How are *DNA molecules* physically duplicated?'

Since 1945, then, biochemistry has finally overcome the obstacles raised in its way by Pasteur and Virchow. More and more of the constituent substances of the cell have turned out to be built up from recognizable chemical materials – having extremely long and complex, but still decipherable, molecular formulae. Their behaviour within the cell can also be shown in many cases to be just what their composition requires – if we bear in mind (as Bernard would insist) the special conditions prevailing in their cellular environment. Indeed, some of them will continue to perform the same chemical operations if removed from the cell and placed in a suitable mixture of substances in the chemist's test-tube. Kornberg, for example, mixed together quantities of the four molecular sub-units into which DNA can be broken down, together with a small portion of DNA as a 'primer', with the result that the DNA 'multiplied' in an almost alchemical way: its power to link up simpler molecules was not affected by removing it from the cell. (The long chain-molecules of which proteins consist have been synthesized in a similar way.) At last we can begin to dismantle the barriers which, after the discovery of micro-organisms and the formulation of the classical cell-theory, still seemed to divide chemistry from biology. The task of reproducing the natural processes by which viruses are formed is already almost within our reach, and the possibility of a crude kind of man-made 'living cell' is no longer out of the question.

By 1962 it seemed to be well established that DNA performs a crucial fraction – and perhaps the whole – of the functions which Weismann had defined for the molecules in his germ-plasm. By a marathon feat of physico-chemical analysis, Crick and Watson of Cambridge have worked out the complex patterns of atomic connexions shared by every isomere of DNA: it consists of a pair of spiral chains intertwined and held together by hydrogen bonds between their sub-units (Plate 15). Molecular biologists are also beginning to fathom some of the chemical processes by which the nucleic acids actually carry out their biological functions. The constituent molecular sub-units of an RNA molecule, which are of several different types, fall into place against the template of a DNA molecule, and reproduce its stable overall form. The RNA molecules migrate into the cytoplasm, and there act in turn as templates for all the innumerable varieties of necessary protein molecules – whose sub-units are of twenty different types. (It is as though the protein molecules were like a newspaper whose form is determined *at second-hand* by the type which the compositor sets up in his galley, even though this type may never directly touch paper or ink. For the type is used to mould a dozen or more white-metal rollers which are taken away and used on the machines by which the actual printing is done. Proteins are made in the 'printing machines' of the cytoplasm, whose RNA preserves in itself the set pattern of the nuclear DNA which shaped it.) For some time it was a puzzle to see how patterns made up from twenty basic components could be determined by a template built up from only four. Presumably the key to the protein 'code' must lie in the permutations and combinations according to which the RNA sub-units could be arranged. In fact, it seems, each protein sub-unit occupies a location determined by an appropriate group of *three* RNA sub-units in combination.

The scope for molecular biology and cyto-chemistry, in deciphering further the joint structures and functions of cells and their parts, is probably unlimited. The next fifty years will certainly transform our understanding of this subject, together with all its implications, as surely as chemistry was transformed between 1810 and 1860 and sub-atomic physics between 1910 and 1960. Two large questions stand, awaiting answers, in the very middle of our picture. First: it is still unclear – biochemically speaking – just *how* normal cell-division takes place. The duplication of the chromosomes in preparation for cell-division must double also the number of separable strands of DNA. So, somehow or other, DNA molecules must be capable not only of acting as templates for RNA but also of *replicating themselves* – which is what Kornberg's experiments demonstrate that they in fact do. Up to now, however, no one has established just what the mechanism of this replication is. Penrose has invented simple mechanical models which can, in suitable circumstances, produce replicas of themselves out of sub-units simpler still. This, at any rate, demonstrates that the idea of a molecule replicating itself mechanically is not inconceivable. Yet how precisely replication happens in the actual cellular environment is a question still under investigation.

Secondly: the questions about embryology, development, and regeneration, over which Bernard jibbed, can still be answered only schematically. In the DNA of the cell-nucleus, we have reason to see a highly stable material counterpart to Bernard's non-material 'creative idea'. Here, without much doubt, is the substance which, biochemically speaking, is chiefly responsible for determining the direction of the processes of development; and there is already evidence that some of the control mechanisms governing the rates of these processes once again exploit the 'feed-back' principle. But it is one thing to recognize a general correspondence of this kind. It will be quite another to work out all the refinements by which the nuclear templates in the cell influence and control the unfolding form of the developing organism. In physiology, as much as in nuclear physics, there are bound to be obstacles as well as pleasant surprises round some of our intellectual corners. But, having come as far as we have, we are entitled to be confident that this problem too can be solved.

FURTHER READING AND REFERENCES

As general sources, consult once again *Great Experiments in Biology*, *Source-Book in Animal Biology*, J. R. Baker's papers, and A. Hughes' *History of Cytology*.

For the late nineteenth century, see:

A. Weismann, *The Germ-Plasm*, Walter Scott, 1893

C. Darwin, *Life and Letters*, John Murray, 1887, and *The Variation of Animals and Plants Under Domestication*, John Murray, 1868

F. Galton, *Memories of my Life*, Methuen, 1908

W. Bateson, *Materials for the Study of Variation*, Macmillan, 1894

The curious case of Gregor Mendel has attracted some attention: the life by H. Iltis (Allen & Unwin, 1932) can be consulted, and the reasons for his neglect and rediscovery are well analysed by Elizabeth Gasking (*J. History of Ideas*, 1959) and by B. Glass, in his collection of essays on the history of ideas presented to A. O. Lovejoy. See also the essays by Bentley Glass in the collection *Forerunners of Darwin*, John Hopkins Press, 1959

On twentieth-century genetics, the standard textbook is that of Sinnott, Dunn, and Dobzhansky (*Principles of Genetics*, McGraw-Hill, 1950). T. H. Morgan's *The Physical Basis of Heredity* (J. B. Lippincott, 1919) is still worth consulting. The best popular introduction to the subject is to be found in:

C. Auerbach, *The Science of Genetics*, Hutchinson, 1962

The most fascinating recent discussion of general biology – including genetics – is:

C. H. Waddington, *The Nature of Life*, Unwin Books, 1963

A sound imaginative and well-written discussion of the interactions between embryology and development, cytology and evolution is:

G. R. de Beer, *Embryos and Ancestors*, Clarendon Press, 1940

On modern cyto-chemistry and its implications for biology, see in particular the many articles on the subject in *Scientific American* (especially the issue devoted to the cell in September 1961), and also:

C. B. Anfinsen, *The Molecular Basis of Evolution*, John Wiley, 1959

T. O. Caspersson, *Cell-Growth and Cell-Function*, W. W. Norton, 1950

E. H. Mercer, *Cells and Cell-Structure*, Hutchinson, 1961

The Physics and Chemistry of Life, Simon & Schuster, 1958, (publ.

Scientific American, esp. Part III on 'The Structure of the Hereditary
Material')

There is an excellent film on the electron microscope, made and distributed by Associated Electrical Industries Ltd, which brings together a fine collection of material illustrating the topics discussed in this chapter.

EPILOGUE

The Reunion of Matter-Theory

AROUND A.D. 1700 a point was reached in astronomy and dynamics at which the fabric of the heavens was seen clearly and in proportion for the first time. Though our horizons have widened during the subsequent two hundred and fifty years, the Frame of Nature established by Newton has largely survived the conceptual revolutions of Maxwell and Einstein, so in those fields (which formed the subject of our earlier volume) Newton's work represented an intellectual watershed – the pass from which the view was at last familiar. In the present book we have nowhere found ourselves at a comparable watershed. The intellectual revolutions in men's ideas about matter have been unending: the very foundations of physics and physiology have (it seems) been dug up and relaid every half-century. As a result, in these parts of science no comprehensive body of 'common sense' has become established: the fundamental concepts have never remained stable and universal long enough for common sense to take hold. And, by now, some onlookers draw the uncomfortable conclusion that, in fundamental scientific theory as in *haute couture*, the basic categories are at the mercy of fashion – liable to change without warning from decade to decade.

Yet there are reasons for thinking that this conclusion is over-hasty. If we compare the respective conclusions which the arguments in physics and physiology have now reached, a different possibility presents itself: at this very moment we may be reaching the point at which a new 'common sense' can crystallize out. The intellectual changes of the last forty years have done much to demolish, from both sides, the barriers which, since 1600, divided organic from inorganic Nature; and the prospect opens up of a common system of ideas equally adapted to problems in both groups of sciences. If this development could be realized it would create an all-embracing 'natural philosophy of matter', and restore the Aristotelian unity of the animate and the inanimate. But this unity would be restored on a new basis. Life for Aristotle was a self-evident property of matter: its possibility did not need explanation. The New Science set life and matter right apart: living things were treated either as the results of an extraordinary cosmic chance or as the deliberate productions of an Almighty Designer. Neither of these seventeenth-century alternatives satisfied the legitimate demands of natural philosophy, since neither made the existence of living things intelligible and natural: either way, life was treated as something *superimposed on* matter.

Today we can see, forming under our hands and eyes, the possibility of a reunified view of matter and life. And this is so just because our fundamental assumptions about matter have at last gone beyond both Aristotle's and Newton's. For us, matter is intrinsically neither developing nor inert: potentially, it can be either the one or the other. The chemical elements, as such, are neither organic nor inorganic: they have it in them equally to form gases and crystals, viruses, DNA, and cells. And this reordering of our ideas is based on no mere quibble: our theories of matter have been transformed down to the very root. Classical nineteenth-century science was still in crucial respects a Demokritean system: it treated the atoms of matter primarily as 'bricks', and left unsolved the Stoic problems of coherence and organization. There is no such Demokritean bias about contemporary wave-mechanics. The physicist's fundamental units are no longer bricks: they are now *dynamic* units, defined by characteristic patterns of energy and activity; and they join together not in simple chains or aggregates, but by forming out of their separate wave-systems stable 'concords' or harmonies, which have new capacities and activities of their own. Thus the principles underlying matter-theory today are neither teleological alone, nor mechanical alone. Instead they are *architectural* – going beyond the old distinctions between form and function, structures and activities. We find in Nature a hierarchy of active forms, which runs from sub-atomic wavicles, through atoms and molecules, nucleic acids and viruses, to cell-parts and cells, organs and complete organisms. (The sequence is not closed at either end.) At every level of analysis, from protons and electrons up to living creatures, the objects which Nature is composed of have to be characterized in terms both of their structures and of their activities.

The steps in this sequence of levels are neither arbitrary nor absolute. In the world as we know it, it is useful to distinguish between the different modes of physical and chemical organization – sub-atomic, atomic, and molecular. But the boundaries are all blurred. The term 'atom' no longer marks off a discrete indivisible entity: it serves rather as a dotted line which we draw round a nucleus and its cloud of associated electrons – and in many cases (e.g. in metallic crystals) this boundary is purely fictional, since the electrons in question are largely pooled. At the biological level, likewise, cells and genes remain the units into which living creatures and cellular nuclei can conveniently be analysed for working purposes. Yet genes, like atoms, have now been split, and even Virchow's central doctrine – so fruitful a century ago – that material objects are either cellular organisms or non-cellular non-organisms, is subject to qualifications and exceptions. The whole class of *viruses* comprises non-cellular creatures whose behaviour and properties place them squarely across the frontiers of the living and the inert. Chemically, they represent simple associations of proteins and nucleic acids. They can be analysed and synthesized, extracted and dried, just like the most undoubted inorganic crystals; and, if they were never known except in that form, one would not hesitate to label them as 'inorganic' and 'inert' (Plate 16). Yet, if placed within a host-cell, they exploit the new environment, and multiply themselves just as though they – rather than the original nucleus – were the focal objects directing the activities of the living cell: in this capacity one is compelled to accept them as the simplest type of parasitic organism. So the distinction between living and non-living things can no longer be drawn in *material* terms. What marks them off from one another is not the stuff of which they are made: the contrast is rather one between systems whose organization and activities differ in complexity. If we are free to think of cell-parts as species of giant molecules, we may think of individual atoms as extremely simple organisms. The different grades of structure and the different grades of activity form a single hierarchy.

This agreement is not, as one might think, a sheer coincidence:

on the contrary. If the activities of an object are to be intelligible at all, its material structure must be of such a kind as to make these activities possible. Unless the solar system had the sort of structure it does, eclipses could not occur: though the layout is one thing and the eclipses are another, it is by studying the disposition of the different bodies in the system that we understand how eclipses are possible, and on what conditions they take place. In the same way, when we have fully surveyed the 'layout' of the DNA molecule, we shall presumably come to see how replication, too, is possible, and on what conditions it will ʝake place – why a molecule of that design, placed in the right conditions, *could not fail* to replicate. Expanding and refining the concept of organization, one must expect similar correlations at other levels. Biological organization is not the same as life; but it is, clearly enough, the material pre-requisite for life. Only in a creature with the necessary organization are vital and mental activities possible and intelligible; and we must understand this organization if we are ever to explain the possibility of life, and the conditions needed for its occurrence.

This conclusion has one implication which people sometimes find unwelcome: namely, the inference that all our activities – even our thoughts – have a material counterpart or correlate. So long as it seemed that inorganic Nature 'slavishly obeyed the laws of mechanics', this hesitancy was understandable. Yet it was never *necessary* to suppose that mental and vital activities happened without any material counterpart, entirely 'of their own accord': historically, in fact, this was a purely temporary heresy. If humans and animals are capable – as they manifestly are – of mental and vital activities, their material organization must, as surely as that of the solar system, be of a kind that makes these activities possible. Aristotle and Galen assumed no less!

If the last absolute distinctions between the organic and the inorganic are fading, and grading, into differences of degree, that is another indication that our theories of matter may be reaching maturity. For a long time cosmology rested on a similar absolute distinction, between the sub-lunary and the super-lunary worlds: with the coming of the new seventeenth-century perspective this opposition lost its sharpness – the undoubted differences between the two worlds were easily explained within the wider theory.

Such an absolute distinction frequently turns out to be a distinction we had not wholly understood: we felt obliged to insist on it, simply because we lacked an adequate theoretical perspective. So the very fading of the absolute distinctions, which were such a feature of classical physics and physiology, may yet turn out to be a most significant aspect of twentieth-century scientific thought. The uncrossable frontiers, between compounds and mixtures, atoms and radiation, matter and energy, the living and the inert, were intellectual expedients which mark the classical theories as partial and incomplete. And the most far-reaching outcome we can hope for from twentieth-century matter-theory – which includes both quantum mechanics and molecular biology, as well as half a dozen other specialities – is a common system of fundamental concepts, embracing material systems at every level.

We have travelled a long way from Miletus and the Ionians. The craftsmen who preceded Thales had no theoretical hold on the materials they handled: the affiliations of their crafts were religious rather than philosophical. The Greek philosophers thought up a whole batch of theoretical questions, and six or eight rival forms of answers, each with its own attractions. But they themselves carried their theories beyond rivalry to reconciliation: their questions, though penetrating, remained abstract and divorced from the craft tradition, and the alchemists' attempts at a marriage of crafts and philosophy turned out to be abortive. How different our own position appears! Our intellectual grasp extends throughout the cosmos, and has brought to light the material processes going on at every scale – from the thermonuclear furnaces of the stars, down through the protein-factories of the cytoplasm, to the changes of wave-pattern which take place when an atom swallows a photon. And this intellectual grasp is paralleled and completed when we turn to the practical sphere. We have exceeded the dreams of the craftsmen, the alchemists and the medicine-men, and by now we have the means either to satiate or to destroy ourselves.

Yet though our contemporary science, and its more worldly offspring technology, may be so different in their fruits from the natural philosophy of the Greeks, the genealogy connecting them back to Greece is unmistakable. Werner Heisenberg in the twentieth century describes his theoretical problems in terms that Anaximander would have understood (see page 52):

It is impossible to explain . . . qualities of matter except by tracing these back to the behaviour of entities which themselves no longer possess these qualities. If atoms are really to explain the origin of colour and smell in visible material bodies, then they cannot themselves possess properties like colour and smell. . . . Atomic theory consistently denies the atom any such perceptible qualities.

The central questions of matter-theory (which have preoccupied us in this volume) have been the same ever since the birth of speculation in Ionia. How are living and non-living things fundamentally related? What light do material structure and design throw on activity and function (or vice versa)? Are material things aggregates of separate units, or manifestations of integrating forces? And, to go to the very central point in the bull's-eye of the subject: In what common terms can we make unified sense of the whole architecture of the material world? That was the question to which Thales addressed his mind, and it is still the central question in matter-theory today.

In cosmology, the crucial problem presented itself to men from outside, the moment they looked up reflectively at the night sky. In matter-theory, the crucial problem came from within men's minds. This ambition, to find a common set of principles making sense of all material things, had demanded that concepts and observations should always progress together. Similar patterns of thought have recurred in our story at different epochs because, at different stages and levels, men were faced with intellectual problems similar in their fundamental forms. Thus our theories have served, not merely to generalize our observations (the Baconian myth), nor merely to clarify and order our ideas (the Cartesian myth): rather, they have had a more complex function. They have laid down the principles regulating our interpretation of the facts, in a way that has had to be adapted both to Nature and to Man – both to the world we are seeking to understand and to the demands of the intellect which is our instrument.

Epictetus spoke of the power of Man's mind to fathom his environment, and reason out a mode of life, as 'the God within Man'. Ever since Thales, men have striven to match the powers of the mind to the powers of Nature, and their efforts have been fantastically successful. It is perhaps the most remarkable of all natural events that a species has grown up in an environment, and has ended by understanding it.

There are many wonders, but none is more wonderful than Man. For he has learned the arts of Speech, and of wind-swift Thought, and of living together in Neighbourliness.

Sophocles was fortunate, for he had not tasted the fruits of our knowledge. The irony is that one species should combine the insights of a Newton with the fears and appetites of fools.

Index

Abuqasim of Cordova (d. *c.* 1013), 135

Ackernecht, A. H., *Rudolph Virchow, Doctor, Statesman, Anthropologist*, 407

Aeneas of Gaza (*fl.* A.D. 480), 39

Aether, Newton and the, 217–23, 285

Agriculture, art of, 34
  myths and, 35–7
  the calendar and, 36, 37

Aidoneus, 56

Air, as a basic form of matter, 54, 55, 65
  nature of, 232–5

Albert the Great (*c.* 1206–80), 155

Alchemy, 120–50
  aims of, 136–43
  in Alexandria, 124–30
  beliefs of, 166
  Christian attitude to, 143–4
  craft element of, 130–36
  distillation and, 134–6
  dyestuffs and, 133, 134
  fathers of, 136
  in Islam, 144, 145
  jewels and, 133, 134
  medieval, 155–7
  metals and, 132, 141, 142, 143
  phlogiston theory and, 237, 238
  recipes of
    to make artificial silver and gold, 147
    to prepare alcohol, 149–50
    to prepare mercury, 147, 148
  traditions of, 143–7
  tribikos in, 149
  wider influences of, 143–7, 166–73, 193

d'Alembert, Jean (1717–83), 279

Alexander of Aphrodisias (*c.* A.D. 200), 154

Alexander the Great (*c.* 360–323 B.C.), 122

Alexandria:
  alchemy in, 124–30

as a centre of culture, 102–11, 121–30, 136
  Greek philosophy in, 124, 126–30, 136
  inhabitants of, 121, 122
  language of, 122
  religions in, 122
  temples of, 126, 127
  trade in, 122

Anaxagoras (*c.* 500–428 B.C.), 45, 54, 58, 61, 79, 244

Anaximander (*c.* 611–547 B.C.), 51, 52, 54, 432
  pendulum theory of, 53, 54

Anaximenes (*c.* 556–480 B.C.), 51
  breath theory of, 54, 55, 66

Anderson, T. F. (b. 1901), 332, 333

Anfinsen, C. B., *The Molecular Basis of Evolution*, 425

Anti-matter, possible existence of, 336

Apprenticeship, system of, 27

Aquinas, Thomas (*c.* 1225–74), 154, 221

Arago, François (1786–1853), 283

Arber, Agnes, *The Natural Philosophy of Plant Form*, 268

Archimedes (*c.* 287–212 B.C.), 34, 103, 121, 157, 158
  hydrostatic balance of, 34, 157

Aristarchos of Samos (*fl.* 280–264 B.C.), heliocentric astronomy of, 69, 77

Aristotle (384–322 B.C.), 14, 35, 45, 46, 59, 64, 65, 89–100, 112, 123, 204, 220, 221, 263, 264, 265, 430, 137
  astronomy of, 137
  on biological sciences, 89, 90, 91, 96–100, 108, 113, 114, 116, 117, 351, 393
  cosmology of, 99, 100, 110, 365
  De Generatione, 154
  as a disciple of Socrates, 89
  influence on medieval scholars, 153–7

438

INDEX

'Send no more roses to assuage your guilt, Mr Oberholzer,' I told him smilingly. 'Such flowers may, as you have already so painfully discovered, later explode while you are still in the blast area.'

Frits Bühler Krom
DER KOMPETENTE KRIMINELLE:
eine Fallstudie (Tr. D. Keel)

CHAPTER ONE

They stopped the car by the gateway in the wall on the lower coast road. Then, after a moment or two, the three of them climbed out stiffly, their shirts clinging to their backs. It had been a long, hot drive.

From the shade at the end of the terrace I could see them clearly through the binoculars.

Professor Krom, the older man, I already knew; there could be no doubt about him. The younger man and the woman, however, had to be identified from recent snapshots taken by private enquiry agencies on the subjects' respective campuses. Although I can never take photographic identification quite seriously – I have seen, and used, too many false passports for that – these two, I decided, looked sufficiently like the persons they were supposed to be for me to assume that they were indeed those persons.

The car was a rented Fiat 127 with Milan registration plates. Their baggage, except for the hand stuff, was on a roof-rack. There was no unauthorized fourth person inside. They appeared, for the moment, to have adhered to the terms of the agreement I had worked out with Krom.

For several seconds they stood staring up at the Villa Lipp. Then, lips began to move and gestures were made. One did not have to be a skilled lip-reader to know what was being said.

'Are we expected to carry our bags up all those steps?' That was the woman, running sweaty fingers awkwardly through her hair as she spoke.

Krom, the leader of the expedition, gave her a fatherly pat on the shoulder. 'I doubt it, my dear. But why don't we go and find out?' He looked up again, showing me his teeth this time; he had realized that I had to be watching. 'I'm quite sure he's there.'

'And laughing his head off.' Dr Connell, the younger man, was eyeing the house with dislike and massaging his aching neck muscles. He had done all the driving. 'I'll bet there's an upper access road, too,' he went on. 'No one builds a villa like that without a driveway. This is pure one-upmanship. The son-of-a-bitch just wants us to arrive pooped.'

He was not entirely right. True, I had omitted the access road from the sketch-map I had sent Krom; but not simply in order to cause them discomfort. What I had wanted, too, was plenty of time in which to examine them and their belongings before they could examine too closely me and mine. Not that they would see many of my belongings in that expensively rented petit palais, but they would all see Yves and Melanie as well as me. There was no way of preventing their doing so – we had been rendered, to some extent, expendable – but the attendant risk could at least be minimized.

Evidence of the need for such precautions soon became visible.

Once they had decided that there was no point in their just standing there and that they had better start climbing, Connell took what at first looked like a portable radio from the car before he locked it. Then, when he turned, I saw that what he had in fact was a tape-recorder.

This flagrant violation of the agreed ground rules did not greatly surprise me. Dr Connell was, my sources had informed me, that sort of young man; the academic counterpart of the boardroom Wunderkind, always confident of being able to talk anyone misguided enough to disagree with him into seeing things his way.

Well, Yves would know how to deal with him. The one who had begun to interest me more, from a security point of view, was the woman, Dr Henson.

As they climbed the lower flight of stone steps and passed

the fountain at the foot of the main stairway, she swung the embroidered satchel she had been carrying slung on her left shoulder over to her right one. The satchel looked ordinary enough, the sort of object that a slacks-and-shirt woman of her kind might normally carry. What bothered me was that, judging from the way she had to heft it across her body, the contents of the thing were much heavier than one would have expected them to be.

I spoke to Melanie as I went inside.

'Before you go out to meet them, tell Yves that the woman may have something in her bag that shouldn't be there. I'll be in my room when he's ready to report.'

While I waited, I went through the three dossiers again and reread my own notes on them.

The subjects, in order of both temporal and academic seniorities, were:

FRITS BÜHLER KROM, Professor of Sociology and Social Administration
Nationality: Dutch
Age: 62
Civil Status: Married, two sons, one daughter.

My own office had turned up that information after a few minutes with standard reference books. The only additional information that I had been able to get about his personal life, as opposed to his professional life at the German university where he worked and about which every piddling little detail seemed to be known, was that he had eight grandchildren with a ninth on the way.

GEORGE KINGHAM CONNELL, Assistant Professor, Department of Social Sciences
Nationality: USA
Age: 36
Civil Status: Married, one daughter (by first wife who divorced him), two sons (present marriage).

I had a note which said that he was currently in Europe

9

to attend by invitation a seminar at the University of Freiburg im Breisgau, West Germany, and that his family was at a Maine lakeside summer resort.

The American agency commissioned by me to carry out the Connell investigation had complained about the deadlines I had imposed on them. They had, however, managed to gather in the time available a surprisingly large amount of campus gossip. One item reported 'a widespread belief' that certain members of the university Board of Regents were objecting vigorously to any renewal of Dr Connell's contract which might result in his promotion to associate rank and securing of tenure. The objectors were all, it was said, lawyers.

GERALDINE HOPE HENSON, Research Fellow, Faculty of Social Sciences
Nationality: British
Age: 33
Civil Status: Divorced, no children.

At the end of a detailed account of her career and an estimate of her credit-worthiness, the British agency had added a cosy note. Henson had been her maiden name and after her divorce she had gone back to using it. To her many friends, however, she had always been known affectionately as 'Hennie.'

Krom, Connell, Henson.

Social scientists all, but with not much else in common, apparently. Then, one looks at the titles of some of their published books and papers and the picture changes. All three of these scholars are not only criminologists, but criminologists of a new and peculiar breed; they all have the same kind of bee in their bonnets.

Krom's *The Lombroso Fallacy in Contemporary Criminology* and *Frontiers of Criminal Investigation* may not be as conspicuously iconoclastic as Connell's *The Myth of Organized Crime* or Henson's *The Professional Criminal – Six Studies in Incompetence,* but his preface to the monumental *Criminal Statistics 1965-1975, an Analytical Appraisal* makes his position clear. Along with such authorities as John A. Mack of Glasgow and Hans-Jürgen Kerner of Tübingen, as well as younger scholars like Connell and Henson, he had joined the ranks of those criminological heretics who believe that most current ideas about criminal psychology, criminal biology and criminal psychiatry are either fallacious or irrelevant. They believe this because they hold that what criminologists have been studying so assiduously over the years is not the criminal as he or she may exist, but only those one or two species of the genus which are, and always have been, catchable.

They also believe, despite the angry merriment of old-school policemen, for whom the idea is naturally upsetting, in the existence of an entire criminal species of sub-genus about which little or nothing is as yet known: that of the Able Criminal.

Krom's description of the species is one of the more celebrated. It was part of a lecture delivered at a meeting of the International Police Association in Berne. Although he himself, writing in German, prefers to identify his quarry as *Der Kompetente Kriminelle,* on this occasion he was, in deference to the majority among his polygot audience, speaking in English. Having uttered the phrase Able Criminal aloud on a lecture rostrum for the first time, he then went on:

'I am not, my friends, in any way alluding to the Master Criminal of blessed memory, that beguiling figment of nineteenth-century fictional imaginations who so often fell prey to amateur detectives, but to a present-day occupant of the real world.

'The Able Criminal, male or female, may be presumed to possess a high IQ, to be emotionally stable and 'well adjusted,' to exhibit none of the personality defects said to be characteristic of the accepted 'criminal types' and to belong to none of the much-publicized crime syndicates so dear to the romantics in some of our law-enforcement

11

agencies. He will, except in the protective cover role of worthy citizen, be unknown to such agencies and unsuspected by them. He (or she – gender has no relevance here) has no discernible and hence no classifiable *modus operandi,* and unless disease or advancing age causes deterioration of his faculties, he is virtually uncatchable.

'Of the kinds of crime he commits, fraud is naturally high on the list; yet fraud is not, for some of the species, the only, nor even a principal, source of revenue. Here in ~~Berne it will be unnecessary~~ to remind you that the laws on income tax evasion – not avoidance, evasion – vary widely between our different countries. In America and Britain evasion is a crime. In Switzerland it is not, in a great many other parts of the world, in places like Monaco, Grand Cayman, Bermuda and the New Hebrides, there are no income taxes to evade. Within the stratified complexities of international tax and corporation law the opportunities for the Able Criminal are boundless. On the evidence which has been available to me – unhappily not evidence of the quality upon which our democratic justice likes to depend – these opportunities include large-scale but non-prosecutable embezzlement and blackmail, plus undetectable forgery as well as property crime, chiefly connected with heavily-insured works of art, of the more traditional sort. I do not have to tell this audience that where there is crime for gain on that scale, however sophisticated it may be, there too will be found, sooner or later, its inevitable accompaniments, gangsterism and violence.'

Krom had gone on to list some of the technical difficulties to be overcome in researching the species, and had compared them with those which had confronted the physicists who first set out to investigate the behaviour of energized particles in a cyclotron.

'The investigators might *think* that they knew what was going on inside, but until they had devised an exact way of knowing what was going on, the validity of their suppositions could not be assessed.'

Connell, in his doctoral thesis, had commented sadly on the comparison. 'Professor Krom might have added that while physicists have long since solved those and many other sets of even more complex problems, we, the new criminologists, are still grappling with the most basic among ours. We have not yet learned to recognize source material as such even when we are staring at it.'

Dr Henson, writing in *The New Sociologist*, had been explicit about her difficulties.

'No matter how ingenious the investigative techniques employed, the likelihood of the student learning anything that our able criminal would prefer to keep secret is small. The writer, and she does not think herself uniquely handicapped, has had to depend largely for her data-gathering upon methods of enquiry which only the charitable could call serious. To put it bluntly, they involve unscientific fumblings with minor strokes of luck; for example, the accidental unearthing of a conventional criminal informer who talked unwittingly of matters the real significance of which he himself had not even begun to grasp.'

She had made her point. She might have been wiser to have left it at that. Instead, she had gone on to lambast some of her critics.

'Understandably, members of the older schools of criminology, recoiling from the difficulties, have chosen to deny the able criminal's existence. They have preferred either to continue cultivating the already over-cultivated study fields of juvenile delinquency and Mafia-style organized crime, or to dabble in forensic medicine.'

The critics had hit back fiercely. Among the politer was one who reminded her that phenomena which are so very difficult to observe without 'unscientific fumblings' frequently turn out to exist only in the minds' eyes of the committed few who claim to have observed them. The able criminal could well be compared in that context with such aberrations as the Unidentified Flying Object and the little green men from outer space. And were there not simple persons who still believed in ghosts?

Poor Dr Henson. With that truthful but unfortunate reference to fumbling she had handed her opponents the only weapon they could effectively use. Yet, her frankness did not go unrewarded, for the controversy it aroused brought her to the special attention of Professor Krom. He had known of her book, of course, but now he was reminded of her, and of the views she held, at a decisive moment.

Something remarkable had happened to him and he needed kindred spirits with whom to share the experience.

Connell has emphasized the difficulty for the new criminologists of recognizing a source when they see it. Henson has spoken of the remoteness of even that opportunity. Only Krom, with all his experience, having stumbled upon a major and reliable source, having recognized it as such and then decided patiently to wait and watch, may now know how lucky he has been.

I know of only two other similar cases of this magnitude. In both, the consequences for all concerned were most unpleasant. There were failures of nerve and regrettable lapses into primitive modes of behaviour, not quite as unexpected as those upon which I have to report but no less outrageous. In neither of those cases, however, were there any survivors.

So, whether he is prepared to admit it or not, Krom was lucky in a number of ways. The most important of them, undoubtedly, was the discovery of his windfall source in me.

By the failures of the world in which I move I have been accused in my time of possessing nearly all the anti-social qualities. It has been said that, both in my business and in my private lives, I have been consistently sly, treacherous, ruthless and rapacious, vindictive, devious, sadistic and generally vile. I could add to that list. But no one, *no* one, has ever yet suggested that I would even

14

condone a resort to violence by others, much less promote or organize the use of it myself. Squeamishness? Timidity? Think what you please. I have seen enough of violence to convince me that even where it appears to succeed, as in some struggles for political power, the success usually proves in the end to have been more apparent than real.

I do not, of course, expect justice; that would be too much; but I believe that I am entitled to a fair trial before the only court I recognize, the only court whose judgements I now value; that is the court of public opinion.

Now that the real 'Mr X' has been identified by me and the full extent of his perfidy is no longer a secret, those who are prepared to consider the evidence with open and objective minds – evidence that proves beyond doubt and sans whitewash that far from being the villain of the piece I am his principal victim – should be allowed to do so.

If Krom is still reluctant to risk his precious reputation by disclosing in their proper perspective those facts which are known to him, but which he finds inconvenient, then I must do the job myself. Perhaps, too, Connell and Henson will be prompted by their integrity as scholars, to say nothing of common decency, to back me up. If they are not so prompted, well, for once, my own welfare and that of men of more conventional goodwill may be promoted together. For once, it is in nearly everyone's interests that a whole truth be generally known.

The house-phone buzzed.

'Paul?' It was Yves.

'We have complications,' he said. 'Dr Connell has protested at my taking his tape-recorder from him. Said that he had had no intention of using it without permission, and insists that taping is his normal way of setting down case notes. Would be lost without it. Pointed out that he had carried it openly, and after obtaining Krom's reluctantly-given permission to do so.'

'What did you decide?'

'To let him have it, conditionally, because we might find it useful too, if you see what I mean.'

'I think so. What conditions?'

'I said that it would be placed in his room and must remain there. He could use it, but no voice tracks were to be made other than his own. I can easily wipe anything we find objectionable later on. Meanwhile, I'll check it out for added circuits.'

'Okay. Now, what about Dr Henson's shoulder bag?'

'Paul, that is far more serious. The heavy object you observed turned out to be one of those plastic cases which women use now when travelling to carry cosmetics in small quantities. They are fitted with leak-proof bottles and little jars to save weight.'

'Then why was it heavy?'

'Because of an arrangement of objects packed in the cavity below the main tray. They included a camera.'

'Oh, for God's sake! What kind?'

'Special job, but based, I think, on a body belonging to that small underwater Nikon. Among the accessories with it we have green and infra-red filters and two lenses, one a close-up. A very classy outfit. Must have cost a fortune.'

'What did Dr Henson have to say for herself?'

'What one would expect, I suppose. No intention of using it without permission. Indignant when reminded that you had made a point of disallowing cameras in the protocol she signed. Hit back. Tape-recorders were also verboten. Connell was carrying one. Were we going to make an equal fuss about that?'

'How did Krom and Connell react to all this?'

Yves sound surprised. 'Oh, they weren't present. I saw each separately.' He paused. 'But, Paul, she had more than just the camera stuff in that compartment.'

'Not a gun, I hope.'

'No, something perhaps a little more dangerous. A small aerosol spray. It had a printed label saying that it was a nail-varnish remover.'

16

'Which you didn't believe.'

'The nail-varnish remover that the women I know normally use comes in bottles, not aerosols. The label didn't look right either.'

'What did you say?'

'I asked her to show me how it worked on one of her fingernails.'

'And?'

'Refused. Why should she spoil a perfectly good manicure for my amusement?'

'But you weren't impressed.'

'Paul, she doesn't *have* a perfectly good manicure. I think the aerosol's loaded with that Swedish chemical they are using these days for examining suspect documents like forged cheques, the stuff that reacts with amino acids to bring up latent fingerprints on paper so you can photograph them. They come up purple. Hence the green filter for the close-up lens.'

'Hence also the fact that she wouldn't spray it on her fingers. The stuff is called ninhydrin and it's highly poisonous, even in solution. Someone must have warned her.'

'Doesn't surprise me. The whole compartment, the whole kit, looks as if it had been thought out and packed in a lab by some police or other intelligence-gathering outfit, for use in the field.'

I sighed. 'How about Krom? Anything up his sleeves? Radio bleepers? Poisoned darts?'

'No, he was clean. I've got the key of their car, I'm going down now to drive it up.'

He would also search the baggage thoroughly after it had been taken up to their rooms.

'Where are they now?'

'Melanie's giving them soothing drinks.'

'Let me know when you've cleared the baggage. I'll go down then and introduce myself to our guests.'

With characteristic politeness he had refrained from

17

commenting on the crass absurdity of the words I had just uttered.

There would be no need at all for me to introduce myself to Professor Krom.

Unfortunately, he and I had already met – and more than once.

That was the cause of the whole trouble.

I can still hear him pronouncing what could have been my death sentence, as well as his own.

'You were too kind, Mr Firman. In future, when one of your employees is called to meet his Maker, I strongly advise you to send no flowers.'

That is what he *actually* said, not what he now claims that he said. At the time there was none of that rubbish about exploding flowers and blast areas; and the word 'guilt' was certainly not used, 'smilingly' or in any other way.

What guilt, anyway? Only an idiot would attribute a sense of guilt in this case to me.

I am not the defendant.

I am the plaintiff.

Professor Krom's account of the events I am describing differs radically from mine; and it does so, I believe, chiefly because his was written while he was still too disturbed by his experiences at the Villa Lipp to think clearly. He is, after all, an elderly man unaccustomed to explosions. It is likely that, in all important respects, my account is the more balanced of the two.

That said, however, his initial achievement remains and should be recognized for what it is: a triumph of chance over all reasonable probabilities and, from his point of view at any rate, evidence that some of his theories may ultimately be capable of proof. His single-minded professional persistence aided by a photographic memory produced a moment at which two apparently dissimilar persons seen in totally different and unrelated contexts were suddenly identified as one and the same.

I was the person thus identified, and news of the identification had been given to me two months earlier during one of the tax-haven seminars organized by Symposia S.A.

The place was Brussels.

That much admitted, the record may now be wiped clean of some of the mud with which it has been so freely bespattered. I wish to state categorically that neither the Symposia group of companies – specifically: Symposia AG, Symposia SA, Symposia NV and Symposia (Bermuda) Ltd – nor its connected consultative body, the Institute for International Investment and Trust Counselling, are in any country or in any way contravening or subverting established law. Not even our keenest competitors in the field of trust counselling have, however eager they may have been to take advantage of Krom's so-called 'revelations', dared to suggest otherwise. The idea is preposterous; and anyone who still doubts this has only to look at the long list of those bankers, trust officers, international lawyers and tax accountants who attended the April seminar, and at the names, all famous in the international business world, of the experts they came to hear. Men of that calibre understand and respect the law. The last thing they wish to do is to consort with criminals.

The subject of that particular seminar was of fairly general interest, a survey of the various pieces of anti-avoidance legislation currently being introduced by some ill-natured western governments, and the number of registrants was high. There were one hundred and twenty-three of them; and anyone foolish enough to suppose that organizing such affairs is in itself a road to riches may like to know that Symposia's net reward for that week's work was a mere twenty thousand dollars. Nobody can say that *that* part of the tax-avoidance business yields high profits. Without its fringe benefits the game would simply not be worth playing. Through organizing these affairs we get to know people and we get to know things.

Not that we ever spied on anyone; I don't mean that. If anything, as I now realize, we were too easy-going. Naturally, we always took an interest in the identities of those who attended our seminars, in their countries of origin, the passports they carried and the fields of their specializations; but those little dossiers we compiled were primarily for the benefit of our faculty lecturers. From the start it was always Symposia policy to admit to our seminars, however delicate the subject matter, all who were prepared to remit with their applications cheques for the registration fees. We expect the major government revenue services to be represented and they usually are, often adding – especially when the lecturer is himself a former revenue official – a certain liveliness to the discussion periods. The atmosphere, though, is essentially one of friendly rivalry and mutual respect. Both sides are simply doing their jobs as best they can and with pretty clear ideas about one another's strengths and weaknesses. Discretion is practised, of course, but almost never to the point of play-acting. I know of only two cases of persons registering under false names.

One was a journalist working for a French left-wing scandal sheet. The seminar he attended was devoted mainly to the subject of discretionary and exempt trust concepts. He pretended to be a lawyer. In the article he wrote following this masquerade, he managed not only to mount a totally irrelevant attack on multi-national corporations but also to reveal that he did not quite know what a trust was.

The other case was, as we shall see, different.

The journalist had been spotted immediately. Krom was not spotted at all; chiefly because the name under which he registered was not false enough. It had been borrowed, with its owner's knowledge and consent, so that the usual intelligence cross-check turned up nothing to alert us.

In my official capacity as Director of the Institute it was natural that I should take the chair and introduce the speakers at one or two sessions. The first of those I presided over was in the afternoon of the second day. It ended at five. An hour later Krom introduced himself to me.

His method of doing so had an unpleasant touch of the macabre in it and was for me, I freely admit, highly disturbing. No doubt he intended it to be.

The receptionist telephoned me in my room.

He was a man who knew me and my voice well. He still asked carefully if he was speaking to Mr Firman.

'Certainly you are. What is it?'

We usually spoke French. Now he began speaking in English. He was obviously reading what he had to say.

'I am asked to state, Mr Firman, that Mr Kramer and Mr Oberholzer of Zürich are waiting in the lobby here to see you.'

Since they were both dead men – Kramer being literally

dead and Oberholzer figuratively so – the announcement gave me quite a jolt.

I said: 'I see. *Both* these gentlemen are there?'

'That is what I am instructed to say, sir.' The tone of his voice was unnaturally formal. I thought it possible that he believed he was dealing with a police matter.

As we were in Brussels, I knew that possibility to be remote. We were on excellent terms with the authorities there. In fact, if I could have assumed that it was only a police matter, I would, at that moment, have been much relieved.

'I'll be down in a few minutes, Jules.'

'Thank you, sir.' Still very formal, painfully so.

I didn't wait a few minutes. I went down straight away and by the emergency stairs. This enabled me to get a look at the vicinity of Jules's reception desk without crossing the lobby.

There were some new arrivals at the hotel checking in, or waiting to do so, and there was quite a crowd by the desk. None among them was known to me or looked in the least like a person who could have intimidated an experienced hotel receptionist.

Jules was pretending to study his reservation plot-board on the wall behind the counter, and I could see, even at that distance, that he was in a state of shock. I had another, more careful, look around, then went over quickly and elbowed my way through to him. The indignant looks his two assistants gave me were easy to ignore. I tapped him on the shoulder. It was as if he had been expecting arrest and was now resigned to it. He leaned wearily against the wall before he turned.

He was, I knew, in his sixties. Now, grey and sweating, he looked eighty and unlikely to last much longer. When he recognized me he fluttered his hands and started to protest weakly against my invasion of his territory. I cut him short.

'Stop yammering. Where are they?'

'There's only one, the man in three-two-six. But . . . '

22

'Name?'

'Dopff. He is over in the corner by the big flower arrangement, and he is watching us speak. I beg you, Mr Firman, please . . . '

I did not wait to hear what he was begging me to do, or not do, but turned and walked straight across to where the man was sitting.

My memory for names and faces is good, very good, but it has its limits. I could remember that a person named Dopff was registered for the seminar and that he was from Luxembourg, but I couldn't recall his profession. That meant only one thing: whatever he was - lawyer, banker, amateur tax-evader, or government spy - he had been checked out as a potential client and, as such, found wanting.

As I approached, I recognized him; he was the elderly man who had been sitting in the middle of the third row an hour or so earlier, listening with rapt attention to my introduction of the main speaker. I had noticed him partly because he had actually seemed interested in my ritual listing of the speaker's qualifications - they were all there printed in the official programme he had in his hand - but mostly because he appeared to wear a permanent smile. The smile, I had noted later as we were all leaving the conference room, was an optical illusion which vanished when you came closer to him. It was produced by the combination of an upper lip shaped like a circumflex accent and a mouthful of large, very white teeth, the kind that look like cheap dentures even when they are not.

He was showing them to me now as I approached him; only this was no illusory smile; it was a blatantly triumphant grin. Had I not needed badly to know who he really was, what he wanted and what sort of threat he constituted, I would have walked straight on past him just for the pleasure of watching the result through the mirror on the adjacent wall. I took refuge instead in courtesy. The really heavy-handed, old-world stuff can make it possible for one to discharge an enormous amount of anger without the object of the anger becoming fully aware of it. He may suspect but he cannot be certain. With luck, one will cause him considerable unease without giving him any excuse to take offence.

Unfortunately, with a man as sure of himself as Krom, this form of attack can never be wholly effective.

The common language of our seminar has always been English, so it was in English that I addressed him.

'Mr Dopff, is it? I understand that you wish to see me.'

To the grin he added an insolent stare. 'No, Mr Firman, that is not at all what I wish. I have already seen you, clearly and unmistakably, before. That was in Zürich five years ago when you were calling yourself Oberholzer.'

'My name is Firman, sir.'

He went on as if I had not spoken. 'So, I have seen you twice. What I intend to do from now on is to talk with you.' He patted the arm of the empty chair beside him. 'Why don't you sit down?'

I remained standing. 'I am sure that you will understand that I am a busy man, Mr Dopff. I simply came to tell you that the receptionist here gave me a strange message, from you he tells me, about two persons of whom I have never heard. It seemed proper and sensible to let you know that the message was either garbled or misdirected. That is all.'

He showed his teeth again. 'That garbled message brought you pretty quickly, Mr Oberholzer.'

'The name, I repeat, is Firman.'

'At the moment it is, yes. But it used to be Oberholzer, and I have no doubt that there have been, and still are, a great many other identities in your repertoire. How annoying it must be for you to realize that this time you can't just run for it.'

I gave him my little bow. 'Except to escape the acute boredom of this conversation, Mr Dopff, why on earth should I run anywhere?'

He was unruffled. 'You ran in Zurich. Here, as you have

obviously realized, you must try to bluff your way out. No head-start possible, no suitable cut-outs available and no inconspicuous exits handy. Agreed? So why not sit down and join me in a little whisky? In spite of your impressive outer calm, I am sure that you would find it helpful.'

At that moment I had almost decided that he was some sort of private detective, a retired fraud-squad type. Anyway, it was time to counter-attack.

I sighed and sat down in the chair beside him. 'Very well, Mr Dopff. You want to talk. May I suggest a subject?'

'Why not?' He snapped his fingers for the waiter. 'We can always change it.'

'Then, since the subject of indentity seems to interest you so much, why don't we have a look at the one you're using?'

'By all means.'

The waiter came then and took the order for more whisky. It was given in what sounded to me like Flemish.

'For a start,' I said, 'I don't think you're a Luxembourger.'

'Absolutely right!' Beaming smile. He might have been playing a guessing game with a favourite grandchild.

'And your name is not Dopff.'

'Right again. My good friend Maurice Dopff, who lives and works in the Grand Duchy, registered for this affair and then found himself unable to attend. He kindly allowed me to come in his stead.'

'Do you really expect me to believe that?'

'Of course I don't. He allowed himself to be used as cover.' He fished out a visiting card and handed it to me. 'Permit me to introduce myself formally. The name is Krom.'

I knew at once exactly who he was. In the tax-avoidance game our coverage of legal and financial publications of all sorts and nationalities is as comprehensive as we can make it. The Institute and Symposia between them employed a multi-lingual, and very expensive, full-time research staff of eight as well as numerous part-timers. With us, good intelligence is as essential for survival as discipline and foresight. Our coverage of specialized technical journals dealing with law enforcement at policy-making levels is extremely thorough. Krom's allusions to tax avoidance and evasion in the published version of his Berne lecture had been sufficient to ensure its being brought to my attention flagged with a red sticker. Even if he had not initiated our acquaintance by playing games with dead men's names, I would have known enough about Krom to be wary of him.

My first ploy, then, was to pretend that I knew nothing while working to find out more.

I gave the card a perplexed look. 'Well, Professor, this is all a bit surprising. As you can imagine, we get lots of peculiar characters at these seminars of ours, all sorts of nosey-parkers, including, I have to say, some of our competitors in the tax haven area. We don't object. If we can teach them something, well that is what we are here for, to teach. It *is* though a trifle irksome, I admit, when they make fools of themselves by wearing disguises.' I contrived a sudden look of anxiety. 'You really *are* Professor Krom, I hope? This – ' I held up the card – 'is not, by any chance, a disguise within a disguise?'

He had been watching me intently and with a certain air of disbelief. Now he shook his head slowly. 'No, I am Krom. Why? Were you hoping that I wasn't?'

'On the contrary, I was hoping that you were. You see, this is the first time we have had the pleasure of entertaining a Professor of Sociology. This is an occasion. Still – ' perplexity again – 'I'm afraid I don't yet see the connection between your field and ours. Unless, that is, you are seeking advice on how best a good Dutchman may avoid those onerous Netherlands taxes.'

He suddenly grinned again and clapped his hands softly. 'An excellent performance,' he said, 'really excellent. Just for a moment there you nearly made me forget. Forget Oberholzer and Kramer, I mean. You see, Mr Firman, my field is criminology.'

It was time to show *my* teeth. I said: 'You'll find no able criminals here, Professor Krom.'

He positively giggled. 'From defence to attack, eh? The pretence of ignorance is abruptly discarded in order to disconcert. Splendid impertinence!'

I went on as if he had not spoken. 'So I'm afraid your little fishing expedition will have to be written off as a waste of time. Sorry.'

Protesting hands. 'Oh, but it has got off to a most successful, a most promising, start!'

The drink arrived just then. I was glad of the diversion. The man was proving hard to handle, and I needed time to think. I could have done with more. It was necessary to find out from him what he considered success without actually asking, and I made a complete hash of it.

When the waiter had gone again I said: 'Then you must be easily satisfied.'

He read me instantly. 'I can well understand, Mr Firman, that you are curious.'

'I'm surprised, certainly.' No point in letting the adversary *see* your discomfiture even if he must have sensed it. I kept going. 'You bait your hook with some mysterious substance labelled Oberholzer and Kramer, and catch an empty beer can. If you think that's good fishing, naturally I'm surprised.'

The teeth flashed triumphantly. 'You've missed a trick, Mr Firman!'

'I am sure that you intend to tell me which.'

'Of course I do. You fell into the trap of failing to ask yourself an obvious question.'

I smiled. 'How do you know what questions I ask myself, Professor?'

'I know you haven't asked yourself this one because you haven't asked me for the answer. Consider. You are told that Oberholzer and Kramer are waiting to see you. Correct?'

'I am told that two persons of whom I have never heard are waiting to see me.'

An upraised forefinger flicked the quibble aside

27

contemptuously. 'Yet, in your anxiety to set eyes instantly upon the person who uses these unknown names, you quite overlook the oddity of the channel of communication he has chosen to use.' He paused before going on. 'Do you usually in this hotel receive messages about visitors from the receptionist? Doesn't the concierge's, the hall-porter's, department function here?'

I managed, not without difficulty, a careless shrug. 'It functions, yes, and quite efficiently. I presume you thought that a busy receptionist was less likely to remember your face than the concierge who gives you your room-key and who might also be unsympathetic to practical jokes.'

He gave me a kindly look. 'Not bad for a spur-of-the moment invention, but it won't do, will it? Hindsight content far too high. If you had never heard of Oberholzer and Kramer why would the possibility of a practical joke occur to you? No, you failed to ask yourself why I had gone to the receptionist because the questions uppermost in your mind just then were – who is this joker, what does he want and how dangerous is he?'

I drank some whisky. I had begun to need it. As if to humour him, I put the question: 'Well, why *did* you use the receptionist to send me your message?'

He gave me a nod for good behaviour, but no immediate answer to his question.

'In spite of his being one of the more active members of your private espionage organization,' he said, 'I think I may know more about that receptionist than you do. Naturally, all your known associates have interested me for some time. Where possible I have built up dossiers on them. However, once I had decided that the birthplace of our collaboration would be here in Brussels, work on all your local contacts was intensified.' A peculiar twitching of his facial muscles began as he added: 'The possibility of an abortion occurring was, to this fond parent, a totally unacceptable risk.'

As his face went on twitching and he gazed at me

28

expectantly, I realized that he thought he had said something funny and was waiting for a laugh.

When all he got was a blank stare, the twitching ceased and he said tolerantly: 'Perhaps you would find a military analogue more to your taste.'

'Perhaps.'

'Well then, this was the kind of operation in which success can only be won by immaculate preparation leading to the achievement of tactical surprise. A note delivered to your room, or left in your mail-box downstairs here, would not have worked. You would have had time to think, time to investigate and prepare defences, possibly time to make arrangements for my discomfiture. Or even,' he added coyly, 'not knowing of the precautions I had taken to safeguard myself, time to organize my removal from the scene.'

I looked suitably offended by the insinuation. 'For a criminologist you have a somewhat lurid imagination, Professor.'

'I was not, of course, being entirely serious, Mr Firman.' The teeth made a jovial showing, but the wariness in the pale-blue eyes told a different story. He believed not only that I was an able criminal but also a person capable of murder. I made a note of the fact. That sort of belief, senseless though it may be, can sometimes be quite useful.

'But,' he was saying, 'you are right about one thing.'

'Good.'

'The concierge might, as you say, have found the verbal message strange. There could have been several possible consequences of his doing so. You might, as we have seen, have been in some way forewarned and thus forearmed. Even more important, he might, without thinking, have talked, gossiped, and so compromised the entire operation. I had long perceived, you see, that if our collaboration was to be fruitful, absolute secrecy, in the early stages especially, was essential. *That* is why I chose the receptionist to deliver my message. He will not, I assure you, repeat a word of it, or of your subsequent questioning of him, to any third party. The poor fellow is far too frightened to disobey me.'

'I noticed that he had been frightened. What did you threaten him with?'

'Threaten him, Mr Firman? It wasn't necessary to threaten him.' He found the accusation quite astounding. 'As I told you, I have done, and had done for me, much intensive work on your people. This man spied on you, so it occurred to me to wonder if, perhaps, he spied, or had once spied, for someone else. I was simply looking in a routine fashion, you understand, for parallel associations. Well, I have friends in Bonn who are interested in my work and they have access to the BND and its archive of Nazi SD files. And what do you think? During the Nazi occupation here our receptionist avoided forced labour recruitment by becoming an SD informer. Naturally, since he had never been exposed here – the victorious Allies couldn't be bothered with the non-German small fry and the Belgian Resistance never had free access to the files – he had come to believe that the past, or that little bit of his particular past, was buried for ever. Did you know about it?'

He was still trying to sell me the proposition that, no matter what game we ended up playing, he would hold a winning hand.

'No,' I said. 'I didn't know.'

'So it was unnecessary to use threats. All I had to do was speak to him using his old German code-name.'

'I see. And you didn't consider that a threat?'

He swallowed most of his drink – talking had made him thirsty – and savoured it with a genteel little smack of the lips before he answered.

'No,' he said finally, 'I didn't consider it a threat. Nor, by the same token, would I consider that the conflicting interests which will be the basis of our collaboration need be thought of as threats by either of us. We are both sensible men, are we not?'

'I am beginning to have doubts, Professor. That is the third time you have spoken of our collaborating. Collaborating in *what*, for heaven's sake?'

This time he showed me all his teeth and a stretch of molar bridgework as well.

'I intend,' he said, 'to make a complete, full-scale case-study of both you and your remarkable career, Mr Firman. For that, I shall require your close collaboration. Total anonymity will, of course, be guaranteed so that nothing need be left unsaid. You will be the great Mr X.' He gave a little snicker. 'In other words, I intend to make your craft and its associated skills as well understood by, and as recognizable in, the law-enforcement agencies of the world as common-or-garden burglary is now. Yes, Mr Firman, I intend to make you famous!'

Mat was in London, negotiating, on behalf of Chief Tebuke and the native population of Placid Island, the final settlement of their claim against the Anglo-Anzac Phosphate Company; or rather he was going through the motions of negotiating on their behalf. Everyone who counted knew that he was in fact negotiating more for his own ultimate benefit than anyone else's. They also thought that they knew what he wanted for himself out of the settlement. His connection with, then amounting to control of, the Symposia Group was at that time a very well-kept secret.

We maintained a fully-staffed office in Brussels. With its help, I was able to reach him by telephone soon after seven.

The emergency routine in use at the time involved sending a preliminary alert through a London cut-out via telex. That brought him to a safe phone to receive the call. Inevitably, though, there was some delay. I filled it by re-examining the file on Krom.

It had been his Berne lecture that had brought him to my attention, and it was to the lecture that I now returned.

One of the things that had struck me about it at the

time had been his casual use of the word 'criminal'. In my opinion and, I think, in that of most modern lexicographers, a criminal is one who commits a serious act generally considered injurious to the public welfare and usually punishable by law. Krom seemed to believe that anyone possessing the imagination and business planning skills needed to evolve a new way of investing time and money in order to make a profit, was automatically a criminal. The wretch need not have committed any illegal act to earn him the distinction. If he had been original and his originality had succeeded, that was enough. For Krom he stood condemned.

This is Krom on my old friend Carlo Lech's last fling:

'The classic coup by Able Criminals – we do not know exactly how many were involved, but it is believed that there were four partners in the venture – is, of course, the famous butter affair. For the benefit of those delegates here whose governments have seen fit to abstain from or avoid, membership of the EEC, I should explain that between member states there is an elaborate system of import-export subsidies. What these clever rogues did was to buy a large consignment of butter, a trainload of the stuff, and send it on a European tour, claiming each time it crossed a frontier, subsidies for its fictional transformation into some other butter-fat product. At the end of the tour they sold off the butter for what they had paid for it and pocketed between them ten million Deutschmarks in subsidies. Later operators in this field have not even troubled to buy the goods they manipulate in this way. Their transactions exist *only* on paper. Value-added tax rebates of non-existent but thoroughly-documented export transactions are currently in vogue. EEC regulations are constantly being changed, of course, to stop up the holes in them, but new holes continue to appear. Needless to say, even when such a criminal, or the corporate cover behind which he works, has supposedly been identified, there is no effective means of instituting a prosecution.'

Well of course there isn't. No criminal law has been broken, and nothing injurious to the public welfare has occurred; not, that is, unless you consider the spectacle of EEC bureaucrats going about with egg on their faces injurious to the public welfare. There are, in fact, large sections of the European public who find such sights highly beneficial, and worth every centime or pfennig of their cost.

And not even Krom, by the way, had been altogether unaware of the inconvenient questions which his theories invited. He had dealt with them, cutely, by asking them before his audience could do so.

'Why, I may be asked, should the word "Able" be used to categorize this well-adapted but minor sub-genus within the human race? Would not the term Successful Crook be at once more accurate and more suitable? My answer must be that it would not. The word "crook" is imprecise and the word "successful" would in this context be misleading, for it could be taken to mean "fortunate".' The Able Criminal is, no doubt, fortunate in that he is successful; but he is successful not through some happy series of accidents or because the police authority concerned with him is incompetent; he is successful always and only because he *is* able.

'Why, then, is he a criminal at all? What, if he really exists, can possibly motivate him? The desire for wealth and the power that goes, or is said to go, with it? Hardly. Men capable of planning and executing the butter coup or having the fiscal wit to create illusory businesses which make real profits could surely become multi-millionaires quite – I was about to say "legitimately" – perhaps I should say instead "legally"'. As legally, anyway, as unit trust managers or currency speculators are said to conduct their respective operations.

'But our Mr X is not attracted by the blessings of legitimacy and legality, only by the extent to which the appearances of them may be put to use. He is a white-collar criminal in the sense that he is an educated one, yes;

33

but his crimes are the products not of breaches of trust
– the hand in the till, the falsified accounts – but of breaches
of faith. And the faith he breaches is that of faith in
established patterns of order. He is, in short, an anarchist.

'What kind of anarchist? Well, of one thing we can be
certain. He will not be stupid. He will not have taken to
his heart the works of the ineffable Marcuse, nor troubled
himself with the ravings of those hapless social philosophers,
those paladins of the lollipop set, Raoul Vaneigem and Guy
Debord. He will believe neither in the Spectacular Society
nor in Situationist Intervention. He will not be a carrier
of bombs in plastic shopping-bags. But his tactical thinking
will have much in common with that of some of the better-
disciplined urban guerrilla groups – those who work by
confounding bureaucractic controls and exploiting the
resultant confusion for profit. Whether that profit be
ideological or solely financial is a matter which need not
concern us here. The first step is to recognize the nature
of the difficulties facing us. In the jungles of international
bureaucracy, including those of the multi-national
corporations, there is always plenty of dense undergrowth
in which able men may conceal themselves and from which
they may mount attacks. The task of those attempting to
flush them out will never be easy.'

We had one room in the office suite which was regularly
checked for bugs. I sat in there to take the call to Mat.

Our conversation lasted less than a minute. Most of it
consisted of code-words suggesting that we were in the
fertilizer business. They conveyed, however, first a top-
priority blown-cover alert from me with a request for orders.
From Mat came an instruction to go to London forthwith
by the company plane, and be prepared to return to Brussels
that same night. The journey was to be made unobtrusively.
If possible it should not be known that I had left the hotel
at all.

Finding the pilot took time because he was in bed with

some girl; but he had obeyed standing orders, which ensured that he was always on call in an emergency, and, once found, he responded promptly. For the salaries we paid we expected efficiency. When I got to the airport he had already obtained a clearance to land at Southend and filed a flight plan. Customs clearances presented no problem. The only baggage I carried was my Brussels room-key with its heavy brass number-tag. By eleven-thirty I was in London.

Mat usually stayed at Claridge's, but this time he had chosen to hole up in a rather seedy Kensington hotel.

I had twitted him about it when I had seen him some weeks earlier. What, I had asked, had he been trying to prove? That he was just a simple island wog being victimized by the wicked monopoly capitalists who had stolen his forefathers' birthright? And whom did he hope to impress with this nonsense? The British Foreign and Commonwealth Office people he was dealing with, who knew to a man that he was a graduate of the London School of Economics and had attended Stanford Law School? Or Anglo-Anzac Phosphate who thought of him chiefly as the expert on Pacific tax-haven trust laws appointed by a Canadian bank to make sure that many mangy old Chief kept his nose clean and got his sums right?

There had been no answering smile. About some things one no longer makes jokes.

'Paul, there is only one person I have to impress at the movement, Chief Tebuke. You ought to know why, without my having to spell it out for you. If we want real power in an independent Placid Island with a dollar-linked currency and beneficent corporation laws, the appearance of that power must be vested initially in the historically acceptable indigenous figure who can give it a glaze of respectability. The granting of independence must seem, especially in North America, to be a belated act of simple justice to which no honest man, whatever his race, creed or colour, could possibly object. For how long did the Australian Government tolerate the fiscal independence of

Norfolk Island when they found that it was taking a slice our of their tax cake? Just as long as it took to pass the legislation cancelling Norfolk's right to take it. No effective right of appeal existed because there was no indisputably valid claim to sovereignty. Any rich fool can buy an island and proclaim it a sovereign state. On the mainland he need not even be so very rich. All he needs to do there is back an up-and-coming separatist movement, or a bunch of dissident army officers, and play it patiently by ear. But how or what he buys into is unimportant. It's getting the recognition that counts. Not just a tolerated measure of autonomy, but *de facto, de jure,* UN-approved, copper-bottomed sovereignty, the works.'

'I only asked you why you weren't staying at Claridge's.'

'And I'm telling you. In this case the key to recognition lies in Chief Tebuke, our symbol of both legitimacy and self-determination. In order to control him I must retain his trust and affection. In the islands, trust and affection are based on the strict observance of certain social rules, which you might choose to call etiquette but which I prefer to call a code of manners. I am not the Chief, but an adviser. Therefore, I must live in a lesser place. He happens to be impressed by the Hilton. So, I must not live in Claridge's where heads of state are known to stay. I could live on a lower floor of the Hilton, of course, but the less I see of him the better. This is well out of his way. What's the matter with it anyhow? I've lived in worse hotels and so have you. You're getting soft, Paul.'

That one had been rather more long-winded than usual, probably because he had thought it necessary to mix some falsehood in with the truth; but, apart from that, you could call it a typically sanctimonious Mat reproof.

It has been said that the vision of the apocalyptic horsemen reveals only that St John must have had poor eyesight. Just *four* horsemen? For heaven's sake! Listen man, even *twenty-*four would have been too few.

The suggestion is, of course, that the consequences of

war are of infinite variety and by no means always evil. Like many other platitudes, this one, too, has an element of truth in it.

Among the consequences of World War II in the Pacific, for example, the accident of Mathew Williamson's exposure to the world Boy Scout movement, and subsequently to the works and philosophy of Lord Baden-Powell of Gilwell, would probably be accounted by most right-thinking persons a good thing; and if there are those, more familiar perhaps with the ideological content of the works, who feel inclined to question that verdict, let them keep their thoughts to themselves. One thing is virtually certain: without the benefit of the Chief Scout's teachings, Mat – he was given a Christian name and baptized at the Methodist mission while he was in Fiji – would never have become the extraordinary businessman he is.

In view of the *kind* of businessman he is, that may seem odd; but I doubt if the author of *Life's Snags and How to Meet Them, Sport in War, Scouting for Boys* and *Lessons from the Varsity of Life* could ever, even in one of his least humourless moments, have envisaged the effects that his homespun pragmatism might have upon the mind of a lad of Mat's peculiar antecedents, natural talents and disposition. His books were, in a sense, gospels, but they were not designed to withstand interpretation by a half-caste Melanesian sorcerer.

Mat's father was an Australian sea captain named Williamson, his mother the daughter of a village headman in one of the Gilbert Islands. There is no record of the pair ever having been married. She had lived on board Williamson's ship, a freighter owned by one of the phosphate companies, and Mat, whom she called Tuakana because it meant 'eldest', was born in the company dispensary on Placid Island. She had, though, no more children after him.

When he first told me about Placid we were sitting on the verandah of a hotel in the New Hebrides' capital, Port Vila, having breakfast. He was in his middle thirties then, an imposingly handsome, dark-skinned man with russet hair. I had assumed that the hair colour was a product of his mixed blood, but found later that in some of the islands it was quite common. However, eyes as blue as his were not. I found them disconcerting. They have had the same effect on others I could name.

I was not too disconcerted to ask questions, though. That, after all, was what I was there for, to ask questions. So, I asked him where he came from and so received the first of many lectures.

'As we were taught at the mission school,' he began, 'the great Captain James Cook gave English names to many of the places he discovered or explored in the wide Pacific Ocean. So good of him, so kind.'

It was said in a high-pitched, nasal voice, startlingly unlike his own, and further distorted by a regional English accent that he later attributed to Birmingham. He has an excellent ear. I am sure that if I had ever met the missionary whose voice he was imitating that day I would have recognized the man instantly.

The voice was discarded as abruptly as it had been assumed when Mat went on, 'You know what I think, Mr Smythson? I think that by the time of his last voyage he was becoming bored with the problem of finding all those new names. I also think that he had a copy of Dr Johnson's dictionary with him and was just going through it page by page. You smile? I'm serious. Fiji had its own native name, of course, even then, but north-west of it what do we find? Ocean Island, Placid Island, Pleasant Island. You see? Successive discoveries all in alphabetical order, even though they're separated by a thousand miles. Placid and Pleasant are, anyway.'

'And very different, I imagine.'

'Oh, not at all different. In fact, very much the same.' He cut a slice of papaya. 'Neither of them was ever placid or in the least pleasant. Both, however, used to possess millions of tons of phosphate deposits. Most of these,

38

naturally, have long been strip-mined and removed, leaving us with lunar landscapes of unlovely grey coral. We were both occupied briefly by Imperial Germany before becoming British colonies. In 'forty-two we were both occupied by the Japanese, who used us as communication centres, and later heavily bombed by the Americans. Both of us subsequently became UN trust territories administered jointly by Britain, Australia and New Zealand, who still wanted what was left of the phosphate. I was born on Placid.'

'I can understand your feeling bitter.'

'Bitter?' He grinned. 'Why on earth should I feel bitter? We were barbarians. You will note that I say "we". I include myself. What would we in our ignorance have done with so much old bird-crap, so much phosphate? Nothing. Our exploitation by the Powers was the best thing that ever happened to us. Even the American bombing was good. Simple people enjoy loud bangs. Unfortunately I was not there to hear them. When the Japanese attacked Pearl Harbour, my father was considerate enough to leave me to be educated in Fiji while he took his ship off to fight for the British Empire.'

The Methodist missionaries who received him had been in for some surprising experiences.

At ten, Mat had had no education other than that provided by his parents and by his travels with them in the ship. From his father he had learned to read and write English and the mathematics of navigation; on his travels he had picked up smatterings of several island languages; from the ship's crew he had learned about the recreational facilities available in Australasian seaports; and, of most importance to him at the time, from his mother he had learned the pagan legends of her forebears. From her too, he had learned about the power and practice of magic; above all, he had learned the secrets of death-spells and other rituals, defensive as well as offensive, through which personal safety or power over others might be achieved.

In the summer of 1942 news came that Mat's father had

gone down with his ship, and a number of refugees from Singapore, off the coast of Java. Later that year his mother died of a kidney disease. It was at the time of his becoming an orphan that Mat was baptized.

The staff at the mission school, delighted to find that they had a gifted child to teach – in mathematics he was considered a prodigy – cannot, however, have deeply regretted the death of his mother. Having fought the good fight against pagan superstition with the weapons of Christian superstition for so long, they must have been disheartened to find out their gifted child could frighten the living daylights out of his wretched classmates with an ancient death-curse. He had shown no interest in the religion he was now being taught. His sudden enthusiasm for Scouting, strange though it may have seemed at the time, was undoubtedly accepted with considerable relief.

I once talked to a retired colonial officer who had served in Fiji for the last three of the seven years that Mat spent there. He had known about Mat chiefly because he had been concerned as an official with the arrangements of the boy's higher education; but that had not been the only reason. He had recalled with amusement that, even as Mat was winning a scholarship and applying, with the help of Government House, for the grants which would enable him to live as a student in London, his name was being submitted for the honour of King's Scout.

'I'll bet they didn't know *that* at the London School of Economics,' he said, then chuckled again. 'Do you know, there was a time when that boy was actually accused publicly by the parents of another, older boy of sorcery and weaving spells. It wasn't a proper court case because they were both minors and because there was no law dealing with junior witch doctors, but there had to be an investigation of the complaint and I was told off to handle it. Know what the cheeky young bugger did?'

'Mat Williamson you mean?'

'Yes. At the enquiry, he handed me, very respectfully,

a list of the questions that he would have addressed to the other boy's parents had he been the defendant in an adult court of law. As, under the circumstances, he was not allowed to ask them, would I please do so? Well, it sounded such a reasonable request and he looked so solemn and upset that, like a bloody fool, I agreed. Should have looked more carefully at the questions first, of course. The parents' complaint was that, as a result of the spell, their boy had suffered agonizing stomach cramps for a week and that the spell had defeated all medical attempts to relieve the pain. That list of questions was like a medical cross-examination, only worse because it gradually became like a parody of a real one. Began all right or I wouldn't have started on it. What had been the diagnosis of the District Nurse? Colic. Had she prescribed medicine? Yes, but it hadn't worked, and so on. Then he really cut loose. What about bowel movements? What had the faeces looked like? Liquid or solid? Small or large? Round or sausage-shaped? Was there accompanying wind? What did it smell like? I wouldn't have gone on but for one thing. Every other question made evidential sense. Had the boy had such attacks before? How often? Real questions. But it was the others that counted. You know, those people have rather a broad sense of humour. They began to laugh and that was that. Nothing much I could do. It wasn't a court of law, but whenever I hear of a case being laughed out of court, I think of that list of questions. If I could have found the little monster guilty of something, I'd have done so cheerfully.'

'But you didn't.'

'Of course not. I was too busy trying not to laugh myself. But afterwards I gave him a ticking-off. Not that he cared. Too clever by half, young Williamson. And I'm not saying that just because he made an ass of me and also won a scholarship. Lots of those very bright teacher's pets are emotionally immature. He wasn't. He had the sort of insights that a great many so-called adults never begin to acquire. He was also a bit cruel. He'd know exactly what was going

41

through some other fellow's mind and use the knowledge to frighten him by dressing it up in that magical hocus-pocus of his. Cruel, as I say, but funny. As for the Boy Scout stuff, that was funny, too, if you looked at it from where he stood. Tribalism, that's what he saw, with lots of stern rituals and the chance to exercise a natural talent for leadership. A very spry lad, and a very deep one, that.'

'As a matter of fact he still quotes Baden-Powell.'

He sniffed. 'They say that the Devil still quotes the scriptures, I believe. I'd say that Mathew Williamson's idea of a good deed for the day now would be lending his best friend a pound and getting an IOU from him for two.'

In fact, Mat Tuakana, as he was calling himself then, made his first million not by using his own money, but by arranging for other persons to spend theirs.

He was twenty-two when he graduated from the LSE. One of his student friends there was a native of what had formerly been the Dutch East Indies and was then emerging as the Republic of Indonesia. The friend's father had long been a Sukarno man, was close to the new President and had valuable patronage at his disposal. American aid to the new state was being given generously. In Djakarta educated men of ability who were neither Dutch nor Chinese were in short supply. When Mat and his friend arrived they had no trouble at all in making themselves useful. In a country where the average life expectancy was then no more than thirty years and the number of university graduates as a percentage of the population was approximately zero, their youth was no handicap. Within weeks they were in positions of authority and responsibility that in most other countries could only have been reached after years of determined in-fighting and conspicuous dedication. In Indonesia, too, positions of authority and responsibility were also, then, positions of considerable personal profit for those who held them. Mat's job in the Ministry of Trade and Industry was to act as a purchasing agent. The money he used was allocated from the millions of dollars of US aid which arrived in the form of American bank credits, and what he bought was what American advisers to the new regime appeared to believe the Indonesian people most needed: useful things like refrigerators, room air-conditioners, radio sets, modern plumbing and cars that would make the place more like home.

Of the millions of dollars that Mat spent on buying such things, some, naturally, stuck to his own fingers. He got two commissions on each deal, one from the agent selling the merchandise for its US manufacturer and another from the merchant to whom he allocated the stuff when it arrived. He made his million in a little under two years and then, sensing that change was in the air and knowing that, while it is always a mistake to be greedy, in Djakarta at the time it was often a fatal mistake, he got out.

He had many American contacts now, so it was to America that he went. He was also given much advice on how best to multiply his million. This he ignored. The advice he took concerned his education. From Americans whose judgement he had come to respect he had learned that the great American law schools are not simply places where men and women are taught to practise law, but places where excellence in other kinds of social and political management is nurtured and developed. Believing his education to be in many such respects incomplete, he had applied to Stanford and, on the basis of his excellent showing at LSE, had been accepted. With the million sensibly invested, I am sure that he had no trouble at all in enjoying his spare time there.

Whether or nor he enjoyed the rest of it I have never discovered. The only time I ever asked him he evaded the question. It may have been that those who assessed him there ultimately saw through him a little too clearly, and allowed him to know that they had done so.

The Kensington hotel was made up of two large, Victorian, terraced houses joined together and given a revolving-door entrance. The night porter was obviously a tippler, but still

43

more or less sober when I arrived. Mat's name sobered him still further and, after telephoning up to announce me, he managed to operate a curious old lift. The hotel may have been sleazy, but Mat had made the best of it. Since I had last been there he had taken over most of the second floor with, according to the porter, four rooms en suite.

The largest had been made into a sitting-room and Max was waiting for me there. So was Frank Yamatoku, his boy-friend.

Frank is a Japanese-American whizz-kid from California who made a killing in the porn trade there before Mat found him. Frank's innovation had been in movie theatres. He had started in Los Angeles with the one house, a couples-only place in which there were water-beds instead of seats and triple-X films showing around the clock. When he had had six of these places going, he had sold out to a syndicate, thoughtfully giving the Vice Squad a list of the syndicate's members as soon as he had cleared their cheque and was in the overseas departure complex of the airport. Frank has a lot of imagination and is an absolutely brilliant accountant, but until Mat found him he often took risks and lived dangerously.

Mat had cured him of those tendencies, I thought, but I would still have found it difficult ever to like Frank. He knew it, too, and the feeling was mutual. Even though I knew that he was working on the fine print of the Placid Island settlement with the Anglo-Anzac accountant, I was not pleased to see him there with Mat.

'You made good time, Paul,' Mat said. 'No further problems?'

'No further problems, no. But the one I'm here about is quite enough, I assure you.' I looked at Frank and then back at Mat and waited.

After a moment Mat gave me his lazy smile. 'All right. Would you excuse us, Frank?'

Frank stood up. 'Surely. Good to see you, Paul.'

With a nod he left. I was quite sure that he would listen

to what Mat and I had to say to one another, but even so it was better without him there.

'A drink, Paul?' Mat motioned towards the sideboard.

'A little later perhaps, Mat. We have that man Krom, the criminology professor, on our backs.'

He became very still. He knew who Krom was. All the stuff about the man and his views that had been passed by the researchers to me had been passed by me to Mat. He was now mentally reviewing it. After he had done so, he relaxed again.

'Tell me, Paul.'

I told him about the first stage of the Krom encounter and waited.

'A foolish man,' he commented, 'but you don't consider him stupid, I gather. If you did you wouldn't be here.'

'No, he's not stupid. He is, however, a little frightened by the step he has taken.'

'Frightened of you?'

'Of me, of us. He has friends in the Dutch Ministry of Justice sympathetic to his views on our business activities. He has friends of like mind in West German intelligence. The man under whose name he is attending the seminar is a rich Luxembourger with political connections. All were advised confidentially of Krom's reasons for attending and of his professional intentions before he came. He has also left affidavits concerning the Kramer affair with university colleagues.'

I paused and again waited for comment. After a moment he began to whistle softly. According to Baden-Powell, the good Scout smiles and whistles under all difficulties. Mat had given up smiling under difficulties, but the habit, acquired as a boy, of whistling under them he had never lost. The tune was always the same, that of a treacly Victorian ballad entitled 'Just a Song at Twilight'. He must have picked it up from some homesick Britishers. It sounded very odd coming from Mat's lips. He says that Baden-Powell himself admitted to having sometimes had trouble over his

45

whistling. Frequent use in public of this antidote to difficulty during the Boer War had given him in some quarters a reputation for eccentricity and callous indifference to the feelings of others.

The whistling stopped. 'What leverage has he?'

'He has been working on Symposia, and me, for a long time. He has identified me in the Oberholzer role. He knows other things. He can't know all and publish it himself *without* naming names, he threatens to leak what he does know to an American or German news magazine *with* names.'

'All he's got is hearsay. He's bluffing. You should have played polo with him, Paul.'

Another Baden-Powell prescription. To play polo with someone in this context is to out-manœuvre him by edging him away from the direction in which you want to go. The metaphor was first used by B-P, I believe, in his essay on the joys of pig-sticking.

'It didn't work, Mat.'

'You should have double-talked him.'

'I did. I asked him to define crime. I asked him if he didn't think that it was largely a fiction created by politicians posing as legislators and legislators pretending that their motives are free from political pollution. Didn't he agree that ninety-five per cent of so-called crime is committed by governments against, and at the expense of, those citizens in whose names they pretend to govern?'

'Yes, that's double-talk all right. What did he say?'

'That it was double-talk. You have to understand, Mat, that what he really wants now is to satisfy his professional vanity. You read his Berne paper. It amused us. Others, his professional peers, are not in the least amused when their lives' work is dismissed as irrelevant. In many quarters he's been attacked as a crank. He now wants us to help him demonstrate that, far from being a crank, he is the great innovator, a Darwin of criminology.'

'By publishing a casebook *without* naming names? Oh, I know that medical textbooks do it. Patient X and patient

46

Y. The identities don't matter, not unless the doctor reporting the case is suspected of being a quack seeking to prove an untenable pet theory with invented evidence.'

'Exactly. In such a case, he either has to produce the patient or qualified witnesses to substantiate his evidence. That's what Krom proposes to do. He has his witnesses already picked, one American, one English, both qualified persons. We meet in private for a four-day period during which I give them the story of my life. Place of meeting to be of my choosing. Strict security to be observed by all, especially witnesses who will be given only the sketchiest of preliminary briefings, enough to engage their interest and ensure their co-operation, without giving anything substantial away. The text of this briefing will be agreed by Krom and me. All names, places and so on to be changed in order to protect the guilty. That's what he wants, and in my opinion that's what he means to get, no matter what it costs.'

He started whistling again, then abruptly stopped. 'I think you've allowed yourself to be conned, Paul. I think you should tell him go jump under a train and that if he makes slanderous or libellous statements about you, or the Institute, or the Symposia Group, we'll sue them *and* him till the pips squeak. Remind him that, in the circumstances, he will be a source no publisher can protect in the usual way. He'll have uttered his threats to the plaintiff in advance. He wouldn't have a hope.'

I shook my head. 'It's no good, Mat. I tried all that. I told you, he knows things. One of his juiciest suspicions is that Symposia is hooked into the Placid Island project. He only needs start a rumour to that effect to cause trouble. Do you still think I'm allowing myself to be conned?'

That did it, as I had known it would.

Mat's cynicism about the Placid Island deal is a pretence; it always has been, although he would never dream of admitting it. As a boy, he had heard of another phosphate island once called Pleasant, which had re-discovered its aboriginal name of Nauru. As a man, he had seen that same Nauru, whose whole history was so like that of Placid, cast off her old trust-territory shackles, achieve independence from the British Commonwealth and become the Republic of Nauru, with prospects as a tax-haven.

Now it was Placid's turn. Placid had a better climate than Nauru and better port facilities than Nauru, which lacks a natural harbour. Placid was Mat's birthplace. With Mat to preside over its fortunes and its future – poor old Chief Tebuke could have a whole floor to himself in the Placid Hilton if he lived long enough – with Mat to provide the inspired leadership that his people so eagerly awaited. Placid was destined to become the most remarkable, the most prosperous sovereign state in the entire South Pacific.

Is Mat an able criminal as defined by Professor Krom? Possibly, but he is certainly no anarchist. What he wants is a kingdom, and if the national flag has not yet been designed – a pandurus leaf on a field of gold? – the banknotes almost certainly have. If sociologists like Krom must paste labels on men and women in order to classify them, I would say that Mat is, as I am, an adventurer; that is, in the old pejorative sense of the term, a healthy and intelligent person who could labour usefully in the vineyard, but who prefers instead to live by his wits.

There was no more whistling from Mat. He stared at me now with cold dislike.

'What does he know about Placid?'

'That I went there last November. He knows that Symposia turned down the offer of an interest in Nauru. He knows that Symposia has stopped steering its clients towards the New Hebrides and has something else cooking. He knows that a Placid settlement is imminent because word has got round that our competitors are trying to get a foot in there through Anglo-Anzac.'

'You said that he was frightened of *us*. Did you discuss me?'

I had, in fact, tried hinting at his existence. Why, I had

48

asked Krom, should he assume that in what he called 'the Symposia conspiracy' *I* was number one? How did he know that I wasn't just a figurehead, part of an elaborate cover-story designed to protect someone else? My intention had been to shake his confidence a little. All I had succeeded in doing was making him laugh. He *knew* that I was number one, so would I please stop trying to talk my way out of the situation.

I had no intention, however, of telling Mat all that.

'No, Mat, we didn't discuss you. Your name wasn't even mentioned. Obviously, he must know of you, the *eminence grise* of the Placid Island lobby. If he reads the financial papers I mean. That PR outfit Anglo-Anzac have working for them will have seen to that. But as for your personal connection with Symposia, he couldn't have a clue. If he had, he'd certainly have said so.'

There was a long silence, and then he quite visibly relaxed. 'So, Paul, you're the only one who's been blown so far. It's not *us* he's dealing with, but you. And all that he's looking for is dirt about operators like you and old Carlo Lech. Is that right?'

'You might have put it a little more delicately, but yes, I suppose that's about right.'

'Then you'd better go along with him, hadn't you? Throw him an old bone or two and hope that he keeps faith, eh?'

'Yes.'

'And that his witnesses keep faith. You're going to have to do rather a lot of trusting, aren't you, Paul?'

'That *had* occurred to me. I'm going to have to take out quite a lot of insurance too.'

'Well, we can afford it. You'll need team help too. Yves would be your best bet on the technical side, I think. And Melanie I know you like.'

I should have guessed then what was in his mind. Yves, we had both agreed in the past, was a first-rate man; but we had disagreed about Melanie. Although he is sexually double-gated, Mat's judgements about women are rarely

49

sound. I considered, and still do consider, Melanie to be one of the best cover-builders and analysers there is. She learned her craft with the Gehlen organization and is brilliant. For some reason – perhaps because she is as brilliant at penetrating the most complex covers of others as she is at erecting full-proof lie-structures for her own side – Mat had never trusted her. He suspected her, he said, of being a security risk.

I should have asked him whether he had changed his mind about her, whether he had forgotten that he had told me of his suspicions or whether he was, in his tortuous way, giving me fair warning of what I could expect.

I did not guess, so I did not ask. He would not have answered anyway, but asked who I would like instead of Melanie. There would have been a reminder, too, that once he had delegated responsibility he never interfered. He might also have started quoting Baden-Powell on a Scout's honour.

Instead, we discussed which old bones could best be used to satisfy Professor Krom's appetite.

CHAPTER THREE

By the time Yves had cleared the visitors' baggage, the sun was down behind the tamarisks on the headland; and, for the first time since Brussels, I was feeling something like my normal self.

Yves's first report had made me too angry to think sensibly. It had not been until I had cooled off that I had perceived the obvious: that I had been presented with an opportunity of improving my position; not of escaping completely from the predicament I was in, but of improving my chances of surviving it without suffering permanent damage. I was certainly better off than I had been an hour earlier. How much better off would depend on how skilfully I could manipulate the modified situation.

Mat had spoken of tossing Krom some old bones as if all we had to do was to open some handy closet and dismantle one or two of the skeletons that had been hidden in it. I had gone along with the pretence, and he had let me do so; but we had both known that what Krom would expect and insist on getting was not a bag of old bones but his pound of raw, red flesh. It had also been tacitly understood that the only place from which the stuff could safely be extracted – safely, that is, from Mat's point of view – was my own personal deep-freeze. As he had so charmingly pointed out, I was the one who was blown, not he.

That Krom might himself somehow make things easier for me, even unintentionally, was a possibility I had not even considered before.

Among the ground rules I had agreed with him in Brussels had been one that gave me the final say on all matters concerned with the security arrangements at our subsequent 'conference', and another that laid it down, as a precondition of my giving him any information in the presence of witnesses, that the witnesses would be bound in all respects by the same security restrictions as those he himself had accepted.

I had not needed Mat to tell me that I would have to do an awful lot of trusting. Well, I had trusted and at once I had been let down. Krom's witnesses had turned out to be about as trustworthy as that legendary Lebanese scorpion. So what about Krom himself? Was it likely, *really* likely, that he, when it came later to publishing my confidences, would prove to be any more reliable? Perhaps, in the end, I would be less seriously injured if I simply called his bluff and told him to do his worst without my willing co-operation.

I could not really do that, of course, out of loyalty to Mat; but Krom could not be sure that I wouldn't; he might well feel that he would be wise not to drive me too hard.

Anyway, I now had him in the wrong and would shortly rub his nose in the fact. If he wanted his pieces of raw flesh he was going to have to sit up and beg. That meant that he would get tired sooner and possibly be more easily and uncritically satisfied. If my luck held, I might not have to throw him any of the juicier bits at all.

At least I now had a bargaining position, or thought that I had.

They were in the cool of the drawing-room off the terrace and sitting in a stiff little semi-circle. Melanie, petrified by having to pretend for an hour to be the hostess, was doing her impersonation of a grande-dame. I had warned her when we had worked together before that it made her sound like a retired *poule-de-luxe* hankering after the good old days, especially in her rather peculiar English, but she had convinced herself in the end that I had only been joking. It is odd that someone who can build up with such marvellous ingenuity roles for other persons to play should perform so dismally when called upon to act a little herself.

She was in the middle of an anecdote about Coco Chanel

which she had picked up from a women's magazine. Krom's eyes were glassy with boredom. Dr Connell was glowering at her. Dr Henson was holding an empty tumbler in cupped hands and staring into it as if it were a crystal ball.

In the doorway I paused and clicked my heels slightly. Melanie stopped talking instantly and stood up.

Krom rose more deliberately and pointed at me. 'This,' he said to his witnesses, 'is Mr Paul Firman.'

I waited one more moment, until they were all on their feet, then I went forward with my most charming smile to greet them.

Connell made an instinctive movement as if to shake hands, but I ignored it and let one formal little bow serve them all. The sooner they were reminded that they were uninvited as well as unwelcome guests the better.

'Welcome,' I said. 'So glad you had a safe journey. This, as you have no doubt gathered, is my secretary, Miss Melanie Wicky-Frey, but – ' I broke off and threw a reproachful glance at Melanie – 'I see that your glasses are empty.'

Krom was the first off the mark. 'Thank you, Mr Firman, but we are travel-weary. What I think we would all like at the moment, if you will be so kind, is to be permitted to go to our rooms.'

'That is,' said Connell tartly and in pretty fair French, 'if his Algerian truffle-hound has finished snuffling through our bags.' He went on quickly as I opened my mouth to reply. 'And if, Monsieur Firman, you could spare us the protestations of injured innocence, we'd appreciate it. We are, as the Professor says, tired.'

I gave him the thinnest of smiles. 'Oh, I wasn't going to protest, my dear sir, though Mr Yves Boularis might do so if he heard himself described as an Algerian. He is Tunisian. Of course your luggage has been searched, and most thoroughly. I must remind you that, even though you seem to speak French quite well, the language agreed upon for this conference was English. Am I not right, Professor?'

Krom cleared his throat. 'Yes, quite right, Mr Firman,

though I think Dr Connell has a point. We all submitted with good grace to a body search, but is it really necessary that we should be treated with such deep suspicion, almost as if we were policemen in disguise?'

'Yes, Professor, I am afraid it *is* necessary.'

He gave an exasperated sigh as I went to the sideboard and poured myself a drink. Then Connell started again. My not shaking hands had rattled him.

'I suppose you're referring to that little tape machine of mine,' he began, and drew breath to continue.

I shut him up by turning to Dr Henson.

'What do you say?' I asked her. 'Am I being unreasonable, or are you forgetting that you signed a paper agreeing to abide by a set of rules while attending this conference?'

On closer inspection, she was an attractive woman with delicately structured facial bones, fine eyes and a mouth which suggested all sorts of possibilities. Not all of them would be agreeable, however; that brief marriage of hers must have been a harrowing affair. At that moment she was wondering how she might convincingly convert her embarrassment into anger and failing to find an answer. Finally, she just shrugged.

'You are not being unreasonable, Mr Firman. I haven't forgotten the paper I signed.'

'Thank you, Dr Henson. Now, do you mind telling me and your friends here whether it was your own idea to photograph and fingerprint the persons you were to meet in this house, or someone else's?'

Krom let out a kind of yelp.

Connell started a protest. 'Now wait a minute! Are you accusing Dr Henson of . . . '

But Dr Henson preferred to take care of herself. 'No,' she broke in crisply, 'he is not making an accusation. He is asking an awkward question about the special cameras and other equipment found concealed in my handbag.' She surveyed us challengingly. 'The answer is that it was *not* my idea. The camera and other things were given to me, with instructions, by the head of my faculty, Professor Langridge.'

Krom yelped again. 'Langridge! You mean that you told *him* about this conference?'

'Of course, I was taking a leave of absence. Short, yes, but at a time when I was expected to be present. Ought I to have disappeared mysteriously and drawn public attention to myself?'

'You told Professor Langridge *where* you were going and on what errand? Couldn't you have accounted for your absence in some other way? Was it necessary to be so indiscreet?' Krom was becoming very angry indeed.

'I don't make a habit of lying to colleagues, Professor. Besides, I didn't *know* where I was going until lunchtime today.'

It was time for plainer speaking. 'You told Professor Langridge that you were going first to join these two gentlemen in Amsterdam?' I asked.

'Yes.'

'Did you know, when you told him, that he often does little jobs for British intelligence?'

She flushed. Connell muttered, 'Jesus!' She still had the empty glass in her hands and for a moment I thought she was going to throw it at him. Instead, she put it down carefully.

'I knew,' she replied, 'that he did some work for the government. But there's nothing remarkable about that. Scholars of most disciplines sometimes accept research commissions from ministries or sit on official department committees. I had always assumed that what he did for the Home Office, or whoever it was, had something to do with his long-term study of the European probation service. A reasonable enough assumption, I think.'

'When did you discover that it had been a false one?'

'About a week after I told him that I was proposing to take this time off. One day he called me in and showed me the camera and other stuff.'

'You didn't object?' This was Krom again.

'Of *course* I objected!' Dr Henson was nearly as angry as he was by now. 'We had a flaming row about it, if you must know. An extremely unpleasant argument, anyway.'

'Which he evidently won,' said Krom bitterly. 'How?'

'He began by asking, yet again, what our exact intentions were. By "our", he meant those of us who have concerned ourselves with investigations of the able criminal. What was our object? Did we intend merely to establish his existence, in the way, say, that a microbiologist might, having established the existence of a dangerous viral mutation, simply record the fact? Or did we intend to make use of any knowledge or proofs we might acquire about such persons to assist others in eradicating them?'

Connell grunted sympathetically. 'Yes. I've had that one. What did you reply?'

'That I didn't know, that the question was in any case both premature and hypothetical as well as grotesquely unfair to microbiologists. He then said that his "masters" – he actually used the word "masters" like some pompous senior official – that his masters were already convinced of the existence of this new kind of offender and were determined to eradicate him.'

'Did he say what evidence they had?' Krom was almost boyishly eager now. The tidings of yet another band of converts to his private religion had quite dissolved his anger.

'Naturally, I asked, but I soon realized that he didn't really know much. He did, though, make two statements of interest. This wasn't a Home Office matter any longer because conventional police forces hampered by rules and restrictions were helpless in these areas. Not much in that. But he also said that for the less-inhibited forces acting on Treasury orders, *and* in concert with foreign counterpart services where collaborative relations existed, it would be a different story.'

She paused. 'And then he threatened me.'

'Sounds a sweet guy,' Connell remarked.

'He said that if I refused to co-operate, that is endeavour to get photographs and prints and report fully and secretly on my return, his so-called masters would place me under surveillance of a kind which would frustrate the whole exercise. It's not as stupid as it may sound. He knows, you see, how I feel about our work in this field.'

'I suppose he was talking about harassment, men in trench coats breathing down your neck.'

'And your neck too, I imagine, Dr Connell.' She turned to me. 'What about it, Mr Firman? How far would we have got? Turin?'

'No farther, certainly,' I replied. 'Naturally, the possibility of one or all of you being under surveillance had to be considered, and not necessarily surveillance of the obvious kind with which Dr Henson was threatened in order to ensure her co-operation. Professor Langridge's masters had other options available to them. I had you very carefully watched all the way.'

Connell snorted disbelievingly. '*All* the way, Mr Firman? Taking that amount of trouble to cover yourself costs money.'

'Yes, the overheads on an operation of this sort can be quite heavy.'

'Of *this* sort? I thought this operation was supposed to be one-off, unique.'

'It is.' I gave him the needed rap over the knuckles. 'But I was speaking in general of operations involving inexperienced persons, for whom, or from whom, one needs protection. Naturally it is expensive, but you don't have much choice. Either you accept the expense when the need for it arises or you resign yourself to the prospect of being very soon – what was Professor Langridge's word for it? – oh yes, eradicated.' I turned and looked Krom in the eyes. 'A serious question must now be asked,' I went on. 'We have breaches of security on your side and also gross breaches of good faith. How, under these circumstances, can we possibly continue our conference as planned?'

I did not really expect him to throw in his hand; he had too much at stake for that, but it was worth a try. The more defensive he was forced to become the better.

He responded shakily at first. 'I agree that you have cause for complaint, Mr Firman, but no damage has yet been done. Has it?'

'No damage? I don't understand. To me, the whole situation now seems completely compromised.'

He rallied. 'Why? Thanks to your own caution, security has been completely preserved. As for good faith, Dr Henson has admitted that she erred and satisfactorily explained the dilemma that led her to do so. You have the apparatus given her by Professor Langridge. What has been lost?'

'Trust, Professor.' In Brussels I had used Mat's phrase about trusting on Krom. I had also used it several times on myself. I used it again now. 'So far I have done an awful lot of trusting. In return I have been rewarded with deception and equivocation. As things stand at this moment, it seems to me that I have less to lose by telling you the deal is off and that you can do what you like with your researches to date, than by continuing to accept bland assurances that your side of the bargain will be kept because you are honest folk, and that it is only I and my associates here who are villains.'

He showed his teeth. 'Oh no, you don't, Mr Firman. Who is deceiving or attempting to equivocate now? We on one side have been completely open and frank. Stop overstating your case.'

I laughed shortly. 'You're bluffing, Professor. Shall I ask Dr Henson or will you? When she took that apparatus and agreed to use it, what did she intend? With whom did she mean to keep faith when she brought it here? Professor Langridge and his masters or you and me?'

Connell said, 'Oops!'

Krom thought it through, then glowered at Henson.

From her came a shrug and an exasperated spreading of the hands. 'Several answers,' she said, 'all of them muddled. My first thought was simply to leave the camera and other stuff behind in England, but then I realized that leaving it would create complications.' Another spread of hands. 'Where was I to leave it? In my flat where it could be found by the friend with whom I share the place? She works for Langridge and adores him. Ought I to have tried explaining the whole situation to her? And how could I be certain, that even though I'd promised to co-operate with these people, they wouldn't send someone to watch me anyway? All things considered, it seemed sensible to go through the motions of co-operating by taking the box of tricks with me. Does anyone mind if I smoke?'

She started fumbling in her satchel, but Melanie was there so promptly with cigarette box and lighter that any respite Dr Henson may have been hoping for was brief. When she saw that we were all just waiting for the more crucial parts of her explanation and that no one felt disposed, at that stage, to assist her by making any sort of comment, she continued.

'In Amsterdam the only place I could have left it safely was in the airport consigne. But if I was being watched, and I still don't know whether I was or not, that would have given the game away completely. How could I have returned with my lie about having failed to use the camera through lack of opportunity, when they knew that I'd ditched it at Schipol Airport? So I put off doing anything about it and waited to see where we were going. It was after Turin when I first began to wonder if perhaps I had been making a mistake, if perhaps I'd allowed my personal dislike of Langridge and his Secret Service nonsense to cloud my judgement, or distort it sufficiently for me to reject any and every argument that he put up without even pausing to consider it. However, it turned out that whether I liked it or not, one of his arguments, along with some of the phrases he used to advance it, *had* stuck in my mind.'

Connell said, 'Aha!' an exclamation she ignored.

'Professor Langridge said – ' and she ran her fingers

through her hair again in the way I had seen from the terrace – 'he said that this conference as I had described it, seemed to have more to do with journalism than with scholarship. And not even investigative journalism of the socially useful kind. It sounded to him more like one of those exercises in sensationalism currently favoured by the popular press and the seamier television channels. A news or TV feature is manufactured out of interviewing at a secret rendezvous some notorious terrorist or other wanted criminal.'

She began now to stride about, slicing the air with the edges of her hands as she spoke. It was obvious that she had begun to reproduce Professor Langridge's physical mannerisms along with his rhetoric.

'And what is the object of these journalistic antics?' she demanded at the ceiling. 'I will tell you. For the new media which indulge in them the object is readier access to the eyes and ears of audiences of cretins. For the crooks and thugs who are the star performers the reward is a big jar of the most marvellous cosmetic ointment of all – free publicity. Smeared with that stuff even the most odious of men and the most detestable of causes can enlist a measure of popular sympathy and support. Many distinguished politicians as well as eminent divines have become involved in such tawdry enterprises, so why not an ageing Dutch professor of sociology?'

She avoided looking at Krom, who seemed to be more amused than annoyed by what she was now saying, and continued to talk at, or to, me. 'The team-leader gathers the brainwashed and compliant subordinates before setting off into the wide, baby-blue yonder. What is different about this adventure? Two things. Journalists working for the established media are to some extent privileged. Unless the casework upon which *we* are engaged happens to confer on us quasi-medical standing we most certainly are *not*. And neither are your collaborators. The only way you could refuse information about these criminal contacts you propose to make, should you be challenged on the subject by a lawful authority, would be by a pretence of ignorance.'

She paused, and then, with a grimace of disgust at the whole recollection, became herself again. 'His other point made more sense. Reporters on secret-interview assignments are invariably, and for their employers' as well as their own legal benefit and safety, accompanied by a cameraman, an assistant to fetch and carry and somebody to operate a tape-recorder. Even if the person to be interviewed elects to wear a hood or mask, a camera is still there to authenticate the fact that he has done so, and if he chooses to make a voice-track analysis difficult by speaking into a water glass, the tape-recorder will take note of that too. Why is this Mr X so shy? Is it because, and *only* because, he wishes to preserve his total anonymity and all the cover identities with which it is ringed, or is the truth rather more drab? Could it be that Mr X is just another professional incompetent after all, and that, far from being unknown to police anywhere, he is very well known indeed to those forces with access to Interpol files? Only photographs and/or fingerprints on the subject could establish the truth.'

'We have a specimen like that who sits on our Board of Regents,' said Connell. 'He's known as The Syllogist.'

'The conclusion I came to,' Dr Henson continued firmly, 'was that I didn't yet know nearly enough to make even a preliminary judgement. When I heard what Mr X had to say, and formed an opinion of him, then I would review the position. Meanwhile, I would attempt to conceal the camera and ninhydrin spray.'

It occurred to me that for a person who professed to dislike lying to colleagues this was a pretty cool admission. I was about to say so when Krom cleared this throat loudly. Thinking that he was about to deliver the admonition, I let him go ahead.

He didn't even slap her wrist.

'I think that answers the question in all its aspects,' he announced. 'Our agreement stands.'

'Of course it stands,' said Connell. 'Naturally, with a deal like this there are going to be little misunderstandings which need clearing up.'

Obviously, none of them had the smallest sense of right and wrong. I had one more try.

'They may be cleared up to your satisfaction, Dr Connell,' I said, 'but they are very far from being cleared up to *mine*.'

Krom grinned at me. 'But it's not *your* satisfaction that has to be considered, is it? If it were, the chairman of the Symposia Group and director of the Institute of International Investment and Trust Counselling called Paul Firman would long ago have disappeared in a puff of smoke, to emerge three or four days later with an entirely different identity in Sao Paulo or Mexico City. We wouldn't be standing here at all. But we *are* standing here, and we are doing so because Paul Firman can't afford just to disappear. Time and affluence have done their work. His cover is too well established now and his face too well known. He may even be involved in a pension plan. He is caught between two evils and he has sensibly chosen the lesser of them. Am I not right, Mr Firman?'

I almost gave up, but not quite. I managed, apparently unmoved, to meet his eyes. 'We'll see later who is right and who is wrong, Professor,' I said. 'Meanwhile, dinner will be in an hour. Melanie, perhaps you would be good enough to show our guests to their rooms.'

The listening post Yves had chosen was a storage loft over the garage. It had the advantage of being accessible from inside the house via an inner door to the garage, yet well away from the servants' rooms.

When I got there the receivers covering the guest rooms had already been switched on and I was in time to hear Melanie telling Connell that she hoped he would be comfortable and to ring if there was anything he needed.

Yves nodded to me gloomily.

'You handled them well down there, Patron,' he said, 'but I think it is hopeless. *Nous sommes foutus.*'

'It's only a matter of time. That lot will never be able to keep their mouths shut about anything. They're supposed to be intellectuals, persons of probity. One feels tempted to treat them as common crooks.'

'It can do no harm if we *think* of them in that way. In fact it might be a good idea.'

He gave me a sidelong look. 'When we started here, I had a feeling that there was a lot I didn't know. Letting your arms be twisted by a party of amateurs, however clever they might be or think they were, didn't sound like you, Patron.' He paused. The fact that he was calling me Patron instead of Paul meant that he was really worried. He added a sigh for good measure. 'You handled them well, as I said, but you handled them carefully and gently. I'd have pushed their faces in and told them to walk home.'

'If it were as easy as that they'd never have arrived.' I had been listening to a bumping sound coming from one of the rooms. Now there was a loud scraping noise. I wanted to change the subject anyway, so I asked what it was.

Yves plugged in the earphone he was wearing. This action enabled him to concentrate on the sounds from the room without ceasing to cover the rest. 'It's Krom,' he reported after a moment or two, 'trying to locate our bug, I think. He's been dragging a chair from place to place, then standing on it, probably to peer at the cornices through that pocket monocular he had tucked away in his suitcase.'

'Any chance of his seeing the bug?'

'Well, if he knew what it looked like he just might spot one end of it, but I don't think he will. Anyway, he couldn't get at it. It's in the chandelier, and you know how high those ceilings are.'

'He could fall off the chair and break a leg trying to get at it.'

'He has nothing to try with. I went over the curtain rods

63

and put extra fastenings on them. If he tried to get one of those down he'd make a noise as well as a mess.'

There, in a few words, are summed up several of Yves's virtues. His vices were not then in evidence.

His versatility was wholly practical and selective. He did not waste time learning how to make amateurish electronic monitoring gadgets; he made sure of picking the most reliable equipment by seeking out the little man near Lausanne who supplies the CIA.

When resourcefulness and imagination could be enlisted to solve unfamiliar problems economically, they were permitted to do so; the curtain rods, which might have been decked revealingly with alarm-bell circuits, were simply fastened more securely to their supporting brackets.

A voice came suddenly from Connell's room. He was speaking into his tape-recorder.

'Research project Alpha-Gamma, cassette one, side two. As from Villa Lipp, near Cap d'Ail, France,' he said. 'July 13, 19.30 hours. Arrived, accompanied Krom and Henson, at 17.30 approx. having followed route and instructions already noted. Query. Is this room bugged? Casual inspection which says no as likely to be wrong as right. Lacking equipment necessary to make proper check, no point in speculating.'

As Yves nodded his approval of that sensible decision, Connell went on.

'Our party was met by woman who described herself as Firman's secretary. Age, fifty plus. First impression that of Madame de Stael pretending, with aid of faded, little-girl-type prettiness, to be bird-brained. Hair rinse: brunette with approximately one centimetre grey-auburn visible near scalp. Named by Firman as Melanie Wicky-Frey. Rhymes with tray, but I'm not sure of the spelling. Fluent English, but strong accent with mixed American-British usages. Must ask Krom, who has European ear, for his diagnosis of nationality.'

A longish silence. Then: 'On second thoughts, no. Don't

ask Krom anything. You won't get a straight answer. He's a jealous little god about this project. Continue. Secretary Melanie then hands us over to lean and hungry character named Yves Boularis. Expression, mournful yet threatening. Reminded me of that termite-clearance inspector who gave me such a hard time when we were selling house on Cheviot. Diagnosed this Yves as Algerian butler. Wrong on both counts. Not butler, but some sort of right-hand man. Also doubles as security guard. According to Firman, not Algerian but Tunisian. My present disinclination to believe a word the man Firman says – have a suspicion that there's one who could enjoy lying for its own sake – leaves doubt in mind, however. Who trained Yves to search baggage and frisk? The French? Had big fight to keep this recorder, but sweet reason, or my open fury, prevailed. However, Henson got into serious trouble, and thereby hangs a tale.'

He proceeded to tell it to the recorder, while we listened in turn to Dr Henson taking a bath, and Krom, who had by then abandoned his search for electronic monitoring devices, breaking wind.

When we came back to Connell, he was comparing the British use of men like Langridge in amateur espionage roles with the deeper penetration of the American academic world by US government agencies such as the CIA.

He went on: 'Have left description of Firman character till last. Reason? Call it insufficient evidence. Just can't make up my mind. First impressions, all tenuous. Caucasian, yes. Country of origin? Take your pick. Anywhere from the Caspian to Gibraltar, including Cyprus and Malta. Can't I pin it down a bit? Sure. He has a one-hundred-and-ten per cent British accent. Only other guy I ever met with an accent like it is an American with a Lebanese passport who works for UNESCO and was educated at the English High School in Istanbul before going on to the Sorbonne. He has brown eyes too. Very helpful. Be more specific. Age: mid-fifties, maybe younger. Difficult to judge. Height: two inches shorter than I am, say five-eleven. Looks like weight-watcher, sunlamp-user and wearer of steel-grey toupee. Could also look, with only a little help from the imagination, like ageing movie star who never really quite made it to the top, but who got out at the right time, with self-esteem and investments still intact, to make a killing in California real-estate. Hell, I don't know. Maybe what I am looking at is a retired con-artist who gets his kicks now out of sticking pins into the pretensions of academic clowns like us. Could be. He's already needled Krom, and Henson took quite a beating; though she did, after all, set *herself* up for that. Maybe, as old Krom started to say in Amsterdam before the sheer horror of the idea switched it off, he isn't Firman at all but a covering stand-in. Oh no, forget it. This guy's no stand-in; he reads the lines too well. Want to know something, Connell? As long as he was a deduced, theoretical phantom of the opera, a conceptual bundle of joy who stuck in the Establishment's craw, you believed in the existence of Mr X one hundred per cent. Now confronted by a person who says he *is* Mr X, you cop out. You say: "Him? Can't be. He looks human!" What did you expect? Bela Lugosi? The Man in the Iron Mask? Or hadn't you given that side of the matter any thought? Ah, well, you're tired now. So how about a shower and a clean shirt? Then, just watch and wait. Okay? Okay. More anon.'

There was no more then from any of the receivers. After a few seconds, Yves switched both them and our own recording tapes to voice-actuated operation.

'An observant man,' he commented.

'Describing you or describing me?'

'Both, I thought. And the woman is even more dangerous, Patron. I think we are doing now what you have always said we should never do.'

'I've said that we shouldn't do many things.' His gloom was beginning to depress me.

'But, in particular, you have said that we should never step out into the street without looking up first to see if the woman on the floor above is about to empty a chamber pot.'

'I have never said anything so crude. I did once say that one should always look carefully where one is walking on certain streets.'

'Same thing, Patron. If you don't look, you're in the shit either way. I think that is where we may be now, and I would like to understand why.'

'Later, Yves,' I said. 'Later, perhaps.'

There was no point in confirming his fears before it became necessary to do so.

We dined on the terrace.

Personally, I dislike eating in the open air at any time, even when there are no insects to plague one; but it was a very warm night and, as Melanie had said, with six at table and the cook's sister-in-law in from the village to help the husband serve, a few moths fluttering around would be a preferable discomfort to that of the staff body-odour in a confined space.

All three of our guests, advised by Melanie that the most casual clothing would be *de rigueur*, had decided to take her at her word. The white-haired Krom in faded blue slacks with a pink linen sports shirt looked positively elegant.

I gave them a white Provencal wine before dinner. None of them refused it, and the large round table at which we could all sit comfortably made for general conversation. At least we looked relaxed though, of course, there had been no real lessening of tension. Their suspicion of me, only slightly modified by increasing curiosity, still hung over us; but their readiness to be physically comfortable declared at least a kind of armistice.

It did not last long. Refreshed by his shower and change of clothing, Connell had soon forgotten his decision to watch and wait. He was ready for action again.

It took the form of hitching his chair closer to mine and telling me in a confidential undertone that he had been trying to place my accent. 'I know it's British, of course,' he added quickly, 'but British from whereabouts? I know it's not Australian or South African. I suppose it could be . . . '

He got no farther, Krom was half out of his seat and leaning across the table with teeth bared.

'No, Dr Connell, no!' He swallowed a couple of times trying to get rid of some of his anger before it choked him. 'No, I shall not need that sort of assistance from you in questioning Mr Firman about his origins and background.'

He had begun in his vehemence to spray saliva, and Dr Henson hastily moved her wine glass out of the line of fire.

Connell was looking utterly astounded. It was a facial expression of which he made much use I was to find. 'Of course, Professor, of course, of *course*. I was simply making an idle enquiry.'

Krom was neither deceived nor appeased. 'It was agreed between us, let me remind you,' he grated on, 'that all enquiries of whatever kind will be made by me. Here, everything will be conducted throughout in the way that I decide and only in the way that I decide. That was positively agreed.'

'Sure, Professor, sure it was agreed.'

'But not,' I remarked distinctly, 'by me.'

They all stared at me except Yves, who poured himself some more wine. I continued: 'I will be the one who decides which questions are answered and which are not. I will also decide the areas of business activity concerning which information may be given. No, Professor, it's no good you huffing and puffing. Since our meeting in Brussels I have had plenty of time for reflection and decision. After Dr Henson's demonstration of her disregard for her agreement about confidentiality, to say nothing of Dr Connell's less covert breach of his, my conviction that none of you is to be trusted has been further strengthened.'

Krom made a gargling sound of disgust and sat back

in his chair. 'No, Mr Firman, no. No more wriggling, please. Will you not even now accept the fact that you are hooked?'

'When you accept the fact that the fish on the end of the line is not after all the one you thought you had, yes.' I did not wait for him to answer but turned to Henson. 'Why did they give you ninhydrin to bring here, Doctor? Do you know?'

'Oh, not that again!' from Connell.

Krom did some more gargling.

She took no notice of either of them. 'Apparently,' she said 'quite a lot of people still don't know that one can raise fingerprints from matt-surfaced papers if one knows how. They didn't think it would be prudent for me to try stealing something else you'd handled and start dusting it in the old fashioned way. Besides, the results wouldn't have been as good.'

'Supposing I hadn't handled the papers while you were here?'

'They said you would. As long as your hands were warm, a book, a newspaper or even a paper napkin would work. As a last resort I was to ask you to read the typescript of a book review I have just written and get your opinion on it as well as your prints.'

'I'll gladly read it, Doctor.'

'Unbelievable!' blared Krom.

'Rubbish!' I said irritably. 'What about you and your friends in West German intelligence, Professor? When they ask you confidentially for the precise details of your adventures in the quest of Mr X, are you going to remain, after all the kindness they have done you with their files, resolutely silent? Of course you aren't. None of you is going to keep his mouth shut. He won't be able to. So, what you are going to be given is not all the truth, if there is such an entity, but bits of it. And you, Professor, can take your choice. Leak what you know and you get nothing more. Play it my way and you get something.'

69

He thought about it, then glowered at me suspiciously. 'How much?'

'Some days in the life of Herr Oberholzer?'

'I have one already.'

'No, you haven't. You can't begin to know what happened that day. You don't even know what crimes you might accuse him of.'

'Extorting money by threats. Blackmail. There are more, but those will do to begin with.'

I laughed sufficiently to choke a little over my wine. 'Extortion, Professor,' I said when I had recovered, 'is, as you must surely know, the standard cry raised against those who collect, or try to collect, payment from delinquent debtors. Blackmail is often used to describe letters from creditors beginning with the word "unless". Oberholzer was no debt collector in any case. If that's all you have . . .'

'I am not speaking about debts incurred for goods or services legally supplied. I am speaking of the exactions of criminals.'

'But the services which we supplied were always perfectly legal. Is it a crime to give good advice?'

'Some advice, yes. To advise a man who has himself committed a criminal act how he may, by giving you money, avoid the consequences is certainly criminal.'

'And, Professor, if you ask for information instead of money?'

Henson giggled and Connell smirked, but it took Krom a moment or two to grasp the implication. It did not please him. He straightened his back.

'Very well, if such hair-splitting amuses you, I have, in the interests of social science, become an extortionist. Maybe you will find it less amusing, Mr Firman, if I now ask you to start paying up?'

'Of course,' I looked at Melanie. 'Would you mind getting the copies of file number one for me, my dear?'

70

Krom stared at me suspiciously as she went. I sipped my wine and took no notice of him.

The moment had arrived, as I had known it would eventually, and I was prepared to serve Krom what I believed would look, smell and taste like the meat for which he had asked.

The work they are doing in the food laboratories nowadays to make protein artificially is really amazing. I believe that they have even been able to produce it from really unlikely substances such as oil. The only trouble with the artificial stuff, though, is that it doesn't really taste of anything much. You have to add a meat essence to give the concoction flavour.

If you are feeding social scientists, especially criminologists, you have also to add to the artificially produced material a little truth.

When I saw Melanie returning along the terrace I turned to Krom. 'In expectation of our meeting,' I said, 'I have prepared papers concerning Oberholzer, his employer and later senior partner, their business associates and their business activities over a period of three years. They are papers for discussion of and, of course, I am prepared to be questioned by you on them. My answers may or may not satisfy you. We shall have to see.'

At that moment, the butler announced that, at the other table on the terrace, dinner was served.

Melanie had timed it perfectly.

Their eyes were on the files she held, their stomachs were thinking about dinner.

One can divide one's adversary without necessarily conquering him, of course, but any division is better than none. I had won at least something; not a battle, still less a campaign, but perhaps a minor skirmish on an outer flank.

The first course was a duck-liver paste. For the occasion I had called it Pâté Oberholzer.

I don't care for such things myself.

The others ate all of it.

CHAPTER FOUR

Krom said that he intended to write my life story and now has the audacity to claim that he has done so.

What rubbish the man talks! He does not even know where I was born. And why does he not know? Because *he* did not ask. Because, *he*, with this fatuous obsession of his, this determined inability to distinguish between a criminal and a businessman, prefers to assume that I must wish to keep such facts about myself secret.

Utter nonsense!

If he had not intervened so energetically when Connell had asked me where I came from, I would almost certainly have answered. There was no reason why I should not have done so.

I was born in Argentina, and my family was, still is, one of the many there of British origin bearing commonplace British names. In our case, as with others like us, intermarriage with and absorption by the Spanish-descended majority has, chiefly for religious reasons, been a slow process. When I was born, even though we had been in the country for well over a century and thought of ourselves as more Argentine than British, our name was still free of Spanish collaterals and my birth was duly registered at a British consulate as well as with the local municipality. All very schizoid. With us, British nannies still supervised the upbringing of children, and we were still sent to England at the age of eight to endure the torments of its boarding schools. My father thought it proper in 1914 to join the Royal Navy. In 1939 I joined the British Army no less matter-of-factly. If I withhold the family name I do so for good reason. I have dual nationality, and the possibility that the protective cover which this could give me might, after all these years, become an asset is one that I cannot now ignore.

Allegations of the kind Krom has made, consisting of one part fact stirred into nine parts fantasy, are always the hardest to refute; and, in this instance, the task has been made still harder because the fragments of truth embedded in his slablike case-study were supplied by me in what he persists in calling my 'confidential papers'. He also makes much of their having been supplied in front of witnesses. What effect that could have on the value of the papers as evidence is beyond me. If I had handed him a forged ten-dollar bill, would the presence of Connell and Henson as witnesses have rendered it genuine?

The first paper – how much grander the word 'paper' sounds than the more appropriate 'hand-out' – dealt with some of the circumstances leading up to Krom's seeing Oberholzer in Zurich and some of the consequences of the whole incident.

And that was *all* it was, an incident. Krom's presentation of it as if he were Zola discovering for an amazed public the iniquities of the Dreyfus case is, no doubt, for anyone who knows the truth, pretty funny. Far from funny is his clear and instantly recognizable picture of me dressed up to look like the super-villain of his imaginings.

Melanie, who helped me concoct the texts of the 'papers' and who was responsible for some of the juiciest red herrings in them, thinks that we overestimated him. She says that we relied too much on the scholarly scepticism allied to an ability to evaluate misinformation that ought to have been there, but which were not. In other words, we were too clever.

I say that we underestimated his capacity for self-deception. We gave him a kaleidoscope to play with and he used it as if it were a reading glass.

If there must be a picture, let it be a warts-and-all photograph, not a caricature; and if the world, or that small portion of it inhabited by criminologists and policemen, really wants to know about poor old Oberholzer, let it be one of his own many voices that is heard. My account will be full, reasonably accurate and free from Krom's distortions. It will not, of course, be free from *my* distortions. I happen to be one of those who believe that the ability to tell the whole truth about anything at all is so rare that anyone who claims it, especially if he does so with hand on heart, should be regarded with the deepest suspicion.

I can only attempt to be truthful.

I met Carlo Lech for the first time when I almost had to arrest him near Bari. That was in 1943 after our landings on the heel of Italy, when the Eighth Army had moved north to Foggia. I was in the British Field Security Police at the time, and I almost had to arrest him because a corporal in the detachment of which I was in command was an officious bloody idiot.

But what, it may be asked, was an English-Spanish bilingual doing in Field Security in Italy? Was this the British Army once more up to its ancient game of putting square pegs into round holes? No, it was not. During the year after I left school, I learned to speak very good Italian.

Where his children were concerned, my father was generous and, though far from being imaginative, always scrupulously fair. I was the youngest of his three sons, and when, in the summer of 1938, he was notified by my housemaster that my year in the sixth form had ended less disastrously than had been feared, I was offered the same choice of rewards as my brothers before me. I could go to a university before going into the family business; I could spend a year and two thousand dollars travelling in Europe before going into the family business; or I could have the sports car of my choice and go into the family business right away.

My brothers had both taken sports cars. I chose the year in Europe.

In three months I had spent the two thousand dollars

– having had a very good time doing so, though – and was flat broke in Cannes. A cable would have brought me a steamer ticket home, a sermon on the value of money, and, of course, immediate entry into the family business. I didn't send the cable because I didn't want to go home and didn't want to go into a boring family business which already had more junior executives than it needed anyway. As any good con-man will tell you, it takes most people a long time to spot the fact that a spender has turned into a sponger, and in places like Cannes it can take even longer for a credit-rating to slip. I gave myself a month to get out of the hole I was in before I ran screaming to Daddy or started doing silly things that could get me into trouble with the police. I made it in three weeks. I got a job as steward on a yacht.

The owner was an Italian banker and some of the reasons for my being hired were simple.

The Munich crisis had led in France to a partial mobilization, and the French steward had been one of those called up. It was not known when he would be released or, since he had insisted that local union rules entitled him to a full month's wages on leaving, whether, when released, he would trouble to return. At that end of the season it would be hopeless to look for an experienced replacement. The rest of the crew, including the cook, were Italians, who did not care who poured the drinks and served the meals and made the beds. I had Argentine papers and, as the yacht was registered in Genoa, there would be no nonsense about labour permits and unions that the owner could not deal with later should he decide to keep me on. Meanwhile the job was strictly temporary.

Among the less simple reasons for my getting the job was the fact that the owner's wife had picked me up one morning at the Carlton beach. She had done so under the impression that I was a virgin youth seeking reassurance and instruction from the older-yet-still-amazingly-attractive woman she believed herself to be. Both my clothes and the hotel at which I was staying were of the expensive kind, and when I confessed to her that I could no longer afford to tip even the boy who put up the beach umbrellas much less pay my fare home, she had at once blamed the gambling tables for my predicament and easily understood, without my having to tell her of it, my fear of parental retribution. I never tried to disabuse her of any of those notions. She was friendly in bed, only sometimes demanding, and she always smelt nice.

With her husband my credentials were of a different order. The school to which I went has never been considered as better than reasonably good; but he happened to have heard of it, and the idea of having an English public-schoolboy – even one who was Argentine – as a servant seemed to appeal to what I assumed to be the Fascist sense of humour. I think that his original intention may have been to discipline his wife, and at the same time strike a blow for Il Duce and the corporate state, by firing me after a few days, or as soon as I had sufficiently demonstrated my incompetence. If so, I disappointed him. Being a steward on a yacht is not all that different from being a junior boy in the kind of school I had just left. I may also have misjudged the nature of their personal relationship. Possibly it did not include the friendliness with which she treated me. Perhaps, in that marriage, she was the one who had the disciplinary whip hand.

I very much hope so, because, although I have during my life encountered a great many unpleasant men and women, I still after all these years remember him as being one of the nastier.

When the weather broke on the Riviera we cruised south, first to Ischia and Capri, and then on down to Tripoli. There, east of the town, the owner had land, on which he played at citrus-growing, and a tarted-up farmhouse. His wife explained that he owned the place not because he wanted to or because it was profitable, but for some mysterious political reason.

76

We spent several days doing nothing much while he had meetings with the Governor and other local administrators. Then we started off on a cruise that was supposed to take us to Benghazi. A north-west gale ended that, and within thirty-six hours we were back in Tripoli. There it was announced that the yacht would now be laid up for its annual refit, with just the captain retained to oversee the work. The rest of the crew would be off to their homes in Italy for the winter months. The owner and his wife moved into the house.

Nobody having told me where I stood, I counted my savings, wondered whether I could expect a tip from the lady, and eventually asked the captain if I was entitled to my fare back to Cannes. He mumbled something about my not having a labour permit, and then said he would enquire. Until the boat went into the yard to have its bottom cleaned, I could sleep on board. I was reminded of the end of one of those terms at school when there had been not enough holiday time in which to go home, and nothing much else to do but spend too much pocket-money.

To my surprise, the captain remembered to enquire about me without being reminded. Next day, I was sent for by the owner.

It was the first time I had been to the house. You took a bus to the nearby village and then walked along a dirt road between lemon groves.

His study was a hideous room with a tessellated floor and red, leather-covered walls. The writing table was a Second Empire monster with a matching chair of throne-like proportions. He had a mop of white hair and very black eyes. Sitting in that enormous chair, he looked like an illustration depicting the king greedy for gold in an art-nouveau edition of Grimm's fairy tales.

'I understand,' he said, 'that you wish to return to France. Why, young man? In order to gamble away all the wages I have been paying you these past weeks?'

His wife had told me of his stuffiness about gambling,

but I had forgotten about it, along with the fiction that I was a gambler myself. So, instead of replying that what I did with the money I earned was my own affair, not his, I answered his silly question as if he had been entitled to ask it.

'No, Sir. I merely wish to regularize my position. As the captain pointed out, I still have no labour permit for Italy or Italian possessions.'

It could have been more happily put. He gave me a long, smouldering stare.

Then he said deliberately: 'For the work you are paid to do in Italian possessions, the only necessary permission is mine.'

I was very innocent in those days. It took me a moment or two to grasp what he had said. When the penny dropped, though, several things seemed to happen at once. For the only time in my life I felt myself blushing. I had an almost overwhelming desire to hit him and, along with it, an equally compelling determination to get out of the room before I did anything stupid. Good sense won. I turned quickly and walked to the door.

'Come back here,' he snapped. 'I haven't finished with you.'

I didn't go back, but I stopped and faced him again. After all, I still had to know what the score was.

'You had better understand me,' he continued. 'I have considerable influence with the authorities both here and in Rome. I could have you in prison within the hour if I chose. I could also have you deported. In that case, you would certainly pay your own travel expenses. The only way that you can, as you put it, regularize your position is to do as you are told, not by that fool of a woman, but by *me*.'

He let that sink in, a smile hovered. 'You may even find it less inhibiting to do as you are told here, rather than on the far side of a yacht bulkhead.'

When he was sure from my expression that I had

thoroughly understood him, he sat back and seemed to relax. 'I leave for Rome tomorrow afternoon and shall be away for some weeks. You will place yourself at my wife's disposal for as long as she continues to find you useful. When she has finished with you, then you may go.' He paused, savouring the final insult before delivering it. 'One other word of warning. There *are* some possessions of value to me in this house. Don't try to steal them. My servants will know immediately if anything is missing. Now get out.'

I left without seeing her and walked to the bus stop in the village. When I got back to the yacht, however, there was a note from her waiting for me. It said that I must ignore her husband's bad manners. They were the result of too much association with politicians. She would expect me for lunch on Friday. From then on I would be *her* guest, not his. In case I had not yet been able to make arrangements for cashing cheques with a local bank, she was enclosing five thousand lire to cover taxi fares and any other incidental expenses I might wish to incur.

At that time five thousand lire would have gone some way towards *buying* a taxi, the kind of taxi they had in Tripoli anyway. Two days later I moved into the farmhouse; but one thing I had to ask her about before finally deciding to stay. Had she known from the first that he had listened to us?

The question seemed to perplex her. 'But he didn't listen to us from the first,' she said. 'How could he have listened to us in your hotel?'

'I mean on the boat.'

'Oh, walls on boats are always so thin.' She dismissed them with a shrug. 'But what does it matter? Who cares what is heard? It is what one *feels* that counts.'

It did not seem worthwhile trying to challenge that statement.

I stayed there over three months, and by then my Italian, although never altogether free of Spanish intonations, was fluent. By then, too, I had come to the conclusion that

I wasn't going to be needing it for very much longer. Hitler had invaded what the French and British governments had left of Czechoslovakia. A few weeks later, and to show that he could be just as bold and bloody if he put his mind to it, Mussolini had ordered the invasion of Albania. From Rome, too, came word that the yacht would that summer be cruising only on the west coast of metropolitan Italy. Her husband added, as if as an afterthought, that an Italian steward had been hired and would report for duty when he himself joined the boat at Naples. The captain would be advising her of his sailing orders.

It was time for me to go. I left, by a ship bound for Marseilles, on my nineteenth birthday, though I didn't tell her of the coincidence. I don't think she was all that sorry to see me go – she was one of those who like change – but a birthday would have added unnecessarily to the emotional content of the parting. Perhaps, now I think again about it, she taught me quite a lot.

From Marseilles I went to Paris and lived, within my means this time, at a small hotel in the rue de l'Isly. In spite of the fact that my year of 'travelling in Europe' was almost over I was not unduly troubled by the thought that I might soon have to return home. That was probably because it was almost impossible to live that summer in Paris without knowing that there was going to be a major war; and because, as a result, I did not really believe that anything was going to turn out as planned for very much longer. Still, as a precautionary delaying tactic, I wrote to my father suggesting that it might not be a bad idea if I went home by freighter via New York, so that I could visit the World's Fair and see what our foreign business competitors were doing in the world market. I could, I assured him smugly, easily afford it.

I need not have bothered. Mail travelled slowly in those days, and, by the time my letter reached him, the German-Soviet Non-Aggression Pact had already been signed. During the last week in August 1939, I cabled him saying that, subject to his blessing, I proposed going to England in order to join either the Royal Navy or, failing that, the RAF.

His blessing I duly received, but soon had to cable for supplementary assistance: more money and some introductions in the right quarters. Of course, at the beginning of the war, none of the British services was prepared to cope with floods of raw recruits, least of all the Navy and the RAF. The best he could do in the way of introductions not only landed me in the Army but also in one of the most boring parts of it – a searchlight battery stationed in East Anglia.

All I remember now about the winter that followed was how cold it was, and that in March we moved to a site farther south which seemed even colder. In May we were moved again, suddenly, to Wales; not because we were needed there, but in order to leave the hutted camp we had occupied free to receive troops evacuated from Dunkirk. In Wales we were told that the artillery regiment to which our battery belonged was to be converted from the searchlight role to that of mobile Ack-Ack with Bofors guns. Older officers and men were to be weeded out and transferred to static units. The qualifications of all personnel were re-examined and reassessed. The process happened to coincide with Italy's entry into the war and the issue of an Army Council Instruction requiring returns from all units listing the names of NCOs and men who could speak Italian. My name was one of three sent in, the other two being those of British-born Italian waiters. In due course, we were summoned to a barracks near Durham where we were interviewed and tested by an officer who spoke phrase-book Italian with a Scottish accent. He said, in the importantly secretive way which was then fashionable, that we were probably needed for guard duty at the new Italian internment camp on the Isle of Man.

I never knew what happened to the waiters, but two

months later I was sent to an infantry battalion bound by troopship for Egypt and the Western Desert.

After we arrived, the battalion delivered me to the Intelligence Corps. Theoretically, I was there as an interpreter. In practice, I was used from the start to interrogate the Italian prisoners-of-war who were then pouring in by the thousands. An officer, with an NCO escort, was supposed to deal with each POW separately, but there were just too many of them for that sort of nonsense. So the work was split up. To give me a semblance of authority, I was made an acting-corporal and told to behave like a stage sergeant-major. It was all a great waste of time. During the months before Rommel's first big counter-attack, I interrogated many hundreds of POWs and wrote an equivalent number of reports on them. Never, during the entire time, did I learn anything of military value that I had not already learned from the intelligence briefings we were given. The only higher-ups who took any real interest in our findings, were the political warfare people. Once or twice I was able to quote in my reports things said by a more-than-usually demoralized prisoner – generally one with wife trouble – or gripes, spotted in the letters from home some of them carried, that could be used in propaganda.

I was confirmed as corporal and there was talk of my being commissioned, but nothing came of it. Instead, I was transferred to Field Security Police and posted to Italian Somaliland as an acting-sergeant. After more than enough of that – why anyone should ever have wanted the place passes all understanding – I was posted to Eighth Army in time for the invasion of Sicily.

To see how it was that I came to arrest Carlo, you have to know what the Field Security Police in Italy were supposed to do. Some who were there at the time may need no reminding, but it may help others to recall that our opposite numbers in the American sector of the front bore a rather more dashing title – Counter-Intelligence Corps.

The CIC and ourselves both had the same job and we did it in more or less the same way. While the ordinary military police were concerned briefly with military matters such as convoy traffic control, drunks, deserters, POW cages, stockades and so on, we dealt with the problems arising from the presence all around our forces – and, in the towns and villages, *among* them – of large numbers of civilians who, until recently, had been actively or passively on the side of our enemies. Some of them, a few but some, still were. Our main task was to see that, in the forward areas where such things mattered, those who were against us and in a position to do something about it were either removed or neutralized.

Of course things were rarely as simple as that.

If a farmer stole a pair of army boots because his own had gone to hell and he had to start ploughing his land again, was that petty theft or sabotage? Was an old whore wounding a soldier by hitting him in an eye with the heel of a shoe merely defending her democratic right to the rate for the job, or was she giving aid and comfort to the Waffen SS division dug in across the river north of us? And then there were the black marketeers who flogged bottles of a turpentine-like liquid they called peach brandy to the troops in exchange for cartons of army rations. How did you cope with that sort of traffic? By telling the troops that they were ruining their lives?

Well, no. What you did was try to catch the black marketeers, and you did this by checking as constantly as you could on the driver and occupants of every civilian vehicle moving in your area. The CIC used jeeps with two men in them. We used one-man motorcycle patrols.

It was one of my patrols who brought in Carlo.

The first thing I heard of Carlo was the sound of his car, a clapped-out Opel that made more noise than the patrol's motor-bike. When both engines had been switched off, I heard the corporal telling the owner of the car to stay exactly where he was. The corporal then came down to report.

'Highly suspicious, this one, sir,' he said. He called me 'sir' because I was by then a Warrant Officer 2nd Class, a sergeant-major. He also handed me a gasoline permit and laissez-passer issued in Naples by AMGOT.

I drew a deep breath and counted silently to ten.

AMGOT – Allied Military Government Occupied Territories – was one of the crosses the army had to bear at that stage of the campaign. AMGOT, it seemed to us, had been recruited by a committee of highly-placed saboteurs from the dregs of those ghastly pools, which both the American and British armies were obliged to maintain, of officers who had been commissioned in haste or ignorance and later rejected by unit after unit as unfit for any sort of responsible duty. Some were just stupid, some were alcoholics, a few were failed crooks and more remarkable, and from our point of view the more dangerous of these, were those amiable, personally charming and often cultivated eccentrics who, having served honourably in peace-time regular armies had, over the years, quietly become gaga without anyone ever having noticed the change. They were more dangerous not only because they were often of quite senior rank, but because many of them tended to hold political views which even Gabriele d'Annunzio might have found reactionary. Their tendency to form warm personal friendships with the former Fascist bosses they had been sent to replace, and also to confirm them in office, caused much resentment in the Allied armies.

Naturally, some of the AMGOT scandals were successfully hushed up. The Town Major in Sicily who used his authority to buy up all the best buildings, including the hotel, at cut prices for his own post-war account, was quietly court-martialled and sent home to serve a short prison term. Only a few ever heard about that. The gasoline-permit racket and the shenanigans that went with it were less easily covered up.

They reached their full absurdity when a CIC patrol on the outskirts of Naples stopped an Italian civilian driver whose car looked unusually well cared for and asked for his permit. The driver responded sullenly. He slowly produced a wallet from his pocket and was about to extract the permit when the CIC man reached in impatiently and took the whole thing. Inside, he found not only the AMGOT permit and a considerable sum of money, but also a Gestapo permit to operate the car issued less than three months previously. The driver was later identified as a senior Fascist Party official who had denounced Badoglio as a traitor for arresting Mussolini, urged his countrymen to stay loyal to the Nazi alliance and, when possible or convenient, stab the invaders in the back. He was on the Allied wanted list. The CIC put him in jail. Twelve hours later he was out, released on the orders of a senior AMGOT official.

This was too much for the CIC, who promptly leaked the story to war correspondents. Questioned by them, the AMGOT spokesman began, not too badly, by admitting the facts and agreeing that the whole affair was absolutely deplorable. But, he continued, they were all men of the world who knew that, in occupied territories where states of emergency existed, occasional compromises, distasteful though some might consider them, had to be made. AMGOT had been given the responsibility of governing the country *pro tem,* but no one had explained how it was to be governed without the aid of experienced local administrators accustomed to giving orders and seeing that they were obeyed. Where, might we ask, were the democratic administrators willing and able to take over the duties of those he was being urged to discard? We had had serious outbreaks of typhus. Was he now being asked to permit outbreaks of typhoid and cholera because the senior city sanitary department engineer had once been a member of the Fascist Party?

The spokesman had chosen that moment to pause for breath. Unfortunately for him, there had been one correspondent there who particularly disliked rhetorical questions. He was on his feet instantly. But what, he asked, about this man who had been arrested and then released? Was *he* a senior sanitary engineer? 'Colonel, is he *any* kind of a sanitary engineer?'

That was when the spokesman had made his mistake. Instead of continuing to conceal his contempt for the newsmen, he had suddenly let it show.

He had smiled at the questioner. 'No, my dear sir,' he had replied sweetly, 'the gentleman is not a sanitary engineer, but – ' a slight pause – 'I happen to know that he plays an excellent game of bridge.'

Naturally, the whole story was at once censored, but the censors could not stop it spreading by word of mouth. It was at this time that some wag thought up the bitter little joke motto, *Amgot mit Uns*.

So, all that interested me about Carlo's gasoline permit and laissez-passer was the name of the officer who had signed it. As the name was unfamiliar, I was unable to tell how much weight the permit-holder might have behind him. Accordingly, I rang signals and asked if they could put me through to CIC Venafro. Signals said that they would try. Venafro was then on the right flank of Fifth Army on the other side of the mountains from us, but signals could sometimes patch me in through HQ Caserta.

I called the corporal to come back down. There was still a faint possibility that he hadn't made a complete fool of himself.

'Was he carrying anything in the car?' I asked.

'No, sir, just himself. But he's way off his permitted route, and out of his area as well.'

'Did you ask him why?'

'No, need to, sir. Standing orders. He shouldn't be here.'

Hopeless. You could never persuade that kind of idiot that, in some circumstances, he might get better results by using standing orders as threats rather than by blindly obeying them.

'I take it you've told him that he's going to be arrested?'

'Of course, sir. He already *is* under arrest really. Clear case. Shall I bring him down now?'

'Not yet. I'll let you know. Has he said anything?'

'Not a word, sir. Shall I question him?'

'No. *You* keep your mouth shut too.'

After a while signals came through to say that they had raised CIC Venafro. The man in charge there was an officer – trust the Americans to do things properly – but he never pulled rank on me and we had always managed to co-operate amicably. We had first met in Sicily.

'Hi, Paul,' he said. 'What can I do for you? Or do you want to do something for me?'

'I'm not quite sure, sir, which it is. One of my lot has brought in a man named Carlo Lech.'

There was a small silence before he said: 'Paul, I think you may need help, but I don't think I have the right kind. Lech is a well-known bridge player. You didn't, by chance, catch him with any of the actual goods on him?'

'No.'

'Then you'd better let him go before someone starts reaching for your balls with a pipe-wrench.'

'He's out of his permitted area.'

'You could ask him why and then let him go.'

'If I'm going to have to let him go, sir, I'd like to ask him more than that. He's been picked up and my man has logged the fact. I've got to have a good reason for letting him go. He's got to buy his way out and not too cheaply. He's from your side of the mountains. If you were here what would you like to ask him?'

'Two nights ago twenty thousand cigarettes went missing off a truck between Caserta and here. There was an MP riding shotgun. His case is that the cigarettes were never loaded. I'd like to know what really happened because it's happened before and some of the loot has ended up right here. Makes it look as if you're a jerk who doesn't know what's going on in his own back yard. And if Mr Lech knows any good anti-Fascists, men of distinction whom we can persuade to come out of hiding so that we can give them posts as mayors, city councillors and police chiefs where their untainted records and democratic convictions can publicly demonstrate . . . '

'Yes, sir. I've had that directive too. I'll see what I can find out about the cigarettes and call you back if I get anything. Funny name for an Italian, Lech. Sounds more like German.'

'It's Austrian. He's one of those Tyrolese Italians, injured in a road accident when a teenager, which kept him out of any of the services. Party member though, and a smart lawyer. Watch yourself, kid.'

I cleared the line, then told the corporal to send the prisoner down but stay upstairs himself.

At that time Carlo was more than twice my age, a short, compact man with greying dark hair, grey-green eyes and one of the kindliest expressions I have ever seen. You felt instantly that he was longing for you to say or do something, anything that would give him an excuse to let the smile that seemed always to be trembling on his lips blossom forth. Except for the leather overcoat he wore, which was too long and had obviously once belonged to someone else, he was neatly dressed. His slight limp, a legacy of the road accident, did not seem to bother him much. He walked down the broken stone stairs as if he were used to them, and he was taking off his greasy grey-felt hat as he did so.

At the foot of the stairs, he stopped, looked carefully at the crown on my battledress sleeve and then said in English: 'Good afternoon, Sergeant-Major.'

I replied in Italian. 'Good afternoon, Mr Lech. Please sit down.'

He inspected me again and then, after examining carefully

the rickety wicker chair I had offered him, sat down opposite my blanket-covered trestle table.

I was curious. 'What were you looking for in the chair?' I asked.

'Lice, Sergeant-Major. I can't stand them and, as a civilian, have no access to the military's new ways of getting rid of them.'

Several years later, he told me that that had been the moment at which he had made up his mind about me. 'I saw you as a son, the kind of son I would have liked to have, one with whom, and at whose side, I could do business. I saw you, above all, as a potential associate, a friend and partner whom I could trust, under any circumstances, even when his private hubris was involved, not to behave stupidly.'

He may have been telling something of the truth. Carlo had a sentimental streak that few who ever did business with him can have suspected. He also had a son, a handsome, clever but rather vain boy, who later disappointed him profoundly by going into the Church.

Nevertheless, our first meeting was for me more like a family quarrel than the meeting of minds he chose later to recall. The moment he was seated, I perched myself on a corner of the table from which I could look down upon him, and attacked.

'You are driving a vehicle in this area without a valid permit and have, I understand, admitted doing so knowing that it was an offence. Am I right?'

'Knowing that it was a minor, technical offence, yes, Sergeant-Major.'

'There are no minor, technical offences in this area, Mr Lech. An offence is an offence. Where were you hoping to go and why?'

'To Bari on business. I explained all this to your corporal.'

'What business?'

'Supplying the club for senior officers in Naples with brandy, Sergeant-Major.'

'*Peach* brandy?'

He looked shocked. 'Oh my God, no. The colonels and brigadier-generals would never commission me to supply them with that sort of rubbish.'

I noted that in spite of his shock at the idea of peach brandy entering a senior officers' club, he had tried to pull rank on me with his colonels and brigadiers and at the same time managed to flourish the word 'commission'. I had to mangle that line of defence before he could develop it.

'Are you claiming that you are in this area illegally but justifiably because you have been specifically ordered here by a senior British or American officer? If so, have you some written authority to substantiate your claim?'

'Oh no, Sergeant-Major, there is nothing like that. It is really quite simple. When persons of consequence ask the person of no consequence for his help, he endeavours, if he is wise, to oblige them. I am sure that if you would care to telephone General Anstruthers – ' he had difficulty in pronouncing the name but made a brave try – 'he would confirm that good brandy was requested. Of course,' he added thoughtfully, 'I doubt if the General will take kindly to being questioned formally by a warrant-officer on such a trivial matter.'

I tossed a packet of cigarettes into his lap. 'Any more,' I suggested, 'than the General will take kindly to the knowledge that his name is being used illegally as a black marketeer's laissez-passer.'

He handed back the cigarettes without taking one, so I went on. 'Whereabouts in Bari is the brandy?'

He threw up his hands in protest at the question. 'Sergeant-Major, if I were certain that it even existed, I would not be committing this trivial breach of the regulations which you are now exploiting. I am told that the brandy is there, six cases of it, but I am not told where. For all I know it may by now have been – what is the word? – "liberated" by the British army. Or it may be that the original bottles have been refilled with wood alcohol. I have a contact, yes, but I do not know him personally and so cannot possibly buy sight unseen. But I explained all this to your corporal.'

'Who is your contact?'

'The man formerly in charge of what was the bonded warehouse.'

'If the brandy is there and up to standard, what do you propose to do about it?'

'If the price is not absurdly high, I shall buy it and then take it back to the General and his club wine committee.'

'In your car?'

'Certainly, in my car, and with a bill of sale to prove that the goods are my property.'

'What makes you think I'll let it through, Mr Lech?'

'Unless you are attempting to solicit a bribe, which I doubt, why should you even think of stopping it? Tell me, Sergeant-Major, how do you define this new term or phrase you use, this "black marketeer"?'

'One who has authorized dealings in goods that are rationed or otherwise in short supply.'

'Is dealing with pre-war French brandy unauthorized? I hope you are not one of those socialists, Sergeant-Major, who object to the law of supply and demand controlling prices merely because persons like me risk their capital in order to make a fair profit.'

'What is a fair profit?'

'If I succeed in buying this brandy, I shall add forty per cent to the price I have to pay. Bearing in mind the fact that, in addition to my normal overheads in a transaction of this kind, I must suffer the mental strain of trying to convince a suspicious British Field Security policeman that I am not a crook, is that excessive? I shall be glad to let you have a bottle for the same price as that which I shall charge the General. Is that what you call black-market dealing?'

I had, after all, been warned that he was a lawyer. 'All right, Mr Lech,' I said, 'let's try a different commodity. Two nights ago, twenty thousand cigarettes were stolen off

91

an American truck somewhere between Caserta and Venafro. How would you describe the acting of selling them?'

'In civilized countries, Sergeant-Major, and in some uncivilized ones, dealing in stolen property has always been an offence.'

'But one which you would never commit yourself.'

'Certainly not. I have no need to commit it.'

'You wouldn't know, by any chance, who stole those cigarettes?'

'No, but I know *how* they were stolen.' He waited for me to ask him how.

'Well?'

'Would the knowledge be of use to you here in your area, Sergeant-Major, or are you thinking unselfishly more of your colleague in Venafro?'

He could not have made his meaning plainer. If I wanted to hear more, he expected a clear run to Bari and back, with no 'technical' obstacles in his path. It wasn't a bad deal, so I nodded.

'I'm thinking of both us now, Mr Lech, so your information had better be good.'

On his private island, ten years later, we analysed that part of the conversation as if it had been a game, a form of exercise.

'I watched you very closely,' he said. 'You were throwing away an apparent advantage because you knew that it was essentially worthless. I could have had you in trouble with your own people within hours, and you must have known that too. Yet, you hung on by switching currencies. Sterling was out, but there was still the dollar. Your reply, reminding me of the more lasting penalties to be incurred by arousing American displeasure, could not have been bettered.'

The verdict of a bridge-player enjoying the benefits of hindsight. At the time he had protested vigorously.

'Of course my information is good, Sergeant-Major. Indeed, it is impeccable. Most petty professional crooks share the same weaknesses. One of them is that they can never refrain from boasting of their successes. In the matter of the cigarettes, it was arranged in advance with the military policeman on the truck that the driver, his accomplice, would stop on the way and leave the load unattended for five minutes in order to deal with a sudden call of nature. The place arranged for the stop was near the village of Galleno. There is no soft shoulder on the road just there, so it would be an easy place for a truck to pull off, and then get back on again, without getting stuck in the mud. I dare say that a very quick search might find some of the cigarettes still in the village.'

'Thank you, Mr Lech.'

I gave him back his AMGOT papers and then filled in one of the duplicated pro-formas we used for civilian vehicle movement control in the Bari area. While I was doing the filling-in I thought that I might as well see what his reactions would be to the question about anti-Fascists.

To my surprise, he did not laugh.

'Here in the south,' he said, 'you will find only three kinds of person who will claim seriously that they have long been anti-Fascist. First, there are the village priests, or most of them, as you must know well. Then, there are the very few real Communists, getting old by now. They are mostly still underground awaiting their moment. And finally there are the madmen.'

'Madmen?'

He stood up. 'Who, unless he was a priest or a Communist or in some other way mad, would have resisted Party pressure to conform for twenty years? And who but madmen, could look around them now at the destruction of what little had been built up in this pitiful country and declare that it is better so or that the punishment was necessary?' He brushed the thought away as if it were a cobweb across his face. 'In the north, we shall no doubt find things very different. You will see. We will both see. There are Communists who will be less old and better organized. I am at present cut off from my family in Milan, but even when I last heard from my wife, before the arrest of Mussolini, the situation had already begun to change radically. The partisans had begun to organize themselves instead of talking.'

He took the pro-forma from me, examined my signature and then spelled out my name. 'Is that right, Sergeant-Major? Good. I have no doubt that we shall be meeting again and I wanted to be sure. May I ask, I wonder, where you learned to speak Italian so well?'

'If we ever meet again, Mr Lech, I will be glad to tell you.'

'Oh, we shall certainly meet again, Sergeant-Major.' The smile had finally broken through. 'Thank you. Thank you very much.'

With a stiff little bow he turned and went up the stairs. By the time the racket of his car had died away and the corporal had been told why his prisoner had been sprung, signals had got me Venafro again.

My colleague was pleased with what I had to tell him and looked forward keenly to passing it on to the MPs commanding officer, whom he disliked. I did not trouble to tell him, though, about Carlo's views on anti-Fascists. He would not have liked them and might even have considered such talk subversive.

Two days later I returned from a session at Corps to find a package on my table. The orderly on duty said that it had been delivered by an Italian in a car holding a movement permit signed by me. Inside the package was a bottle of Martell V.S.O.P. and a bill for two thousand lire made out on paper with a printed heading in English. *CARLO LECH Doctor of Jurisprudence,* followed by a Naples address.

I wasn't going to pay two thousand lire for a bottle of brandy even though it was certainly worth more than that at the time, and it would have been most inadvisable to keep the bottle without paying at all. The prissy corporal who had arrested Carlo would be sure to hear of it and start telling everyone that I had accepted a bribe. On the other hand, the idea of sending the bottle back seemed offensively high-minded. So, I went to the senior Divisional HQ warrant-officer and asked his advice. He agreed that the price made it look like a bribe but also thought it too good a thing to miss. His suggestion was that the bottle be raffled in the HQ mess with tickets at fifty lire apiece, all monies in excess of two thousand lire to go to the Mess Comforts Fund. The bottle was won by an Ordnance Corps staff-sergeant. We had an air courier service to Naples which I used to send Carlo his two thousand lire, in AMGOT notes, together with a typed receipt for his signature.

The receipt was eventually returned. Under his signature Carlo had written: 'Many thanks. See you soon.'

CHAPTER FIVE

I have said that I gave Krom and the witnesses a white Provençal wine before dinner. That is quite true. What I failed to mention was that this was no ordinary Provençal white. I mean the kind that may be drunk with, say, a fiercely garlicked bouillabaisse and survive the ordeal.

What I gave them was the very light-bodied, dry white that comes from the immediate vicinity of the small port of Cassis near Marseilles. There is not a lot of it to be had, and it is very good in its unobtrusive way. It is, though, quite delicate – a bouillabaisse would kill it stone dead – and has to be treated gently.

Unfortunately, the cook's husband, who had the temerity to call himself a butler, was convinced that the only proper way to chill any white wine was to refrigerate it, or even, I suspect, to give it an hour in the deep-freeze.

I had already warned the fool against such brutality, but that night, possibly because it was so warm outside, he ignored my orders and served it far too cold. The result was that it tasted very much like water.

And that was how Krom proceeded to drink it. Yes, I know he had had a long, hot day, had sweated a great deal and was probably a bit dehydrated; but the bottle of Evian provided for him in his room should have taken care of that. What he seemed not to realize was that the liquid he was swigging down so thirstily – he consumed well over a bottle before dinner – had the normal alcoholic content of other white wines from the region of about eleven per cent. Or perhaps he did realize it. Perhaps he would have been happier if we had all had a boozy pre-prandial session of double dry martinis or schnapps.

I don't know. I can only say that before dinner he certainly drank too much, and that during dinner he continued to drink too much and ate, once the pâté had taken the edge off his appetite, practically nothing.

In a way, I can understand his not feeling hungry. That evening, as far as he was concerned, was the culmination of many years of dedicated labour. I happen to believe that the dedication has been misguided and that the labour will ultimately prove to be fruitless; but that is not how he sees things at present, nor how he saw them. He believed that he was within reach of a goal, physically within reach of it. The files Melanie had brought in just as dinner was announced now lay on an adjacent coffee table. If he had stood up and reached out, he could have touched them, and he was having trouble keeping himself from doing so. His eyes flickered towards them constantly to make sure that they were still there. The burgundy that came with the veal went down almost as quickly as the Cassis.

'Nice wine, Mr Firman,' Dr Henson remarked.

'Thank you.' It *was* nice for a wine that had only been bought two weeks earlier from a local merchant, but I had not expected her to notice it. I had thought of her more as a claret drinker.

'But not nice enough to impair our judgement, eh?' Krom beamed glassily on his witnesses.

'One would hope,' said Connell pointedly, 'that while we are on an important field expedition nothing should be allowed to impair our judgement.'

'There you are wrong!' Krom stabbed a forefinger at Connell and then began waggling it like the arm of a metronome. 'I will tell you in advance something that you would later have had to discover for yourselves.' The metronome stopped and the forefinger began stabbing at me. 'Where this man is concerned, no unimpaired judgement can be made. Why not? Because he is like one of those creatures of the cephalopod family such as the octopus or squid, which, when attacked or threatened with attack,

97

discharges an inky liquid to form a cloud in the water behind which it may retreat.'

Yves nodded appreciatively. 'Calmar,' he explained to Dr Henson. 'Good to eat, but only when cooked in the Italian way.'

Krom ignored the interruption. 'And what does this ink consist of? What is its composition when Mr Firman has brewed it? I will tell you.'

'We know,' said Connell. 'The answer's hog-wash.'

'Pardon?'

'You're forgetting, Professor. You gave us this lecture on the way down. Every time Mr Firman feels that he is in any way, even marginally, threatened, up goes the defence that, if anything not quite kosher has been done by anyone, ever, and he's been around at the time, it was never he who was basically responsible for what happened. He, it appears, has always been one of life's number-two men, always putty in the hands of some ruthless, clever, wicked number-one. Right?'

'Well . . . '

'I know I'm not putting it quite the way you did, Professor, but I think that's roughly the way your readings on him come out when they're processed. You call that sort of tactical fluid discharge octopus ink. I call it hog-wash. What do you call it, Mr Firman?'

'In this case I think that I have to mix the metaphor a little and call it wishful thinking. Professor Krom clearly does not wish to believe that the cephalopod he caught was not the largest in the ocean. A natural reluctance on his part. But if he really believes that my version of the events which interest him is so little to be relied upon, I don't understand why any of you is here.'

Connell said quickly: 'Olé. Nicely fielded.'

Krom rumbled back into action. 'Has it not yet come to your notice, Dr Connell, that when a structure of lies about a sequence of events is superimposed upon a schema composed of fixed points of known truth concerning those same events, more can be learnt about the liar by comparative analysis than can be learned by listening to and endeavouring to make sense of so-called confessions?'

'I wonder, Professor,' Dr Henson asked blandly, 'if we could have a concrete example of that method of working in the case we are now discussing.'

'Certainly. Mr Firman maintains that, at the time I identified him, he was *not* in control of a considerable organization running a small, but staggeringly lucrative, extortion racket. He also denies that his operation was based on information gained by the suborning of bank employees and others holding positions of trust. He claims instead, absurdly you may think, that he was the helpless agent of an Italian criminal named Carlo Lech.'

This was too much, even from Krom. I stopped him. 'Just a minute, Professor. I have never said that I was anyone's helpless agent, and I have never said that my friend Carlo Lech was a criminal. I did say that we were for a time in partnership and that he was the older and senior partner. I also said that he was an extremely capable business man and that he had other partners besides me. At the time, you may remember, you told me that Carlo Lech did not exist, that he was a figment of my fertile imagination. Didn't you use those very words, Professor?'

'I did and I was right to do so. The Carlo Lech of whom you spoke and are speaking now, your "friend"', *was* and *is* a figment of your imagination. Oh yes, there used to be a Carlo Lech in Milan. No doubt about that. He was a highly respectable and respected corporation lawyer. That doesn't mean that he was necessarily an honest man, of course, but after our talk in Brussels I made the most careful enquiries about him. Unfortunately, he died five years ago so we cannot ask him personally what he thought of you. He had, though, a son who is a priest. This son had never heard of you, or anyone like you. His second child, the daughter of Maria, wasn't born until nineteen forty-six. Mrs Lech was, as you may or may not know, twenty years younger than her husband. The daughter married a young American orchestral musician, a cellist of talent whom she met in Milan, and now lives mostly in the United States. Shortly before Carlo Lech died, she gave birth to his first grandson, Mario. I wrote to her asking about you, but she knew nothing.'

'Even the most doting Italian father would be unlikely to discuss his business associates with a young child, particularly associates who used assumed names.'

'She wasn't a young child when I saw you in Zurich. Were you her trustee in Vaduz? Ha! That left the widow, who seems always to have been a semi-invalid and who has been for the past two years in a sanatorium. She now suffers from Simmonds' disease which is, I believe, something to do with the pituitary gland. She was not available for interview. Had she been available, though, I have little doubt that her reaction would have been the same as her son's. She would never have heard of you.'

He paused to let it all sink in, and to empty his glass again, before he delivered the *coup de grâce*.

'The Carlo Lech you described to me,' he said, 'never existed.' And then, perhaps to convince himself as well as his witnesses, he repeated the word that mattered to him most and thumped the table with his fist as he did so.

'Never!'

In spite of the note I had received after our first meeting saying 'See you soon', it was, in fact, nearly two years before I saw Carlo again.

A lot had happened in the interval and, as far as I was concerned, not a moment of it had been pleasant. Crawling up the leg of Italy with an army which had gradually been stripped of its best British divisions so that they could be used in the battles for France would have been, for me, a lowering experience anyway. Specialist units like the one to which I belonged did not go with their divisions. We were part of the Italian front, for eternity it seemed. The succession of east-west defensive lines which it is so easy to build in that country, where the mountains and the rivers lay them out for all the world to see, let alone German generals, ensured that the attackers, no matter how brave they were, no matter how well and skilfully led, had to suffer repeatedly the despair and frustration of having to pay exorbitantly for every minor success. And the reward for a minor success was always the same; your first glimpse of the next obstacle to a major one. I have heard of no campaign in modern war that was accounted enjoyable by any of those engaged in it, but the Italian must, in terms of futility as well as ordinary beastliness, have been among the nastier. In war's forward areas, the sights of the dead unburied and of the wounded before they have been cleaned up are not always the worst; and the battlefield depression that follows a hard-fought victory is often, no matter what the staged press pictures like to pretend, indistinguishable from that which follows a defeat.

It was just after we reached the Gothic line and I was quartered in yet another wrecked house, north of Ravenna this time, when Carlo came to see me again.

I almost failed to recognize him. Gone were the long leather coat and the greasy felt hat. He was dressed in what would now, I suppose, be described as a para-military uniform. He wore GI ankle boots, the kind that British officers were always trying to get hold of, those made of an inside-out leather that looked a bit like suède and had rubber soles; and on his head was a black beret. It was his topcoat that impressed me most, though. This was the short turned-sheepksin job that was issued to some of the units operating in the mountains above the snow-line. It was also worn by some of the more dress-conscious senior officers among those of the fourteen nationalities then serving on the Fifth and Eighth Army fronts. On the otherwise badgeless Carlo, the coat bestowed field rank at least.

'I've tracked you down, you see,' he said by way of

greeting, and handed me a bottle wrapped in a copy of the *Stars and Stripes*. 'Whisky,' he added, 'but there's no bill this time.'

It was late afternoon and getting dark. I lit a pressure lamp, got two beer glasses out of the mortar-bomb box used for mess stores, and opened the bottle.

We raised our glasses to one another in silence and drank. Then he said: 'You are looking older, Sergeant-Major.'

'I am. A year and a half.'

'I was merely observing, not offering a shoulder to cry on that you neither want nor need.'

'What can I do for you this time, Mr Lech?'

His near-smile twitched a bit. 'For the present, thank you, nothing. I had meant to visit you again before this, but events and my work made it impossible.'

He went on to give me a rough idea of what had happened to him. He was now based in Rome and working for the reformed Military Government, mostly in his professional capacity as a lawyer.

When war travels slowly and devastatingly from one end of a country to the other, it is obvious that in its wake a multiplicity of legal problems, few simple and many highly complex, are going to have to be solved. Most, of course, will concern damaged property, often, except for the land it once stood on, totally destroyed. Who used to own it? What has happened to him or her, or, if the owner was a corporation, it? If the one-time owner is now defunct does a known successor exist?

He had seen and heard a lot on his travels about the country.

About his wife and family, he said only that he had been in direct touch with his wife, and that she was well. I gathered from other things he said that he had been in some way assisting British and American liaison officers in co-ordinating partisan activity behind the Gothic line. Questioned about it, though, he at once changed the subject.

'Last time I saw you,' he said, 'I asked you where you

had learned to speak Italian. Later, I tried to find out about you from the British Adjutant-General's department at army headquarters, but they preserved security most ingeniously by pretending not to understand their own filing system.'

'It was probably no pretence. But yes, I did say I'd tell you all if I saw you again. You mean you're still curious?'

'More than just curious. Interested.'

So, I gave him a reasonably full, though in parts censored, curriculum vitae.

I soon found that the censorship had been unnecessary. He was not in the least concerned with my moral character, about which, he told me later, he had already come to a firm conclusion. This was, that I could be counted upon never to do anything which it was not in my own best interests to do, and that my direction as to where those interests lay at any specific moment would always be swiftly, as well as shrewdly, reached. Tripoli, except for the name of the banker on whose yacht I had served, was waved away as of no consequence. He did not want to hear about adventures. It was far more important to learn that I spoke Spanish. How about French?

'I get along. Schoolboy grammar, plus additions to my vocabulary picked up in Cannes and St-Germain-des-Prés.'

But you learn languages easily, it seems.'

'Learning Italian when you already speak Spanish isn't difficult. I think there is a book that makes it easier both ways. Do you want to learn Spanish?'

'No, no, no. You speak English. You should have little trouble learning German.'

'Why should I learn German?'

'Because I think that it is soon going to be a very useful language to have.'

'Don't you mean Russian?'

'No, German.'

I must have looked blank. You have to remember that this was February 1945 and the Western Allies and Russia between them were tearing Germany apart. Anyway, Carlo saw that explanation was needed.

'As soon as this is over, Sergeant-Major, I intend to go into business. Oh, I shall re-establish my legal practice too. That is necessary to the business as well as important in other respects.' He looked into his half-empty glass. 'You see, I intend to go into the business of managing other people's money.'

This, in itself, did not seem to me to have much to do with German being a useful language for me to learn, so I said nothing. Then, suddenly, he leaned right back in his chair and raising one hand to shade his eyes from the glare of the pressure lamp, stared intently at me for a long time, several seconds.

Finally, he said, 'Paul, what are *your* plans for when this is over?'

It was the first time he had called me anything but Sergeant-Major. I remember noting the fact and also being extremely puzzled. It seemed to me that I was about to be offered some sort of job; but what, in God's name, could an Italian lawyer contemplating going into the arcane business of managing other people's money want with a man of not quite twenty-five? The young man spoke three languages, true, but was he not totally inexperienced in any business other than that of acting as a security policeman during a war? Obviously, I had been mistaken. He was not about to offer me a job. Therefore, he must want something else from me. Play it straight, then; that is to say, cagily.

'Well, I said. 'I suppose that I shall go home and see my family. There's a job there, if I want it.'

'But in the meantime, what?'

'I don't think there's going to be much meantime.'

'There, I fancy, you are wrong,' he said. 'For you, there may be more than you think. I expect that you have heard talk of demobilization plans.'

'Of course. There'll still be Japan to be finished off, but

not for the old sweats. I hear they've already started sending the long-service men home from Burma. It's to be first in, first out, with a points bonus for every month of overseas service. On that basis, I should be home three months after it's over, even going by a slow boat.'

He shook his head. 'I intend no disrespect, but if you had been a fighting soldier, an infantryman, an engineer, a gunner, that might have been a reasonable expectation on your part; but you are not in those categories. I believe that, even after the Nazis are finished here, Allied troops will still be needed. There will be problems with the Yugoslavs about Trieste and other places, there will no doubt be problems with the French. Above all there will be immediate internal problems, social, economic, and political, which will not be solved without the presence for a time of occupation forces. With partisans in absolute control of vital areas in the north, we could not even administer a direct economic-aid programme without armed help. Your governments may choose to replace what you call the old sweats – I suppose you mean the experienced men – with younger conscripts or those who have seen less service, but specialists like you will have to stay on. You will be asked to volunteer.'

'Or else?'

'That's right. Or else stay on anyway, but forgo the rewards that would have been yours as volunteers.'

'Thanks for warning me. One our people managed to get sent home and given a psychiatric discharge a month or two ago, I was surprised how easy it was, once he'd really decided.'

'Baby talk doesn't become you, Paul. I think that you would prefer to stay in Italy for a year or eighteen months and make your fortune.'

'In the army? That sounds as if we're back to black marketeering.'

He sighed irritably. 'It is absolutely essential that you rid yourself of this absurd idea that I am a criminal or that I have criminal instincts. I am a lawyer who respects the law. Illegality is for the immature and the foolish. The wise man has no need of it.'

'Sorry.' He seemed genuinely put out, so I poured him some more of his own whisky. 'But,' I went on, 'you must admit that when anyone speaks of making a fortune out of the army, the mind instantly turns to thoughts of . . . '

'No, no!' he protested. 'While *in* the army, not *from* or *out* of the army.' He made one of his brushing-away-a-cobweb gestures. 'The kind of cheating you are thinking of is already being done on a scale that you could not possibly emulate, even if you wanted to. And the scale is increasing. I told you, I have seen and heard a lot on my travels. There is an American quartermaster, for example, who is at present, according to my estimates, over thirty thousand dollars ahead in canned-food deals.'

'Then we *are* talking about the black market.'

'No, we are considering a problem that arises out of it. In a nutshell it is this. What does the quartermaster do with his money when the time comes for him to go home? Does he carry it in his musette bag? *Does* he?'

'I gather that you think that to do so would be unwise.'

'From his point of view, catastrophic. I can tell you that the Judge-Advocate's department is already preparing court-martials against two splendid old soldiers, regular army veterans, who were simple enough to do just that. Given the opportunity, any fool can steal money. It's accounting for the possession of it later that is difficult. Do you know that one of those fellows was stupid enough to claim that he had won it all in crap games? The trouble was that he couldn't remember any of the other players. I can tell you this. When the time comes for the rest of these lines-of-communcation and base-area bandits to go home, or even be transferred to other theatres, they are going to find that there are obstacle courses for them to run that they never knew about and that they can neither beat nor avoid.'

'So what would you advise the quartermaster to do with his thirty thousand dollars?'

'Advise him to give them all to me, so that I can take care of them for him.'

He himself obviously found nothing strange about what he was saying. It called, consequently, for a careful reply.

'Carlo, you are, as I have reason to know, a trustworthy man. But, with respect, I don't see how you are going to persuade a man who has made thirty thousand dollars by cheating to believe that you, to say nothing of the rest of his fellow men, aren't just as crooked as he is. Isn't that the way the crook's mind works?'

'Certainly, it is. For that precise reason he must be sold new ideas. First, if he is an American, he must be made aware of the various hostile moves that can be made against his thirty thousand by the United States Government and its Internal Revenue Service. For instance, that part of his nest egg which is in occupation money will be made worthless after a certain date unless it is declared beforehand. In order to declare large sums he must be able satisfactorily to explain them. That part of the whole which is in Italian currency cannot be converted outside the country except by payment through his own home bank. Once more he must explain. In the same way if he remits dollars in amounts which exceed his accumulated base pay, he will also be required to explain. In other words, he must either lose all or he must trust, *and* pay, someone else to do what he cannot do for himself; that is, convert that portion of his equity which is not in dollars into currencies which will remain negotiable. Then, the whole of it must be kept safe until such time as he can reclaim it without ever having had to account to anyone for his possession of one cent. How will we perform these unique and quite invaluable services for him? My dear Paul, I will tell you.'

Thirty years were to go by before the Watergate investigation brought the word 'laundering' into metaphorical association with the word 'money'. In 1945 we did not use that particular figure of speech; but in fact 'laundering money', the process of giving large sums which have been criminally acquired the appearance of having been come by legally was what Carlo then began to describe.

Mr Q, the quartermaster, would hear, as if by accident, not only of the obstacle courses in preparation but also about an Italian lawyer of the highest repute who specialized in foreign tax law and was an expert on international currency dealings. How did Mr Q imagine that all those rich Italian industrialists had managed to get the hell out and stay rich when all the rest of Italy was on the bread line? Obviously, they had switched all their loose cash to currencies and places in which it was safe, and it was this wonderful little lawyer who had made it possible for them to get away with it.

Once Mr Q's agile mind had grasped the fact that here might be a way of concealing his own ill-gotten gains until the heat was off, an introduction would be arranged and Carlo would go to work.

Of course, Mr Q, your problems can be very simply solved. No trouble at all. I will arrange to have your money converted into gold-backed bonds and deposited in my Lugano bank. As soon as you wish to reconvert and receive the money, you write from America and tell me so. In reply you will hear news of the sad death in Europe of a distant relative of yours. Your family emigrated originally from where, Mr Q? Denmark? Then the relative will die in Copenhagen and the money that this so-generous cousin bequeathed to you will be paid in Danish kroner. Any questions?

'Yes, Dottore Lech. How do I know that I can trust you?'

'A sound question, Mr Q. I like hard-headed clients who take nothing for granted. You trust me initially because I am trustworthy and of good reputation. You sit here in my office confident that nothing which is said here will go any farther. You entrust your money to me because I shall give you, first, a notarized receipt for it and, second, the name of the bank in Lugano where it will be held to your credit in an anonymous numbered account. Do you know about anonymous numbered accounts, Mr Q?'

Naturally, he didn't. In 1945 the numbered Swiss bank account was not the hocus-pocus cliché beloved of knowing crime-reporters that it was to become in later years. Refugees from the Nazis had used it, as the Swiss had intended it to be used, as a defence against Gestapo enquiries and Gestapo reprisals. Subsequently, top Nazis and Fascisti, having second thoughts and wanting to hedge their bets, had used it as a defence against the dark suspicions of diehard comrades and the awful penalties that awaited defeatists.

To Mr Q the concept was new and immediately reassuring. He hung upon the Dottore's words; and if he never quite got around to asking how it was possible for a numbered account to be opened for him in a Lugano bank without anyone *at all* in the bank knowing his identity, it was understandable. In Italy and sitting on thirty thousand hot bucks it all sounded just great.

Now, of course, it all sounds so wide-eyed and artless that just recalling it makes me smile. Nevertheless, it worked. Parts of the set-up still work. When we started, it worked in all its parts because Carlo had thought everything through carefully and realistically down to the smallest detail. Not even Mat Williamson denies that Carlo was a superbly imaginative planner.

His choice of me as the contact man, the intermediary who knows how one can get in touch with the legendary Dottore Lech and what miracles the great man can perform is an example.

'Why me?' I had asked.

'Because a man like Q would automatically suspect a fellow-American who dangled information like that before his eyes of being an agent-provocateur; and he could very well be right. You, a British non-com, one those upper-crust limeys whose voices make them sound as if they're pederasts even when they're not, could never be suspect.

And what more natural than that someone in your line of work should hear about someone like me? From our own point of view, you have freedom to move about and make new contacts. With the cessation of actual hostilities, that freedom will tend to increase, and so will your freedom to invent reasons for extending your liaison with the Americans.'

'What about the British Mr Q's?'

He raised his right hand as if he were about to swear an oath or deliver a blessing, and then said very sharply: 'No!' After a pause he went on slowly: 'Never, Paul, as long as we are associated, will you ever approach any of your own people, no matter what you may suspect or know about them. Remember this. Nothing we ever do will ever be illegal with our own, our respective, national authorities. In your case, talking about currency transactions to an American soldier, or a Polish or a French one, you would be taking negligible risks. Talking to a British soldier of the same things, you risk being charged with an infinite variety of military offences. If we trifle a little with the law, it must always be the law of others, never of our own. Besides, most of the marketable commodities are now supplied by the Americans, who also control the main storage and distribution facilities. I expect that state of affairs to continue. Oh yes, there will be, as there are now, British, French and Polish fingers in the black-market pie. I have no doubt of that. But most of the fingers will belong, apart from those of my own countrymen, to Americans. That is where the serious money will end up.'

'But what happens to the money, Carlo? I mean, if it's left with us for safe-keeping.'

He was surprised that I should find it necessary to ask. 'Naturally, it remains the property of our client. That we will have the use of it to finance our own market operations will be none of his business, any more than it is the business of the man who banks his money in the conventional way to oversee the banks' investment policies. In many ways we shall, indeed, operate exactly like a bank, but a bank unfettered by petty rules and restrictions.'

'At most ordinary banks the client can go and withdraw his money if he wants. Will he be able to do that with ours?'

'Certainly he will! He can have his money any time he wishes, plus a generous share of its earnings during the time we have managed it. Our own charges will seem modest when we are found to have doubled his money for him. The fact that we may have quadrupled it for our own account need not concern him. Of course,' he added thoughtfully, 'complications are bound to arise. They always do when laws are broken.'

I waited. Carlo was thinking how best to enlighten the innocent without seeming to condescend or over-simplify. He was a courteous man.

'Consider,' he said at last, 'the position of a client of ours once he is back in his home town, a civilian again with perhaps a job and even a wife and family. How different it will all seem. And how unreal this faraway treasure of his will soon become!'

He contemplated that agreeable vision for a moment before sighing his way back into the real world. 'But let us assume a bolder spirit, or one who cannot bear the thought of money lying, as he thinks, idle in a Lugano bank. There are such men, Paul.'

'Yes, Carlo, there are, especially among those who have made killings as black marketeers.'

'Especially, you think? Among those who were always pilferers, thieves, even before they went into the army, stupidity is to be expected, I agree. But from those late development delinquents who will use our services we can count upon more sense, I believe. Take our prototypical Mr Q for example. Longing for, or possibly needing, money, he decides to send for his nest-egg in the prescribed manner.'

'You mean he chooses to inherit? Yes? Well, we then have to find the equivalent of thirty thousand dollars in

Danish kroner and remit from Copenhagen. Or do we just ignore him?'

The smile blossomed. 'Ignore him? That is the last thing we do. On the contrary, we at once arrange to have sent from Copenhagen direct to his local home town paper the magnificent news of this remarkable legacy and of the romantic story which lies behind it.' He looked at me expectantly.

'What romantic story?'

'What does it matter? You are being obtuse, Paul. Think of Mr Q and the strange position in which he would find himself. Think of questions that would be put to him. Who is this mysterious relative? Why has nobody ever heard of him or her before? And it would not be only the local newspaper reporter who wanted answers. His friends and, above all, his family would want answers, too, and they would examine them somewhat more critically. Almost as critically as the Internal Revenue people. How quick they would be to note the source of Mr Q's surprising windfall and to request a copy of the probated Will when one became available! Do you know, Paul, I believe that Mr Q would very soon be countermanding his instructions to us and telling his local paper that the whole thing had been a case of mistaken identity. Same name, wrong man.'

'What about his notarized receipt! He could come here and collect.'

'He could, but would he? Have you thought of all the anxieties, the heartaches, that receipt must already have caused him? He will have realized, remember, almost as he saw me signing it, that to be found with that piece of paper in his possession could be as damning as to be found counting the money itself, perhaps more so. There could be no plea for leniency on the score of ignorance. Al Capone went to prison for income-tax evasion, not for the way he had made the income. No need to remind Mr Q of that. How he must, in the end, have hated that beautiful receipt!

112

Where did he hide it when he left for home? In the lining of his tunic? In one of his shoes?'

'Supposing he went to Lugano?'

'They have never heard of him or his numbered account. He would have to come to us, where he would at once learn that, for security reasons, we had some months earlier transferred the money to a different bank. All is perfectly safe. What currency would he like it in? Or would he prefer to have it transferred to his domestic account? You see? He is back with his original dilemma, only now, from the tax-evasion standpoint, the offence is even more serious. He had an illicit hoard of dollars. Now, it has made a profit on which he ought to pay capital-gains tax if he were an upright, God-fearing citizen. But he is no longer that, and he knows it. Perhaps, if he has confided in his wife and she is a woman of courage the pair of them will risk all and smuggle it back to the United States. Or try to do so. We would be failing in our duty, I think, if we did not warn them most seriously of the nature of the risks they would run. At the same time we might remind them that, if they leave the money with us to increase and multiply, there is nothing to prevent their using it later. They might eventually decide to buy a *résidence secondaire* in Italy, or somewhere on the Côte d'Azur, which they could rent when they weren't luxuriating in it themselves. Then, no one ever need know anything.' He paused, closed his eyes and breathed in deeply as if he were already enjoying on Mr Q's behalf the cool evening breeze scented by pine trees. Then he opened his eyes again before narrowing them slightly. 'You see, Paul? There would never be, there *could* never be, a run on *our bank*.'

Does that sound like an anarchist speaking, Professor Krom? – a man against all settled order and systems of law?

I don't think it does. To me it sounds like a man who enjoyed making money not by breaking laws but by circumventing them, not by destroying order but by utilizing it in unorthodox ways.

Yes, Carlo was vain; indeed he revelled in his own cleverness; but the respect that he professed for the law was absolutely genuine. He was, too, something of a moralist and strongly disapproved of black marketeers.

He disapproved because he considered them parasites. He would have been affronted, though, by any suggestion that the same word could, with equal justice, have been applied to us. I only know of one person who had the temerity even to hint at the suggestion, and the consequences for that person were unpleasant. Carlo could, when angered, become quite vindictive.

In that respect he was different from Mat Williamson. Mat does not have to be in the least angry with a man before deciding that he must be destroyed.

The years immediately following VE day were great ones for parasites. Allied aid supplies, mostly American but some British, poured into Italy and West Germany at a prodigious rate.

However, since this is not a history of the post-World War II black markets – the writing of which I happily leave to a scholar of the Krom school of fantasists – I shall merely give some idea of the scale of them by reporting that, during our first eighteen months of operations, Carlo was 'entrusted' with nearly half a million dollars derived from the Italian markets *alone*.

I say *alone* because before long we were getting word of much larger sums needing our services in Germany.

The early reports from Carlos' man in Lugano told of a chaotic situation. Big money was being made, but those making it, mostly American senior NCOs and junior officers in transportation and supply units, seemed unaware of the difficulties into which they would soon be getting. This was not simply because they were new to the game, but because in West Germany the rules were complex and the conditions of play tended to promote over-confidence. For instance, there were three distinct occupation zones, in two of which – the French and the British – exchange control restrictions were maintained on their national currencies. In the British zone, these restrictions were enforced by a Special Investigation Branch squad of remarkable ferocity. So, the American wheeler-dealer, who already benefited from his access to the most sought-after market commodities, also enjoyed the advantage of being able to do business in the only freely convertible currency available, the dollar.

Soon, stories began to come in of American soldiers crossing into Switzerland for 'Rest and Recuperation'. On arrival, most of them made for the nearest bank. Perfectly natural, one would have said, if all that those fine boys were doing was exchanging a few of their dollars for francs to spend locally during their furloughs; but that, it seemed, was by no means all that some of them were doing; lots were opening bank accounts.

This, of course, was before the mere possession of a Swiss bank account by an American or British citizen rendered him, at least in the eyes of his native Revenue men, at best a jail-worthy tax-evader if not a Mafia narcotics-pedlar as well; but murmurings about refugee Nazi funds being protected by the Swiss bank secrecy laws were already getting louder, and a newspaper story about a black market in antibiotics involving occupation medical-corps personnel had caused a considerable fuss. As always when the nostrils of higher authority are assailed by smells of corruption other than their own, the cries of outrage and disgust are promptly followed by sounds of loophole-stoppings and stampings-out, of tightenings-up and clampings-down.

In the American sector, by the end of 1946, an efficient laundry service of the kind Carlo could provide had become essential. I do not claim that his was the only one in the field – we had our imitators by then – but it was unquestionably the safest and most reliable.

In November, having at last been told that the army no

115

longer required my services, I asked for a travel warrant to London and was demobilized there. Acting on Carlo's instructions, I then obtained a British passport as well as renewing my Argentine papers, before returning to Milan. From Milan I went to Lugano, where I spent a week or so learning a few more ropes. From Munich, I wrote to my family explaining that I had gone into the scrap-metal business.

The code-name given to me by Carlo for use when I needed to authenticate confidential messages was 'Oberholzer'.

In 1956, Carlo had an operation for the removal of his gall bladder. The surgeon who performed it somehow bungled the job, and later in the year a second operation became necessary. He recovered all right, but it was a long, debilitating illness and it changed him. I don't mean that he aged prematurely, though I have noticed that serious illness can have that effect on persons in their sixties. With Carlo what happened was that, as his physical health returned, the pattern of his characteristic psychological responses seemed gradually to intensify. He became an exaggerated, larger-than-life version of himself. Things that would once have only made that smile of his blossom, now made him laugh aloud. Things that would once have been dismissed as annoyances now produced outbursts of rage. It was as if, in the struggle to regain his health, he had been obliged to shed the emotional weight of several old but crucial inhibitions. The result was in many ways a more engaging man, but also a more formidable and sometimes frightening one. I have said that Carlo could be vindictive. After his illness he could be cruelly so. The man who could dream up the butter-train coup was also capable of applying himself with relish to more disagreeable amusements.

His claim that ours was a bank on which there could never be a run had proved to be justified. On that score we had no anxieties; and, after 1951, when the double-taxation conventions between Switzerland and the US and UK came into force, the possibility of a run ceased to exist altogther. Our 'customers', a cagey bunch of crooks with finely-tuned survival instincts, could never all go crazy at the same time.

That is not to say, however, that some of them did not over the years withdraw their deposits, having devised their own ways of accounting for them. Some of the ways worked. Few attempted, though, to use the legacy method of getting their money, and most who did chickened out, as Carlo had predicted they would, before the pay-off was finally made.

The typical American customer seeking to close his account with us was usually in Europe on a business or vacation trip. Mostly, they wrote, after leaving the United States and generally from London or Paris, to announce that they were on their way. Those who went unannounced direct to Lugano were referred to Milan, and Carlo was immediately given advance warning either by telephone or by one of our couriers. When such customers arrived they were usually, and quite naturally, a bit flustered. Doubt and greed, plus a little anger and a lot of fear, make a disturbing emotional mix; but most were easy to handle.

The one who so upset Carlo was exceptional in a number of respects. To being with, he was not flustered, only bloody-minded. Furthermore, during the time that had elapsed since I had signed him up in Germany, he had returned to the United States and, under the GI Bill of Rights, qualified as an accountant. In addition, he had married a woman, also an accountant, whom he had met while they were both attending a post-graduate course in business administration. She had worked then for a firm of Wall Street investment bankers. After their marriage they had gone into business together, starting an employment agency specializing in trained data-processing staff.

This customer was so different from our prototypical Mr Q that I shall call him Vic – as in Victor and victim.

When I first met him, Vic had been dealing with the already overcrowded market for stolen PX goods, but later, thanks to a lucky posting and a promotion, he had been able to switch to army truck tyres and make real money. By the time his tour of duty in Germany ended we were holding over seventy thousand dollars for him, and he, although he had met Carlo only once, held nine of the notarized receipts. The courier service we operated made such transactions fairly routine, once confidence had been established at an initial meeting, as well as safer. The meeting usually took place near Zug, where Carlo's holding corporation was registered.

Vic gave no advance warning of his arrival in Milan, and none was received from Lugano because he had not bothered to go there. I had other projects to supervise by then, and was dividing my time between Milan and three other cities. It was by chance that I was there when Vic descended on us. A lucky chance, I think; not because the occasion was in the least enjoyable, but because it made me think more carefully than I had thought before about Carlo. Naturally, he called me in to greet his old client and my old friend.

At first, Vic showed no signs at all of bloody-mindedness. He was not exactly affable, but cool, polite and collected. He had a brand-new Gucci brief-case which he carefully placed on the floor between his legs. Then he told us what a wonderful little woman he had married and why he hadn't troubled to go to the bank in Lugano.

A month earlier they had been talking about expanding their business, of opening a second office in Chicago. They had spoken of the additional capital that would be needed and of the problems of borrowing it they would have to face. In the watches of the night Vic had revealed for the first time that while in the army he had not always been a simple soldier.

Mrs Vic had heard his confession with surprise but only token distress. They were both human, weren't they? Once

118

her surprise had worn off curiosity had taken over. Her Wall Street experience had given her some knowledge of Swiss banking customs. *What* sort of an account did he say he had? An *anonymous* one? Didn't he mean numbered? No, he meant one hundred per cent anonymous numbered. Well, honey, I have news for you. There are numbered accounts, but not one hundred per cent anonymous ones. Okay, your name's not on the account externally, but it's on it internally. The only anonymity lies in the fact that no more than five key bank personnel can match the name to the number. Exactly how did you open this account? What sort of application did you sign?

Now, Vic turned narrowed eyes in my direction. 'How many other suckers did you sign up, Paul baby?'

'You had an anonymous account.'

'There's no such thing.'

'There's no such thing *now*. The rules were changed when the double-taxation conventions were signed.'

'Bullshit!'

I gave him the weary look. 'If you yourself had not insisted that, for security reasons, contacts between us could only be made on *your* initiative, you would long ago have been formally notified of the situation. Why project your paranoia on us? If you had simply gone to the Lugano bank you would have been referred here automatically.'

'Well, now that I'm here *un*automatically, where's the money?'

I looked at Carlo. He already had his hand on the intercom to the outer office. He flipped the switch and said in English: 'Send in the current confidential fiscal account of Mr Vic.' To Vic he said: 'I am assuming that you can produce the original receipts that I notarized. You have them with you?'

'Sure.' He reached for the brief-case and took out an old-fashioned pouch file of the kind that is tied with a linen tape. He undid the tape, took out the receipts and spread them out elaborately in the shape of a fan. 'How many peanuts are they worth now?' he asked unpleasantly.

What interested me at once was their condition. I had seen a number of those receipts produced for inspection in Carlo's office, and always before they had looked unfit even for his elegant waste-basket. Either they had been dog-eared and greasy from years of furtive handling and re-examination, or so creased, folded and refolded to suit strange hiding-places that they were nearly falling apart. Vic's were all clean and smooth. As well as being astute and impertinent, he was also, it seemed, overwhelmingly sure of himself.

Carlo's senior secretary, the matriarch, came in with the statement of account and placed it reverently on the desk in front of him.

Normally, that is faced with with a client who had minded his manners and was there merely to enquire about the state of his dream money, Carlo would have let the account lie there for a few minutes while he chatted away knowledgeably about some new sculptor whose work had caught his eye, or the follies of currency speculation, or anything else that had happened to come into his mind as he sat there. The truth was that the accounts, which were always updated twice a year, were his own particular pride and joy. He did them himself and they were masterpieces of obfuscation. One of his greatest pleasures was to see a client, on examining an account, purse his lips and then nod vaguely as if it were all perfectly understandable. He believed that the preliminary chit-chat – what he called his abracadabra – helped the process along by bemusing the client.

With Vic, however, abracadabra was obviously not going to work. Besides, the fellow annoyed him. Almost before the secretary had left the room, Carlo leaned forward and tossed the account folder in Vic's direction.

Vic caught it neatly, opened it and spent about ten seconds glancing at each of the three pages inside. Then, he slapped it shut and skimmed it back so that it plopped on to the desk right under Carlo's nose.

'Mr Lech,' he said, 'I left you with seventy-three thousand dollars of mine. In eight years those dollars have become one hundred eighty-six thousand somethings. First question, what kind of somethings? Lire?'

Carlo put the account folder aside as if the sight of it now offended him. 'American dollars, of course,' he said. 'You have more than doubled your money.'

Vic did not look in the least pleased. He just said: 'How? How have I doubled it? Tell me, Mr Lech.'

Carlo touched the account folder without looking at it. 'It is all here, Sir. I thought you understood figures.'

Vic made a spitting sound. 'Sure I understand figures, when I know how they've been cooked. You, or rather your boy Paul here, now tells me that my money hasn't been in that bank after all. So where has it been?'

'Acting on your behalf, we held it in a deposit account.'

'Ah, now we're getting somewhere. Acting on my behalf, you said. Right? So what did you invest it in? German blue chips? Schering? Siemens? Daimler-Benz? Hoechst? What was the portfolio?'

Carlo had a small ebony-edged silver ruler which he used as a paperweight. With it, he suddenly rapped on the desk. 'That is enough, sir,' he said sternly. 'I am a lawyer, not an investment banker. You found it convenient to utilize my services in order to hold your money in trust. I have held it in trust. It is more than intact. You can receive it back at any time you wish, less my proper fees but plus compound interest at bank rates as they have fluctuated over the relevant period. You have more than doubled your money. What is your complaint?'

Vic sat back, as if relaxing, then cocked an eye again at me. '*What* kind of an account do you charmers say you put it in?'

'A deposit account.'

He made his spitting noise again. 'Now, I *know* you're lying. If you had opened anything at all in my behalf, it would have been a discretionary investment account. No, let's cut the crap now, eh, Pauly? I've done my homework, I figure that, over the last eight years you've had them to play with, you and Mr Lech have made a cool million out of my seventy-three thousand. That would be par for the course. Now, you tell me you've doubled my money plus a few bucks, less your fees of course, and ask me what my complaint is. Are you serious?'

What did he think we were? Nice guys about to vote him a pension as sucker of the year? He had indeed done some homework, but not as much as he thought. In fact, thanks to the Lugano bank's post-war policy of investment in German industry, we had made over two million dollars out of his particular nest-egg. Now, it remained only to get rid of the man.

'How would you like your money, Mr Vic?' I asked. 'A draft on the Chase-Manhattan in Geneva? A telex transfer to your own bank in the United States? Cash?'

He examined us both carefully for a moment or two without answering. Carlo began tapping on the desk-top with his ruler.

Then, Vic broke his own silence with a short laugh. 'The shyster and his shill!' he said.

Carlo stopped tapping and I saw that he had gone quite pale. His colloquial English was not good, but it was good enough to understand the word 'shyster'. Rather than let him say something he might regret, I got in first.

'Don't push your luck, Vic,' I said. 'We could always ship it back as truck tyres. It's cash, I take it. Dollars in century bills?'

'Fifties or centuries, but I want them right now.'

Carlo reached for the intercom and told the matriarch to get the bank on the phone. That was unnecessary because we kept a cash float of half a million dollars in a safe deposit box. He was playing for time; to think, presumably, though what there was to think about just then I did not immediately understand. When the bank was put through, he said first that I would shortly be requiring access to the safe deposit vault. Then he told the procurator at the other end to wait and, looking at Vic, asked him in Italian if, in view of the large sum of money he would be carrying, he would like a bank escort to his hotel.

I gathered, correctly, that this was a test question to see if Vic understood Italian. When it was evident that he did not, Carlo repeated the question in English.

No, Vic did not need an escort, thank you very much; he could take care of himself.

Carlo said goodbye to the procurator and then went on speaking in Italian to me.

'Paul, I want the receipt from him for the money to be witnessed by someone at the bank. Make a ceremony of it. And I particularly want those old notarized receipts of mine back. Then, I want to know as soon as possible which hotel he's in. Offer to share a taxi with him and drop him off. Then phone me the name of the hotel immediately. Unless it's within a couple of minutes of here don't wait until you get back.'

It was not the moment to ask him what he was up to, so I went ahead and did exactly as I had been told.

Vic made difficulties about signing for the money, but the actual sight of it and the solemnity of the bank officials quietened him down eventually. The old receipts he handed over without a murmur. Only about half the money was in hundreds and he had trouble stuffing it all into his nice new brief-case. He rejected my suggestion that we share a taxi – now that he had the money he seemed scared of me – but he let me flag one down for him and tell the driver where to go.

I called Carlo from the nearest cafe and reported.

'Good,' he said. 'You have all the receipts? Splendid. Now please bring them back here, Paul.'

When he had the originals spread out on the desk he looked at them as if they were old and much-loved friends.

'How could such an otherwise cautious man be so stupid?'

123

he asked. 'If they had been mine, I would have set light to every single one myself before I handed you its ashes.'

'He was too worried about the receipt that *he* had to sign.'

'That is why I asked for it. Oh yes, it will be useful, but it will be the first ones which will count. Look at the dates! How interesting, and how devastatingly conclusive.'

'Conclusive of what?'

He did not answer straightaway. 'What is that name he called you, Paul?'

'Shill?'

'Yes. What does it mean?'

'Mostly it's the slang word for a professional gambler's accomplice who is there to make winning look easy, but con-men and other crooks also use shills. A shill is a person, man or woman, who persuades the victims to come and try their luck, to let themselves be swindled.'

He sighed. 'One would think we had *lost* this foolish man's money, instead of doubling it. Well, he must pay for his insolence. As soon as you phoned me I arranged to have him tailed from his hotel.' He responded to my raised eyebrows, 'I wish to know what he does with the money.'

'If he has any sense he'll put it in a bank.'

'Yes, but which bank and where? It is too late today, but perhaps he will travel overnight. Where to? Lausanne? Basle?'

A wild thought occurred to me. 'You're not thinking of taking it back off him, Carlo?'

'It would serve him right, but we are not thieves. No, I simply wish to know which branch of which bank he chooses.'

'Then what?'

'The American Internal Revenue Service pays a ten per cent reward to informers who give them proof that a US citizen has failed to declare income.'

'You'd inform on Vic?'

'I? Great heavens, no! I have an associate in New York

124

who will do that. I will just send him the evidence. Think of the wringing hands when the IRS descends on our friend Mr Vic with their demands for back audits. What was the source of these large sums obtained while you were serving in the army and for which we hold receipts? Why did you no report them? You refuse to answer because to do so might incriminate you? Then answer this. We have evidence here of a capital gain by you of over eighty thousand dollars. Why was that not reported? Where is it? We'll tell you. It's in such-and-such a bank. And before you add perjury to the rest of the crimes you're going to be charged with, let us remind you of this. Swiss bank secrecy doesn't protect persons who can be shown to have committed criminal offences like stealing US army property. What a fine time they will have!'

I was beginning to feel sorry for Vic. 'You'd do that to him for a ten per cent pay-off?'

'Of that pathetic reward I shall not accept one cent,' he said contemptuously. 'My reward will be the satisfaction of *my* sense of the fitness of things. He insulted me. He insulted you. He will be punished, as a criminal, such as he, deserves to be punished, for his crimes against his country's laws.' He sat up very straight in his chair and gazed fixedly at the Moretto landscape on the wall behind me. Finally, he made the cobweb-brushing gesture he still used to punctuate thought processes. 'All this has taught me a lesson, Paul,' he added.

'You mean that, if we're going to blow him to the IRS, he's liable to blow us too?'

'Certainly not! What crimes have *we* committed? I was merely reflecting that it might be time for us to spread our wings again and to fly in a new direction.' He raised his elbows sideways, dropped his hands, then tensed his fingers into talons as if he were a bird of prey about to kill.

'Oh?'

'Yes. In future, Paul, we will have no more dealings with

illegitimate money. It is contagious, it carries infection.' One of the talons brushed away yet another cobweb. 'By devoting ourselves diligently to the new arts of tax avoidance, I think that we may be able to create for our clients, and certain others, impenetrable and indestructible shields against the rapacity of governments.'

He went on to explain in detail what he had in mind.

I have admitted that, after he had recovered physically from his illness, I sometimes found Carlo a little frightening. The revenge he had taken on Vic, simply because the man had been foolish enough to speak his mind, worried me quite a bit, but the plan of action he then proceeded to lay out was wholly rational.

The idea derived from his belief – a widely-held belief, I know, but one that was in his case based on special knowledge – that the very rich are always also very stingy.

Thus, if you were able to show a rich man how he could avoid paying large amounts of money to the government which presumed to tax him and his corporate enterprises, he, in his turn, would be ready to pay a much, much smaller amount of money to you in the shape of a fee.

At least, he would be ready to do so for a time. That, sooner or later, he would become reluctant to pay you as he had previously been reluctant to pay the tax collector, was inevitable. Ultimately, he would probably try to cheat you as, once upon a time, he had tried to cheat the tax man. Therefore, you bore that possibility in mind from the start, armed yourself with appropriate sanctions and made sure that, if or when the attempts to cheat you were made, simple mechanisms to ensure their failure were triggered automatically. Ideally, Carlo thought, our relationship with our clients should be one of mutual, and permanent, trust.

Who but Krom could have had the breathtaking audacity to speak in this context of 'international parasitism' and make wild allegations about a 'multi-million-dollar extortion racket'?

CHAPTER SIX

I am not the only one who has found Krom hard to take.

Had our stay at the Villa Lipp not been cut short so suddenly, Connell and Henson would surely have ended by quarrelling with him. Obviously, they respected his earlier work and so were prepared to put up with a certain amount of his nonsense, including a lot of tipsy pontificating; otherwise, they would not have been there; but even on that first night, before we knew that things had gone seriously wrong and that we were in danger, there were signs of strain.

Krom had objected strongly to Connell's asking me questions; and I had made a bet with myself that, in due course, I would hear him insisting just as strongly that only he was entitled to to receive my 'papers', and that only he would have the right thereafter to decide who saw how much of what was in them. I won the bet too.

When the coffee had been served, I told Melanie to pass round file number one to our guests. Krom stopped her instantly by clutching at one of her arms. He was as stricken as a child who has just been told that the bright new toy which was to have been his alone must, after all, be shared.

'I think, Mr Firman,' he said with a show of teeth, 'that, in your own interests as well as ours, the distribution of all documents ought to be strictly limited.'

'I quite agree, Professor,' I stared hard at Melanie's arm until he released it. 'There are only three copies of that document, one for you and one each for your witnesses. I shall insist that the last two be returned to me to destroy as soon as they have been read and compared with your text.'

He tried to think of an inoffensive way of saying that he did not want his witnesses having access to material that was really his, and his alone, in case they stole bits of it from him. Naturally, he failed; there is no inoffensive way of saying such a thing. He tried stepping around the difficulty.

'Notes should be taken.'

'Of course. And I am sure that they *will* be taken,' I said cheerfully. 'Dr Connell has a tape-recorder and Dr Henson has a shorthand-writer's notebook in her suitcase. I dare say she also has an excellent memory.'

Henson suddenly laughed and received a glare from Krom.

She at once raised both hands in apology. 'Sorry, but I had an unworthy thought,' she explained. 'It crossed my mind, only for an instant but quite distinctly, that Mr Firman couldn't care less how many notes are taken because he has no intention of letting us see or hear anything that could in any way compromise him.'

Yves broke in angrily. 'There, Doctor, you are greatly mistaken. This meeting alone compromises him, and us.' His outstretched hand included Melanie.

'Don't worry, Mr Boularis,' Krom tried clumsily to pat him on the knee and seemed to resent Yves's instinctively flinching away. 'But don't deceive yourself either, or let him deceive you,' he went on with one of his saliva sprays. 'Your friend Firman was compromised years ago when I saw him in Zürich.'

Connell stifled what might have been the start of a low moan. 'Ah, yes,' he said, 'we're back to the celebrated Oberholzer-Firman identification. Are we now going to be allowed to hear exactly what was so compromising about it, or is that still "pas devant les enfants", Professor?'

He sounded as if he had become as tired of Krom as I had. Before the elder statesman had time to do more than glare and show teeth again, I had signalled to Melanie.

This time she went the other way round the table so that the witnesses received their copies of the file first.

'Read all about it,' I said to Connell.

The witnesses' behaviour towards me since then has left much to be desired, inevitably perhaps; but I still regret that security considerations, now known to have been irrelevant, prevented my giving them more of the truth than I did. They might have learned something, not only to their own advantage, but, of more immediate consequence in this time of trial, to mine.

This is how it really came about that Krom saw me in Zürich.

The warning telegram did not reach me until late on Tuesday, over twenty-four hours after Kramer had been taken ill.

The text of it said only that he was in the emergency heart unit of the Kantonsspital in Zürich. The signature, however, was in a code form meaning that not only was there material urgently awaiting collection but also that the strictest security precautions should be taken. Use of the code signature showed that, ill or not, he had written or dictated the telegram himself and that his mind was still functioning.

I was in Lisbon at the time and the message had been re-transmitted from Milan by Carlo; and I mean by Carlo personally, not by some trusted underling to whom the job had been delegated. If that sounds an odd way to run a business making net profits in the five-million-dollar-plus region I shall have to agree, it was odd; but that was because the business was odd.

Carlo kept up his office with its appropriate staff in Milan mainly as a front. Otherwise the only persons we employed were our six couriers, four men and two women, who did exactly as they were told and never asked a question except when the answer was needed to clarify an instruction. All other operations in the ten cities we used as bases were handled through the neutral channels of 'business accommodation' services which provided mail-forwarding and phone-answering together with addresses to put on our

129

various letter-heads. Our consultancy work was always done in hotel rooms. For the profits we made, our overheads were negligible.

The business I was doing in Lisbon had reached a delicate stage and it was impossible to respond to the warning message as promptly as I might have done. I don't think it would have made much difference though. When I received the message, the Kramer relationship was already unsalvageable. All that would have been different, possibly, would have been the nature of the trap set for me.

Anyway, it was Thursday before I could leave Lisbon. I reached Frankfurt later that day and rented a car. I was in Zürich at nine-thirty on Friday morning.

Why did I drive when I could more quickly have got there by air? Mainly because, if you are in western Europe and want to have a confidential business discussion on the other side of a frontier, it is more secure to travel by car. The days when an elaborate carnet recorded every frontier transit which the car and its passengers made are gone. All you need is an international certificate of insurance and they generally don't bother even with that, much less your passport; at most road frontier crossings they just wave you through. Airlines, on the other hand, keep copies of passenger flight manifests that can be checked by anyone with the right kind of muscle, and at lots of airports you may get your passport stamped. Train controls can be stickier than road, too, because the officials have more time. The only persons who should never use road frontiers are smugglers, because on some roads the Customs people like to play games. Instead of lining up beside the immigration squad, they move their check-point three or more kilometres back along the road on their side where a build-up of traffic doesn't matter. Then, they have plenty of time to nail the ones with the evidence on them, just as the poor slobs think they are free and clear.

I am not a smuggler and I use the roads. I did, though, go to the Zürich airport and park the car there before taking an airport bus into town. Anyone then becoming interested in my movements would have assumed that I had arrived by air. I got off the bus at the Haupt-Bahnhof.

From there I phoned the hospital and learned that Kramer had been dead for two days.

It was too early in the morning, I felt, to telephone a newly-created widow. To pass the time, I had a second breakfast while I decided how best to handle the phase-out-and-forget routine in this particular case. At that point, strange as it may seem now, the only grave difficulty of which I was aware was that of remembering the widow's first name without having Kramer's personal file there to check on.

I got it eventually – Frieda. After breakfast I went for a stroll and found a department store where I was able to buy a black tie.

By then it was ten-thirty, so I went back to the station and called the Kramer apartment.

The voice of the woman who answered was that of someone younger than Frieda; the married daughter, I found. She accepted my condolences politely enough on her mother's behalf, but when I asked if I could speak to the mother there was a marked change of tone.

'Is that, by any chance, Herr Oberholzer of Frankfurt?' she asked.

'Yes, I am an old friend of your father's.'

'So I have been given to understand.' Her tone was now distinctly cool. That could have put me on my guard, but didn't. Those nursing private griefs often resent attempts, real or imagined, by outsiders to share them.

'I am speaking for my mother,' she went on briskly. 'She has asked me to tell you that the funeral will be at eleven tomorrow morning. The crematorium is on the Käferholz-strasse. Flowers, if you wish to send any, should be delivered to the chapel of the hospital mortuary before nine-thirty.'

'Thank you. I am grateful for that information. However, I hope to pay my respects and offer my personal sympathies to your mother before then. I propose to call on her this morning, just before noon if that would be convenient.'

'No, Herr Oberholzer. I am afraid that that would not be convenient. Only family members are here today. But my mother has anticipated your anxiety and concern. She asks me to assure you that your papers are quite safe and that you may collect them at any time after the funeral tomorrow. There will be sandwiches and coffee here for those who can stomach them. Goodbye, Herr Oberholzer.'

She hung up.

Even then I wasn't really worried. Under the emotional stress of her husband's sudden death, Frieda had obviously been talking too freely about things she would have been wiser to forget; but, as her knowledge of them was necessarily limited to what Kramer would have told her in an unlikely fit of total indiscretion, it represented no serious threat to me, just a nuisance. Because she had disapproved of me and my relationship with her husband – though she could scarcely have disapproved of the money it had brought in – I was being made to stay in Zurich when it was neither necessary nor advisable for me to do so, and to attend a funeral.

Persuading wealthy tax and exchange-control evaders to pay you for advising them is not difficult; not, that is, when you have the right sanctions at your disposal; but, unless you are very careful, it can be dangerous.

It must be accepted that any rich man who chooses to *evade* his country's fiscal laws when, simply by taking a little trouble and obtaining good advice, he could *avoid* them, has to be, however superficially astute, basically stupid.

When, therefore, he has to pay up in order to conceal his folly he is unlikely to accept the loss philosophically. On the contrary, he will quite often go to extravagant lengths to avenge the 'outrage'. I know of one case in which the idiot actually went out, bought himself the most expensive rifle on the market, had it fitted with a telescopic sight and began practising to become a marksman.

The fact is that a lot of these very rich men can behave remarkably like old-fashioned psychopathic gangsters. Protecting your set-up from lunatic vindictiveness of that kind calls for more than ordinary care and attention. Where security is concerned, you have to be a trifle paranoid.

The moment Kramer's daughter hung up on me, I should have immediately gone back to my car and hit the road for home and a good dinner. I was married at the time to my second wife. She was really an excellent cook.

The wrong kind of greed, that was my trouble; greed, plus slow and very sloppy thinking. Kramer had said in his telegram that there was important material to be collected. So, there was I hanging about in the expectation of collecting; just as if nothing had happened; just as if Kramer had still been alive and well.

The weather was horrible, a bitter wind was blowing showers of wet snow. If I had been travelling on one of my real passports I might well have checked in at a first-rate hotel where I was known and would be cosseted. Luckily, I was travelling as Reinhardt Oberholzer. I say 'luckily', because if I had been using a real identity nothing I could have done would have saved the situation. There are some paper-trails that cannot be diverted or cleaned up because, before you get busy with your little spiked walking-stick, the hounds will be there in the field waiting for you.

So, thank God for the Oberholzer passports.

Yes, that's right, Krom. Passports, plural. We used five. I had one. The four men couriers had one each, which they used when they were acting as cut-outs.

Carlo's unorthodox thinking would have sent any trained intelligence man crazy. For example, he had picked the cover name Oberholzer originally because it was neither common nor uncommon but middle-ordinary in most German-speaking places. In an Anglo-Saxon community, Underwood or Overton would be in the same bracket. So far, quite orthodox. But what happened when the cover wore thin and began to unravel?

Orthodox opinion was that you promptly junked both it and its occupant. Carlo did not agree. By hastily junking a cover, to say nothing of the person who had been using it, you might well supply confirmation of what had until then been only a suspicion. You might even create suspicions where none had existed except in your own imagination. Was it not better, surely, to present the opposition with a fresh set of doubts to resolve by putting a second man into play, one who in some respects strongly resembled his namesake, yet in others was confusingly different? If suspicions had existed before, would they not now be allayed? Or, if not wholly allayed, would not the reasons for them now have to be reassessed?

In view of the nature of the opposition we faced, an opposition which had always to rely upon reluctant or havering witnesses telling as little of the truth as they dared, such a reassessment could have only one result. 'Doubt demoralizes' was one of Carlo's favourite maxims. His tactical description of the Oberholzer-style multiplication manoeuvre was 'dispersal' or, if he felt like being facetious, 'defence in width'.

I once played against a good three-card-trick man for over an hour. I knew exactly what he was doing and how he was doing it, and still he beat me three times out of five. That was how the Oberholzer game had worked. Only we had been winning five tricks out of five, until I lost one that made it necessary not only to change the name of the game but also some of the rules.

Zürich is a busy city and unless you have made reservations in advance or are a known and valued client in a particular establishment, central hotel rooms are not always easy to find. Since I could not go to a place where I was known, I went to the tourist bureau at the station, where they operated a hotel booking service.

Now I may have been careless that day, but I was not

completely feckless. When you are using a cover, you always, and automatically, use it as little as possible simply in order to protect it from unnecessary wear and tear. So, when I gave my name to the girl at the tourist bureau I instinctively resorted to an old ploy.

In most countries, officialdom tends, when identifying you, to put your surname first and your given name or names after it. In many parts of Asia this name order is socially usual as well. On the European mainland and in South America, the social and administrative usages tend to overlap. Your insurance policies may describe you as OBERHOLZER, Reinhardt or Reinhardt Oberholzer. On a formal occasion among strangers you may click heels and introduce yourself as Oberholzer Reinhardt, while at a less starchy function you are dear old lovable Reinhardt Oberholzer. To the travel-bureau girl I gave my name as Oswald Reinhardt, slurring the Oswald slightly so that I could always claim, if necessary, that she had not been listening attentively.

By the time I had returned to the department store, bought an overnight bag and a change of linen and was back at the bureau, they had a room for me. It was in a second-category place up by the botanical gardens. The receptionist there had my name as O.Reinhardt from the bureau, and did not bother to look closely at the Oberholzer passport I fumbled with before filling out the police card.

The hotel was on a pleasant street with lots of trees which probably gave it quite a rustic outlook during the summer. Unfortunately, it was also next door to a church with a clock tower. This had a full set of chimes which were, I soon found, in robust working order. The receptionist, showing me to my room, said with a false but practised smile that many guests enjoyed the sound of the clock striking. The prospect of going back to the tourist bureau and starting afresh was unattractive, so I asked the way to the nearest pharmacy.

It was several streets away in a little shopping district

which appeared to serve a quarter which was mixed business and residential. In a miniature supermarket I bought half a bottle of whisky. In the pharmacy I bought, in addition to razor, soap, face-cloth and tooth-brush, some ear-plugs. Then, deciding to return to the hotel by a different route, one that I thought might be less exposed to the wind, I saw the flower shop.

Now, although I like flowers and normally find flower shops agreeable places, I am not one of those who cannot resists them. It was just that, in this particular shop, there was a remarkably handsome girl visible through the window. She was spraying the leaves of some philodendra, and the way she was raising her arms did something for her. As I slowed down to admire the view, the sight of her happened to coincide with an irresistible urge to get in out of the cold wind again plus the thought that a wreath from Oberholzer at the Kramer funeral might serve both to modify his women's hostility and to fortify their discretion.

So I went in.

When the girl was not spraying plants placed high up on wrought-iron display stands, her posture was not so good, but she was cheerful and friendly. She wouldn't recommend a wreath, she said, because her partner, who was the real expert at making wreaths quickly, was away with 'flu. If I insisted, she would do her best to make a nice wreath in time, but as it would have to be at the hospital mortuary before nine-thirty the following morning, she really thought that flowers would be better. What about some of those hot-house roses over there? Of course, they wouldn't last beyond tomorrow, but in this weather neither would the flowers in a wreath. You couldn't just send greenstuff, could you? If I decided on the roses she would see that they were well wrapped and, as she was the one who would be doing the delivery, taken straight into the mortuary chapel when they got there. For a German like me they wouldn't be all that expensive, and if I took the lot – the red, yellow and pink would look lovely together – she would give me

136

a discount. She was a good saleswoman with some miserable roses on her hands which weren't going to last the weekend anyway.

Once the bargain was struck, though, and I was seated at a little table writing conventional words of sympathy on a card to go with the flowers, and sealing it into one of the envelopes provided, she became curious. She knew from my accent that I was neither Swiss or Austrian, but she couldn't decide whether I was a north or south German, nor could she figure out my relationship with the dead. When I had declined her offer of a receipt and she was ringing up the sale on the cash register, she remarked that they didn't have many foreign visitors, buying flowers up there and asked me where I was staying. When I told her she looked genuinely concerned, but at once said bravely, but with even less conviction, what the receptionist had said, that lots of people liked the sound of the bells. She was no longer curious about which part of Germany I came from. She knew now that I would not be back, not in that quarter of Zürich certainly. When I left the shop, she was putting my condolences to the family Kramer into a little plastic bag that would protect them from the weather.

I lunched well, far away from the hotel, spent the afternoon in a cinema and had a good, early, dinner. The night, though, was dreadful.

The ear-plugs did little to help and the whisky less. Every time the clock struck, the windows rattled and you could feel vibrations through the bedsprings, or at least I fancied that I could; and, of course, after a bit you ceased to think of sleep and simply lay there waiting for the next assault.

At three in the morning I took a chair-cushion, the duvet and all the pillows and blankets I could find, and made up a sort of bed in the bathroom where, I had noticed, the sounds from the clock tower were slightly muted. There, I managed to doze through two lots of quarter-hour chimes before the bathroom floor made itself felt and four o'clock shattered the last hope of sleep. I sat up for the rest of the night in the one armchair, with the duvet over my head.

Excuses, it may be said. The man makes a fool of himself. Clearly, he has to blame someone or something, so he picks on a church clock and a sleepless night.

Not so. My mistakes on that occasion had all been made the day before. What is remarkable is that, having suffered the sort of sleepless night after which a man normally needs tranquillizers if he is to function at all, I succeeded in behaving with such decision and efficiency.

I sat in the armchair until five-thirty. Then, I shaved, bathed, put on my new white shirt and black tie and waited for daylight. At six-thirty, while it was still dark, I went down and consulted the night-duty concierge about the possibility of getting a taxi. He said that it might take a while, but that he would phone for one. When he had done so, I asked him about getting some coffee. The kitchen did not open until seven. Casting about in my mind for other ways of killing time, I thought of my bill and asked if I could pay it. Yes, I could. A surprise, until I caught the look of resignation on the concierge's face. I was evidently not the first guest in the place who had been in a hurry to get away. Nor would I be the last. Very early departures were normal.

So, I paid the bill and said that I would return later for my bag. That was my first piece of luck.

A taxi came eventually and I went to the Carlton-Elite Hotel. There, in the restaurant, I ate a large American breakfast and read the German-language papers. Later, in the lobby, I read the Italian papers and did the Paris *Herald-Tribune* crossword. By then it was nearly time to go to the funeral.

To the doorman I explained my wants; a taxi or a hire car with a driver who would take me to the crematorium, wait and then drive me to an apartment in the Hottingen district. That was where the Kramer apartment was. The doorman said that a hire car would cost no more for that sort of journey and would be more comfortable. He could have one there in five minutes.

It was a black four-door Taunus and the driver was an elderly man with beautiful iron-grey hair and a thin, sad face. He knew exactly where the crematorium was and obviously enjoyed funeral work, of which, he told me gently, he did a great deal.

'Was the departed a close relative of the gentleman?' he asked as he fought his way out of the central traffic.

'No. He wasn't a relation of any kind.'

'A close friend of the gentlemen perhaps?'

'A friend, a business friend.'

'Ah.' He cheered up at once and proceeded to give me some man-to-man advice. 'Then the gentleman will probably be wise to sit at the back of the chapel during the service. That way, one is able to avoid at the conclusion too much involvement with the close relatives if one does not wish it. A brief word of sympathy to the chief mourner in order to show that one has been present is all that is necessary then before leaving.'

'I expect you're right.'

I spoke distantly and he got the message. I heard no more about the theory and practice of funeral attendance. Unfortunately, he had made me think.

I had, in fact, been 'close' to Kramer and his wife for several years. But was I a friend? Even a business friend? A more accurate description, and one that Krom may smack his lips over if he wishes, would be 'co-conspirator'.

I recruited Kramer at an Interfiscal Society Congress in Monaco.

A director of one of the big-three Swiss banks had been there to give a lecture on his country's bank secrecy laws. It was a good lecture, neither as defensive nor as plaintive as such public-relations exercises usually are, and I said so to a man from the same bank who had accompanied the director to the Congress. That was Kramer and he was strictly middle management. He was there, I gathered, partly so that the director should be seen to have some sort of ADC in attendance, and partly to latch on to any worthwhile business that might be floating around among the delegates to the Congress.

The director was the man with the personality, the financial mastermind. Kramer had his dignity, too, but it was that of the good soldier. He would rise no higher in the bank hierarchy. He obviously knew this and was, for an otherwise sensible man, surprisingly bitter over what he saw as an injustice. He spoke over-respectfully of his superiors in the bank. The sardonic smile, of which he made much use, was the final give-away. He was, I decided, open to an approach.

I made it over a drink in the Hôtel de Paris.

'What I don't understand,' I said, 'is the nature of the penalties that your secrecy laws impose. They seem so light.'

'You think so, Mr Firman?'

'Well, supposing an officer of your bank, a man in the head office where you work, is approached by a stranger who is – oh, what shall we say? – an agent of the American Internal Revenue Service? Not impossible?'

He restrained his inner amusement. 'It has been known,' he said solemnly.

'Right. Now, supposing the agent offers this officer of yours three thousand dollars for the name of each and every American citizen on your books and the size of his account with you. What is to stop your man accepting?'

'Assuming that our man, as you call him, has management status in the bank sufficient to give him access to the information requested, what would be most likely to stop him, leaving aside the question of how law-abiding he might be, would be the risk he takes if he accepts.'

'A twenty-thousand franc fine and six months in jail maximum? With a hundred thousand dollars, and most likely much more, in an entirely different bank, what's he got to lose?'

'I don't think our director made it quite clear, Mr Firman,

140

that the penalty of fine and imprisonment you mention may be applied for every single offence proved against the accused and that the sentences would run consecutively. Ten offences against the secrecy law would mean five years in prison, twenty offences ten years.'

'But with zero risk the question hardly arises, does it? Do you mean to tell me that it doesn't happen all the time? I can tell you of a dozen cases. In one, the British Treasury got all they wanted on a dozen accounts for a measly two thousand dollars.'

He was drinking a silver-fizz, a long drink made of gin and egg-whites mostly. Some women like it and barmen usually provide a straw to drink it with to save the lipstick. He now removed the straw from his glass before he answered.

'There is no such thing as zero risk, Mr Firman.' He folded the straw in two and put it in an ash-tray. 'And what I mean is that, for the kind of information of which you speak, three thousand dollars per item is too little by half.'

It was so easy that Carlo became convinced that Kramer was a provocateur and had to be persuaded that there was no risk on our side. Above all, he said, I must not put myself in the dangerous position of pretending to be an IRS agent. I asked Kramer once whether he thought I was from the IRS, and it was the only time I ever heard him laugh. He said that I was not the IRS agent type. I was never able to decide whether he had intended that as a compliment or not. In time he must have arrived at a very clear understanding of the ways in which the information he supplied me with was used.

One thing I can state with confidence. During the years of our association, Kramer received from us, and in my opinion earned, considerably more than that notional one hundred thousand dollars we had discussed in the Hotel de Paris.

When we reached the crematorium chapel where the

service for Kramer was to be held, the tail-end of a procession of mourners was just mounting the steps to go inside.

'Excellent timing,' said the driver.

In front of the chapel entrance there was quite a large semi-circular forecourt with cars parked around the rim of it. A black Cadillac limousine with a driver waited by itself in front of the chapel steps. This was obviously the car that had brought the chief mourners and would presently take them away. There was, I noticed, a group of three men draped with cameras and camera equipment huddled by the entrance. I assumed that, since at least one senior bank official would be there to pay last respects to an employee, one photographer would be from the bank's PR agency, with the other two covering or hoping to cover for local papers.

As I got out, the driver showed me where he intended to park. I followed the last of the mourners inside and was allowed by an usher to take a back seat. There was taped organ music – Bach, of course – coming through loudspeakers, and on a stone catafalque at the far end of the chapel was Kramer's coffin. There was a single wreath of flowers on the coffin itself but the floor around the catafalque was covered with wreaths and flowers. I couldn't see my roses but assumed that they would be somewhere there. It is difficult to be certain about numbers, but I would say that the seating capacity of the chapel was a hundred, more or less, and that over half the seats were occupied, mostly by business-suited men. A good turn-out.

The service was conducted by a Protestant pastor and was brief. Then, sliding doors rolled slowly into place, hiding the catafalque, so that the removal of the expendable inner shell of the coffin, the part with the corpse in it, to the functional section of the crematorium could take place unobserved by the mourners. The piped music began again. It went on for about ten minutes. When it ceased, the pastor went to Frieda Kramer in the front row of seats and said something to her. After a moment she stood up and, on the arm of a man who was probably her son-in-law, began to walk slowly back along the chapel aisle. The funeral was over.

The others started to follow. After a bit I joined the procession. A man near me told his companion that one collected an urn with the ashes in it a couple of days later.

Outside, Frieda was standing by an open rear door of the Cadillac as, one after the other, the business-suited men and the women in peculiarly awful hats came to commiserate and express solidarity.

I joined the reception line not because I wanted to but because I saw that she had spotted me. Since there was something I wanted from her, there seemed no point in giving offence by going direct to her apartment without uttering a word of sympathy there in public with everyone else. So, hat in hand, I went forward.

As I did so, Frieda said a word out of the corner of her mouth to the daughter who immediately reached inside the car and picked up something from the back seat. The people still between me and the Cadillac made it impossible to see what it was. The payers-of-respects shuffled forward once more.

I heard a woman mumbling to Frieda something about the deep sense of loss that everyone who had known her dear Johann was experiencing and hastily composed a similar speech for myself.

Finally, the man immediately in front of me sidled out of the way and my turn had come.

Until then, Frieda had been standing there stiffly with her elbows at her sides and both hands clasping her handbag just below her breasts as if she were afraid that someone there was going to try to snatch it. She had looped back her black veil and had her double chins held high ready for the attack. I found myself wondering if she already knew how surprisingly rich she was. As she acknowledged the mourners, you could tell who were friends or family and who were acquaintances she scarcely recognized. With the former she would allow herself to be embraced, with the latter she would incline her head stiffly, ignoring the proffered hands and simply saying, 'Thank you, thank you.' But always, so far, she had kept her handbag pressed against her solar plexus.

It was I who broke the spell. There could have been no question of my embracing her, so I did what the other acquaintances had done and proffered a hand for rejection.

That is to say, I *started* to proffer a hand. It was already on its way to her and the preliminary 'My dear friend' was already on my lips, when her handbag shot outwards and upwards, grazing my knuckles.

She was not, in fact, trying to hit me. She was simply using her handbag to point with so that there should be no doubt in any of the spectators' minds about whom she was pointing at. She was pointing at me and, still pointing, when she spoke.

'This,' she said loudly and clearly to those present, 'is Reinhardt Oberholzer.'

At the same moment several other things happened.

A blunt instrument hit me quite hard on the right shoulder. It was the edge of a brief-case wielded by the daughter. The brief-case must have been the object she had taken from the back seat of their car.

'There are your papers, Herr Oberholzer,' she snarled, and let go of the brief-case.'

As I caught it, I heard in the sudden silence that had fallen the clack of an SLR camera shutter. Almost at the same moment, a second photographer let fly with electronic flash. Both of them immediately moved in on me for more pictures.

Krom says that he was right behind the photographer with the flashgun, though I didn't see him. I don't say he wasn't there, just that I didn't see him; and the fact that I didn't see him doesn't surprise me in the least.

He says that I looked stunned. I *was* stunned, I have a mind that is capable of working quite quickly to solve reasonably simple equations and, as I caught the brief-case, my mind had informed me with breathtaking clarity that I was in some danger and – though I deplore the vulgarity there are times when one must be forthright – perilously close to finding myself up shit creek.

After the brief, horrified silence from everyone, except the cameramen who went on taking pictures, I decided that it was time to go. So I put the brief-case under my arm and then, with a little bow to Frieda, turned and walked over to my hired car.

The driver had neither heard nor understood what had happened but he had seen the photographers at work. That meant only one thing to him. He grinned as he opened the car door for me.

'I see that the gentleman is a person of importance,' he said.

'Yes.'

All *I* saw was a police car parked thirty metres away with a plain-clothes man leaning through the window to use the radio. His eyes were on the car I was in and he was obviously calling in its registration number. I have never been in a police identification line-up and been tapped by witnesses as the guilty party, but at that moment I learned exactly how it must feel to be in that predicament.

'Get moving,' I said.

'To Hottingen, sir?'

'No. There is no need for that now. Just go, but go slowly for a moment.'

He was going slowly anyway down the long crematorium driveway, but I still had to have some time in which to think.

I had been set up by the Kramer women and publicly identified as Oberholzer. Photographs had been taken of me, but of no one else at the funeral. The police had been in on the deal. I had been given a brief-case. It was new and nasty, the kind of thing that could be bought for a few francs at a cheap stationers, and I did not think that there were papers or anything else in it. There had to have been a reason for their having given it to me, but any attempt at analysis of the *kind* of reason would raise questions that I couldn't possibly answer at that moment. I had too many questions to cope with already. The brief-case could wait. The over-riding factor was the police involvement. What offence had I committed under the Swiss Criminal Code?

Well, I could be said to have induced a bank employee to breach the secrecy laws. That was an offence. But where was the witness to support a case against me? Kramer was dead. Frieda? She was co-operating with the police, it appeared, but why? And what would her evidence against me be worth in court? Nothing, because I would simply maintain that Kramer had approached me. What lies he may later have told his wife were no concern of mine. On the other hand, the Swiss police had a way of putting a foreign suspect in jail and leaving him there for a few months while the judicial authorities mulled over the possible charges that might be brought against him.

The first priority, then, was to get rid of the car with which I was associated, the one in which I was riding, the one with a driver who would both talk and invent. Next, I had to get out of the canton of Zürich and then out of Switzerland itself as quickly and as unobtrusively as possible.

'We'll go direct to the airport,' I said.

'At once, sir.'

Only then did I open the brief-case.

I had been right about there being no papers in it, but it was not empty, inside, were two of those transparent plastic slip-covers that many European businessmen use to keep loose papers or small amounts of correspondence tidily together without too many paper-clips. I knew that Kramer had used them because, on one of the rare occasions after our first meeting when we had met outside Switzerland, he had shown me how he kept the various sets of document copies that he thought I should see, after he had returned the originals to their proper places.

The volume of useful paper – statements of account, buy and sell orders in respect of investments, yearly audit sheets – had been small and those relating to the persons or corporations in which we were interested at any one time he had been able to keep in a single attache-case. It had been fitted out with one of those concertina-like contraptions that turned it into a miniature filing-cabinet. Into each division went one of the plastic slip-overs. Along the outer edge of each was stuck an identifying strip of Dymo embossing tape with his own code name for the account holder printed on it.

He had always, for 'sensitive accounts', used blue tape instead of the normal black. Sensitive accounts were those belonging to clients of the bank who had been judged 'unpredictable' – that is to say, marginally insane by ordinary standards – and who remained clients only by virtue of the size of their funds and the voting power of their shareholdings.

Both the empty slip-covers in the brief-case his daughter had given me still had their code name tapes on them, and both were blue. One was KLEISTER and the other TORTEN. Kramer had had a love-hate thing about cakes and pastry – he had always been overweight – and his choice of blue names had invariably been used as a reminder that, for him, such things were bad. I knew Kleister and Torten all too well. The former was a Spanish land-owner, the latter the founder and board chairman of an American pet-food manufacturing outfit with European subsidiaries. They had in common two things: both were exceedingly rich and both suffered from that kind of obsessional madness which has been called, when it has affected whole families, vendetta or feuding, but which in their case may best be described as acute personalized revanchism. Or, to put things more simply, pure bloody hatred of one particular group of their creditors.

Those two had been the most persistently difficult of the clients monitored by Kramer, and in the end Carlo had felt obliged to discipline Torten. With the Spaniard, Kleister, the threat of discipline had been sufficient because he was more vulnerable. The mere possession of a foreign banking account of the kind he had was a serious offence under the Franco regime. Torten had chosen to do battle with the Internal Revenue Service, but Kleister had paid our fees. On the other hand, Kleister had also employed an expensive international private enquiry agent to identify his 'persecutors'. By one of those strokes of ill-luck against which not even a Carlo Lech can insure himself, the enquiry agent discovered – not because he was all that clever, but because Torten, when drunk, could be monumentally indiscreet – that the method of paying his fees that Torten had been instructed to employ was the same as the one his client Kleister had described. So, he brought the two men together.

Kleister went to America – the terms of Torten's bail pending his final appeal had involved surrendering his passport – and an alliance was concluded. A council of war followed at which it was decided that as soon as they had discovered who we really were and where we were to be found, they would have us killed.

The expensive enquiry agent had hastily washed his hands of those particular clients. Carlo's response, when word of the threat had filtered through to him, had been to demand a bonus payment from Kleister and to furnish the IRS with a supplementary dossier on Torten.

That had been over a year earlier. Kleister had paid the bonus and Torten was serving a prison sentence of three years for tax evasion, having already paid a heavy fine for the same offence. It was expected that he would be put on probation after serving a little over a third of his sentence. We had heard no more talk of our being sought out and killed. It had seemed likely that K and T were at last beginning to behave rationally.

The sight of those two names in that brief-case, though, gave me a peculiar feeling, chiefly one of anger. I had no doubt that they were there with the knowledge of the police. What was I supposed to do? Panic and throw myself under a bus? Tell them what the words really meant? Give them the missing recipes for Kleister and Torten a la Kramer? Beg for mercy? Confess to some unspecified crime? Drop dead?

I shoved the things back in the brief-case and very nearly wound down the window with the idea of throwing the whole lot out. Then I thought of how upsetting that would be to the driver, and calmed down. Anyway, we were nearing the airport.

When we got there I told him to go to the Departure area and murmured something about the urgent necessity of my getting a plane that would, if I changed at Frankfurt or Munich, get me to Hamburg that afternoon. Then I paid him liberally, saw him drive away and went through to Arrivals.

I had to assume that the police had put out some sort of alert on me, so I hadn't much time; but there were two things that had to be done before I started running.

In the Arrivals area among the rental car company desks was one belonging to the company I had used for the car from Frankfurt the previous day. So I told them where the car was on the park, gave them the ticket for it, turned in the keys and paid with my Oberholzer credit card. The police could make what they liked of that. I hoped it would tend to confirm what the driver would tell them, that I was on my way to Hamburg. It would take them ten more minutes or so to find out that there was no Oberholzer booked on any of the flights out to West Germany destinations.

The other thing I had to do was contact Carlo, or at least get an urgent message to him. I put the call through to Milan with the help of the restaurant telephonist, who didn't mind earning twenty francs for pressing a few buttons on her new PBX. It was just before noon and Carlo hadn't yet gone to lunch. I told him cryptically as much of the bad news as he needed to know at that moment and what I proposed to do about it. I then asked for immediate courier assistance and specified a rendezvous. Carlo did not argue or question, but said that I might have to wait a little. Then he hung up.

I went back outside to the bus stand. There was one just leaving. I rode, as I had done the day before, as far as the Haupt-Bahnhof; but this time I took a train from there, the one that left just after one o'clock for Geneva via Lausanne. There was a restaurant car but I stayed away from it. The man who clipped my ticket between stops along the way might remember me if asked, but there was no point in adding a waiter to the list of those who had seen the last of Reinhardt Oberholzer.

At Geneva the wind was even colder than that in Zürich, but there was no snow and the sun was shining. I walked to the rendezvous, an English tea-room in the rue des Alpes.

I had to wait an hour before the courier arrived. She was a small, stocky Frenchwoman in her mid-sixties, very lady-like but also quite formidable. A few months earlier two louts had attempted to snatch her handbag in the Paris Metro. Both had had to receive hospital attention for severe cuts and bruises before being charged by the police. The cuts appeared to have been inflicted with a razor blade.

She came into the tea-room, paused for a split second to locate me and then beckoned.

'You'd better come now,' she said. 'I'm double-parked.' With that she left.

I had the money to pay the bill ready on the table. All I had to do was get my coat from the rack by the door and follow.

She had a Renault with Paris registration, and the moment I was in the passenger seat beside her she was off. There was no conversation; she just drove, quickly and carefully, until she came to a main crossing where she turned on to the Avenue Henri-Dunant. Unless you drive north or north-east to Lausanne or the Jura, practically every main road out of Geneva will very soon take you out of Switzerland and into France. The Avenue Henri-Dunant joins the road to Annecy and I thought she was going to take that. Instead, she turned suddenly into a big filling-station with an automatic car-wash.

It was one of the men couriers, who, when those things began to be introduced, first pointed out what an excellent security device they could be. For the space of about a minute and a half it was possible to cut yourself off completely from the world outside. There was no bug yet invented that could penetrate the defences of a car going through a tunnel of steel and concrete to the accompaniment of the sounds of huge brushes spinning against a car body and water being sprayed through dozens of high-pressure jets.

So, for a time, even though the chances of a courier's car having been bugged were small, all message exchanges of a confidential nature were delivered, whenever possible, inside cars travelling through car-washes. Silly really, because the message either had to be shouted above the din or written out and handed over. After one or two mistakes had occurred messages were always written and, since no bug was going to pick them up anyway, the use of car-washes for security purposes died out. One of the fringe benefits of the experiment, though, was that for the year or two it lasted, the trade-value of couriers' cars showed a slight increase.

This courier had written the message out before we got to the car-wash.

Carlo had been brief: *Phase out entire Paris operation, repeat entire, then come and see me soonest.*

Before the car was under the blast of the hot-air dryer she had retrieved the message, put a match to it and mashed the remains in the ashtray.

We left Switzerland and entered France in the early-evening commuter traffic. Nobody on either side bothered with passports or anything else. Once over the frontier, the courier made a right turn and drove via Bourg to Chalon. From there I went by train to Paris.

When Carlo had told me to 'phase out' the Paris operation he had meant that he wanted every possible paper trail cleaned up; and when he had emphasized 'entire' he had been referring to something that not even the couriers knew about. This was that we rented a furnished two-room *garçonnière* in Paris. The object had been to enable me to come and go without registering in hotels. The place was rented on a year-to-year basis so that no question of residence arose. The *gérant,* who handled the apartment concerned was a crook, naturally, and I dare say that if he could have found out who the mistress was for whom I kept the place, there would have been a little gentle blackmail. She didn't exist, though, except as a phantom presence represented by half-used make-up containers and scent bottles, some clothing, and a passion for the works of Simone de Beauvoir evidenced by a whole shelf of them, mostly falling to pieces from much re-reading. Melanie had done an excellent job in that case too.

The reason for Carlo's decision to close down the apartment as well as cutting off our accommodation service contacts was clearly based on the fact that all the clients monitored by Kramer had been dealt with through Paris, coupled with the conclusion arrived at by Carlo that everything even remotely to do with Kramer had become a threat to our security and must, therefore, instantly be discarded or neutralized. Why he should have come to that conclusion I did not then know, but it was not the sort of matter one could discuss at length over an open international telephone circuit.

The immediate difficulty was the weekend.

The accommodation service was relatively easy to cut off, because that was paid for quarterly in advance and all I had to do was write them an Oberholzer letter terminating the agreement on the last day of the year. Any communications received henceforth should be reported or forwarded to our Rome office – another accommodation service which relayed correspondence to Frankfurt.

Getting rid of the apartment was not so easy, because the *gérant* headed for the country on Friday morning and was not to reached again until Monday afternoon. It was no use my just walking out, leaving everything and hoping for the best. A new tenant, or a policeman, or a forensic expert, must be able to walk into that place when I, and my true love, had vacated it and find no trace whatsoever there of any identifiable human beings. In addition, the *gérant* must be utterly convinced not only that he knew all, but also that he was going to have to forgo the kick-backs he had once received from the now grief-stricken Oberholzer and look around promptly for a replacement sucker.

During the weekend all I could to was enlist the sympathy of the concierge's wife, who had used to keep the apartment clean for me, and get her to pick up the belongings of the woman who had betrayed me by going back to her husband, as I could not bear to touch them. Quite an affecting moment it was when I took the suitcases down and put them in the taxi.

I got rid of them by going to the air terminal and buying a one-way ticket to Toulouse. I can't recall the name I used – something like Souchet, I think – but I remember that I had to pay excess when I checked the bags in because of the weight of Simone de Beauvoir; but with one lot of baggage on its way to Toulouse and limbo, all I had to do then was pack up the spare suit and other things I had kept there for my own use, and wait for Monday afternoon.

It was Tuesday before I reached Milan.

Carlo looked down as he listened to my report, and after I had finished he was silent for a while.

Finally, he stirred, heaved a sigh and said bleakly: 'I think we are in trouble, Paul.'

'We've been put to some inconvenience and expense, yes. We may also consider it necessary and advisable to abandon

153

some profitable clients. The Oberholzer cover will have to go, of course. But we've had these spots of bother before, Carlo. No doubt we'll have others in the future. This is a nuisance, yes. Trouble? I don't think so.'

'We have been lucky,' he said contemptuously. Luck was something he had always despised. 'But you miss the point, Paul. I say that *we* are in trouble.'

'You mean our partnership?'

'As it exists now, yes.'

'Carlo, *I* didn't kill Kramer.'

'Did you take steps to enquire into the circumstances of the death?'

'No point. He was dead and his wife and daughter were making it clear that the less they saw of me the better.'

'I wasn't suggesting that you should have enquired from them. I myself enquired through Lugano.'

'And?'

'Kramer was taken ill in his office. He had a heart attack, as you heard. But, an hour earlier he had been questioned at length by men from the police section concerned with offences against the banking laws. The strain on him must have been considerable, don't you think?'

'Yes.'

'What would you have done if you had known what I have just told you?'

'I'd have got out.'

'Exactly. Lugano also reports that, after you had been identified and photographed at the funeral, police visited the hotel where you had stayed overnight. What had you done, Paul? Registered as Oberholzer?'

'Of course not. And there was never any chance of their finding me at the hotel. I paid the bill before I went to the funeral. All I lost by not going back there was some dirty laundry.'

'And the chance of meeting the men who had brought on Kramer's heart attack, surely. How did they know where to go? A few quick phone calls? Nonsense! Zürich is too big a city for that. How did they know?'

I thought back. 'The flowers,' I said slowly; 'it must have been the flowers.'

'What flowers?'

I told him the truth. Telling lies to one another was something we had never done.

'The police must have checked all the cards that came with the flowers,' he said morosely. 'When they found yours they checked the shop that had sent them. That must have narrowed their field of search considerably.'

I could have remarked that it had in fact pinpointed the hotel because I told the girl where I was staying when she had asked me; but enough was enough.

'So,' he went on, 'in addition to your photograph they now have a specimen of your handwriting and almost certainly your fingerprints as well. And you object when I use the word trouble? You amaze me. You have become soft through having so much money, Paul, and I fear, something of a liability.'

'What do you want us to do? Split up?'

'Obviously you can see the difficulties in that course as well as I can. We both need time to think. Meanwhile, though, you must make yourself scarce. I think you should go to the island for a bit.'

The island he had bought was in the Bahamas. He said his wife loved it, my wife adored it, I loathed it.

'Anna will like that,' I said.

'Your wife will stay where she is,' he said curtly, 'where a wife should be, in the home looking after your child while you are away on business.'

'Very well.'

'I will come over next week perhaps. Then we can discuss the future, without emotion, like sensible men.'

'All right.'

It was a month before he turned up. I was being punished. And it *was* punishment, from the start. You went to New

155

York or Miami and thence to Nassau. Then you took an island-hopping plane almost to Caicos. Finally, you headed back north again in a stinking little tub that did a grocery round of ten or twelve of the 'Out islands' delivering mail, gasoline, kerosene and bottled gas along with canned meat, powdered milk, bottled water and other necessities. At one of them, Carlo's cabin-cruiser picked you up and took you still farther off the map.

Anyone who holds the belief that a West Indies island all to yourself except for some servants, is bliss, has to be crazy about sun-bathing, spear-fishing, underwater photography, or re-reading mite-infested paperbacks. If he does not enjoy any of those things, the boredom is deadly and complete. In November and December on that particular island it usually rains heavily, too.

Carlo's house was comfortable, I admit; but I had noticed on previous visits that it was still more comfortable when he was there to chivvy the cook and tell her exactly what he wanted done. Even on the day he arrived and was too tired from the journey to do much chivvying, the standard of cooking rose perceptibly. That evening the food was eatable.

Afterwards, he asked me whether I had given any thoughts to my future role in our partnership.

'My only thought has been that I seem no longer to have a role.'

'I don't agree. I have been observing the progress of the trends in tax-avoidance, not evasion mark you, avoidance. A few years ago, when you said that word, certain names came automatically into mind as tax havens. What were they?'

'Monaco, Liechtenstein, the Channel Islands, Bermuda, Curaçao perhaps, Panama, possibly Switzerland.'

'And now? What names would you add?'

'The Bahamas, British Virgin Islands, the Caymans, the New Hebrides, all sort of odd places. You need a geographical dictionary to find some of them.'

'Yes, and what are we doing about it? Nothing.'

'What would you like done, Carlo?'

'I would like a survey made by someone upon whose judgement I can rely. I cannot go myself because there is too much going on in Europe that I must attend to personally – ' he was at the time preparing the butter-train caper – 'but you will know what to look for and be able to assess the prospects. We should consider investing where it is necessary to safeguard our position against later competition.'

We discussed it for four days, and then left the island; he to go back to Milan, I to scout the Caribbean before flying west to the Pacific.

I never saw Carlo again.

Krom was fidgeting with the file in his hand and I knew that he couldn't wait to get at it.

'I have a suggestion, Professor,' I said.

He looked at me suspiciously. Was I about to play some last-minute trick?

'Yes, Mr Firman?'

'I suggest that we now adjourn this gathering until tomorrow morning. Naturally, when you have read what I have written there, you will have questions to ask arising out of it. Would eight-thirty here be too early for a breakfast meeting?'

I looked at the other two to see how they felt about it, but Krom was not consulting them.

'I agree,' he said firmly. 'Eight-thirty.' He got to his feet a bit unsteadily, pulled himself together and remembered his manners. 'I must thank you for an excellent dinner. Good night, Mr Firman.'

Adroit use of the backs of the rest of the terrace chairs enabled him to steer a reasonably straight course into the house. Connell gave me a sly look.

'What was there about that white wine, Mr Firman?'

'Nothing, except that it was served too cold.' I stood up.

They took the hint and also said good night.

Yves and I finished our wine. Melanie said that she was going for a walk.

After ten minutes or so, Yves and I went up to the loft over the garage. There was silence from Krom and Henson; they were reading to themselves. Connell was making sure that his copy of the material was going to remain available for future use by reading it to his tape-recorder. Only an occasional grunt of surprise or doubt showed that this was the first time he had been through it. It was interesting to hear it all being read out – truth, rubbish, and half-truth – all as if it were some sort of Holy Writ.

I was listening, fascinated, when he was interrupted by a knock on his door. He switched off the recorder and went to answer the knock.

Dr Henson's voice said: 'Sorry to bother you. I've just had this note from Krom shoved under my door. Have you had one?'

'Wanting a pre-breakfast meeting in his room at seven-thirty? Yes. I've had one.'

'Do we accept?'

'If our lord and master wants to make sure in advance that he asks all the questions and leads for the prosecution, why not? He'll take charge anyway.'

'I suppose so. I heard you talking. What were you doing? Recording it all on that thing?'

'Yes. Why?'

'Since you've been allowed to get away with it, how about giving me a copy of the transcript?'

There was a pause, then: 'Dr Henson, may I call you Geraldine?'

He made it sound like a joke and that was the way she treated it. 'Don't be a fool, Connell.'

'Gerry?'

'My friends call me Hennie, and I assure you that, as a nickname, it's quite appropriate. Good night again.'

'Good night.' The door closed and he went back to his dictation.

It was at that moment that we heard stumbling footsteps on the bare, wooden stairs up to the loft.

It was Melanie and she was looking flustered. She was also out of breath.

I signalled to Yves to turn the sound down. 'What is it, Melanie?'

'I went for a walk you know, and I *think* – only think mind, Paul – that this place may be under surveillance. Cars stationary on both upper and lower roads. It's difficult to be certain at night, but I thought you'd better know.'

CHAPTER SEVEN

All three of us had a bad night, but at least Melanie and I got some sleep. Yves had none.

About an hour after Melanie's warning, he returned to the listening post over the garage to report his preliminary findings. Since he had spent most of the hour crawling between bushes and being bitten by insects, he looked a mess.

He borrowed my handkerchief and dabbed at some large scratches on his hands and arms while he explained how he had got them. There had been parked cars on both roads, as Melanie had said. He had seen one on the lower road by the garden gate and two, one on each side at distances of about a hundred and fifty metres from the entrance. It had been in the oleander thickets along the upper boundary fence, where he had gone to take a closer look at the two cars outside, that he had run into trouble. At some time, the chain-link boundary fence had been damaged by a car or truck going off the road after taking the bend too fast. Concrete posts had been put up to prevent a repetition of that particular accident, but the gap in the fence had been temporarily blocked with a barbed-wire entanglement which no one had bothered to remove after the fence had been repaired.

Still, he had been able to get a look at both cars by waiting for the headlights of the occasional passing car to show them up. Each had two persons in it, though of what sex he had not been able to see, and each had a local Alpes Maritimes 06 registration. Each also had its front wheels on full left lock. In addition, both on the lower road and the upper, the places at which the cars were parked were where the roads widened slightly. If you wanted to park on those roads for any ordinary reason – you wanted a smoke and a chat, you wanted to neck or eat a sandwich – those were the places you would logically choose. Not as logically, perhaps, if you wanted to mount a simple surveillance operation against the Villa Lipp because your view of it would be so restricted; but if you wanted to prevent any of the occupants leaving the place without your knowing or, if you wanted to prevent their leaving by car altogether, you were in exactly the right position. You had the lower gateway under observation if they tried leaving on foot, and with your two cars on the upper road you could foil any attempt at a get-away by road simply by starting up, driving four metres and then standing on the brakes. If you kept your ears open for the sound of engines from below, you could have the road blocked on both sides of the entrance before the escaping cars could reach it.

And, of course, we, or rather Melanie, could be imagining things.

I would not have blamed Yves in the slightest if he had thought that possibility as being one at least worthy of discussion. In fact, he did not even hint at it. He appeared to respect Melanie's instincts as much as he respected his own.

'One parked car would be of no importance,' he said; 'two would be an interesting coincidence. Three parked cars at this time and in those places and postures I will not accept as explainable in terms other than those of surveillance until I hear that explanation. Then if I am able to snap my fingers and say, "Of course, how stupid of me," I will go to bed. Meanwhile, I must continue to ask obvious questions. Who are they? Who are they working for? What are their orders? Why are they behaving as they are?'

'There's one other explanation you might try on yourself,' I said. 'This is a rich neighbourhood. Oh, I know there may not be much in the way of valuables in the Villa Lipp, but one or two of the pictures ought to be marketable. The owner is known to be absent. They could be a gang casing the joint.'

'Then why aren't they doing so? Why are they just sitting there, all six of them, where they can see so very little but can so easily be seen? And why six? Looking a house over before deciding to rob it is a one-man job and he comes in the daytime with credentials from an insurance company. One is forced to conclude that these people mean to advertise their presence, that they mean to be seen.'

'Perhaps they're selling protection. There used to be a gang along this coast who'd strip your house of everything, including the carpets and kitchen stove, if you didn't pay them.'

This was ignored. Yves had turned to Melanie again.

'I might not have gone for a walk,' she said doubtfully.

'But they *did* see you?' he asked.

'Oh yes.'

'Did they see that you had found them interesting or suspect?'

'I doubt it. I can't be sure.'

'Then I think,' he said, 'that we should see what happens when they know that they have been spotted.' He thought for a moment. 'Patron, either they are very close in because they intend to do something violent almost at once and will not allow anyone to escape, or they are applying psychological pressure to make us leave.'

'They might be out there to make us run, but I don't think they could be meaning to do anything violent unless they knew that, apart from your revolver, we aren't armed. There aren't enough of them. It really comes back to your first question. Who are they?'

'I could go and ask them,' Melanie said.

She does sometimes say stupid things. 'All you'd get would be a blank stare,' I said.

'I think,' said Yves, tactful as ever, 'that there may be a simpler way of letting them know that we are aware of them. We could just close the entrance gates. They can be seen from where the cars are parked.'

'Do they close? With all those shrubs growing through and around them, I would say that nobody ever closed them. They're probably rusted open.'

Yves tried not to look reproachful. 'When we moved in, Paul, oiling the hinges was one of the first things I did. The lower road gate also.'

'Sorry. Can they be locked? I know there are plenty of ways of getting into this place, but if one were going to be violent, charging in by car with a bunch of armed hoodlums would be the most intimidating.'

'There is a chain in the garage. I could arrange things so that undoing the chain from the closed gates would be a noisy operation.'

'Then do that, please. The lower road gate, too, if you can.'

'That has a lock and a key.'

He went off. I heard the distant sound of the front gates closing and then a rattling of chain. Almost immediately afterward, Melanie, who had been sitting by an open window in a room nearer the driveway, came to report that, on the gates being closed, both cars had at once started up and been driven away.

After Yves had dealt with the lower road gate, he returned to report that, on his opening and slamming it noisily before locking it, the third car had also left. He had one additional item to report. Just before he had done his opening and slamming act, he had heard someone's voice. It had been his impression that the voice had been coming through a small loud-speaker of the kind you would expect on a miniature walkie-talkie set, and that the set had been in the hands of the car passenger. He had glimpsed for a moment a short, chromium-plated whip-antenna, of the kind used on such sets, sticking at an angle through the passenger-side window space. The words he had heard the voice uttering had been: ' . . . now. Okay. Out.'

163

The three words had been spoken in English, though by what nationality of English-speaker he firmly declined to guess at. All that seemed likely was that he had been hearing the end of a conversation between an occupant of one of the two cars which had been on the upper road and the passenger in the single car on the lower. The rest of the conversation had taken place while he had been moving from the main gate down to the one in the wall.

'So,' he concluded. 'What is the next move, Paul?'

'You could get some sleep. We all could.'

'Someone must keep watch in case there is an alarm to be sounded. You have our guests to deal with in the morning and so you must be rested. If had better be me who mounts guard. Melanie could relieve me for an hour, perhaps, so that I don't begin to see things that aren't there.'

'All right,' said Melanie. 'At two o'clock, say?'

'Okay, Paul?'

'Very well. Divide the watch between you as you like. I shall have to take a sleeping-pill now, I'm afraid, but I shall set my clock for six-thirty unless either of you wakes me before. I'll also monitor our guests' get-together at seven-thirty. If anything of interest happens outside, one of you will let me know, eh?'

In spite of the pill I had a poor night.

This wasn't because of the watchers outside the villa; at least, not directly because of them. Yves had brushed aside what I had said about protection racketeers, but that was the explanation I had settled for in my own mind; and I had done so because, at that point, I had believed it to be the most likely one.

There *are* such racketeers operating on the French Riviera, and, as their demands are not really exorbitant, it is, especially for foreigners, simpler to pay up than to take moralistic stands and suffer the consequences. The latter can be tiresome as well as costly. A German I know who has a house on Cap Ferrat, but who refused to pay a few thousand francs for protection, had the whole place emptied while he was away, the gang having brought in removal vans to do the job. The police received the owner's complaint sympathetically but without surprise. These things sometimes happened. After such forceful demonstrations the protection people obviously had much less trouble collecting dues, even from hard cases like my German friend. Though I could see that a man of Yves's temper might well find it unacceptable, my assumption that, with the cost of everything going up, it had become customary to put the bite on summer-season tenants as well as owners seemed reasonable enough. I quite expected to receive by mail the following morning, in addition to the good news that a protection service was available, a subscription form to fill in and return with my cheque.

So, it wasn't worry that kept me awake, but my old trouble; the inability to wait before trying to solve a problem until all the available facts are in. Strange as it may seem, the problem that nagged, and went on nagging long after its solution had ceased to matter, was that of figuring out how best to use the presence of external enemies to get Krom and his witnesses out of my hair.

At seven, I went down to the kitchen, complained to the cook that indigestion from the dinner the night before had kept me awake, and appropriated the pot of coffee she had made for her husband and herself. Along with it, I had one of the petit-pains just delivered by the village bakery. The husband told me that during the night some unauthorized person had shut the outer gates. I said that it had been I who had shut them in order to keep out stray dogs. Obviously, and not surprisingly, he thought I was off my head.

I had one cup of coffee in my bedroom and took a second through to the garage loft.

Krom's seven-thirty meeting started more or less on time. Connell was the first to arrive.

After they had exchanged greetings and told one another how tired they had been and how well they had slept, Krom

165

said: 'I chose this room for our meeting because it is free of listening devices.'

'You know that for a fact, eh, Professor?'

'I have examined the whole room carefully myself.'

'And didn't find a thing. Ah, well . . . ' Connell left his doubts at that. 'Do you think we could get a cup of coffee if we rang that bell there? Until I've had coffee in the morning, I don't feel altogether . . . '

He broke off as Dr Henson arrived. More good mornings. She, too, had slept well.

Krom said: 'Coffee would be desirable, but I think it is more important that we get down to business before we meet Firman. I take it that you have both read this paper? Yes? Then, I would like first to hear your general views on it.'

'On the whole true? On the whole false? Or on the whole half-and-half?' asked Henson.

'That for a start, yes.'

'I say half-and-half.'

Connell said: 'So do I, but I can't make up my mind which half is which. I'm hoping for help there from you, Professor. The part about the actual confrontation at the crematorium must be true because you were there and saw it. But how did you actually come to be there? It would help a bit if we could now be told, I think.'

'It would indeed,' Henson's voice.

Krom cleared his throat. 'This will all, of course, be in my book, but I think I can trust you two.'

He could have said right out that, if they dared repeat as much as a word, he would arrange slow and painful deaths for them, but his tone conveyed the message plainly enough.

Henson uttered a strange sound which was probably an involuntary giggle quickly masked by a cough.

'That's what we're here for, Professor,' said Connell. He managed suddenly to sound like the sheriff of Dodge City in a television western.

Krom hesitated, unsure how to take the performance.

Then, deciding to ignore it, he went ahead. 'I had obtained the permission of the Federal judicial authorities in Berne to look into the background of a number of cases of blackmail or, to be more precise, extortion, involving persons and corporate entities who banked in Switzerland. These cases had been brought to my notice by an international private enquiry agent who had sometimes made use of tips I have been able to give him. This time, as well as giving *me* information he thought I should have, he sought advice. These cases of extortion in which he had been asked to act, sometimes in a defensive role, sometimes as a negotiator, covered a period of three years or so. The cases all had two elements in common. They involved tax evasion or breaches of exchange-control regulations under a variety of national jurisdictions, and they involved an organization calling itself a debt-collection agency with branches in most of the countries of Western Europe. Unfortunately, he had had little success to report to his various clients. Given a defensive role, there was nothing he could do except advise them to pay up. Told to negotiate, he encountered nothing but blank walls. He realized quite early on that he was dealing with a front, a facade, in this collection agency, but that those behind it were both well informed and impeccably disciplined. His clients, on the other hand, were mostly, as he put it, 'at sixes-and-sevens' from the moment they became victims until they eventually decided to pay. None of them was ever able to deny the allegations of evasion or breach of regulations, at least not for long, and only one or two had the will or gall to fight anyway. There are always a few men and women who prefer fighting to surrendering, even in a cause they well know to be defective, even when they know that they cannot win or draw, that they have to lose. One can only marvel at such lunacy.'

It might have been Carlo speaking.

For a moment or two I found myself wondering what sort of a man Krom would have become without the burden of that overweight super-ego he carries around. What would have happened to all the 'anarchy' of which he is so afraid? Might he not have become one of our less scrupulous competitors?

An agreeable day-dream, but still a day-dream; he was on again about the troubles of his fat-headed friend, the private enquiry agent, who had unwittingly caused me so much inconvenience. I made myself pay attention.

'It was these diehards among his clients about whom he was specially concerned. And not simply because well-publicized losers were, if known to be his clients, bad for business. He feared too – as we shall see, rightly – that such unbalanced persons could easily decide to take the law into their own hands and commit criminal acts of violence. He wanted the whole matter properly investigated by some responsible police authority. *He* could do nothing more. The essential initiatives, he though, could only be taken in Switzerland, though obviously not by him. With my academic connections there I might do better.'

'And you *did* do better,' Henson's longing for coffee was also now becoming audible.

'A little, yes.' Krom was savouring every moment. If his witnesses thought that they were going to hurry him along with polite proddings they were much mistaken. 'A little better,' he repeated, 'but *only* a little. Both the judicial authorities and the police had certain ideas on the subject of those extortion cases which I found it difficult to counter. They were aware, of course, that there were leakages of information from several of the so-called big banks and from some cantonal and private banks as well. These they were naturally determined to locate and stop, because Swiss law, *their* law, was being broken and the guilty must be found and punished. In so far as the information I brought them about specific leakages helped them to that end, they were interested. But when it came to talk of organized extortion, they lost interest.'

Henson let out a squeak of incredulity. 'The Swiss lost interest in an extortion racket?'

I was grateful to her. It was the question that had popped up instantly in my own mind.

'They didn't believe that it existed,' Krom explained. 'They thought, at that point, that I was merely trying to prove a pet theory. They said that, in order to do so, I was confusing two quite different anti-social activities. One wasn't even a crime. They were referring to the traffic in titbit information that was then being carried on with various US government agencies. For instance, there was the racket worked by those who sold luxury goods like furs and diamonds to rich Americans. In places such as London, Paris and Antwerp, the persons who did the actual selling often earned extra commissions by informing on their clients to the US Revenue as soon as the goods were sold. When a client was caught for smuggling, the informer received a percentage of the fine as a reward. Not nice, or kind, or good for business in the long run, but not illegal. Besides, it didn't happen in Switzerland. What they were interested in, as far as I was concerned, were the bank employees who allowed themselves to be suborned and the wicked men and women who did the suborning. Among those last group, I am afraid, Dr Connell, agents of the United States Internal Revenue Service, which, with the blessing of the American Congress, had made no secret of its hostility to Swiss secrecy laws. Those agents, with their big money bribes, were then considered the prime villains. It had been thought at one time that Oberholzer might be an important IRS man, or possibly even CIA.'

Connell laughed. 'Oberholzer, an American government man? With *that* accent?'

'You have accepted a Secretary of State with a German accent,' said Henson crisply. 'I see nothing extraordinary about Oberholzer being thought of as a possible IRS or CIA agent. Firman's accent – and I take it that we *are* talking about the same man – isn't contemporary British anyway. I'd call it expatriate mid-Atlantic. The same could be said of his vocabulary. If he had a Hungarian-American accent you wouldn't find the CIA notion in the least odd.'

'True.'

'And we are not talking about what, in retrospect, we may think, but what the Swiss knew and believed from time to time,' Krom reminded them. 'I said that not all the victims of the Oberholzer organization were prepared to submit. Among those who chose to fight were two clients of the enquiry agent – one Spanish, the other an American – whose cases had certain common denominators. Both had their accounts in the Zurich head office of the same bank. At least three other known victims also banked there. The other common denominator was the method used by the so-called debt-collection agency.'

'The one of whose methods Firman so much disapproves?'

'The one of whose methods he *says* he disapproves, yes, Dr Henson.'

'I didn't understand how that worked anyway,' Connell said. 'I made a note to ask him a question about it. How do you make a pay-off that can't either be watched or traced?'

'A good question,' Krom said. 'I will add it to my own list of clarifications required. Anything else?'

'The part played in the incident by Frau Kramer and the daughter bothers me,' said Henson. 'What were those two up to? Assisting or obliging the police? Getting back at Oberholzer for corrupting the good Kramer? Covering themselves against the charge that they had compounded a felony? That identity parade after the funeral doesn't sound like a good police idea. Why didn't they go through with the original plan and get Oberholzer out at the apartment? Then, he couldn't have run, not the way he did anyway. And what was the idea of giving him those plastic slip-covers with the code-names on them? That makes no sense at all.'

'Oh yes, it does, young woman,' Krom chuckled. 'And, as it happens, the sense that it makes ties in with your questions about Frau Kramer's place in the affair.'

I listened intently to the next bit because I was just as keen to know the answers as Dr Henson, more perhaps; the same questions had puzzled me at the time and, at intervals, ever since.

'Frau Kramer,' Krom went on, 'could not, I think, have ever made her husband a very happy man. She was one of those women who, at the same moment as they complain that their men do not climb higher and faster on the ladder of success, hang on to their coat-tails to make the climb more difficult, perhaps impossible. They are moral saboteurs, you might say. To be specific, Kramer had reached, as do many men in the organizations, his natural level of maximum attainment without either understanding why he would go no higher or recognizing and accepting his own limitations. In this refusal to accept he was abetted by his own wife. But when it came to Oberholzer's approach, things were undoubtedly different. Ambitious women of Frau Kramer's type often have broad streaks of self-righteousness in them. They desire the ends but reject the means. Or, rather, they do not wish to hear about the means.'

'As if Lady Macbeth were to say that she didn't want to know,' remarked Connell.

'Pardon?' There was a short silence while Krom grappled with the allusion. 'Well, yes, perhaps. I am sure Frau Kramer *did* know of the Oberholzer arrangement. It was just never openly discussed, so that she could say, with her hand on her heart, that she had never been told.'

'Hence her and her daughter's dislike of Oberholzer,' commented Henson.

'The daughter's attitude was determined much more by the adverse affects on her own marriage, and position of respectability that a criminal scandal would have had. After Kramer's second coronary attack in the hospital, and once she knew that he was quite unlikely to survive a third, Frau Kramer's chief concern was for the money her husband had accumulated. All she wanted to know was whether or not she would be allowed to inherit it. Naturally, the police were in no hurry to enlighten her. Equally, she was in no position to ask questions about her husband's private fortune without admitting that she had been a party to concealing the criminal acts that had made it. The daughter would probably have been prepared to abandon the money, or the prospect of it anyway. The mother could never have done that.'

'Didn't they have a lawyer to advise them?' Connell enquired.

'Of course. But what use is an honest lawyer when what you need is a dishonest one? No, she chose instead to give co-operation to the police. This, the police accepted gratefully, but remaining stiffly correct, without allowing their gratitude to show even for a moment.'

'Were you present at the original Kramer interviews?' asked Connell. 'I mean before he had the heart attack.'

'Oh no. That would have been quite improper. I was kept informed though. I was also there when the decision was made to allow Kramer's encoded telegram to be sent, in the hope that it would bring Oberholzer, his pay-master, to Zurich. As we know, it did.'

Dr Henson sniffed. 'Even such a stupid woman as Frau Kramer must have known that the police couldn't try and convict a dead man. If he *embezzled* that money from the bank and it could be proved that he'd embezzled it, even without his being there, things might have been different. As it was, the police had no case against either her or Oberholzer, and probably no claim to any money there might have been lying around.'

'You would be surprised,' said Krom, 'how great an appearance of power a senior Swiss policeman can convey just by looking absolutely serious. Except in one thing. Frau Kramer did exactly as she was told. The exception was in the matter of where the identification of Oberholzer before witnesses was to take place. She refused, practically at the last minute, to have Oberholzer in her apartment.'

'On what grounds? He must have been there before, she

must have known him before, or how could she have identified him?'

'She said that until the police had told her that Oberholzer was a criminal she had not known.'

'*Had* the police told her?' Connell asked.

'Of course not. Challenged on the point, she maintained that the interest of the police in Oberholzer had been enough to tell her. It was obvious now that Oberholzer was a criminal. Her husband, who had known the man slightly, had been questioned about him, but had known nothing. Now, she was being questioned. She also knew nothing, but would assist the police in identifying the villain, anywhere but in the apartment sacred to her husband's memory and to her own memories of their happiness together.'

She hadn't *needed* a lawyer, I would have said.

'There is still the question of the code-names,' Dr Henson was reminding Krom.

'I am not forgetting it, young woman. My good relations with the Swiss authorities obviously do not depend alone upon academic associations. When I am given information it is given on the understanding that the arrangement is reciprocal. I pick their brains, and they pick mine. In this case I helped them discover the real names of the two enquiry-agent clients, the Spaniard and the American, who had defied, or tried to defy, the Oberholzer organization.'

'Kleister and Torten, you mean? Oh, I see. You matched the code-names with the details found by the police in Kramer's private files.'

'Precisely.' Krom did not like Connell stealing his thunder like that, as he went on to make clear. 'But the question asked was not 'how did the police get the names?' but 'why did they give them to Oberholzer?' I will tell you. It began as a joke.'

'Huh?'

'Yes, I agree. A somewhat macabre joke but a joke nevertheless. My police friends had made enquiries about the then whereabouts of Kleister and Torten and found that Torten, the American, had since his release from prison on probation, been enjoying his freedom in Florida. Kleister, his old ally, had recently joined him there. What was more, he had joined him not just for a brief holiday, it was understood, but on a permanent basis. Both men were widowers, and, in spite of their costly troubles, both were still wealthy. It seemed likely that they might be preparing to resume operations against the Oberholzer extortionists. For two men of their ages with money to spend and a cause that they could think of as a crusade, what could be a more pleasurable way of passing the time than finding a man they both hated, and then arranging for his murder?'

'Yes,' said Connell. 'I can see that there'd be room there for loads of laughs.'

'I remember my police friends saying in their droll way that, if Oberholzer were going to be murdered, they would prefer that the crime be committed outside their jurisdiction because they would not have their hearts in the investigation. Someone suggested that they might give Oberholzer a warning of the danger by mentioning Kleister and Torten to him verbally. Later, when the confrontation was moved from the Kramer apartment to the crematorium, they put those marked folders with the code-names in the brief-case because they intended to stop and interrogate Oberholzer at the airport when he tried to leave. Their object, since they could not prosecute him, was, first, to intimidate him, second, to trip him if they could into some damaging admission about his relationship with Kramer and, lastly, to make it clear that he was considered an undesirable alien who would be well advised to stay out of Switzerland. They thought that the code-names in the brief-case might prove useful as an element in the interrogation. In fact, as we now know, he eluded them at the airport, though more by luck than by ingenuity. However, the warning of the code-names did not, it seems, go unheeded. He is still alive.

I wonder about Kleister and Torten. Perhaps he knows. Perhaps I will ask him.'

'Well,' said Dr Henson, 'one thing's explained. I can see now why he objected so strongly to that field kit of Langridge's that I tried to smuggle in. With one set of fingerprints on record in Switzerland against an old identity, the last thing he'd want would be another set of prints, one attached to his current identity, circulating internationally. The two would almost certainly be matched. I must say, though, that he doesn't strike me as a man who has been labouring for years under a threat of death from a pair of half-witted tax-dodgers. If anyone's had the pleasurable time, I'd say it was he. Most regrettable no doubt, but my guess is that he doesn't know what a twinge of guilt feels like and that he has always thoroughly enjoyed himself.'

'He will not be enjoying himself for much longer, my dear. Of that I can assure you. As for us, I think it is time that we went down to breakfast.'

I was ready, seated at the table on the terrace waiting for them when they came down.

They all told me, in response to my polite enquiries, how comfortable they had been and how well they had slept, thank you, at the same time managing to make it clear that solicitude would get me nowhere and that, now they were rested, the sooner we got down to business the better. None of them asked how *I* had slept.

The coffee was not nearly as good as the earlier pot I had had, but they drank it appreciatively and ate their croissants. Krom did not wait to finish his, however, before going into action.

'We have all read with interest your first paper,' he said, spraying crumbs with the sibilants, 'and, while we find some of it useful, we all agree that it is far from satisfactory.'

'Full of holes,' Connell explained.

'And doth protest too much,' said Henson in her

Langridge's voice, 'against accusations that, as far as I know, haven't yet been made.'

'I'm sorry,' I said. 'Perhaps you should all try reading it again, and more carefully.'

Krom swallowed the rest of his coffee and reached for more. 'I myself have read it three times,' he said; 'and with each reading it has seemed less and less illuminating, except in one respect.'

'I am relieved to hear that my failure has not been total.'

'Sarcasm will not help you. What is illuminated so brilliantly is your determination to disclaim all responsibility for anything and everything concerned with this large-scale criminal activity except the humble part you played in it as a kind of superior, but none too competent, messenger boy.'

'Incompetent, yes. Humble? I sincerely hope not. The last thing I want to do is give false impressions.'

'Flippancy is even more tiresome than sarcasm, Mr Firman, so let us have no more of either. We at any rate are serious, and – ' he whipped a folded sheet of notes from his shirt pocket – 'to begin with, I propose to ask you a series of questions.'

'As long as you understand that I may decline to answer those I don't like, go ahead.'

'You said that you had prepared a number of discussion papers and that you could be questioned on them. You did not say how many papers, only that they would cover your activities as Oberholzer for a period of three years. My first question is, what is the scope of the activities described? How is the material as a whole organized?'

'It's mostly anecdotal, I am afraid, like the first paper. So much is hearsay, of course. I can't help that.'

'No, not if you persist in trying to convince us of the existence of senior partners whose orders you meekly obeyed, or separate groups of evil men who did any dirty work that your leader might deem necessary. If you could abandon that pretence it would be helpful.'

'I said that I would try to answer your questions, Professor, not debate your assertions. You asked about the scope of the activities described in the other papers. I have tried to answer your question. Dr Connell complains that the first paper has holes in it. Do you agree with him?'

'I go farther. For me, it is in all respects unsatisfactory.'

'Not exciting enough do you mean, Professor? Not enough murder and mayhem?'

Connell tried to take over. 'He means that there's too much shadow and not enough substance. For example . . . '

Krom stopped him with a look.

'Dr Connell was about to raise a question which we all seem to have asked ourselves. Accepting for a moment the fiction that you were never a principal, only an agent, what about this debt-collection agency that you say was or is employed by your employers to extort their fees? Where is it based? How does it work? Please tell us all about this remarkable institution, Mr Firman.'

I smiled. 'That is the subject of one of the papers you were asking me about.'

'An entire paper?'

'It was a complex organization. And please note that it no longer exists. It was originally based in Luxembourg, with branches in Hanover, Rome, Paris and London. It went out of business years ago.'

'Soon after I saw you in Zürich, in fact.'

'The two events were not related, Professor. In any case I'm sure you would prefer to read what I've written on the subject rather than have it piecemeal.'

Dr Connell stuck his neck out again. 'Does what you've written about explain how you, that is they, got the money without the victims' knowing where it went?'

I waited expectantly for Krom to intervene, but this time he let the question through without protest. No doubt he was curious himself.

'I don't think I understand,' I said. 'By victims you mean debtors, I take it.'

'Call them what you like. I call them victims. Now, how did it function? I guess the process of collection would start with a letter saying that the Luxembourg Finance Corporation, or whatever you called it, had taken over the debt and so kindly pay up without further ado or get clobbered. Right?'

'*I* didn't call the agency anything, and the Lech-Firman partnership was very far from being its major client. Its name, by the way, was Agence Euro-Fiduciare.'

'Meaningless, but looks respectable I guess. Okay. Now, how about that first move?'

'It would be of the kind you described. It sometimes produced results.'

'But not often?'

'Not often, I would say, no.'

'So then you got tough. Yes, I know. *They* got tough.'

'When the agency purchased the debt from us they would naturally receive an account of the services we had rendered the client. This account would include a complete statement of the client's financial situation according to our records.'

'Everything *not* on record back home, you mean?'

'A *complete* statement, as I said. This would include all assets, however held and where held, sometimes together with a summary of the last official tax return made by the client to his domestic revenue authority. Where exchange controls had been evaded, copies of the relevant documents would be provided instead. If, say, from some fringe of the sterling area, money had been transferred to finance a transaction in real-estate or gold, this would be documented as a reminder.'

'Oh boy!'

'At the same time new instructions about the way the debt was to be paid would be issued.'

'I'll bet they would. That was one of the holes I wanted to see filled in. How was it arranged so that Kleister, and others like him who strongly resented and resisted being screwed, didn't know, when they'd finally decided that they *had* to pay up, who'd been screwing them? Their first thought would have been you as the tax-consultant. Right?'

'The partnership always dealt at arm's length.'

'You mean through cut-outs, I take it. Okay, so when things got tough, they weren't able to find you. Right? But they *could* find Euro-Fiduciare, eh?'

'The agency had its own methods,' I said austerely. The pieces of real meat I had to give were not going to be tossed over in response to the first yaps.

Connell didn't like being told to wait. He tried jumping for it. 'So do kidnappers-for-ransom,' he said; 'have their own methods, I mean. So do blackmailers and extortionists. But there is a moment all of them have to face. That's the moment when they pick up the money. Okay, they tell the mark to leave it in the middle of a desert in used twenties and a transparent bag with "Don't Fence Me In" painted on it in red, but they still have to go there and pick it up. That's when things usually start going wrong. Their helicopter has engine trouble or the pilot turns out to be a gamma-minus navigator who puts down nowhere near the loot. The police have been brought in by the victim or his family after all. The bills have been chemically marked and are, used or not, traceable. Some cop or FBI man hidden behind a rock there watching the pickup gets bitten by a rattlesnake and yells. A gun goes off accidentally. Anything and everything can happen. How did the agency make sure that, whoever else got hurt, they didn't?'

'In my paper on the subject I give examples to show how the whole thing worked.'

I stopped there and poured myself the last of the coffee. Henson was sitting motionless with an unlit cigarette in one hand and her lighter poised in the other. Krom and Connell were both leaning forward expectantly. All three were now, metaphorically speaking, and indeed almost literally, slavering.

'Tell us about it,' ordered Krom.

I shrugged submissively but with no thought of obeying.

179

I knew that if they were allowed to gobble up all the food that had been prepared for them, just because the smell of it had reached their nostrils, there would be none left for tomorrow.

Yes, that's how I was still thinking. I still hadn't realized even then that, for me as host at the Villa Lipp, there wasn't going to be a tomorrow.

'It isn't really all that difficult, Professor,' I said. 'Look at it this way. The popular jargon now calls those services Carlo gave the old black marketeers, 'laundering money'. All the debt-collection people did was set up another sanitary process to suit their own special needs. In my paper on the whole subject, I call it, 'waste-disposal'. Laundered money is money cleansed of its associations with pockets it has been in. Waste-disposal money just disappears into a sewage system, one with so many outfalls that no particular deposit can ever, once it has left the sink, be followed or traced to its ultimate destination.'

Krom looked sour. 'Your metaphor is appropriately anal, Mr Firman, but I didn't ask for metaphors. I want specifics, facts of the kind that a banker or a police accountant can get his teeth into.'

'And facts you shall have,' I said. 'You'll find them all in my next paper. For now, though, you'll just have to be satisfied with paper number one and metaphors. Unless, that is, any of you would like to try solving the money-transfer problem that seems to worry Dr Connell. As a technical exercise, I mean. I don't mind giving friendly advice.'

Krom's lips tightened and he remained silent; but Connell wasn't so fussy about his dignity.

'What sort of friendly advice?' he asked.

'You know that banks all over the world transfer money to one another by means of what's called the "tested-cable" system? You do? Good. Then you'll also know that crooks have used tested-cables to swindle banks, often via their computers, out of millions of dollars which have proved to be untraceable. Well, if crooks can make untraceable transfers, think how much easier it must be when the payers are thought of as honest men and the payees are simple debt collectors.'

Henson made a cooing sound. 'What an absolutely *brilliant* idea!' she exclaimed.

'No, Dr Henson.'

'No what, Mr Firman?'

'I will not be flattered into accepting with only a token murmur or protest the suggestion that using tested-cables was my idea. It wasn't. The head of the collection agency thought it up.'

'Oh? And who was he?'

I wasn't falling for that one either. 'He? It may have been a woman. I don't know, Doctor.'

Krom gave his witnesses meaning looks. 'You see, Mr Firman is a slippery fellow. Do you know that, in Brussels, he actually had the impertinence to tell me that most crime is committed by government, and that delinquency is a function of the class struggle?'

'Oh dear!' Dr Henson choked slightly on the cigarette she had at last lighted. 'That sounds more like cut-price Trotskyism than anarchy.'

'It's double-talk,' said Krom, 'and I told him so. Quite unnecessarily, of course, because he is intelligent enough to know that himself.' He turned his attention to me again. 'We have heard the divided responsibility claim *ad nauseam*, Mr Firman. It is not accepted. You thought everything up. *You* were at the controls of the extortion machine you call a collection agency as well as those of the so-called tax-consultancy which kept it fed with information. Your version of the Oberholzer conspiracy is nothing but a pack of lies. What do you say to that?'

'That you are impolite, Professor, as well as mistaken.'

'Would you prefer me to call it the Firman conspiracy? What does the name matter? However you choose to masquerade now, you were the figure around which it all pivoted. Yours were the controlling hands, yours the organizing mind. That is the central, the essential, fact.'

'Central and essential to your case it may be, Professor. That does not make it a fact. To a man of your academic standing and repute I hesitate to use harsh language in a discussion of this kind, and at the breakfast table too, but I must tell you, and in front of your witnesses, that at the centre of your case is what used to be known as an *idée fixe*. Nowadays, it's called a hang-up.'

He said something loudly about my personal character. What he said was probably quite unpleasant and it may even have been true; but, as he said it in Dutch, I can't be sure. I was about to ask him to translate, when we were interrupted by Melanie.

She did not come out on to the terrace, but called to me from a drawing-room window. I turned and she beckoned. Obviously, what she had to say was not to be overheard. I excused myself and went to the window.

'What is it?'

'Yves wants to see you. He didn't want to show himself because he was rather dirty. He's up in his room.'

'Is it urgent?' I didn't want to leave just then in case they thought I was running away.

'Yes, Paul. I think it is urgent.'

'All right. You go over and tell them that I'll be back in a minute.'

I went up to Yves's room. He had been in the shower and was drying himself. He greeted me with the glum phrase that had begun to irritate me. Only this time he varied it slightly for emphasis.

'*Nous sommes vraiment foutus,*' he said.

'Just tell me what's happened. I'll draw my own conclusions, Yves.'

He gave me the mournfully threatening look that had reminded Connell of a termite inspector he had known. 'I have not forgotten that I am under your orders, Patron.'

'Good. What's happened?'

He smiled disagreeably. 'What has happened is, Patron, that I am becoming more nervous every minute. Have you been all over this house?'

'Most of it. Why?'

'Then you will know that on the attic floor there are two windows from which, if one keeps moving from one to the other, one can in daylight see practically all the land surrounding this house.'

'Yes.'

'At sunrise I moved up there to keep watch with binoculars. At about six-thirty, I saw something I didn't like. It was on that piece of land beyond the lower road to the right of the bay.'

'You mean the headland with the tamarisks on it?'

'Those small trees? Yes. There are bushes too. There was a person there.'

'That land isn't on this property. It belongs to the commune, I think. What sort of person?'

'The first thing I saw was a flashing of light of the kind you get when sun reflects off lenses, but it was difficult to see because the flashing was coming from behind the bushes.'

'Someone keeping the same sort of watch on this place as you were keeping from the attic?'

'That's what I *thought*. I also thought that it must be an amateur, someone who didn't know enough to keep in the shadow of a tree to avoid reflections of the sun. So, when Melanie brought me coffee, I told her what I had seen and went down to take a closer look at the watcher. I thought too that perhaps I might frighten this amateur a little.'

'And?'

'It wasn't an amateur there and I didn't frighten anyone but myself.' He put on some clean undershorts and a pair of slacks as he continued. 'What I had seen flashing was the bottom of two new, shiny cans of tomato-juice cocktail mixture. They had been taped together and hung by black

183

thread from a tree branch so that they were just behind a bush. Attached to the tape was a cord going back through the other bushes for perhaps thirty metres. This served two purposes. It kept the cans pointing in this direction, and it enabled the person hidden at the other end to move the cans slightly as they would have moved if they had been hand-held binoculars.'

'So you followed the cord back and found that the person had gone.'

Yves sat on the edge of the bed and, reaching beneath it, picked up a shoe. 'That is not all I found.' He held up the shoe. 'Please look at that.'

It was a blue canvas espadrille of the kind which used to have plain rope soles but which now have soles of crepe rubber. What was odd about this one was that there were extensive burn marks on it, the sort of marks that you would expect to see if it had been worn to stamp out the embers of a brush fire.

'What happened?'

'I followed the cord to where it ended along a narrow path and then I trod on this.' He reached under the bed again and pulled out a square of charred plywood the size of a chess board, with a long bolt attached to the centre.

'What is it?'

'The pressure plate of a very small, insultingly innocuous, incendiary bomb.'

'What do you mean by innocuous? It burnt your espadrille.'

'If they had wanted to, they could have blown a foot off. This bolt broke a small tube of sulphuric acid when I trod on the board. All it ignited, judging from the smell, was a very small amount of chlorate of potash mixed with sugar. I was glad I was wearing socks though.' He took the shoe from me and poked a finger through a burnt spot. 'They were just having fun, you see, Patron. I don't like practical jokes of this sort being played at my expense.'

'You didn't see *anybody*?'

'No one in particular. The motor cruiser arrived, the big one that anchors off the sand beach near the point.'

'At *that* time in the morning?'

'They like a swim before breakfast. I've watched them through the glasses. A crewman lowers the dinghy for them to go to the beach. One man, two women. They swim in the morning and early evening every day.'

'Did you see anything unusual apart from the booby-trap? Or *hear* anything, like a getaway car starting, for instance?'

'Patron, have you been across the road there?'

'No.'

'All you can see from where I ended up is part of the bay, the part with the little pier where we could bring in a launch for water-skiing, if we had a launch. All you can hear are the sounds of waves breaking on the rocks below and, very faintly because of the bushes, passing traffic on the road. And I will tell you this. After that little *pétard* had gone off I wasn't listening very carefully to anything. I have had time to think, however, and come to some conclusions if you would care to hear them.'

'Of course.'

'We were told last night that we are blown. We have now been told for a second time, and given one or two additional bits of bad news.'

'For instance?'

'That we are not just a little blown, but completely. They know, for instance, how we are organized, Patron.'

'Explain, please.'

'As I understand it, you are here to give information to this Krom and the others. No, I am not trying to pry. I don't want to know more. It's better the way it is. But you are the key figure, the one who is giving out the information to these educated half-wits. Those outside can only want to stop what is being done inside. At the moment, they *seem* to be trying to do this by scaring us into breaking

185

up the meeting. Why? They can only wish to make us run so that they can more easily dispose of you.'

'By "dispose of", you mean kill, I take it. Aren't you imagining things?'

'You're the one with the information, Patron. How else are they going to stop you?'

'You said that they know how we are organized. What do you mean by that?'

'There are *at least* six of them and they are not amateurs. That we know for certain. Six pros cost money. You don't use them only to play practical jokes. Patron, they *knew* that I would see those reflections and go down to find the source of them. *I* and I alone.'

'What makes you so sure?'

'Because if they had thought that there was any chance of your going down, they would have left something a little more important for you to tread on. They would have left something that would have killed you.'

I thought for a moment. He was wrong, and I could have told him why.

In Italy during the war I had seen a lot of booby-traps and the effects on those who hadn't made the right allowances for them. There was one trick the Germans had played that I have never forgotten. The hand-guns that their officers and senior NCOs carried had been much prized by Allied troops. The forward area people used to sell them for two or three hundred dollars a time to the chairborne warriors back in the lines-of-communications and base jobs. When the Germans found this out, they used to leave Lugers or Walthers behind when they moved out of a village and booby-trap them with grenades. The Allied engineer patrols got wise to that soon enough and used to carry lengths of cord with hooks on them. Then, when they saw a pistol left behind, they would put a hook on it and pay out the cord until they found a nearby foxhole to take cover in. Even if the pull of the cord set the grenade off, the pistol was usually undamaged. That game went on until the

Germans found out, from some prisoner they took I suppose, what was happening. So then they used a bit more ingenuity. They'd still leave a pistol lying around, but it was no longer the pistol that they would booby-trap. Instead, it would be that convenient, nearby foxhole they'd fix; and not just with a grenade; they'd plant an S-mine in it that could cut a man in half. That's why Yves was wrong. If I'd seen a cord there leading invitingly into the bushes, I'd have been off, scared shitless, scrambling back to the house as fast as I could go. Once you become boobytrap conscious, or get land-mine jitters, you stay that way for life.

I decided to keep all that to myself though. My convenient protection-racket theory had, since I had left the terrace and Krom's indignation a few minutes earlier, ceased to make even a little sense. Yves was on edge, and now so was I. The immediate needs were calm and as much sense as we could bring to dealing with a difficulty we didn't yet understand.

'What would you advise?' I asked.

'That we should stop covering for certain persons who aren't here and start thinking of our own skins again.'

I didn't ask him who it was he thought we were covering for, because I preferred not to know that he had guessed correctly.

'By doing what, Yves?'

'That's a very conspicuous car we came in.'

He was quite right; a white Lincoln Continental with Liechtenstein plates is a conspicuous object; but he knew that the one in the garage was part of our cover story as tenants of the Villa Lipp and I didn't immediately read his thinking.

'What of it?'

'You asked for my advice. I say we forget our guests, take their small car, just the three of us, and make a quick break for it. Then we hole up in the safe-house and hire help to take care of the opposition.'

'How do you know that there *is* a safe-house?'

'With Melanie planning a set-up, there's always a safe-house.'

'I'll bear the suggestion in mind, but I don't like it at the moment. We know too little. Supposing the opposition turned out to be a government agency. You couldn't hire help to take care of that.'

'It isn't the French. They wouldn't play practical jokes. On their own ground, as we are, they'd have a complete frame-up ready – drug-smuggling or arms-dealing charges, something like that – and we'd be in police hands while they took us to pieces one at a time until they had what they thought they wanted. If it's a foreign government outfit operating with French permission, the last thing they'd want is the sort of trouble we could organize.'

'Maybe. I don't like the jokes any more than you do, but they bother me in a different way. I can't help feeling that whoever's out there must be waiting, hardly able to keep from laughing aloud, to see how soon we start walking like good boys into whatever stew-pot he's got waiting. We've let him know that we're not asleep. Before we do anything more positive than that, I want to know who's paying him or them and for what.'

'Perhaps Melanie was right after all. Perhaps we should try asking them.'

'The first persons we ask are the ones downstairs on the terrace. If any of them knows anything that we don't, it's time we found out. Besides, even if none of them knows anything new, they'll all have to be told what's going on. I don't fancy any more meals on the terrace. We make too easy a target. You'll probably be up again tonight, Yves. Why don't you just get some rest now?'

'Thank you, Paul. Later perhaps. At the moment I would prefer to hear the answers you get downstairs.'

'In that case you'd better bring your shoe and that other piece of evidence. Krom may be more inclined to believe you than me.'

* * *

Krom was not inclined to believe either of us.

At first all he did was cackle with laughter. That ended in a fit of coughing, then, the spluttering and hawking over, he went into a stern-father act broken by giggles whenever his own wit proved too much for him. Not until he had realized that his witnesses had ceased to be even mildly amused did he simmer down sufficiently to deliver a coherent verdict.

'No, Mr Firman,' he declared sonorously; 'yesterday we were tired, and so let you off lightly. Today, things are very different. Today, you will have to lie with much more skill if you expect to be taken seriously, much less believed. Diversionary tactics as elementary as these – sinister watchers lurking in the bushes armed with walkie-talkies, binoculars, booby-traps and bombs – will not help you for an instant. I beg you not to waste our time with them. Let us return to Oberholzer and the account you give of the ways in which the material he gave you was used.'

I glanced at Yves and Melanie to see how they were taking it. Melanie was wearing the expression of mindless impassivity that was her normal response to boredom or stress; and I had expected to see Yves sunk in his habitual gloom. To my surprise and concern, his sallow complexion had gone a shade lighter and his lips were pinched in a peculiar way. It took me a moment or two to realize that he was in a towering rage.

As he caught my eye he stood up suddenly and looked down at me.

'Patron, I apologise. I came down, against your advice, because I expected to hear some questions answered or at least discussed. I now see that I underrated the difficulties.' He pointed at Krom. 'This old bag of piss and wind is too much in love with himself to be able to think, and these others only lick his feet. If you still think you can persuade any of them to listen to sense, that's your affair. I don't think it's worth the sweat. I think, with respect, Patron, that we should now take seriously the suggestion

I made upstairs, and simply warn those you are covering for that from now on they'll have to take their own chances. These people here don't matter. We do. It's up to you, though, and I'm still at your orders. You told me to get some rest. That's what I should have done at once. So, that's what I will do now.'

He started to walk away. It was Henson who stopped him.

'Mr Boularis?' She spoke sharply but with a rising inflection, as if she were asking a visitor who was expected but who had not yet been introduced to identify himself.

He paused and half-turned his head.

'Mr Boularis,' she went on quickly, 'I'm sure that you're tired, but I would be grateful if you would repeat the explanation you gave us about this pressure-plate device.'

Yves turned round now to look at her suspiciously.

'I know,' she added, 'that the explanation you gave ought to have been sufficient, but for someone who doesn't know much about explosives it was a little puzzling.'

Yves answered her with his eyes on Krom. 'I'm surprised that with so much bleating going on you heard anything. What don't you understand?'

'Well, for instance, you described the thing as having been arranged so that the long bolt in the centre of the board acted as a sort of plunger going down into a small bottle holding the incendiary material. The end rested on a tube containing sulphuric acid which it broke when you trod on the board. Is that right?'

'That's how I reconstruct it from what was left.'

'Thank you. What I don't understand, though, is how hard it would be to make and set up such a thing.'

'Quite easy, if you have the stuff.'

'You mean if you know in advance that you're going to make it and roughly when you're going to use it?'

'Yes.'

'How long would it take to make and how long to install?'

Yves walked back slowly, deciding how to answer her.

For a few delicious moments I was able to forget about Krom. One of our guests had suddenly started talking sense and the whole atmosphere had changed. Melanie, I saw, had felt the same. I wondered how long the improvement would last and concentrated on looking as if I hadn't noticed it.

'To fill a glass tube with sulphuric acid and seal it would be tricky,' Yves said. 'The best way would be to use a well-greased rubber cork with a hole in it for the bolt to slide through and break the bottom of the tube. You'd also have to see that the bolt was clear of the acid, or it would simply be eaten away. The whole thing would have to be carefully handled.'

'It wouldn't be something you might decide to do on the spur of the moment?'

'No. With those materials you would not wish to be hurried. An accident could be most painful.'

'So this device was made yesterday or before?'

'Certainly.'

Connell could no longer let Henson score all the points. 'How about siting the ambush? How about digging the hole for the device and doing the installation?' he asked. 'Would you do that at night?'

'Not unless you could use bright lights to see by.'

'So this harassment, or whatever you want to call it, must have been planned well in advance?'

Krom snorted. 'Of course it was planned well in advance. Mr Firman plans all his special effects well in advance. Think how carefully he planned to wave his magic wand and turn the unfortunate Carlo Lech into Beelzebub. Planning to conjure up, out of thin air, this band of goblins and evil spirits to frighten the children into being good, and obedient, and uncritical, would be easy by comparison.'

They all looked at me except Henson who was still watching Yves.

'What would *you* say to that, Mr Boularis?' she asked. 'Why should Professor Krom or Dr Connell or I, or anyone else who has read what Mr Firman is prepared to admit about himself, accept anything he now says at its face value? You see the difficulty?'

'What difficulty?' Yves asked. 'I am a skilled person who recognizes and respects managerial intelligence. What old piss-and-wind there is accusing him of is planning to play pointless, and therefore unintelligent, practical jokes on *me!*'

'And why shouldn't he?' demanded Krom. 'He is perfectly capable of hiring other skilled men to do just that.'

'Of course he is,' said Connell; 'but why should he? I mean where's the mileage in it?'

'In your very own words, Dr Connell,' retorted Krom. '*That's* where the mileage is. You and Dr Henson are now arguing Firman's own case for him.'

'Professor, that's not quite true. You say he's trying to fool us. Okay. That's likely enough. All we're asking is, "why should he try fooling us *in this way?*" Where does it get him? To a point where he can say that he's sorry, folks, but he's being harassed by enemies so we'll just have to take rain-checks? He can't be as dumb as that. He's still over a barrel. You just take what papers he has now and re-convene at a later date. So there has to be another explanation. Either he's stalling for some reason that we haven't yet figured out, or there's an explanation that *he* hasn't yet figured out.'

They looked at me again.

'Quite right,' I said. 'I haven't yet figured it out. If Professor Krom can contain his disbelief for a moment or two, or at least keep it inaudible, I'd like to try again.' I glanced at Yves. 'Either sit down or go to bed. Don't just stand there please.'

He sat down again.

Krom sighed heavily. 'Now comes the rabbit out of the hat.'

I ignored him. 'Nothing can be figured out,' I said, 'until we know who is playing these tricks. The *why* can be answered later. Yves, Melanie and I have the advantage of knowing for certain that I'm not the trickster. Perhaps you too will accept that as true for a moment. The only other things we can be certain of so far are, first, that all the elaborate security precautions we took have been penetrated and, second, that whoever did the penetrating wants us to know it beyond all doubt. As I say, we'll have to leave the "whys" for later. Let's start with the "who?". Yves doesn't think that we're dealing with a French agency because of the methods being used. I agree with him. It could be, though, a foreign agency. German or British say, acting with consent on French territory.'

Dr Henson smiled slightly. 'Unless Dr Connell has some CIA connection that we don't know about, that leaves the Professor and me as those possibly responsible.'

'I'm afraid so.'

'Nonsense!' said Krom and wagged a finger at me. 'Either you have a bad memory, my friend, or you are hoping that I have. Yesterday, you told us that if any of us had been under surveillance we would have come no nearer to you than Turin. You had us carefully watched all the way. How could we possibly have led what you call a "foreign agency" to you, even if we had been prepared to act against our own interests as scholars as well as to breach our security pledges? If we did so unwittingly, then it can only have been because your vaunted supervision of our journey here failed. That is if it ever existed.' He grinned at Connell. 'You commented that it must have been expensive. If it had existed, I dare say it would have been – *very* expensive, *too* expensive. Composing a Firman fairy tale about it would be an easier operation and an infinitely cheaper one.'

The look Connell gave me was hostile. 'How about that, Firman?'

I motioned to Yves. 'Tell them.'

'About the cost?'

'About what was done.'

'Ah.' He cast his mind back. 'Well, there were several good, clean checkpoints. The first stage, you will remember, was air from Amsterdam to Milan and then, by rented car, to the Palace Hotel in Turin. Only Professor Krom knew even that much in advance. At the Turin hotel, you were still clear. The next appointment was waiting, addressed to the Professor. It was for lunch the following day at the Tre Citroni restaurant in Cuneo. There, the sketch-map was handed to you in a sealed envelope with the bill.'

'Aren't you forgetting?' asked Connell; 'we all knew the night before that we were going on to that restaurant in Cuneo for lunch the following day. Any one of us could have blown that.'

Yves nodded. 'You could have, yes. That was why you were given the opportunity. If any one of you had taken it there would have been no sketch-map at Cuneo. But none of you did take it. None of you made a telephone call either that night or in the morning except to order from room service. None of you left letters or notes behind you at the hotel to be picked up later. Overnight your car was examined carefully for beepers. The road to Cuneo is mostly through flat, open country of the kind which makes tailing difficult to conceal from alert observers. You were not followed then, nor when you took the road over the mountains beyond Cuneo. At the French frontier you were also clear. Nevertheless, as you began the final descent to Nice an extra precaution was taken. There was an accident on the road just behind you. Only a minor affair, but it blocked the road for nearly ten minutes. By then, you were either well lost in the late-afternoon Nice traffic jams or already out of Nice and heading along the lower road in this direction.'

They thought it over for a moment or two. Connell was the one who broke the silence.

'Murphy's Law?' he asked.

I shrugged.

'What did you say?' Krom was suddenly on the edge of his chair. 'What law is this?'

Connell smiled kindly. 'Sorry, Professor, I was using an

American folk-expression, a sort of joke proposition called Murphy's Law. It holds that, in all human affairs involving advance planning, anything that can unexpectedly go wrong will invariably do so.'

'What has that to do with Firman's precautions?'

'Well, it means that even if this security leak he's trying to trace was caused by one of our group, it could only have been caused by some outlandish mishap, like a tail, who hadn't for some reason been spotted earlier, accidentally picking us up again outside Nice. Personally, I think it more likely to have been the French police. A little thing like an accident blocking the road wouldn't have stopped them radioing ahead.'

Henson objected instantly. 'It simply doesn't work, you know. Suppose we'd been heading for a high-rise apartment in Monaco. Where were they going to put the booby-trap they'd been working on? If there really is anyone hostile out there, they couldn't have found this place by following us. They must have known in advance.'

'And since,' said Krom, 'we have no evidence that there is anything out there more hostile than the insects who bit Mr Boularis we may conclude that Mr Firman, after a lifetime of successful chicanery, has at last lost his grip. In his anxiety to get rid of me, he has accused us, his guests, of doing something to place him and his employees at risk, something that, *on his own showing* mark you, none of us could possibly have done. I find it very sad.'

Such leaden fatuities ought not to have angered me, but they did. My inner anxiety must have been telling on me. Worse, the invitation to reply in kind proved quite hard to refuse. I started to tell him to save his tears, but stopped myself only just before the words were out.

'No one so far is losing his grip,' I said instead, 'and no one has been accused. As your host, I am simply telling you that the arrangements for our safety and security here seem, in spite of all the care taken, to have broken down.

It was my duty to warn you, so I have done so. There will be no more meals served at the round table by the balustrade over there. So far, these people have only annoyed us. However, they may have plans for more aggressive acts. Whether they have or not, I don't intend to present them with sitting targets.'

Krom gave the balustrade what was supposed to be a terrified look. 'I am amazed,' he said, 'that you don't call in the police.'

'If it becomes necessary to do so, Professor, I shall leave you to handle the reporters. As a sensational news story, the siege of the Villa Lipp should be just the thing for newspapers like *France Dimanche*. I dare say your colleague Professor Langridge would find it enjoyable, too. Meanwhile, if you want to take a walk and inspect the booby-trap site, by all means do so. With luck, the enemy can try playing a practical joke on you. That would make the walk more interesting and, when you get back, you'll be able to tell me how nearly you were killed. Meanwhile, I shall continue with my enquiries. You will be kept informed, of course, of my progress.'

The idea of sensational publicity had shaken Krom sufficiently to confine him to a sneer. None of them made any move to leave, however, and for several moments we all just sat there staring at one another.

Then Connell spoke. 'Going to be a bit difficult for you now, isn't it, Mr Firman?'

'Difficult? I don't think I understand.'

'I mean that looking for leaks now is going to be difficult. Now that we've been eliminated, you've sort of run out of suspects, I'd say.'

I smiled at him. 'Dr Connell, I said I was going to continue with my *enquiries*. I have no further need of suspects.' I paused to let him interrupt if he wanted to. He didn't. 'With you three disposed of, the mystery, or part of it, anyway, is solved. I know now that the leak could have come from only one person.'

Melanie broke the silence that followed by emitting a little gurgling laugh.

They turned to look at her.

'Mr Firman means me,' she said.

CHAPTER EIGHT

Krom and Connell both looked startled. Henson was the only one amused by that odd laugh.

She offered Melanie a cigarette. 'Is Mr Firman denouncing you?' she asked.

'Oh, I don't think so,' Melanie declined the cigarette with a graceful hand movement. 'It's just that, having reminded himself that he and I are the only persons who were supposed to know in advance that this was to be the meeting place, he now finds it convenient to think aloud.'

'He doesn't pause to wonder if he himself could conceivably be the culprit? Two persons were supposed to know in advance, but only one of them could possibly have leaked the information – you. Can that be right?'

'Yes, of course.'

'Of course? You mean that you really accept that verdict or that you have no choice?'

'Oh, I accept.'

'The master is infallible?'

'Naturally.'

Melanie was displeased with me, and her innate bitchiness, usually well hidden beneath the surface appearance of bright-eyed stupidity, was beginning to show through. Had I not intervened then, she would soon have been talking nonsense of a less acceptable kind.

'You mustn't take Melanie too seriously,' I said. 'She has a weakness for ornate overstatement. I am always warning her against it, aren't I, my dear?'

Her instant over-anxious nod aroused Krom's paternal instincts. 'Are you always warning her, too,' he demanded, 'that, as your secretary, she must expect to be used as a scapegoat?'

'No, Professor, I am not. No such warning would be necessary. As an acknowledged expert in the organization of undercover work, Melanie Wicky-Frey knows a great deal more about the selection and management of scapegoats than I do.'

Henson started to say something, but I shut her up by raising my voice as I went on: 'For your further information, she chose this place herself, composed all the cover stories we are using, and advised me on general security matters at all planning stages. What she is complaining of now is that I am not treating her as if *she* were infallible. I don't blame her. As you people should know very well, experts always tend to award themselves immunity from criticism.'

Krom looked expectantly at Melanie, ready to welcome and swallow whole any denials of my dastardly charges she cared to make. When all he drew from her was an empty stare, he sighed and returned heavily to me.

'So, when you introduced her as your secretary, that was a lie.'

'Don't be absurd, Professor. Why should I need a secretary here? I was surprised that you didn't ask. The idea's so obviously preposterous. Actually, Melanie is a wholly special kind of PR expert.'

'A wholly special kind of liar, you must mean. It's hard to believe, though, that there could be anyone more special in that field than yourself.'

Yves cleared his throat. 'Patron, I thought that these people were going to take a walk. If they are not, I suggest that you and Melanie talk in the dining-room. You won't be overheard there.'

He meant that the dining-room wasn't bugged. 'Good idea,' I said and stood up, motioning as I did so to Melanie.

'Ah, no!' Krom was levering himself out of his chair. 'I refuse to be dismissed in this way.'

'No one's dismissing you,' I said; 'but it's clearly impossible to talk seriously here.'

When I started to move, he stood in front of me. As I made to go round him, he grabbed me by the arm.

Connell was on his feet instantly, bleating, 'No, no!' as if I had been about to hit the old fool.

I said to Melanie: 'Go ahead. I'll see you in the dining-room.' Then, I looked at the hand on my arm as I had looked at it the night before when it had been on Melanie. Like other compulsive arm-grabbers, Krom seemed not quite to realize that his habit could be objectionable. When I had to jerk my arm free, he looked cross, as if I had interrupted a chain of thought, and then wagged a reproving finger.

'Your statement,' he repeated, 'was a lie, and, as you now admit, a pointless one. You *have* admitted that, yes? Very well. We don't yet know what kind of man you are, but the evidence so far suggests that, although you may not be a criminal psychopath in any of the generally accepted senses of the word, you possess many of the characteristics often attributed to the so-called moral defective. Still, for the present we shall have to be content with an *ad hoc* classification, such as – oh, what shall we say? Variegated delinquent, perhaps?' His eyes sought the witnesses' approval. 'There is, in any case, one thing of which we can now be certain. Our delinquent is an inveterate as well as a resourceful liar.'

I was weary enough to lose patience with him.

'Where,' I asked, 'did you get this extraordinary idea that you have a prescriptive right to be told nothing but the truth? Does it come up through the seat of your academic chair? Or is there some tatty sociological saint who once taught that all who have to submit to your questioning are, by divine decree, automatically on oath? Of course, that must be it. And what happens when the poor souls perjure themselves? Obviously, burning at the stake would be too mild a punishment. Instead, we are slowly and brutally classified! Right, Professor?'

Connell chuckled, but Krom only nodded encouragingly.

'Slowly and brutally? Yes, I expect you're right, Mr Firman. And so?'

'And so, the only time you'll hear a truth from me is when it happens to suit me better than a lie or when none of the available lies is good enough to stand inspection. Truth games are dangerous, even for children. All I'm playing for is safety, safety for myself and my partners in what you choose to call crime.'

Krom beamed. 'This candour is *most* refreshing.' He switched the beam to Connell and Henson. 'Clearly, this tantrum of Firman's is a direct response to my diagnostic stimulations. We are making progress. If, as he says, defects in his cover arrangements have come to light, now might be the moment for us to probe his defences in depth.'

Although the witnesses could scarcely have failed to notice that Krom, with his third-person plurals, had suddenly conferred colleague-collaborator status on them, neither gave any sign of having done so. Knowing Krom as they did, they probably recognized that, from him, such courtesies could only be slips of the tongue.

'I agree,' said Connell; 'it's time we had a look at some of the nuts and bolts of this set-up. If he expects to persuade us that he's basically incompetent, he's going to have to produce something more convincing than a hunk of charred plywood.'

'Bearing in mind,' said Henson, 'that, according to Mr Firman, Wicky-Frey is the nuts-and-bolts expert, I would feel that we should concentrate first on her.' She flashed her appealing smile at Yves. 'Now, what do *you* think, Mr Boularis?'

She had succeeded with him before; but that had been half an hour ago and he had learned a lot since. He glanced at her casually and then returned to watching the small birds that were hopping about beneath the chairs and feeding on the crumbs from breakfast.

After a moment he said: 'I *now* think, Madame, that you are *all* full of piss and wind.'

201

In the silence that followed this further diagnostic stimulation, I left to join Melanie in the dining-room.

I found her sitting wreathed in tobacco smoke, at the head of the long table.

She rarely smoked except after dinner. The ashtray in front of her and the lighted cigarette in her hand were announcements of her need for relief from the intolerable pain of my displeasure. They also warned me that if I were not instantly apologetic and extremely kind to her, she might be driven to commit ritual suicide by inhaling.

As I had nothing to apologize for, and no intention of being kinder than I felt just then, I made no move to sit down. I have always found it easier to keep my temper and to remain civil when standing.

Besides, my assumption was that, having had ample time in which to review the entire cover operation step by step, Melanie now knew where the leak had occurred, how it had occurred, and who might have had the impertinence to exploit it. Once I knew those things, I expected to be able, having shrugged away surprise and exasperation, to start figuring out ways of capitalizing on my misfortunes. Krom's description of some of my tactical thinking as 'octopus ink' had not been all that fanciful; and yes, even in the dining-room on the morning of that second day, I was still thinking in terms of using the jokers outside the gates to neutralize the jokers within.

Call it the last minute of innocence.

'Well?' I asked.

Melanie stubbed out her cigarette. 'I've drawn a blank, Paul. No, let me finish. I've been over it all as thoroughly as I know how, and several times, even while that horrible little lesbian was pretending to be nice to me. I've nothing to tell you that you don't already know. Nobody was told except you. *Nobody!* And only the two communications codes were issued.'

'Why two? What two?'

She sighed patiently. 'Brussels office has one in their safe

202

for emergency use. Usual safeguards. The other was requested by Mr Yamatoku in London. That was properly authorized. Standard procedure was followed in both cases.'

That was it. I suddenly felt quite peculiar, as if someone had stuffed wool in my ears and started to inflate my head with a foot-pump. Because I knew, almost at once, that if I didn't sit down I would soon fall down. I gripped the back of the dining-chair nearest to me, eased it around slightly and sat.

Melanie says that I succeeded in making the move look as if I had simply become tired of standing, and that at the time she hadn't any idea that I was nearly passing out. Most gratifying. In future, though, it may be advisable for me to carry one of those special medical ID cards with multi-lingual notices on them. I mean notices warning that the bearer has an implanted pace-maker or an allergy to penicillin, or is diabetic, things like that. In my case, the card should read, *Bearer May Refuse To Lie Down When Dead.*

'You say that the issue of this second communications code was properly authorized? What do you mean by that?' I asked her. 'Authorized by whom? *I* didn't authorize it.'

'It didn't have to be authorized by you, Paul. Surely you know that? The cypher requesting confirmation was duly received.'

'You didn't think to ask me why London had a need to know our communications code for this operation?'

'Certainly not. Both the request and the response to Brussels' double-checked conformed strictly to the rules. It was all standard procedure. Why should I have asked you or anyone else? What are such procedures for if not to be acted upon?'

I could see then exactly why Mat had thought her a security risk. He had spotted something that the Gehlen organization had missed. Once a security procedure had been established, she would cease for ever to question any particular use of it. She was insufficiently paranoid.

Our communications code system had been devised originally by Carlo as a means of controlling the courier network when normal routines were interrupted. If, say, a courier had to divert, or be diverted, from his standard movement schedule, the first thing he did when he ceased moving was to call in or cable, via one of the answering services, a sixteen-figure message, dressed up to look like a price-range quotation. Decoded, the figures would give the courier's cover name, the area of the country in which he was located, and a telephone number at which he could be reached. After Carlo's death, of course, when the Symposia Group came into being and the old buccaneering ways had long been discarded, we had no need of courier networks or any other sort of covert-operations hanky-panky. If the decision had been left to me, I would have abolished the communications code system. A modern business ought not to need such toys. It had been Mat's idea that we should keep that particular one.

The reasons he had given for our doing so had looked shrewd as well as sound. The code drill was simple, it had worked well for years, it was cheap to run and, above all, it encouraged personal initiative in our field men. It told them, in effect: 'Don't call us – except to leave your number, or tell us that there's something too big for you to handle on your own – we'll call you.' His real reason for retaining the drill was that it enabled him to keep tabs on Brussels, and all those rich Symposia pies he had his fingers in, without anyone but me knowing of the connection. Even upper-echelon personnel like Melanie, who knew that Frank Yamatoku in London was a number-two man to someone, didn't know that the someone was Mat Williamson.

For Mat, with our communications code and Frank to make the long-distance calls for him, pin-pointing us at the Villa Lipp would have been no trouble at all. If he had been in a hurry and had had access to an Alpes-Maritimes area phone-book with Yellow Pages, the trace job could have been done in an hour.

I now knew, then, who had been responsible for the presence of those objectionable people outside the house. It only remained to find out who they were and what orders they had been given. It says something, I suppose, about the quality of my former relationship with Mat when I record that, faced with an urgent need for answers to what the pit of my stomach told me were life-or-death questions, my first thought was still to ask *him* for them; to ask, moreover, knowing with reasonable certainty that I would receive. The answers wouldn't be wholly untrue, of course, because Mat has always preferred to deal in ambiguities and half-truths rather than straightforward lies; but I knew that, if I listened carefully and ignored the literal meaning of the words, the kind of background music to make them sound convincing would probably tell me a lot of what I needed to know.

Melanie, still the injured party awaiting a well-earned apology, was studying her nail-polish. I sat back and clicked a thumb and third finger gently until she looked up.

'Go back outside,' I said. 'Tell them I have to make some phone calls. I'll let you know what's happening as soon as I know myself.'

She stood up. 'What about the second file?'

'We'll give it to them after lunch, perhaps. Not that it matters now, but the quieter they can be kept the better. I'll see. On the subject of lunch, we'd better have it in here.'

'There's the space beside the swimming pool. That isn't exposed.'

'All right.'

'We can dine there too. It's a long way from the kitchen but dinner tonight'll be cold anyway.'

'Why?'

'It's the Quatorze today. The servants want to get finished early and go to the local fête. They asked, I said they could.'

When we occupied it, the Villa Lipp was still on a telephone exchange that hadn't been fully integrated into the international direct-dialling system. This meant that, although we could be called direct by someone dialling from another country, we ourselves could initiate foreign calls only through an operator. You needed patience to keep dialling until one answered.

In that large house there were only three telephones: one in the entrance hall with an extension in the main bedroom, and, also in that bedroom, the one I was occupying, a phone on a second line with no extensions. I used this second one, having checked it for obvious bugs before doing so. There would have been no point in my calling Mat's London hotel. Even if he had been in and available, he wouldn't have taken an international call through the hotel switchboard. It took me twenty minutes to get through to the London cut-out.

The man on duty spoke very slowly and distinctly as if he distrusted the telephone and would have been happier with a short-wave radio. This was normal. Mat likes using radio hams as cut-outs, and does so in a number of countries; partly because hams are accustomed to staying awake at all hours and partly because some of them can be prevailed upon, in an emergency and for no longer than the few seconds needed to send a high-speed message track, to operate their transmitters illegally. Mostly, he chooses elderly men with pensions to supplement and a mild taste for conspiracy. If they are former Boy Scouts, so much the better.

I gave the number of the phone I was using along with my cover name and said that the matter was urgent. It would be thirty minutes, I was told, before I was called back.

I had fitted induction stickers to both phones, and it was just as well that I'd done so because the return call came through on the other line.

It wasn't Mat, though, but Frank Yamatoku.

'Hi, Paul,' he said, 'still in the same place after all. Is that right? When you gave the other number, we thought you might have moved without telling us.'

'And upset your planning?'

'Oh, we knew you hadn't done that.'

'You did?'

'Sure. We'd have had complaints if you hadn't been in the target area. What's that other number? A second line we didn't know about?'

I'd already had enough of him. 'It's been great hearing your voice, Frank, but it was my old friend I called and my old friend I want to talk to. Is he there?'

'Not right now, Paul. Later maybe. Meanwhile, I have messages. We've been expecting this call for hours, you see. Since last night. Why the delay? We were getting worried. What kept you?'

'Reaction times must be slowing down.'

He chuckled. 'Happens to us all, they say. But you're here now, so never mind. I'll get to the messages. He says you'll want various questions answered, and that the first will be, 'Who?' After that comes, 'Why?'. Finally, there's, 'What shall we do to be saved?' That one must be religious, I think, from the way he said it. You still with me?'

'Listening carefully.'

'Then I'll get straight to the why of it. I don't have to tell you, Paul, that we've both been worried. Not about how you'd handle yourself, naturally, because we both of us know and respect you, but worried *for* and *with* you. So, we began wondering what we back home could do. We wanted you to feel that, when you were fighting that lonely battle of yours out there, you weren't alone. We wanted you to know that you had friends right behind you ready to give a helping hand when you needed it. You understand me, Paul?'

'Frank, it's those friends right behind me, and what they might do before I can turn around and stop them, that I called about.'

'Bear with me, Paul, and let me share our thinking with you. Our first thought was that you were, we all were, in bigger trouble than you wanted to admit, and that you were going to need more than a paper towel to clean off all that shit you stepped in. I mean clean if off so there'd be no lingering odour. What you needed, we figured, was one of those deodorants that does more than just freshen up the air. You needed one that would destroy the opposition's sense of smell. Right?'

'You've lost me.'

'Look at it another way. What happens when one of these penny-ante Third-World governments has big trouble on the home front? You know what happens. It looks around for some foreign enemy who'll take the people's minds off all the troubles at home by standing up outside the gates and drawing fire. Xenophobia, right? Baddies from outside?'

'I see.'

'Of course you do. And you'll also see that, with the kind of non-belligerents you have there with you right inside the city walls, we couldn't take chances. You're not going to fool social scientists of that calibre with Hallowe'en masks and hi-fi scream tracks. They're serious investigators. You have to give them a taste of the real thing or they don't believe, do they?'

'Don't believe what?'

'That this investigation they're making is dangerous, physically dangerous. Dangerous for you, dangerous for your employees, and, thus, dangerous for *them*. In fact, so god-damned dangerous for everybody there, that the quicker they get their asses out the less likely they are to share the terrible fate planned for you. Death through proximity, that's what they have to fear, Paul.'

'They're not going to buy it.'

'You don't know yet what you'll be selling, friend. I'm trying to tell you. That is where we come to the "who" bit. Are you still with me? This is important.'

'Still with you.'

'Now, I'm not personally acquainted with the outfit that's been hired, but I've heard of it and I understand that it's talented enough to rate top money. Can't say more because

I've been told to stay with hard fact. The word to you from our friend, though, is that the tab for the operation's been picked up by three guys acting in concert, three guys whose names he says you'll know. I have them written down. Let's see. Yes, here we are. The names are Kleister, Torten and Vic. Vic who, it doesn't say. Maybe you know.'

'Yes I know.' The foot-pump connected to my head was being worked again.

'Good. Then you'll also know, Paul, that these three gentlemen are all, as far as you're concerned, somewhat prejudiced. That means that, although our friend made it very clear to them that harassment was authorized only insofar as it was needed to carry conviction, the possibility of these nuts over-stepping the mark if provoked ought to be borne in mind. He asked me to mention that specially.'

'I appreciate his concern.'

'I hope you mean, that, Paul, because it's something you should appreciate. He's still fond of you, in spite of everything, and he still wants to protect you if you'll let him. He says that before you went over the hill you played polo real good, and that if you found yourself in an emergency predicament you might still give these characters more trouble and make them real mad.'

'I might, yes.'

'The word is, don't. You'll only get hurt a lot instead of a little. That's only advice, mind. He still has too much respect for you as his old bossman, Paul, to presume to *tell* you. He's only asking you to accept a piece of friendly advice.'

'Is there anything else that I should accept?'

'He said to tell you that he'll be thinking of you all the time. He meant it too. *All* the time.'

'I'll be thinking of *him*.'

'Have a good day, Paul.'

He hung up.

I switched off and immediately pressed the rewind button. After I had played the whole tape through twice, I listened to the beginning of it a third time before writing a note to Yves and Melanie.

Yves, please meet me at CP now after passing this to Melanie, please distribute File No. 2 and then join us.

I found the cook's husband and gave him the note to deliver. Then, I took the recorder from my bedroom and went to our 'Command Post' in the garage loft.

When Yves joined me everything was set up and ready.

I pointed to the recorder. 'I've just taped a call from London on this. First, I want you to listen to the beginning and tell me if anything occurs to you, anything at all.'

He asked no questions, just nodded and sat down.

I started the play-back. After the first couple of sentences I stopped it and looked at him.

'Again, please,' he said, 'and this time as loudly as possible. The speech quality doesn't matter.'

I couldn't get it much louder because induction suckers aren't all that efficient and the recorder's amplifier hadn't much left to give, but I did my best. Oddly enough, Frank's voice quacking away through the tape-hiss was, though still intelligible, less offensive than it had been with the volume lower. I let it run on for a moment or two longer before switching off.

Yves pursed his lips. '*Anything* that occurs to me?'

'Yes, please.'

'You said that the call was from London. I don't think it was.'

'How can you be sure?'

'Calls from London to here are dialled. With long-distance direct-dialling, an electronic time-and-distance charge counter is activated as soon as the answering phone is picked up. It's connected to a computer that bills the customer. I don't know exactly how long it takes to start running – only a small fraction of a second I would think – but if you already have the phone to your ear when the circuit is completed you always hear it. It's like a sound of a stick being dragged for an instant along iron railings. Your recording here begins while the phone is still ringing. If the call had come from London, or Bonn or Amsterdam, we'd have heard the charge counter coming into action when you picked up the phone. The sound's not there. That call was made locally from no farther away than Nice or Menton. And it wasn't made from a pay-phone either. You'd have heard a charge counter start with that too. The sound would have been different from the long-distance counter, but you'd have heard it.' He paused, then added: 'Is that what you wanted to hear?'

'Not what I wanted, but what I expected. I didn't notice until the second time I played the tape.'

'Most people don't hear it at all. The counter normally starts during the time it takes to pick up the phone and put it to your ear. You asked for anything that occurred to me. I also recognize the caller's voice. It's the man I know as Mr Yamatoku.'

He was watching me narrowly for a reaction. I nodded. 'I'm going to ask you to listen to the rest of the conversation, but let's wait a moment until Melanie gets here.'

We had to wait several minutes.

'Questions,' she explained peevishly. 'Paul, you should not have so spoken about me in the ambience of such persons. They are incapable of maintaining the moderations of polite usage.'

The sudden deterioration of her English suggested that the questions had been inconveniently searching.

'Didn't the second file divert them at all?'

'Do you divert lions with carrion when there is fresh meat to be had? These people are most ill-mannered.'

'You're being too fussy,' I said. 'I'll be surprised if those other people with us, the ones we *weren't* expecting, have any manners at all.'

Yves shoved a bentwood chair against the back of her legs and she sat down abruptly.

'What do you know,' I asked, 'about a man named Mathew

211

Tuakana? He sometimes calls himself Mat Williamson. Mean anything to you?'

I was looking at Yves as I spoke simply to notify Melanie that I had called the meeting to order and wanted no more of her nonsense. I hadn't really expected him to answer. In his line of work, he was unlikely to have become involved in any of the futile attempts already made to penetrate the dense covers concealing Mat's operations; but I had been mistaken. After a moment's thought, he nodded.

'Yes, I've heard of him. A Polynesian *métis*. Homosexual. A banker of some sort. Ultra rich. Is that the man?'

'Where did you hear that gossip?'

'I know someone who did some work for him. It's all wrong, I suppose.'

'It's right about his being half-caste, but wrong about the non-white component. His mother was Melanesian, not Polynesian. Also, he's had women as lovers as well as men. Who was your informant?'

An impertinent question that ought not to have been asked. Yves didn't apologize for ignoring it.

'I was also told,' he said, 'that Williamson was one to stay away from if you were free to choose. Some of these ultra rich have a habit of ditching things when they've finished with them, even if the things have only been used once. I'm told Williamson does that with people. Was I wrong there too?'

I hesitated, so naturally he had to pounce.

'Is *he* the one you're covering for here?'

I didn't have a chance of deciding how fully or frankly I would reply. Before I could draw breath, Melanie was talking across to me to answer Yves.

'Of *course*,' she told him, 'it must be Williamson. I should have thought of him before. He's the Placid Island man, the one negotiating on behalf of the natives over the compensation to be paid out by the phosphate interests. He's an economist with unorthodox ideas. You know? The kind of ideas that sound fascinating while they are being

212

used to sell something, but that no one ever hears of again after the deal is set. He also acts for a Canadian bank. If that man had needed protection from Krom, I should have thought the bank would have provided it. Why trouble poor little Symposia?'

By bitching me with that snide reference to Symposia she was trying to recover the dignity lost minutes earlier when her buttocks had hit the seat of the chair.

'He doesn't control the Canadian bank,' I said, 'though his association with it is common knowledge. He *does* control Symposia, however, and he controls it through me. That is very far from being common knowledge and the thing that was to have been hidden at all costs from those with prying eyes and publishing voices, especially from Krom. News that there existed a backstairs financial arrangement between Symposia, the trendy fast-buck artists' favourite tax-haven advisory service, and His Excellency Mat Tuakana, man of the people, King's Scout and patron saint of Placid Island, would kill for ever his chance of getting that international licence to print money he's always yearned for. And he'd never get another chance.'

I turned to Yves again. 'I'm the one whose cover was blown by Krom, so I'm the one who has to make good the loss, hold the fort, stick the finger in the dyke, fall on the exploding grenade or do whatever else is necessary to keep His Excellency's reputation safe, sound and spotless. Yes, he *does* like scrapping people when he's used them. Let's hope he hasn't succeeded with us.'

'*Us*, Paul?' Melanie again.

The look I gave her was as sour as her own. 'I think it's time I revealed, in case you didn't know, that *both* of you were hand-picked for this operation by Mat Williamson himself. And if you think that being chosen by the great man personally for this assignment isn't much of a distinction, you're mistaken. In your case certainly, Melanie, the choice was made with immense care. To prove it I'm going to play back a phone conversation I've just had with

Frank Yamatoku. He's Williamson's left-hand man, Melanie. That's why I was a little upset when you told me that you'd given him our communications code.'

Yves whispered, '*Merde*' as if it were a prayer.

She stared coldly at my chin. 'A capable operations director would have reviewed the standard security procedures before committing the team.'

I wasn't going to argue about that with her. 'When I called Williamson's London cut-out from here, I asked him to return my call personally. It was returned instead by Yamotoku, and it sounds as if he's calling from a local phone not far from here. Listen.'

They listened. They listened to the whole thing three times. Between play-backs I answered questions as truthfully as seemed prudent in the circumstances.

Who, for instance, were Kleister, Torten and Vic?

'No, they're *not*, much as they may sound like it, a slack-wire baggy-pants act out of a third-rate circus. There's nothing even marginally comical about these three. They're old business rivals still nursing their grudges against me for the defeats they once suffered in a couple of big deals. They said I tricked them. You know how it is with losers, *some* losers anyway. They think that winners only win through skulduggery, and that that makes it all right for losers to use skulduggery if it'll give them their revenge. We should try to feel sorry for the poor slobs.'

Of course, neither Yves nor Melanie believed a word of that soap-opera version of the facts; but they accepted its essential element. It was more than likely that I should have former victims gunning for me. But gunning for me with what?

How real was the threat implicit in Yamatoku's reference to the possibility of K, T and V's merry men 'overstepping the mark'? Was such sinister moustache-twirling to be taken seriously?

I told them that, when dealing with Mat Williamson, everything ought to be taken seriously, but nothing at its face value. However, for the purpose of our council of war, a few assumptions could safely be made.

Among those old acquaintances of mine with reasons for disliking me, K, T and V had been chosen not for their ability to exercise restraint where I was concerned – it was known that K and T had once threatened to kill me – but because, in spite of earlier misfortunes, they were wealthy enough as well as crazy enough to pay a team of professional hard men to carry out orders of which Mat approved. When implementing any policy of his involving even a modest cash outlay, Mat always arranged for someone else to foot the bill. He had known of K, T and V because their dossiers had figured in the inventory of Carlo's consultancy accounts which I had inherited; dossiers that I had later transferred to Mat as part of our overall deal.

Yes, Mr Yamatoku's hostility was plainly audible. Unfortunately, the idea, comforting though it might have been, that Frank had merely been indulging his personal dislike of me must be put aside. No doubt he had enjoyed giving me his bad news; but he hadn't invented it. He would certainly have taped our conversation, as I had, but *his* tape would have to be played back to Mat. With that hypercritical audience in mind, an audience prepared to evaluate every intonation, Frank Yamatoku wouldn't have dared to depart from the brief he had been given.

In my own mind the conviction was growing that Frank had a well-prepared, all-eventuality script in front of him when he had been talking to me; but I wasn't quite ready then to start explaining, or trying to explain, Mat Williamson to anyone except myself.

There was something else I had to be sure of first.

Meanwhile, I thought, it might be advisable to get Melanie on my side again.

'You were right,' I told her; 'I ought to have reviewed the standard security procedures before committing them to your care. I apologize. But now, I think, it's time we started formulating decisions.'

'Decisions on whether or not you take his friendly advice, Patron?' Yves had hooked up the small tape-deck to the bugging amplifier and had been replaying my conversation with Frank through the earphones. He flipped a switch. 'What does this bit mean?'

Frank's voice came through the monitor speaker. *'He's still fond of you, in spite of everything, and he still wants to protect you if you'll let him.'*

Yves switched off. 'In spite of *everything*, Patron? What is this everything?'

'He means that he forgives me the inconvenience I have caused him by allowing myself to be seen years ago by a Dutch criminologist in a Swiss crematorium.'

'I am being serious, Patron.'

'I wasn't joking. That's simply Mat Williamson's way of informing me that I am what you call ditched.'

'And *this?*' He had wound the tape on. 'What does this mean?'

Frank's voice again. *'That's only advice, mind. He still has too much respect for you as his old bossman, Paul, to presume to tell you. He's only asking you to accept a piece of friendly advice.'*

'That was put in,' I said, 'with the idea of making it difficult for me to play the tape to Krom. Frank's idea, probably. I'd say Mat let it go through to humour him. He himself wouldn't have bothered. He knows I'll let Krom hear the tape.'

Melanie almost squealed her protest. 'And give him one more excuse to call you a liar? While you were upstairs with Yves, they were talking about you as if I had not been there. You have not convinced them of anything that we hoped and planned for them to believe. Do you know what Dr Connell calls you? "Mr Kingpin", that is what! Paul, you will never succeed now with Krom and these others. You have cut off your own nose with your denials of truth and spit in your own face. You have boasted of your amorality, that everything you say is a lie, and they are virtuously ready to believe that there, at least, you tell the truth. They have made up their minds, and nothing you can now do will change them.'

In an effort to keep my temper, I corrected her before answering. 'You cut off your own nose to *spite* your face, not spit in it, Melanie,' I paused to swallow a bit more anger. 'The situation's completely different now. Can't you see it? Hasn't the penny dropped?'

Yves gave her no chance to reply. He was having trouble with a different anxiety. 'You haven't yet answered the question I asked you, Paul. Do you or do you not take this friendly advice of Mr Williamson? Oh yes, the situation is a little different now, but there is still only one way out of it. Those bastards outside were not put there just to make you call London. We're being set up for a kill, I feel it.'

'You may be right.'

'Well then, Paul, let's do what I said. Let's forget about the guests. This was their idea anyway, and they don't matter now. We should think of ourselves. No consultation. No argument. We choose the right moment, we take the rental car, we head for the safe-house and then stay there until this place has been disinfected by paid bastards of your own.'

I tried to say what had to be said. 'It doesn't work, Yves. There's no right moment for us to choose. For one thing, it's too easy for them around here, too easy to stage an accident. You know? One of those accidents in which all the occupants of a small car are killed when it runs off the road on the corniche? It's happening every day for real. No one would even notice.'

He slapped his right elbow with the palm of his left hand, and then stabbed a forefinger at me. 'Paul, I give you a guarantee! If *I* am driving, anyone who tries to run us off the road – *anyone*, even if he is an Italian kidnap driver – will kill himself before he can scratch our paintwork. That little buzz-box is not heavy, but she steers well and on

217

these roads that is good enough. Good enough, with me driving, to get us away from this fly-trap, free and clear to the safe-house. Paul, I *guarantee* it!'

I glanced at Melanie.

She shrugged sullenly.

My eyes went back to Yves. He thought I was still trying to make up my mind and out came the forefinger again, moving stiffly from side to side this time, to dispel lingering doubt.

'You think I can't do it, eh?'

I said: 'Our cut-out point was the hotel in Turin. Remember?'

'What of it?'

He hadn't even begun to understand. It was possible that his mind was still doing immaculate skid turns on the hairpin bends of the corniche while the opposition cartwheeled down the hillside in flames. A good technician, Yves, but unreliably romantic. There was nothing left to do but speak plainly.

'Yves,' I said, 'I'm sorry, but this fly-trap *is* the safe-house.'

His look of anguish was of the predictable kind and I didn't waste time consoling him. I knew at this point where the score stood. I also knew, more or less, what I would have to do to change it.

'A remarkable man,' Krom said, 'remarkable by any standards.'

He knew, or thought he knew, all about Mat Williamson and had instructed his witnesses on the subject. He had never heard of Frank though. I spelled Yamatoku for him. They wrote it down, and then we all went into the dining-room.

I played the tape through twice. During the second playback both Krom and the witnesses took notes. Finally, Krom sat back and looked questioningly at Henson.

'Any comments, my dear?'

She stubbed out a cigarette. 'Only obvious ones, I'm

afraid. A shadowy figure named Vic has been added to the supporting cast headed by Kleister and Torten. I shan't be at all surprised if we find this Vic popping up again, wearing a devil's suit and a smell of brimstone next time, in a later discussion paper.'

'A note of scepticism is sounded.' He nodded sympathetically and looked at Connell.

'I had that very same thought, Professor. And one or two others.' Connell consulted his notes. 'This Mr Yamatoku, for instance. His speech sounds American – could be from my own home state – and I'm sure we'll find when we check it out that the Placid Island banker, Williamson, has a Nisei accountant of that name on his staff. But that still leaves us with the question of provenance. In this Frank-and-Paul show we've been listening to, is the Frank character the real Yamatoku or is he some bit player hired by the old bossman here to read lines? I am assuming, by the way, that the lines contain hidden meanings that are going to be revealed to us later. To give one example, there is an allusion to the game of polo which at present makes no sense at all.'

'More scepticism, I fear, Mr Firman.'

No cackling now, no raucous sarcasms. Something had happened to Krom while we had been away. My guess was that the witnesses, impressed by Yves's outburst on the terrace earlier, had ganged up on their leader and persuaded him that he would get more out of us if he made less noise himself.

Henson was pretending coyly to have had a sudden inspiration. 'I wonder now! Wait a minute! If Mr Firman could telephone London and have his call returned promptly like that, surely we could do the same. Naturally, we couldn't be certain that the Mr Yamatoku we were talking to – have I got the name right? – was the genuine article, but we ought to be able to test the actor theory. Only a very good one could improvise in that turgid neo-revivalist manner.'

'I thought one of you experts might have noticed that

219

the call was a local one,' I said. 'Would you explain to them, Yves?'

Yves explained.

They listened quietly and attentively in a way that I didn't like. Krom's natural rudeness and the witnesses' sycophancy had been infuriating, and probably bad for my blood pressure, but they had their psychological uses. They had enabled me, for one thing, to view the prospect of him and his witnesses dying violent deaths in the near future with only a token regret. So, I had been left reasonably free to concentrate on avoiding the same fate. The new politeness was not only disconcerting, and thus destructive, but also insidiously depressing. It would have to be countered. As Yves began going into detail, I cut him short.

'You're quite right, of course, Dr Henson,' I said; 'talking to Mr Yamatoku, even if you could, wouldn't help you all that much. Besides, my object in asking you to listen to that highly compromising conversation wasn't to prove anything to any of you. It was to save myself trouble. If you'll just accept for a moment that the man to whom I'm speaking on that tape is Yamatoku and that the "our friend" he's referring to is his employer Mat Williamson, I'll try to explain to you what's happened to change things here without wasting any more time. Agreed?'

Connell talked across me to Krom. 'You have to hand it to our host, Professor. He gives that Number-Two status claim of his everything he's got. He really *does* try harder. Secret watchers and bombs in the night didn't work, so now it's threatening calls from sinister Orientals and sudden cracks of hypothetical whips – all great stuff. But it does make you wonder, I find, about the kind of therapy he's been in, and the quality of it too. Some of these cruelty-is-kinder organismic groups we're seeing around nowadays can do the mind permanent damage.'

Krom squirmed with the agony of keeping a straight face, and then showed me his teeth as if they had all suddenly begun to hurt him. 'You must see our difficulty, Mr Firman.

If we do not take you as seriously as you would wish, you have only yourself to blame.'

'That's quite all right,' I said evenly; 'I'm glad that you're in such high spirits. They may help to make the news I have to give you more palatable.'

'The whip-cracks I could forgive,' remarked Henson; 'it's the false bonhomie that *I* found tedious.'

Krom covered an involuntary snicker by clucking in mock disapproval. 'With Mr Firman working so ingeniously to avoid keeping our agreement, we should be applauding him rather than poking fun. You must be good, my children, *please!*'

Yves stirred and I guessed that he was about to say something obscene enough to disgust even the 'children'. He had my sympathy, but I didn't need his support and snapped my fingers to let him know it. At the same moment, I stood up as if about to leave and then stopped where Krom would be forced to lean back awkwardly if he wanted to see my face.

'I spoke, when I asked you to listen to that tape, of re-negotiating our agreement,' I said. 'Clearly, I was being over tactful. Perhaps it will help you to contain your amusement, Professor, if I tell you that we no longer *have* an agreement. The one made in Brussels is now completely null and void. What we can still discuss, if you wish, is what remains of your ability to blackmail me, and what is left of my ability to give you protection.'

'Protection from what?'

'The consequences of threatening Mathew Williamson. He's not as tolerant of common blackmailers as I am.'

'I've heard of your Mr Williamson, as I've already told you, but I'm not acquainted with him. Nor am I, as you perfectly well know, a common blackmailer.'

'Exactly what you are, Professor, and where, as a result, you now stand are matters that must be re-examined. Do you want to send your witnesses out, or don't you mind if they hear us talking about the messier details of our bargain?'

He showed a few more teeth. 'You're wasting your breath, Mr Firman. I refuse to be provoked. My young friends have experience of the problems of doing research in this field. Why shouldn't they hear the details?'

'Very well. The basic threat you made was that, unless I did and said the various things you wanted me to do and say, you would expose, I quote, the Symposia Conspiracy. That's what you called it. Right?'

'That's what I still call it.'

'Then you must still be, Professor, as big an intellectual and academic phony as you were when you dreamed up the phrase.'

I didn't wait for a reaction, but turned and went through into the drawing-room. It was well-bugged in there – and when an adversary is under pressure it's always better to have a tape, even when there seems to be no way of its ever being used. Besides, it was necessary to have him off balance. That's why I'd walked away after insulting him. A double goosing like that is really painful.

He certainly found it so. He came running. The others followed but he didn't wait for them before counter-attacking. He was too angry to wait.

'You won't get rid of your corruption by trying to hang it on me,' he snapped. 'Ask any policeman! Defence by projection is common among criminals.'

'It's common among all sections of the populace, Professor, including criminologists. I accused you of being a phony. With or without your permission, I intend to explain to your witnesses why I did so.'

I paused to dismiss his unspoken protest before going on. 'Symposia is an organization concerned with tax avoidance by strictly legal means. By coupling its name with the word 'conspiracy', an imprecise but emotive term loaded with associations of illegality, you created an essentially meaningless but potentially lethal smear. You've wasted your talents, Professor. You should have been a politician.'

His martyred God-give-me-patience look brought in Henson for the defence. 'If it was meaningless, why should it have upset you so much?'

I gave her my best smile. 'How did your Professor Langridge put it? "More to do with journalism than with scholarship," was it? Something like that, I think. What would he have said, I wonder, if he'd actually heard his colleague, Krom, threatening to leak the whole smear package to the financial journals and news magazines if I didn't collaborate?' "Collaborate" was the chosen euphemism. Moral blackmail and extortion were the realities.' I faced Krom again. 'Last night you allowed that you were an extortionist. Of course, as you have explained today, you were tired last night. But tired of *what? Only* of travelling, or of hypocrisy too?'

Connell rallied to the cause. 'You still haven't answered the question, Firman. If the charge was baseless, why are we here? Why didn't you tell him to drop dead?'

'I can't believe, Doctor, that you are simple enough to suppose that a smear can always be defeated by ignoring it. Only the invulnerable few, or those past caring what happens to their reputations, can afford to adopt that attitude. I would also remind you that institutions handling, or advising on the handling of, other people's money are among the most vulnerable to this kind of false charge, however baseless it may be.'

'But in your case the charge wasn't false or baseless,' Henson again, with Krom nodding his blessing. 'Your first paper admits as much, not just frankly, but brazenly. Oh yes, you're careful to point out that Oberholzer belonged to your pre-Symposia days, but surely that's mere nit-picking.'

I was finding it difficult to remain cool and had to make a conscious effort. 'Let's be clear about this. What I have admitted is that I once committed offences against the Swiss bank secrecy laws by obtaining confidential information from a bank employee. That offence is, as you well know, one that has been committed time and time again over the years by agents and officials acting for non-Swiss governments. Among them have been the governments of most of the developed nations and a good many from the Third World as well. Within the international communities of income-tax gatherers, fraud-squad investigators and exchange-control enforcers outside Switzerland, the offence is regarded about as seriously as a parking violation. You seem also to need reminding that I have never been arrested in Switzerland or anywhere else, nor even detained for questioning, much less convicted in a court of law.'

Connell went into a world-weary, cut-the-cackle routine. 'Please, Mr Firman. We've seen the bleeding. Now, how about showing us the wound? All you've been given, you say, is a parking ticket. And yet, for the honour of dear old Symposia, you act as if you'd been busted for murder-one. Come *on!* The Symposia Conspiracy isn't about parking violations. It's about an extortion racket that relies for the fingering of likely victims on an intelligence set-up pretending to be a tax-haven consultancy service, and, for the raking in of its blood money, on a network of illegal debt-collection agencies making undercover use of international communications systems. That's what Professor Krom was proposing to shed light on, and that's what he still intends to shed light on. All he did to you was to offer the sort of deal that the law offers crooks all the time and all over the world. 'Turn informer and we won't press charges. Tough it out, or try to, and we'll throw the book at you.' You started by going along with the deal and now you're trying to renege. No need to apologize. We understand how it is. But don't bore us with crap about parking tickets. Okay?'

With almost no effort I was able to laugh. 'When you wrote your book about organized crime, Dr Connell, that was the sort of talk you put in the mouths of the stupider

DAs and the more reactionary policemen. You disappoint me.'

'A nice try, Mr Firman,' said Henson; 'but we already knew that you could read.'

In spite of her confident tone, she was by then having several second thoughts and Krom had spotted the fact.

'He's only digging his own grave, my dear. Don't let us do the job for him.' He tried to sound as if he were at ease, but he was showing scarcely any teeth and his eyes had the wary look I had first seen in Brussels when he had been afraid of me. Now, he was afraid of me again; not afraid this time though, of what I might be going to do, but of what he had sensed that I might be going to say.

He had had two months in which to forget the euphoria of his Brussels victory over me and to start wondering why that success had been so easy.

I found it meanly satisfying now to ignore him and give his witnesses the answers he so anxiously awaited. Besides, they were pleasanter to look at.

I said: 'You asked me why, if this threatened smear were baseless, I didn't tell Krom, the author of it, to publish and be damned. I've given you one answer. All smears that start no-smoke-without-fire talk can be expensive in one way or another. You pay off for the same reason that big corporations often settle nuisance actions against them out of court. It may be cheaper in the long run to pay rather than to argue rights and wrongs. I have given you a second answer. If pushed, we could have called the Professor's bluff and then warned the publisher he went to that this was a source that couldn't be protected by the anonymity custom because this source had already tried to sell us the story. That way, ordinarily, we would have been on fairly safe ground. We didn't adopt that solution because to have done so would have been to take an unacceptable risk.'

'Aha!' said Krom.

I didn't bother to tell him that his relief was premature,

225

but went on addressing the witnesses. 'In amongst all the hearsay, gossip, innuendo and straight falsehood that had been assembled to support the conspiracy nonsense, there were one or two sets of facts. Most were unimportant or irrelevant. One wasn't. I refer to the Placid Island material.'

'What's so remarkable about that?' demanded Connell. 'Placid's typical. It's been stripped of most of its natural assets. The only future it has is as a tax-haven outpost with a few high-rise office buildings. Its one extra asset seems to be this Williamson you mentioned – a banker, and an economist too, with a good academic background, who also happens to be a native of the wretched place. Professor Krom noted that Symposia had made overtures to Placid and was trying to establish a monopoly position there. Was *that* what you didn't like?'

'That's what Mat Williamson didn't like. He didn't like it because Symposia wasn't just *trying* to establish a monopoly in advance, it already *had* it established. The Symposia Group is eighty per cent owned by Mat Williamson and always has been.'

'But I didn't *know* that!' Krom yelped. It wasn't that he was dim-witted, just that a bit of his mind was still refusing to listen to the disaster warning that had begun to paralyse the higher centres.

'Of course you didn't know,' I said. 'Practically nobody knew, or knows *now*. The Canadian bank for whom Mat acts as a consultant in such matters certainly doesn't know. Neither do the officials with whom Placid Island independence is being negotiated. Others in ignorance include Chief Tebuke and the lawyers for the phosphate company which is being squeezed by Mat for compensation. Dr Connell asked why we are here. Well, I'll tell you why I *thought* we were here, if that's still of interest to anyone but the birds. We were here, Professor, so that *you* wouldn't rock the boat, of which I'll admit to owning twenty per cent, by revealing the Williamson-Symposia relationship.'

'How could I have revealed it? As you have said, I didn't know about it.'

No doubt he was still in shock, but it was hard to remain civil. 'I can't believe, Professor, that you are as unworldly as all that. You must suffer from the delusion that only scholars are capable of doing research. You think that the corporate entities which make up the Symposia Group are an open book to you because you've looked at all the available records. They show me as a stockholder and also as a nominee for other voting stockholders. That's as far as you've gone because, thanks to the fact that you once saw me years ago in Zurich, you made an assumption about me that you weren't prepared to modify or even reconsider. From Mat's point of view, that was fine – while it lasted. But would it always last? The first thing any newspaperman worth his salt would do would be to question all your assumptions however pretty they looked. And, having questioned, he'd find ways of getting answers that satisfied *his* professional standards. They wouldn't be your ways, because he'd have to work a lot faster than you people. He'd dig patiently, yes, but he'd use those techniques that governments call espionage or intelligence-gathering, depending on whose side is doing what, and newspaper proprietors call investigative reporting. It doesn't matter what *we* call it. The point is that, if you'd been allowed to hand your Symposia rag-bag to the financial editor of a news magazine, the information connecting Mat Williamson with Symposia would have been found within days and the result wouldn't have been called a conspiracy. It would have been called a 'caper', or worse. It would have been the Placid Island Rip-Off. *Now* do you understand?'

Silence. Krom looked like death.

'Well,' said Connell eventually, 'none of that's happened and no one's yet rocked the boat. So what's changed since you and the Professor made your deal? Our appraisal of the situation was faulty from the start, according to you. All right. So what?'

'Unfortunately, *my* appraisal of the situation has *become* faulty. That's what's changed. In London, the risk represented by the Professor's decision to use blackmail in his quest for information seems, after all, to have been judged uninsurable. That phone call was to tell us so, tell all of us.'

'I see. The best way of making sure that no one rocks a boat is to have no people in it. Then your revised appraisal is, I take it, that those friends of yours outside this place now intend to kill us all. Correct? Or is this to be a selective massacre? Just you? Just us? Some of each? What's the new ouija board starting to say?'

Melanie said brightly: 'It's nearly time for lunch.'

The cook's husband was at the door asking if he should bring the ice for the drinks in there or whether we would be moving out to the swimming-pool area.

I said that we would have the drinks inside. By the time we moved out to lunch by the swimming pool, a lot more had been said and the guests were thoughtful. Connell hadn't pressed me for an answer to his questions. He had probably decided that I had no answers.

CHAPTER NINE

For a few minutes they seemed to have stopped wondering how much truth there was in me, and to be asking themselves a question that their books had always said was irrelevant. Was there or wasn't there honour among thieves?

Could criminal relationships be like those to be found in trade and industry? Were comparisons drawn from what was known of marriages or ménages appropriate? Or was the 'standard' criminal relationship one of convenience and collusion only, like a contract between politicians cancellable without warning by either party the moment it became in any way embarrassing?

No one was very hungry. Henson soon gave up on the loup. I had already done so. It is an overrated fish.

'From what you now tell us, Mr Firman,' she said, 'one would almost believe that, once upon a time, you and Mr Williamson were really quite good friends.'

'We have had a long and profitable business association. Obviously, our relationship had a friendly element to it.'

'Friendly enough for you to compromise your own cover to protect his against the Professor's enquiries. That was *very* friendly, surely?'

'Back in May, it seemed to be in both our interests that I should cover for him. Remember, I have twenty per cent. Maybe that clouded my judgement.'

'Yet now, you don't seem to be very much surprised or upset by the fact that he's betraying you, *and* telling you so, moreover. He *is* betraying you, I suppose. That tape we heard wasn't by any chance a fake?'

Two stiff gins-and-tonic had almost restored Krom's self esteem. 'You're learning, my dear. I've been wondering the same thing.' He cocked an eye at me. '*Is* it a fake?'

'I wish it were.'

Connell's hostility towards me had returned to normal. 'You don't think much of *our* right to the truth,' he said. 'How do you feel about associates like Mr Williamson? I mean, after that call we heard, what's the word now about the usefulness of truth?'

'Carlo Lech and I always told one another the truth. To do so was part of our mutual respect. With Mat Williamson, mutual respect is based on insights of a different order. When a question is asked there, you consider, first, not what the exactly truthful answer would be, but what the questioner wishes to hear from you. No, I'm not surprised by his betraying me, nor by his telling me, in that oblique way, that he's doing so. When you deal with Mat, there's always a chance that he may *try* to deceive or betray you. What you *should* do is make sure that he can't. I thought I *had* made sure. Upset? More annoyed, I think. Mat's a complex creature, difficult to explain.'

He and I had been in Singapore when I had heard of Carlo's death.

My reports on the Pacific tax-havens, existing and potential, had been written. I was waiting for Carlo's acknowledgment of the last one, and with it, the words pronouncing my absolution and telling me that my exile was at an end.

He died of heart failure following a virus infection, according to the Vaduz lawyer who acted for our various corporate set-ups there. The man's vagueness was understandable. There was legislation against Liechtenstein Anstalts pending in Italy as well as moves afoot to clamp down on citizens holding large amounts of their capital abroad. It would have been indiscreet of him even to have visited Carlo's Milan office, and highly dangerous to have communicated with the family. There would have been no business reason for him to do so anyway. Carlo's stashed-away fortune was, and still is, in trusts administered jointly by the Vaduz man, with his partners as successors, and me. Carlo's invalid wife, his son and his daughter all benefited, in accordance with Italian inheritance laws, under the formal will he had made there. The trusts benefit only the daughter, her musician husband and, above all, Carlo's grandson Mario. When he comes of age, that boy will be very rich.

However, according to the first letter from Vaduz, Carlo had, in addition, bequeathed me a piece of valuable real-estate.

This news had surprised me. My own holdings in our joint enterprises were already worth several million and I had discussed the whole subject with Carlo long before. We both had plenty of money, earned by our joint efforts but apportioned in accordance with an agreement made when Carlo had been convalescing after his gall-bladder trouble. Aside from the agreement, neither of us owned the other anything except good faith and a single duty. When one of us died, the other would see, as best he could, that the dead man's family and other private obligations were taken care of in a proper fashion. For the sake of official appearances, the survivor would receive the fees and expenses normally payable to a trustee.

A second letter from Vaduz told me that the piece of valuable real-estate aforementioned was Carlo's island.

Surprise had then become confusion. In spite of my occasional white lies on the subject, Carlo had always known that the island bored me. That was why he had sent me to stew there after the Zurich fiasco. Bequeathing the place to me could have been the kind of stupid gesture that wealthy dotards have sometimes made in order to get the last word in some old and silly argument; but Carlo had not been stupid, far from it, nor had he been the kind of man who would give away a tropical island he had loved to a tropic-hater who would at once proceed to sell it.

The third letter explained all. Carlo's island was the property of a Netherland Antilles real-estate company, the shares in which would go to Mario when he was twenty-one. Meanwhile, I was asked to hold them in trust for him. To compensate me for the time and trouble of maintaining the place, as it had been maintained during Carlo's lifetime – and as I had known it, complete with staff – I would, until Mario was old enough to take possession, have free and unfettered use of the island and its installations at all times, for my own personal enjoyment. Our man in Vaduz suggested thoughtfully that it might be a good idea if, on my way back to Europe, I called in at the island and took stock of the current situation there.

Carlo, an innovator to the last, had found a way of getting the last word in an old argument, and of making a ribald gesture from the grave, at the expense of no one but a cornered trustee. Vaduz would have thought it foolish of me as well as petty if I had refused the task. *Everyone* loved islands in the Caribbean, surely. They must do. Otherwise, why did all those tourists go there?

The only person near to me then who would have enjoyed the joke was Mat. Jokes about people stepping on metaphorical banana skins always made him laugh. Luckily, I never told him that one.

It was the order in which things were happening then, not caution, that stopped me. Mat had already known of Carlo and of my connection with him – I was never able to discover how he had known – before we had met in the New Hebrides. The only consolation for me had been that he had told me about the Lech-Oberholzer operation while still believing me to be a louche character named Perrivale (Perry) Smythson whose brains he was trying to pick about certain loopholes said to exist in the Anglo-French Condominium Law. I had begun by taking him for a local boy who had made good. When the matter of our identities had been straightened out, and sufficient time had been given to mutual inspection, exploratory talks about the possibility of joint ventures had taken us a little farther. I would report our talks to Carlo and get his reactions. A further meeting place convenient for both of us was chosen

– Singapore. Of course, I never heard from Carlo on the subject; the virus must already have been at work; but his unexpected going stirred everything up and made it all move faster. I mourned Carlo and needed distractions. When next I met Mat our Symposia project had become a discussable deal. There had been neither time nor inclination then for banana-skin jokes.

In those early days of our relationship Mat treated me with the deference due to an elder statesman. Some of this, of course, was part of the process of buttering me up and at the same time making me feel old, but not all. I had knowledge that he might find useful. He would listen with more than token attention to what I had to say, even if it involved criticisms of his judgement. For instance, I hadn't approved of the pattern of business deals he'd been weaving around the Pacific, and I told him so.

He went into a long spiel about the vacuums created by the abdication of old imperialisms. There was an urgent need of entrepreneurial skills to stimulate constructive business activity at provincial levels, to bring out the money hidden in mattresses so that it could work for all and to engage the non-Chinese in major enterprises.

'They're either just coming down from the trees,' he concluded, 'or emerging from extremely ancient feudalisms. *Someone's* got to get things moving for them.'

'That's what the invest-in-the-future type con-men usually say when they're finally caught.'

His ability to look mystified while deciding his next move used to impress me very much in those days. 'What have con-men to do with me, Paul?'

'Con-men like that are *also* very difficult to prosecute.'

'Also?'

'Those entrepreneurial skills of yours, Mat, are being used in a way that is well understood by any police-man. By the British, the offence of exploiting credit facilities on the here-today-gone-tomorrow principle is called "long-term fraud". In Germany it's "Stossbetrug", in

France "carambouillage", and in America most bunco-squads call it "scam", I believe. Authorities everywhere have difficulty in getting convictions mainly because they're always short of the kind of auditors who know *what* to look for, *where* to look for it, *and* above all, can work fast enough to grab the paper-work before it disappears. You, Mat, have something extra going for you because, as well as moving from corporate set-up to corporate set-up in an ingenious way, you're also moving backwards and forwards between national jurisdictions. You're almost impossible to catch, except in one area.'

The broad smile. 'I know nothing of sharp practices, Paul. Please enlighten me.'

'Two policemen of different nationalities could one day get together, maybe through reading an Interpol bulletin, and regret that there is nothing they can do jointly to bust you. *But* one or other of them, or both, depending on the countries concerned, might decide to clobber you with a breach of some exchange control regulation. It would still be slow going for them, and they might never get a conviction on the fraud charge, but there's one thing a lot of these law maniacs can always get done quickly. They can have bank accounts frozen pending enquiries. For the victim, I'm told, it can be a nasty, lingering disease that prevents his enjoying life to the full.'

He tapped my arm gently. 'You're absolutely right, Paul. That's been my own view for a long time and I'm delighted to hear that you share it.' He made it sound as if he'd been testing me; and, for all I knew, he *had* been. 'In fact,' he went on, 'I took my name out of it months ago, and not just because I didn't like what some of those rascals I'd trusted were getting up to. It was the local Chinese who decided me in the end. That's one of the clubs that won't be licked and can't be joined. They're natural business leaders, the overseas Chinese. Some people compare them with the Jews – diaspora, ghetto life, preservation of cultural identity despite assimilation, that sort of stuff. I say that's superficial. I say that they're the one multi-national corporation that'll never be busted under any anti-trust law anywhere. Why? Complete local autonomy for every single unit of accounting is there for all to see, that's why. So where's the corporation? It's programmed into their genes. Tell you something else about the Chinese . . . '

He paused. He'd been talking more or less freely to a listener he'd considered as safe. Now, though, there was something that he considered important to be said; so he was reviewing it again before letting me hear it.

'Paul, the Chinese can't be frightened in the same way as the rest.'

By the 'rest', I later found, he meant the rest of mankind.

The nature of his peculiar ideas, about intimidation and the techniques of frightening people into absolute obedience emerged from what he then told me about something that had happened to him in Java. He had, of course, been making his first million at the time, so his recollection of the incident was pleasantly light-hearted.

'Just getting about the place was terribly difficult,' he said. 'There were bandits calling themselves religious patriots raiding the villages, and bits of the civil war still going on everywhere outside the large towns. It wasn't safe to travel by road, even from Djakarta to Bandung, without a military escort, and not all that safe with one. So, all the sizeable towns were jammed with people. A top priority got you a bed, but not much else. A room to yourself? Rare, very rare. The Russians were among the greatest friends of the revolution, but the Soviet Embassy had to function for months from a bungalow in the western areas, though in East Java, and especially in places like Surabaja, Jogjakarta and Semarang, it stayed difficult. That was because the hard-cores on both sides were still using the interior as a battle-field. God, how I hate hard-cores! Give me the pragmatists every time.'

'I hadn't realized, Mat, that you'd ever found it necessary to give that choice any thought.'

'You've never worked for a revolutionary government, that's for sure. Well, I had a top priority then, *and* let me tell you, whenever I had to take trips East I used that priority as if I were Genghis Khan. I'd found that the best way of getting through your business is comfort in those parts was to commandeer a foreign consulate. There were several available. No foreign consuls in them just then, of course, on account of the troubles, but the compounds and houses were still there, and in most cases the old native servants had stayed on. In theory they were there protecting property belonging to friendly foreign governments entitled to diplomatic status and immunities.'

'How did you get around that?'

He gave me a boyish smile. 'Servants protecting foreign property on behalf of the central government were responsible to the central government. When one of that government's officials decided to inspect the property to see if the protectors were doing their duty, they'd better co-operate. Otherwise, they'd find themselves out on their ears or, more likely, in jail.'

'So they co-operated.'

'Yes. But they also resented and hated and wondered how to handle the interloper, this man who was suddenly giving them orders, making them work instead of resting up, sitting at the consul's dinner table, sleeping in their consul's bedroom. What would you have done in their place, Paul?'

'Pretended you were the consul and tried to kill you with kindness, I expect.'

'They could do that and they often did. But sometimes the effort seemed to cost them too much and then they'd try to redress the balance in their favour. That happened once when I was staying in a French consulate. I'd been to dinner with the official in charge of the port installations because I'd had business to do with him. He lived in a compound two minutes away, so, after an early dinner and a brief chat, I walked back to the consul's house. You know how those places are arranged? Square lot of half a hectare maybe, high wall all around with barbed-wire on top as optional extra, house in the centre, separate servants' quarters in back of compound, gap in the wall for gate, driveway from gate to house?'

'I know.'

'Well, when I got to the gate I found it unlocked. In that place and at that time, that alone would have given me pause. I also heard and saw movements inside. There was a moon, so I waited by the gate till my eyes had adjusted to the light and I could see what was going on. Have you met many French consuls, Paul?'

'Not many, no.'

'Those I've met haven't, on the whole, been great hobbyists. There was one who was a bit of an ornithologist and made a hobby of his bird-photography, but I haven't come across any who cultivated their gardens much, except career-wise and metaphorically. I think this particular consul may have had an English wife.'

'You'll have to tell me what you're talking about, Mat. I won't try to guess.'

'That place had a rose garden in front of the house!'

'Not a flower I care for much.'

'But an English rose garden in Java, Paul. It was crazy. They were a crummy lot as you'd expect. Still, there they were, planted right after the Japs had pulled out in 'forty-five, no doubt, and tended with care by Madame Consul until the new war came and the servants had had to take over. Now what I saw, as I stood in the darkness by the gate, was a couple of those servants, the two men, digging up the rose garden and burying something in it. Paul, what would you have thought they were burying at dead of night, eh?'

'With you, a self-proclaimed government snooper, on the property? Small-arms I would say, or possibly the last of the old consular hoard of vacuum-packed Gauloises Bleues.'

'Or ammunition, or stolen car-parts? Sure. As I stood

there just outside the gate, watching and waiting for them to finish the job, I went through all those possibilities and more. I also realized that this had to be a one-off, amateur-night deal or they'd have had a boy out on watch in case I came back early. When at last they did finish and the rose bushes were all replanted, I had to move away a bit because then they remembered that they'd left the gate open and came over to lock up. I heard them giggling over something, but couldn't hear what. Then they went off to their own quarters. As soon as they were out of the way, I let myself in and went to the house.'

'Not stopping to look at the roses by moonlight?'

'I wasn't interested in the bloody roses, and neither would you have been. The trouble was that they'd taken the shovels they'd been using away with them. There was no electricity on at that time of night, so, with just my flashlight, all I could find in the house to use as a digging tool was a silver card-tray kept by the front door. In darkest Java with tray and flashlight! Are you with me?'

'Out there in the rose garden digging up the consul's cash-float box? Could be. I hope the silver tray stood up to it.'

'That tray wasn't solid silver,' he said quickly; 'it was plate.' I hadn't known it then, but Mat's scout training instilled in him a respect for the property of others, apart from their money I mean, that has never left him. 'Besides,' he went on, 'the soil was all loose where they'd been digging. I washed the tray carefully afterwards. There wasn't a scratch on it.'

'How about the consul's cash box?'

He took a deep breath in order to regain lost calm before he answered.

'What they'd buried there, Paul,' he said solemnly, 'was the entrails of a pig.'

Now I may not have known much, at that early stage, about his concern for the preservation of borrowed objects, or about any other by-products of his unusual education, but I *had* already learned that, if you let him adopt his preternaturally solemn tone with you without instantly taking counter-measures, he could become insufferably condescending. He had expected to surprise me, so I was very careful to look unsurprised.

'How did you know they were a *pig's* entrails?' I demanded suspiciously. 'They could have been a sheep's or a cow's.'

'In Java?'

'All right, an ox's entrails maybe.'

'They were a pig's entrails. I know about such things, Paul. Take my word for it.'

'Okay, I take your word. So what? Dried blood and bone meal are supposed to be good fertilizers. Why not pigs' entrails? You said that the roses looked crummy. The poor men were simply anticipating your criticisms by feeding the things while they thought you were safely out of the way.'

'And giggling while they did so?'

'A cultural curiosity. Golden Bough stuff. The peasants of Java consider entrails highly amusing.'

I had been baiting him of course. He had now realized that, and didn't like it. He gave me a long, bleak look before he spoke again.

'They were there,' he said slowly, 'to cast a spell, to render me helpless in their filthy hands.'

'Oh.'

Once he had started on spells, there was no point in trying to comment, or interrupt. He knew what he was talking about and he liked playing teacher. If he sounded on those occasions as if he were explaining the facts of life for the last time to a strangely backward adolescent, that was probably another hangover from his Fijian scouting days.

'Those servants knew that the rose garden was of the greatest importance to the owner. That I wasn't the real owner made no difference. As the person in command of the place, even temporarily, I had taken on the attributes of the owner, his strengths and, above all, his weaknesses.

I was dangerous to them because I could put in spiteful reports about the number of illegals they kept hidden in that compound paying squeeze for a patch of roof and a place of refuge from authority. I was a nuisance to them because I made work for them to which they had become unaccustomed. I messed things up, I wanted food, my bed made, my clothes dhobied. They wanted me out of there but couldn't tell me to go. So what was there for them to do? Only one thing. Reduce my capacity for mischief to a minimum. How? Let the spirits of the dead render me impotent. By what means? Let them emasculate me through my rose garden. Let the embodiment of the most aggrieved and jealous spirits be placed in that earth where I was vulnerable. Got it?'

'Mm.'

'So what do you do when hostile spirits have been put in to subvert and suborn you? You turn them around, make double agents of them, that's what you do. Hah! Those offal buriers didn't know the man they'd challenged. They soon learned. Next morning at breakfast, just to start with. The head man can't wait to run tests, of course, to see if the spell had started to work. So, he changes what they serve me for breakfast. I'd ordered papaya. He brings me bananas. Moment of truth! If I don't notice because I don't remember what I ordered, or if, having noticed and complained, I still accept the substitution, then the spell's beginning to work. I'm spooked and they're getting the upper hand. If, though, I do notice and do complain and tell him to take the goddam bananas away and bring me papaya, then maybe they'll have to wait. Until the next meal, that is, to test again with my food or to see what happens when they starch a shirt so hard that I can't do up the buttons. Maybe the day is adverse. Maybe these entrails need to get a bit riper before the spirits feel comfortable in them. Got to give it time, eh?'

'I suppose so.'

'No time, nothing! You throw a scare into the head man

240

right then and there. You don't accept the bananas. Instead, you ask him what you ordered. You ask him slowly, and as you speak you rap the table in time with the words. He will be a little afraid and say that, although you ordered papaya, the fruit available were not good. Then you address him in the manner of a death spell – a spirit-of-eating-alive type intonation maybe – and tell him that it was mango you ordered, not papaya. Now he's in bad trouble. He doesn't know what to think except that the spirits are not on his side. And that's just the beginning. After that, you see that nothing he does is right. You order meat for dinner and he tries bringing you fish. You give him hell, but tell him you distinctly ordered vegetables. What's he trying to do, poison you? You order meat again. Worried, he tries to back off by bringing you meat. You give him hell again, and this time you threaten to put the lot of them in jail for stealing meat when the country is starving. Now they're really on the skids, I mean panic-scared and shaking. The spirits in the entrails have turned against them. Only one thing left for them to do, isn't there?'

'Dig up the entrails and get rid of them, I suppose.'

'Oh, yes, they'll have to put back the clock, but appeasing the spirits won't be so easy. They'll have to work at it. Work hard. Do as they're told without trying to outsmart you. Be good citizens. Do what comes naturally.'

'What's that?'

'For them? Being obedient.'

I smiled.

He remembered at once that the good Scout is at all times chivalrous, a parfit knight who never kicks a defeated enemy when the slob's down. 'Of course,' he added, 'as soon as they'd decided to behave themselves I was as nice as pie. That's the way spells work, like a storm. One moment it's all thunder and lightning and cleansing fear. Then, when the gods and the sorcerer are appeased, out comes the sun again.'

That was only one of his analogies on the subject of spells

and sorcery. Many of them I came to know quite well. For me, though, the thing he was describing – often quite poetically – was merely a primitive, and only slightly more deadly version of what western man nowadays calls gamesmanship. A death-spell can kill in two ways; by frightening the victim to death or, since few men are totally susceptible to fear, by frightening him into doing something foolish – like taking too many sleeping pills or stepping in front of a bus.

It was Mat's belief that Lord Baden-Powell was a natural sorcerer of great potency, and that, but for the accident of his having been born an Englishman, his world leadership would have extended far beyond the confines of the Boy Scout movement. He would have had the will to use his superb skills and cunning politically.

Mat had made a close study of the Chief Scout's defence of Mafeking during the Boer War. The famous siege, which began in October 1899 and lasted for over eight months, was, according to B-P who commanded the town's defenders, a 'minor operation' and his successful defence against overwhelming odds, 'largely a piece of bluff'.

Mat says that he put a spell on the enemy. An official historian said that he made imaginative tactical use of the modest resources at his disposal. Either or both could be right. By constantly moving his one acetylene searchlight around, B-P made the enemy believe that no night attack could possibly succeed. He disturbed their sleep by using a megaphone to give orders to imaginary trench-raiding parties. He harassed them with snipers who only fired during the late afternoon when the sun was behind them and in the enemy's eyes. His men lobbed bombs at the enemy with fishing rods as if they were casting from a beach for flounders. When he had pushed his line of forts and his trench system far enough out from the town, he even began sniping with field-guns. And all the time he kept up a cheerful correspondence with the enemy who was trying to starve him out or wear him down – the Scout smiles and whistles under all difficulties. In a presumptuous attempt to cast spells – or wage psychological warfare? – in the B-P manner, the Boer Commandant at one point proposed a cricket match between the two sides. B-P's reply could not have been bettered, in Mat's opinion. 'You must bowl us out first before your side can come in.'

With Mat, I have never really been sure where cleverness stops and low cunning begins. Inside that second-rate mind, there could be a third-rate one struggling to get out.

Among things said by Mat that I repeated to Krom and the witnesses was this:

'A man once called me a shark. You know what imbeciles some so-called businessmen are. *He* loses money, so he calls *me* a shark. He thought he was being offensive. I took it as a compliment. Know something? In the islands, my mother's people worship sharks. That's because sharks are the greatest of all the spirits of the dead. Super-saints, you might say, god-like beings. So, when he called me a shark I only laughed. What's wrong with being told you're a god? As a matter of fact, I rather enjoyed it.'

'That was *very* nice,' said Dr Henson.

She and Connell were in her room. After an interval the bed creaked again.

I was alone with the bugging gear in the loft over the garage. Yves had been sent, at his own request, on a tour of the perimeter fences. Melanie was on watch at the attic windows. Krom was in his room studying File No 2, *and* licking his wounds no doubt. He would also be casting about feverishly for some ways of retrieving his position. He couldn't wholly succeed now, but he still had a negotiating position of sorts; and, in spite of the wounds I had inflicted on him, he would make the most of it. More hard bargaining lay ahead.

That is, it lay ahead as long as the two parties at present under attack remained in reasonably good condition.

Connell and Henson had begun to talk again.

'It's the old man's fault,' he was saying; 'if he'd levelled with us in Amsterdam and we'd talked it through with him, even a little, we'd at least have had *some* chance. We wouldn't have had to stand there like dummies while Firman threw curve balls that the old man couldn't even *see*.'

'One sympathizes though.'

'Oh, sure. That Oberholzer identification was his big breakthrough, so everything that came after had to flow from it, whether it should really have done so or not. He was wearing blinkers and we weren't allowed to comment or even notice.'

'Hindsight, friend.'

'Admitted. Even so . . . '

'Even so, what could we have changed? We might have had private doubts, but can you see either of us trying to tell the old man that he'd got the wrong end of the stick? Another thing, Firman's right. If *we'd* been doing the research, we'd have taken months to track down Symposia's tie-up with this Australasian witch-doctor Boy Scout. You know we would. By the way, I think my right leg's going to sleep. Do you mind easing over just a fraction of a . . . ?'

'Sorry.'

'No, that's fine. Don't go away. Were you ever a Scout?'

'Never. Nobody ever asked me to join. Don't tell me you were a Girl Guide.'

'I was wondering about the total ethos of a movement that could accommodate Mr Williamson and his peculiarities with such ease. My brother joined the Scouts when he was a boy, but he's eight years older than me so we didn't discuss the experience while it was happening. All I heard was grown-ups discussing it. He dropped out. I'm not sure why. I do remember one thing he quoted from the Baden-Powell book on scouting. It was the twelfth edition my brother had, an enlarged and revised one. I know that because when he quoted from it, my father pricked up his ears. Thought it might be the Edwardian first edition and therefore valuable.'

'Because the thing quoted was an Edwardian value judgement?'

'Not exactly. The book said that a tenderfoot was sometimes timid about handling dead or injured men or seeing blood.'

'Here's one tenderfoot who still is.'

'Well, Baden-Powell said that if you were to visit a slaughter house you'd soon get used to it. It didn't say how often you had to go. Until you *were* used to it, I suppose.'

'Used to seeing dead men in a slaughter-house?'

'Used to the sight of blood. That's a problem Mr Williamson's never experienced, I imagine. Did you like the shark worship thing? We have an anthropologist who did her doctoral thesis on one of those island groups. I've never completely trusted her or her Pacific-island colleagues. I mean the khaki-shorts-and-beard brigade. You know? Out there, with all those animistic tribes for them to batten on, they can't go wrong. You fancy a sub-culture that's taken to keeping the souls of the departed in used Coca-Cola bottle-caps? All you have to do is seek, find, and then get lots of sixteen-millimetre colour footage before anyone else can. Your reputation's made. If shark-worship hadn't existed Mr Williamson would have had no trouble at all in inventing it.'

'The way I heard it, Williamson has no trouble at all doing anything, ever. That bit about his enjoying being told he's a god had a certain ring. And there were other bits I thought un-Firmanlike too. Our host may be a son-of-a-bitch, but he wouldn't get his kicks out of brain-washing domestic help who couldn't talk back, and I doubt if he'd be capable of dreaming up the entrails story. Hell, I'm beginning to buy his Number-Two pitch.'

'I bought that after hearing Yamatoku. Those whom the gods wish to destroy they first call up with advance warning of the holocaust.'

'It isn't only the gods who like to do things in that order.'

245

'Sorry, my fault. I wasn't thinking just about sour marriages though.'

There was a pause. I waited patiently while they made themselves more comfortable. Then she went on.

'Mafeking was what made me think. Or, rather, the mirror image of it that was held up so thoughtfully to demonstrate the nature of our predicament. It's got everything, *nearly* everything anyway, that we've got here, hasn't it?'

'*Almost* nearly everything, yes.'

'A garrison besieged, but somewhat short of field-guns to snipe with? That sort of almost-nearly do you mean?'

'I was thinking more along the lines that, in this mirror version of the siege, the good old Chief Scout's on the outside doing his whistling and weaving of spells, instead of standing firm on the inside, and either socking it to the enemy with bombs on fishing lines or writing sardonic notes about cricket.'

'There's that, I agree.' But she sounded doubtful. She was nearly there. 'What bothers me isn't in the mirror.'

'Nothing to do with Mafeking?'

'Oh, very much to do with Mafeking. The reason why the siege of Mafeking is remembered and why it added to the language a new word for crowd euphoria, you'll recall, isn't that it made Baden-Powell a popular hero, but that its long-awaited relief caused such wild rejoicing. The *relief* of Mafeking, *that's* what's remembered, not the siege. So, what bothers me is not that Baden-Powell is shown on the wrong side, but that there's no relief column on the way.'

'I see what you mean. No distant trumpeter, no cutaway of the cavalry galloping through murderous enemy fire to the rescue.'

'The police here have motor bikes. But yes, that's part of what I mean.'

'The old man's already rejected the police once. Okay, the situation seems to have changed. But what do we, or they, complain of to the local commissaire. The burns in

Mr Boularis's shoe? Mr Yamatoku's used-car-lot courtliness?'

'Don't you think, friend, that we may still be missing the point? That phone call was a threat, but only if one knew enough to understand why. When we began to see that our leader had made a number of quite bad mistakes, you asked Firman a question. What kind of danger were we in and what was the extent of it?'

'A question he didn't answer.'

'A question that he didn't answer *immediately*. Supposing he'd told us, there and then, that his boss and partner, Williamson, had decided to terminate that uninsurable risk we all represented by killing us. What would your reaction have been? The same as mine, I expect. We'd have tittered merrily then moved on to the next question. "What must we do to be saved?" '

'Still tittering merrily?'

'Merrily enough, I think, to make it certain that any answer we received would be either facetious or evasive. Boularis is no longer even nominally polite to us. Firman's still doing his best, but our academic conceits must bore him stiff.'

'I'm afraid you may be right.'

'So, I think that Firman *has* answered your question.'

'With all this stuff about spell-casting and Mafeking studies?' He was having doubts again.

'Authentic anecdote, I call it. What other currency has the wretched man left? What currency, I mean, that we'd accept from him without saying that it was unquestionably forged?'

'All right. We have our answer. "Yes, you're all for the chopping-block. Sorry." Now, how do we tackle the matter of survival? I think we'd both be grateful if his answer to that was a little less Delphian and didn't have to be interpreted. Always assuming, naturally, that there is an answer and that he has it.'

'Perhaps we should try asking him about that first. I have another suggestion.'

'Shoot.'

'That we don't ask Firman anything more in front of Professor Krom.'

A pause, then he sighed. 'Difficult.'

'Why? Krom, if he ever gets back to civilization, will undoubtedly write all this up as if everything turned out exactly as he had planned it. It'll be back to the dream world for him. We decline to comment on anything except the authenticity of those papers we've seen. End of obligation. What's difficult about that? Do you mind passing me my cigarettes?'

Two reliable allies would be sufficient for what I had in mind. I switched off and went downstairs to the garage.

When I'd found the things I'd been looking for I hid them under the stairs.

Back in the loft, I went through the carton with the tapes in it. The boxes containing the ones Yves had used were numbered. I removed the tapes, adding the one I had just recorded to the pile, but left the numbered boxes in the carton.

In my bedroom I put the tapes away in a safe place before going up to the attic.

Melanie had Yves's binoculars on her lap with her hands folded over them. She looked up as I came in but had obviously been dozing.

I told her to go to her room and have a nap and that I would keep watch for a while.

When she had gone, I used the binoculars to see where Yves had got to on his tour of the perimeter. I spotted him down near the coast-road gate, well away from the house.

I returned to the garage. The job I had to do there should have taken no more than half an hour, but it took me much longer than that. I have never been much of a handyman.

Persons like Yves who can work so quickly and surely with their hands have always made me envious.

But at least I did the job properly; did it without being disturbed or attracting attention and got back upstairs without being seen on the way.

This time, when I searched with the binoculars, I couldn't locate Yves. An hour earlier, that would have worried me.

Now, it didn't. I went down to my bedroom, cleaned myself up and then, after pushing a note under Melanie's door, descended to the drawing-room. The note told her not to bother returning to the attic as I had revised our security arrangements.

Now, there was no point in having a sentry up there.

Now, all I had to do was continue to think clearly and to give Connell and Henson, already heading towards me from the terrace, the prescription for our collective survival.

Oh yes, and I had to decide, too, how to reply to Mat.

He would call, I knew; not just to make sure that his spell was working – he would have few doubts on that score – but to make sure that I remained faithful unto death, and that, if the process of my dying should happen to take longer than planned, I wouldn't spend the extra time drawing unpleasant conclusions and making wild statements to ambulance attendants.

That was the one chore he wouldn't leave to Frank Yamatoku.

Moulding the minds and hearts of men was work for gods.

CHAPTER TEN

The fireworks began soon after dinner.

When the first rockets went up from a boat along the coast off Monte Carlo, they seemed to act on Krom as a signal.

We had eaten simply, as Melanie had arranged, so that the servants could get off early to their local Quartorze juillet fête. While they were clearing the table we had moved to the terrace, though keeping close to the house in what even a sulkily nervous Yves had had to agree was an unexposed area. A drink tray had already been set up for us. I had opened a bottle of brandy.

As the popping sounds of the distant red-white-and-blue bursts arrived, Krom leaned forward and raised his glass. For a moment I thought absurdly that he must be about to propose a Bastille Day toast, but no; he had seen an insect drown itself in his brandy.

'I am glad to tell you, Mr Firman,' he said as he fished out the corpse with the tip of a napkin, 'that I am now prepared to discuss your Paper Number Two and to receive your Paper Number Three as per our agreement.'

'What agreement is that, Professor?'

I had avoided him after my talk with Connell and Henson. They might be allies now, but only allies of a sort. I couldn't expect them, when it came to fresh haggling with Krom over the threats and promises made in Brussels, to ignore his just claims on their moral support. It had been important, therefore, that they had time to get used to the idea of helping me with what mattered without having to oppose me again over something that by then scarcely mattered at all. The solution had been to stay in my room, leaving Melanie to ply From with pre-dinner drinks. Mat wouldn't,

I knew, call unannounced. First, there would be a figurative rolling of drums or a clap or two of stage thunder calculated to strike fear into the hearts of us simple men. One could only wait for such a great moment. I had used the time to get all the tapes properly wrapped and hidden in the small bag I intended to take with me on the escape run, and to check out the local radio-taxi services. The bottle of frozen champagne brought to me by the cook's husband had thawed out sufficiently for me to be able to drink two glasses and the burgundy with dinner had been good enough. The strain had been there all right, but it had been under control. When we had moved to the terrace I had been ready to be kind to Krom.

Now, he was showing me his teeth again, and not just in normal quantities.

'I speak of our original agreement,' he said, 'and it is no use rolling your eyes, Mr Firman. I intend to enforce the original terms in all respects.'

'Using what sanctions to enforce them, Professor?'

He gave me the wide-angle view of his bridgework. 'Twenty per cent of what I could have used before, my friend. Twenty per cent of Symposia instead of one hundred per cent, *plus* the knowledge that, even if it were one per cent and we were dealing with a figurehead criminal, the Director of the Institute for International Investment and Trust Counselling still has to maintain the fiction that he is a man of probity.'

'Any attempt on your part to contend that I'm not, Professor, will land you with actions for libel, slander and defamation of character, depending on how you make your allegations and where. Meanwhile, take my advice. You're going to need all your strength before long, so don't push yourself too hard. I have more files prepared for you and you shall have them in due course. Melanie has the copies ready and waiting. At the moment, however, she's listening for the phone call I'm expecting, the one from Mat Williamson. You can hear it if you like. In fact, I think

251

you *should* hear it, all of you.' I had turned, as I spoke, to Yves. 'That could be arranged, couldn't it, with some of the equipment you have?'

Yves squirmed visibly, then tried to pull himself together. Sulkiness was succeeded by pomposity. 'With respect, Patron, I think that with such a conversation, if it takes place, it would be wiser if you used your own recorder.'

'Yves is sensitive about his special skills,' I explained. 'It was just an idea. I thought you might all like to hear it as it's happening.'

'I'm for that,' Connell said. 'More authentic, I'd say. Don't you agree, Professor?'

'If Mr Firman wishes us to hear a telephone conversation, the question of its authenticity doesn't arise. It may be presumed false.'

I shrugged. 'Well, it's up to you. I thought I'd mention it.'

That was when Yves cracked. He suddenly stood up.

'Patron, why trouble to wait? Why wait for bad news? Because it is polite to do so? I will have no part in it and I have told Melanie so. I think that she now feels the same.'

'About what, Mr Boularis?' Dr Henson was smiling up at him. 'What would *you* like us to do?'

'You?' He looked down at her as if in surprise and then made a sweeping gesture of contempt. 'You can do what you like, Mrs Doctor. You belong with your friends. You can die with your friends. Why should I . . . '

He broke off. Something beyond the terrace had caught his eye. He stared, then turned again, bewildered. He had given up trying now to retain his dignity.

I got up, too, to see what it was that he hadn't been expecting at that moment.

The big motor cruiser which, until then, had arrived only at breakfast time was gliding past the headland into the bay. She was carrying a lot of lights. Beneath the awning over the after deck, there was a dinner table set and awaiting a party of four. Around another table, with bottles and an

252

ice bucket on it, were gathered two couples. The women wore denim jackets with their slacks and one of the men had put on a sweater. It was probably cool out there on the water. There was much animation. I had no binoculars handy, but I didn't think I had seen any of them before.

'I thought there were only three passengers,' I said, 'the one man and the two women who swim from the outer beach.'

'The one in the pullover must be a guest or the other husband.' He gave a strangled sort of laugh. 'They all look drunk to me.'

And indeed they did, in a way; the falling-about, arm-waving way of film extras pretending to be drunk in the orgy sequence of a biblical silent. Sounds of the revelry came faintly across the water. Much louder was the sound of diesels suddenly going astern and the squawk of the chain as an anchor was let go.

To celebrate their arrival, the man in the sweater rose unsteadily to his feet from the cushion on which he had been sitting cross-legged and flung a hand in the air as if to call for three cheers. The next moment he had swooped on a long cardboard box lying on the deck by the table and was staggering forward with it to the bows. The crewman there securing the anchor took no notice at all when the man with the box dumped it beside him and began tearing at gummed-paper fastenings on the lid.

'What the hell's he got there?' Connell demanded. 'Bunting? Fairy lights?'

The guests were standing now too. After Yves's outburst, I suppose, any diversion had been welcome. I saw the crewman walk quickly away. Henson's eyes were the sharpest. Her exclamation was one of outrage.

'Oh no!'

Then, I saw. For a swaying-about, fumbling drunk, the man in the bows was suddenly displaying remarkable dexterity. In the space of a few seconds he had lighted from a single match no less than three strings of Chinese

253

jumping crackers and had them bursting simultaneously all over the deck around him. What's more, he wasn't even bothering to watch them. He was already rummaging in the box for fresh delights.

I could sympathize with Henson's cry of protest. I remember thinking to myself as he lighted the first string that the motor cruiser had to be a chartered one with a bad crew easily bribed. No one who owned or had any other normal concern for such a boat would have allowed a good deck to be scarred in that way. Decks are sacred, and expensive surfaces. The Italian banker had kept sets of overshoes for guests ignorant or oafish enough to come on board wearing leather soles, and smokers on deck had always been required to carry ash-trays.

'Paul!' It was Melanie.

'Telephone,' she said. 'An old friend. And I think it's long distance.'

'On which line?'

'The listed number.'

To Krom I said: 'If you want to hear this conversation with Mat Williamson, there's an extension in the entrance hall. Melanie will show you where.'

I didn't wait to see if he accepted the offer. As I turned away, though, a sudden glow from the sea made me look back.

The vandal on the boat had lighted a Roman candle. As he held it aloft, balls of red fire were spurting up and falling to the deck all around him. His friends began to applaud.

I went up the stairs slowly. Mat would wait and I didn't want to seem even a little breathless when I took his call. After starting the recorder, I waited an extra moment or two before picking up the phone, and then began to speak immediately as if I had just snatched it up.

'Mat? What a pleasant surprise!'

I tried to make my surprise, if not my pleasure, sound genuine, but of course he wasn't fooled.

'Sorry to take you away from the fireworks, Paul, but this is by way of being an emergency. Besides, I'm returning your call to me this morning.'

I had to think very quickly then. He was using the high pitched, nasal voice of one of the English missionaries who had taught at the school in Fiji. I had heard it first when he had told me about Placid Island. It was his anti-imperialist voice, and also the one he sometimes used to make the saying of a highly unpleasant thing seem as if it were funny. He was probably using it now, partly anyway, as a disguise, but it startled me and I knew that I would have to watch myself. I ought not have been startled by an English Birmingham accent. With the recorder going, though, it couldn't be allowed to pass without comment.

'What a strange voice you have, Grandma!'

It was a mistake. He came back promptly, sketching in, for the record, a portrait of the faithful henchman driven at last by mockery into a small loss of temper. 'I said I was sorry to spoil your fireworks, Paul, and I'm sorry to disturb you when you have so much on your plate already, but this isn't a bedtime story.'

'That's twice you've mentioned fireworks, Mat. Where are you? Along the road somewhere? Watching the fireworks too?'

'You know where I am, Paul. There are always fireworks along the coast there on the Fourteenth of July. If I'm a bit upset, that's because I've been speaking to Frank, so bear with me. I've also listened to your conversation with him earlier, and . . . Paul? Are you still there?'

'I'm here.'

'Paul, what Frank said to you this morning was one long lie.'

'You mean one continuous lie or a lot of separate lies strung together?'

'I am *not* joking, Paul. From understandable motives, possibly, but with absolutely no authority from me, Frank has made a dangerous bloody fool of himself. In trying to be helpful by running interference for you, he's done a number of things he ought not have done. He's tried to be clever and only succeeded in being horribly stupid. As he's my responsibility, the first thing I want to do is apologize.'

'Apology accepted,' I tried to throw him. So far, every word he'd uttered had been that of a loyal lieutenant addressing a capricious martinet. I tried to throw him by suddenly becoming a martinet, and by speaking to him in a way that he hadn't been spoken to. I was sure, for a long time, if ever. 'But,' I snarled, 'you said that apologizing was the *first* thing you wanted to do. How about the *second* and *third*? Or have you been sitting around on your black butt waiting for somebody else to do your thinking for you?'

He seemed not to have heard what I'd said. All he did was move calmly into his second-stage position. 'Paul, do you remember that time some years ago when we – you, that is – were thinking of buying into that Malay-Chinese rubber syndicate? We went to stay with those people up near Kedah.'

'No, I don't remember that at all and I've never been to Kedah.'

'*Near* Kedha, I said. You'll remember when I tell you. It was just after that American went for a walk in the jungle and disappeared. The American who'd built up that silk business in Thailand and was taking a vacation in Malaysia? Staying as a house-guest with friends? Remember now, Paul?'

'How about getting to the point?'

'But that *is* the point, that he disappeared and was certainly killed. The local theory was that after he told his friends that he was going for a walk he was accidentally killed, not because he wasn't used to the jungles – in fact he was very much at home in them – but because he fell into a tiger trap the village people had dug there on the path he took. It wasn't the villagers' fault, of course, but they were scared because *he* was an American and it was *they* who'd dug the trap and planted the bamboo spikes. So they buried the body and didn't report it. That's why *our* friends didn't want us to go for any walks outside the compound while we were their guests. Our disappearance would have meant police enquiries, trouble. Besides, I think they liked us. I think they wanted our money, but I don't think they wanted us killing ourselves on their doorsteps.'

'Any more than you want me impaling myself on the bamboo stakes that Frank's been so busily sharpening? That's nice, Mat. I'm glad to know. Where's Frank staying down here?'

'It's not nice for anyone, Paul. And I'm including your guests. I don't know why. If anything should accidentally go wrong in spite of all you've done to protect them, they have to be the guilty parties. I hear through the grapevine, by the way, that two of them at least have intelligence links. I've asked friends about the Brit and they confirm. There's nothing nice about any of it. Oh, I agree with you, that doesn't excuse Frank. He's made a prize idiot of himself. These people he used your private files to learn about and contact, these old acquaintances of yours, were never the simple-minded hayseeds he wanted them to be. He knows that now and he's not staying in any one place. He's buzzing about like crazy, because he also knows now that trying to win medals by relieving you of an unwanted presence was never a good idea anyway. Not without consultation. I've told him. He'll be lucky if he doesn't get the chop. But let's be realistic, Paul. The fact that he knows all this, and that he's doing his damnedest to put things right, doesn't help with the immediate problem. Calling off the kind of people he's had out digging traps for you isn't as easy as setting them on.'

'I don't suppose it is, Mat. Frank's advice, as you'll know, was non-resistance. Yours appears to be a little different and slightly more reassuring – no walks in the jungle. Have I got that right?'

No plain answer, of course. I hadn't really expected one.

It was time for that final, all-important move to the third stage of the ritual. The preliminary declaration that a moral authority was properly vested in him, along with its appropriate powers, had formally been made. In other, cruder words, the softening-up process was over. Now, it was time for the decisive incantation. I know of no simple way of describing that process accurately. The carnivorous plant treating inspect prey with enzymes before eating them is a clumsy comparison. Mat doesn't want to eat his victims; he only wants them to oblige him.

He spoke slowly, and was probably tapping a table or desk in time with the words as he said them.

'Paul, there's something I'm going to remind you of now that I'm quite sure you haven't forgotten. You won't have forgotten this because it was something you once told me. You told me, too, in a moment of personal loss and sadness when you were trying to recall worse things you'd gone through. It was about when you were in the army in Italy, before you got to know Carlo up in the north. You recalled seeing another soldier, one of the men under your own personal command, go to obey an order you'd given. And then, a split second later, he'd stepped on a land mine – an S-mine, you called it – and been cut clean in two.'

A three-tap pause.

'How far away was he from you? Only a few yards, wasn't it? Close enough for you to be deaf for a few days, I know, and close enough for you to see what his guts looked like while his own eyes were still wondering what had happened. Less than a minute to die, though, with all those arteries severed. But the awful thing for you, aside from your having told the man to do something that killed him, came afterwards, didn't it? I mean after the first physical shock, when you realized that, although *you* were still alive, there was death all around you. When you stood there with all that singing in your ears and knew that you'd strayed into a minefield, and that if you moved so much as a fraction of an inch in any direction, or maybe even leaned over

258

a little and changed the weight distribution under one of your feet, *your* guts could be slopping about on the ground there too. So, you did what others have sometimes done when they've found they were in a minefield and seen what a mine can do to the soft human body. No disgrace, not when you're in shock and looking at the results of making the wrong move. Some men would have turned and run blindly. Not you. You froze. And you *stayed* frozen until, eventually, someone from an engineer patrol came. Remember? He was a sergeant. He took you by the arm and persuaded you, and finally *made* you walk. It was a step at a time, much slower than a funeral march you said, left-and-right and left-and-right, until you both reached a piece of ground where tanks had been. The mark of their tracks were new, so from there you had places to put your feet where there couldn't be unexploded S-mines. You walked back in the tank tracks. You listening, Paul?'

'Yes.'

'You asked for my advice. You don't need it. You already know what to do. You're in a minefield. Freeze. Right where you are. And stay frozen until I can get things straightened out and made safe, safe for you to walk away. Will you do that for me, Paul?'

'Yes, Mat.'

It would have called for a serious effort on my part to have said anything else.

Besides, it would have been foolish to have said anything else. Better if he believed that the spell was cast; or, to use the jargon he probably now prefers, that I was correctly programmed.

'I'll be there to take your arm,' he said.

The line went dead.

Green, orange and red lights glowed and flickered in the sky.

From my bedroom there was a good view of the bay,

and I had brought Yves's binoculars down with me from the attic floor. I took a closer look at the motor cruiser.

Most of the deck lights had been switched off now, as if to make the fireworks show up better; but there were several Roman candles burning at once and some of the orange balls from them stayed alight longer than the others on the way down to the water. I could see quite a lot of her.

The stern gave her name as *Chanteuse*, and her home port as Monrovia. She had Liberian registration. By the autumn she would be among the dozens of other boats just like her tied up along the yachting moles of Cannes and available for charter next year. It must have been expensive, I thought, to get hold of her at such short notice. Although there were always a few charterers who had their coronaries in June or early July, and so were obliged to fortfeit their deposits, you had to be right in there with bundles of dollars or D-marks in both hands to buy your way on to the yacht-broker's sucker lists of last-minute clients.

Mat must have hated that; but Frank wouldn't have minded.

That Frank was on board the boat, I now had no doubt at all. I knew where he was, too. The people with the drinks on the after deck were merely set-dressing. There were lights on below. The only place in complete darkness was the bridge. It was a big all-glass affair like a greenhouse, with sloping sides that reflected the glare of the fireworks. He'd be there in the darkness with a walkie-talkie, where he could see and control but not be seen.

The man in charge of the fireworks was using a flashlight to set up a Catherine wheel on a plank lashed to the bow rails. As he stood back and felt for his matches again, the beam shone straight down on the rest of the entertainment, the fun-things still to come.

There was nothing more to see. I checked both phones. Then, I rewound the tape and took the recorder downstairs so that the others could hear what had been said.

Krom tried to stop me. He had been listening on the extension and was very agitated.

'We must call the police,' he said.

'We can't. And time's running out. Keep still and listen.'

They listened. Krom seemed not to hear, though. A tic had started under his left eye, I watched the others. Yves especially. He kept catching my eyes on him and then looking past me over my shoulder. The cassette switched off.

Henson had a question. 'Did the minefield thing really happen to you as he describes it?'

'Not quite as he describes it. That's a Camp Fire Yarn version for Scouts. Mat's a prude, you see, and he has blind spots. He thinks that people are unalterable, for instance. It would never occur to him that the mere fact of my being able to tell him about that paralysing experience meant that the memory of it had become tolerable. After over thirty years, it can't paralyse me any more, only make me curl my toes.' I stood up. 'It's cooler outside and we can watch the fireworks.'

'We must call the police,' Krom said.

Connell had questions. 'What's Williamson think he's doing? Sniping with field-guns?'

'And disturbing the enemies' sleep, too, I imagine. The accent he was using, by the way, came from Birmingham in England a long time ago. It came via Fiji and used to belong to an inoffensive missionary.'

'We must . . . ' Krom began, and then paused. He put out his hands and gripped his knees tightly. 'They're there and he can't stop them,' he went on. 'He won't get here in time.'

'No,' I said, 'he won't, I'm afraid.'

There was no considerate way of explaining the position, either to him or to the others.

The Catherine wheel on the boat suddenly went haywire and flew off into the sea.

'Mat's telling me to freeze because his sorcerer's calculations tell him that, after the softening up I've had and Frank Yamatoku's warning, I'm going to behave irrationally. By talking about tiger-traps and minefields, he thinks he's compelling me to run, head for the hills with most of you following. Herd instinct. He wants us to run the way we came, in two parties.'

'Why us?' asked Connell. 'You're the one who knows him. You're the danger. And why in two parties?'

'I've blown him to you. He knows that, just as he knows that Dr Henson came bearing gifts from a British intelligence branch. The same person will have told him. I'm sorry, but you asked me. It's a special occasion. You get the truth. He just wants to do the killings quietly, with a minimum of fuss and expense. Two small parties are cheaper to kill than one big one. In this case, particularly, because separate explanations would be cheaper.'

'Cheaper?' Henson was indignant. 'And what have explanations to do with . . . ?'

'Killing can be very expensive these days, or it can be cheap. It all depends on what's left behind and how difficult the mess is to explain. On the roads or just off them, they're the easiest dumping grounds. All you need leave behind on them is either another ugly monument to our vulgar autoroute society or, if there are bullets to be found in any of the bodies, another tragic by-product of gangster-ridden monopoly capatalism. That's as long as you don't complicate things for the traffic police by mixing criminologists with the tax-consultants.'

Or by letting a victim talk before he dies. How thoughtfully I had been programmed! Should my final moments be unduly prolonged, I could spend them reminding myself sadly that dear old Mat had been right after all. He'd told me to stand still, and like a fool I hadn't listened.

'Are you saying the Professor's right?' demanded Melanie; 'that we should freeze?'

'No, dear, I'm not. Mat will be doing everything he can to make us run because that would give him what he wants for the lowest price. But he's not too proud to have had a contingency plan prepared and ready. By using the agent in place he has here, he should be able to mount a quick two-birds-with-one-stone operation with no trouble at all. Cars with bodies in them aren't news. A bunch of psychos rampaging through an expensive villa, *and* killing five foreign-visitor occupants, would made headlines. And think of the cost! With all that easy money going on the tycoon kidnap circuit, the reliable people want danger money and fringe benefits if there's the remotest chance of their being caught, or even identified.'

No, better by far if I acted as programmed. Better for me. Better for our friendship. That was what he'd been telling me with the sob in his throat at the end.

Connell said: 'The agent in place you're talking about must be Yamatoku. Right?'

Wrong, and the look that Henson gave me said that she knew it was wrong, but Krom was suddenly emphatic.

'We must stay,' he insisted, 'stay here . . . '

That beautiful spell, woven to impose the sorcerer's will upon me, had failed with me because its beauties had been too knowingly and lovingly displayed for my taste. However, with Krom, not a man to be put off by schmaltz if he found the tune familiar, it had succeeded remarkably; though not in producing the effect Mat had intended.

He hadn't been telling Krom anything in particular, except possibly that this wasn't the *real* Mat Williamson speaking; but Krom had listened and what he had heard had made the most exquisite sense to him. Mat had said freeze, so that was what Krom had found he wanted to do, *all* he wanted to do – stay absolutely still where he was, until some kind stranger came to take his arm and lead him to safety.

It wasn't, I think, that he was over-susceptible to the brand of hypnotic suggestion that Mat favours and can use with such effect when dealing with the unwary, or even – since, as far as I know, Krom was never in his youth caught in a minefield – that the evocation of the intense fear experienced in the past triggered an irrational response to events occurring years later. What threw the man so completely was that set of facts which Mat had used to construct his Makefing-sur-Mer fantasies happened to be not only familiar to Krom but also essential to his own fantasies, those about that arch-liar and able criminal, Oberholzer-Firman. He had known for years that there was nothing imaginary about the two men code-named Kleister and Torten. His original Swiss police contacts had confirmed the men's existence and their strange, psychotic retirement hobby. With those and other vengeful bogeymen like them crouching out there in the darkness, nursing pent-up hatreds and waiting, fingers on the triggers, to kill anyone who broke cover, what else was there to do but stay put and keep your head down until help came?

'Stay here and telephone for the police,' he repeated.

Connell glanced from Krom to me. 'I can see, Mr Firman, why you might think it inadvisable to try busting out of here. I can also see why you'd consider this garrison a bit short on the arms and know-how needed to beat off an attack by trained assault troops. Unless you have guns as well as brandy to hand out I mean. I don't see what's wrong, though, with calling the police. If the Professor thinks it's a good idea and we can figure out a way of requesting protection that they'll take seriously – suspected prowlers, maybe – I say let's do it. And in view of the other prospects and possibilities you've been outlining, I say let's do it right now. Let's call in the relief column, dammit!'

'Yves will tell you why we can't,' I said. 'Tell them, Yves.'

He stared out fixedly at the boat.

'Yves has a gun,' I went on; 'he's the only one amongst us who has, and he's being very careful to sit where none of us can get behind him. He's worried because he's badly afraid of the consequences of failure at the moment. He couldn't shoot more than two of us before the others jumped him, so he's playing it cool, or trying to, and waiting for his friend Frank to tell him what to do next. We can't use the phone because he cut both lines right after Mat's call. I know because I checked. He's not going to let us try finding the place and repairing the lines, I'm sure. The gun's inside his shirt under his left arm. I think we'd like it to stay there.'

Krom nodded. '*Status quo,*' he said, and reached for the brandy bottle.

Henson sighed. 'Oh dear.'

'Oh dear, indeed. Our forthright, no-nonsense Mr Boularis has been very busy here. Busy making booby-traps, busy reporting progress at the lower-road gate, thoughtfully recommending instant flight as the way out of all difficulties, even offering to drive Melanie and me to our own private holocaust in *your* car. Mr Williamson and Mr Yamatoku wanted us to leave in a particular way, so naturally Yves did his level best to see that we did. My goodness, how hard he's been working. Not his fault that I'm nervous of drivers who tell you how good they are. Didn't you wonder too, Dr Henson, how Mat had found out about your connection with British intelligence?'

'Yes, I did. Especially as the only connection that exists is the one I told you about. Mr Boularis wasn't present when I told you about it though.'

'He must have been listening at the door.'

'Or else . . . ' Connell hesitated, wondering if what he had suddenly thought of saying might be tactless. About some things he could be very quick on the uptake. It had been he, I recalled, who had voiced aloud his doubt of modern man's ability to spot a room-bug just by looking for it.

Melanie dealt with him firmly. 'Well, it no longer matters. Look! His friends on the boat are sending him signals.'

A couple of cardboard volcanoes had begun to spout red lava and golden rain.

'Signals to say what?' Connell's mind was still with the room-bug hypothesis, but he looked at Yves.

Yves didn't answer. His face was shiny with sweat.

I answered for him. 'Signals to say that the fun's over, I would think. Now, he's waiting for the bangs he's been warned to expect. Mat Williamson is a great believer in the loud bang as an argument. Simple people respect it. Not-so-simple people can often be fooled by it. As a means of inducing sensible people to behave stupidly or irrationally there's nothing to equal it.'

I was talking by then to keep my own courage up. I had seen the launching rack on the deck out there from the bedroom window. It looked like an office-furniture designer's idea for an umbrella stand made out of a bundle of drain pipes. The firework man had been using the glare from the volcanoes to see by. He wanted no mistakes with that lot.

'Coming back, if you don't mind, to the subject of relief columns,' said Henson; 'you did say something about a need for concerted action when the right moment came and you gave the word. Aren't you leaving it a bit late?'

'No.'

I didn't try to elaborate. It would have been silly to tell her that there wasn't, after all, going to be any word. Allies are notoriously unable to understand why, when the time comes, they are quite often no longer needed.

Besides, at that moment the rockets were fired.

Visually, they had nothing to offer; no graceful arcs of coloured fire, no pretty second-stage bursts to surprise delighted onlookers, no candelabrum flares on parachutes, none of the ooh-aah stuff that was dished out in Monte Carlo. As the first salvo went up, all we saw were the jets of orange flame that lifted the things out of the umbrella stand.

Then, with apologetic plopping sounds, they seemed to give up and disappear.

The explosions on and near the terrace were not big, but they were far from apologetic. I doubt if there were more than a few ounces of HE in any of the charges. That's about what there would be in a modern hand-grenade; just enough to create a really jolting anti-personnel blast-wave with a radius of three or four yards. The shallow hole gouged out of a patch of Bermuda grass could have been made by a dog burying a bone. The stonework of the terrace suffered no more than pock-marks. There were several broken windows though.

No one was hurt, but the effect on Krom was remarkable. With him, the noises seemed to act like the traditional snap of the fingers employed by a stage hypnotist to bring his subject out of a trance.

I must say, too, that for a man of his age with half a bottle of brandy in the bloodstream, his reflexes were amazing. When the first salvo exploded, he did a racing dive on to the flagstones. He had found cover behind the pedestal of a marble-topped table before I had even started to move. By the time the second lot arrived, he was already wriggling and rolling his way over the broken glass by the drawing-room windows towards the comparative safety of the room itself.

'You see? You see?' he was saying as he went.

We did see; at least, we saw that it was necessary to get off the terrace. The third salvo, which broke another pane of glass and left one of the outside chair-cushions smouldering, was followed by a brief silence. Melanie broke in.

'Those people must be insane!'

'Of *course* they are insane,' Krom was lying curled up on the floor, busy searching the front of his shirt for slivers of glass. 'They have been insane for years. They were *driven* insane by our host.'

He may have snapped out of a trance, but all spells were still in full working order.

'Are you suggesting,' Connell demanded in the most disrespectful tone I had yet heard him use to Krom, 'that the middle-aged jerks playing with explosives on that boat are Kleister and Torten?'

'Who else would fire mortar shells to maim or kill their tormentor?'

'Those beer-bellied cretins out there are in their forties.'

'And they are not firing mortar shells,' said Melanie; 'anyone who has ever been near a mortar bombardment would tell you that. Those were signal maroons, defective ones.'

'Not defective,' said Yves; 'only modified for aiming. They have death there. That was a rehearsal. Do you want to wait for the real thing? Take no notice of what Firman says. Get up and go, while you still can!'

Yves was a tryer; no doubt of that. He had much to lose.

I had begun to move and was almost at the door when Henson noticed the fact. As it was important just then that I shouldn't have further attention drawn to me, I gave her a meaning nod. I hoped that she would interpret it as the promised 'word' and as a sign that the time had come for a diversion.

She did not disappoint me.

'How do we *know* that the telephone lines are cut?' she asked Connell accusingly. 'Have *you* tried them? Has anyone tried them? Because if they haven't, I don't feel like taking the man Firman's unsupported word for it. There may be *one* line still working. If so, I think that Professor Krom should immediately call the police on all our behalfs.'

A good effort. Melanie moved in at once to cover the sound of my opening the door.

'If anyone is to telephone the police it must be me, Professor, because I am the official tenant here in this villa. It is I also who must telephone the *gérant* acting for the owners so that the damage can be reported and assessed. Please remember, too, if there is a telephone working, which I doubt, that the name of the tenant and present occupier here is not Firman or Wickey-Frey. It is Oberholzer.'

'Aha!' said Krom happily. 'Be sure I shall remember. Oberholzer! How could I forget?'

The jerrican was of metal and a real World War II veteran, not one of the plastic imitations they make nowadays. It had probably been sitting there in the corner of that garage for years; since one of those times when it had been thought prudent to keep a little gasoline put by for emergencies in case the local pumps ran dry. After which Middle East war had it been filled? The 73? The 67? The Suez fiasco of 56?

I hoped that it hadn't been the Suez, because a top-sergeant who used to flog the stuff had once told me that gasoline stored for years gradually loses its potency. I also hoped that the man had merely been rationalizing his misconduct. Neither of the two cars had much left in its tank, and I wanted an event not an incident; it had to be a huge blaze, one that would quickly be seen and reported but not easily put out.

I was worried, too, about the roof problem. Before I had known that Mat was going to oblige me with fireworks, I had rigged the thing to look like a short-circuit following insulation failure in antique wiring. It wouldn't have deceived an arson investigator, but I had been prepared to face that difficulty later in return for the presence, when needed, of some fire trucks and their crews along with a back-up force of police cars and gawking spectators. The fireworks had given me a cover story potentially better than the one about antique wiring; but would it in fact be better if there were no hole in the roof to show where the firework had smashed through? Wouldn't that look fishier than a short-circuit? Even fishier than the remains of The Device?

I thought for a few moments of taking a hammer up to the loft and breaking one or two roof tiles. I didn't in the end; partly because I couldn't find a hammer, but mainly because I was, I have to admit, beginning to panic.

The rocket-firing could well have been accompanied by a signal to the waiting clean-up team. 'That's zero, kids. Start counting. Give them ten minutes to get themselves together. If the bastards haven't begun to come out by then, you go right in and start earning your money.'

Or words to that effect. Besides, I didn't even know if The Device I'd cobbled together would work. I might even have to waste valuable time finding out. Someone – Yves, for instance – might come looking for me while I was doing so. If, through having sweaty hands and being in too much of a hurry, I botched the job, I might end up having to go in there and try blowing myself to bits with lighted matches.

The passage that led to the garage ended at the inner door of what had obviously once been a cubby-hole, with lavatory adjoining, for chauffeurs. Now, it was cluttered with such things as water-skis, old schnorkel masks, a wickerwork chair with a broken seat and a set of golf clubs with hickory shafts. On the wall by the far door were two switches, one controlling the passage lights, the other the lights in the garage. That second switch was necessary because there were no windows or skylights in the garage. When the big outer doors were closed it was pitch-black inside. I made sure that the second switch was in the 'off' position.

To arm The Device, I had to enter the garage without the lights on and feel my way around the cars to a work-bench against the opposite wall. On the bench was a trickle charger with spring-clip connectors on long leads for attaching the thing to a run-down battery without removing the battery from the car. The Device was made out of the two spring-clips, three adhesive bandages and one of the cigar-lighters belonging to the Lincoln. It was fastened with a piece of string, just inside the unlatched lid of the jerrican – in the place where the most vapour would be.

Arming it meant connecting the mains lead of the charger to the light-bulb socket above the bench. That was its regular source of power. There was no wall outlet. Switching on the light would then do one of two things; either blow a fuse somewhere in the house or, more likely, cause the cigar-lighter filament to heat up and ignite the gasoline vapour.

I could smell the vapour as soon as I opened the door. If the stuff had deteriorated in storage, it still smelled like gasoline, almost overpoweringly so. But could one tell by the smell of it? On the way around the cars I was tempted to take the caps off the tanks or loosen them. I didn't do either of those things though. A tank with no cap on it, or no signs of having burst under pressure, would be the sort of thing an arson man would spot instantly. Forget it.

Even if I'd had a flashlight, I doubt if I'd have used it. The night was very warm and the sun had been on the loft roof directly above for most of the day. The place fairly reeked of gas. I'd have been afraid of even the tiny little spark there might be inside the flashlight's outer case. The faint light from the door into the house, although most of it was blocked off by the cars, gave some help. Memory and the touch of sweaty fingers had to do the rest.

Finding the light-bulb socket over the bench was the most difficult thing. Standing there with one hand above my head, groping for the damned thing, I began to feel disoriented. Twice, I had to stop and find the edge of the bench again to make sure that I was still facing the right way. Once, when I had found the light socket, I dropped the charger lead and had to start all over again. But it was done at last. Only halfway through my sigh of relief did I remember that, now, if Yves or Melanie came along the passage looking for me, and switched on the light by the door before I could stop them, The Device would . . .

I scrambled out of there so fast that I bruised myself quite badly against the rear end of the Lincoln. I also gashed a shin in falling over the foot of the loft stairs. Panic. Bloody stupid panic.

Back outside the door again, with only a residual smell of gas still clinging to me and the pains in my left arm and right leg beginning to make themselves felt, I was suddenly quite sure that none of it was going to work, that I'd forgotten something of crucial importance.

Wearily, I leaned against the door and pressed the switch.

The passage light went out but nothing else happened. I had pressed the wrong switch.

I wiped the sweat out of my eyes and pressed the right one.

The *whoof* of the ignition felt like someone putting a shoulder to the door, not to try to force it open, just to see if it were latched.

Very gently, I unlatched it. It tried, equally gently, to close itself again. I used the handle of a ping-pong bat to keep it from closing completely, and then opened the lavatory window to make sure that there would be no shortage of oxygen inside.

I shut the inner door behind me as I left.

There were raised voices coming from the hall, but I had no way of getting up the stairs without being seen.

'It is for Mr Firman and no one else,' Melanie was saying, 'to decide what shall be done and when it shall be done. He's your host, and you, while you are his guests, must respect his wishes.'

Her defiant whine suggested that she was losing the argument. It was no surprise to find that she was losing it to Krom.

'As we are in danger,' he said acidly, 'such niceties of etiquette hardly seem relevant.'

'Quite right,' I said.

They stared at me with understandable curiosity. As well as having torn slacks, I must also have looked filthy and my shirt was black with sweat.

The curiosity changed to suspicion.

'What have you been trying to do?' asked Connell. 'Make it through the enemy lines?'

'No. Looking for the cavalry.'

Melanie was holding my tape-recorder. I had left it in

the dining-room earlier. I took it from her, then turned to Krom.

'I have to tell you,' I said, 'that it will shortly become necessary for us to leave here. All of us. Any further meetings, if there should be any, will have to be held in another place.'

Krom started to open his mouth. I talked him down by raising my voice.

'No argument. You have time, I think, to collect your passports, money, notebooks and other valuables from your rooms, but no time to pack anything. I must ask you to assemble here in no more than ten minutes.'

When Krom again opened his mouth, I let him speak.

'May guests be permitted to know, what fresh disaster now postpones our detailed examination of your criminal past?'

'Certainly. The house is on fire.'

For a moment I thought that his tic had returned. Then, a most curious muscular spasm flattened the circumflex of his upper lip and covered the teeth behind it.

He was trying to stop himself giving me a smile of resignation.

The departments of Var and Alpes-Maritimes in southern France have suffered much from forest fires involving buildings and lives. As a result, the regional fire services are well equipped and well trained. On the Fourteenth of July an exceptionally high state of readiness is always maintained.

Our fire was first spotted by a man in a villa up on the corniche to the east of us. He reported it promptly, no doubt, because there was a slight breeze blowing from us to him, and because we might have been out for the evening. Fire travels quickly in those parts.

The braying of the approaching fire trucks and police cars began as I was stepping out of the shower.

Yes, I showered. I put on clean clothes too. Anyone who

believes that the best way of convincing the police that you're not an arsonist is to look as if you've been in there fighting the flames with a wet towel and a garden hose, has to be mistaken.

By the time the leading truck turned into the driveway, I was ready to greet it. All I had had to do first was park my small bag with the tapes and other oddments I would be needing later in a safe place on the terrace. There was no point in lugging the recorder along too, so I opened it to remove the last cassette. Someone had already taken it.

Yves? That wasn't the moment to ask. I went downstairs. When the first police car arrived, I was out there with Melanie, wringing my hands, getting in the firemen's way and generally behaving just as any other right-minded person would have behaved in those circumstances.

My story was simple. Madmen on boat. Dud rockets. Old stabling converted for use as garage probably tinder dry. Hadn't seen the fire start at back because dealing with burning cushions on terrace. Phones by then out of order. Witnesses, including distinguished Professor, would confirm. Thank God you're here.

I named the boat and told them to look for burn marks on her deck. No, they wouldn't be the kinds of burns you could wash off with soap and water. Power tools and much time would be needed to get rid of those scars. When they caught the villains, as they surely must, I would dearly like to be on hand with a shot-gun. Yes, I understood that one mustn't take the law into one's own hands and that I was overwrought, but no doubt they understood my feelings.

I needn't have worried about there being no hole in the roof to show where the spent rocket had smashed through. When the firemen got there most of the roof had already fallen in. They concentrated on trying to contain the blaze and on confining it to the older, unremodelled part of the building. The senior fireman thought they would succeed, but it would be a long job, and some of his men would have to stay with it to watch for flare-ups. No, he certainly wouldn't advise anyone to sleep in the house. The fire had already got to the main electricity cable, and, when the pipes began to melt, the water would have to be turned off. Better start thinking about a hotel.

Since I didn't intend to be available when the insurance investigators started wondering how best to avoid paying out on the owner's claim, that left the cut-phone lines as the likeliest source of trouble with local officialdom. If they could be seen to have been cut, there would be unpleasant questions asked and suspicion aroused prematurely. I consulted Yves.

'It's all right,' he said; 'the lines came in by the garage and that's where I cut them. The fire won't have left anything for anyone to see.'

'Good. Now I'll take that cassette.'

'What cassette?'

'The one that was in my recorder. The call from Mat.'

'Krom took that. He thinks nobody saw him. It's in his shirt pocket. You could try snatching it. I'll bet he won't give it to you.' His eyes narrowed maliciously. 'Did you know, Paul, that all that beautiful equipment of mine was charged to Symposia? You've lost that lot of tapes too. Bad luck.'

I tried to look as if he'd driven yet another nail into my coffin.

A gendarmerie radio van had arrived to handle communications with the various authorities along the coast who would be concerned with tracking down the *Chanteuse* and bringing in her passengers and crew for questioning.

The cook and her husband returned on their motor scooter, having heard in the village about the fire. The extension to the house that contained their apartment, though badly scorched on the outside, was otherwise undamaged. After preliminary lamentations, they set about making a list of the valuable personal possessions they had left in the kitchen, the laundry, the wine-cellar, the pantry and one or two other rooms adjacent to the garage which had also suffered. A colour TV set, that they claimed to have bought themselves and installed in the pantry next to the freezer, was high on their list. The insurance investigator who diagnosed arson would have a choice of suspects.

The upper road had been closed by the police to non-essential traffic as soon as the alarm had been given. The coast road, however, became jammed with sightseers who had stopped their cars to watch the fun. Motor-cycle police had to be sent to move them on.

A television crew, who had seen the fire while covering a 'folkorique' happening up at La Turbie, were allowed in to get pictures for the regional news. Yves slipped away immediately, and so did I. Fortunately, the TV men didn't stay long. The blaze was already under control. I avoided the cameras by taking refuge in my bedroom, and used the time, with the aid of a candle from one of the sconces in the hall, to pack the rest of my things. I also smudged those surfaces likely to yield clear fingerprints to anyone looking for such things. The cook's husband and the daily woman would get around to cleaning up when we had gone; but, since the whole place wasn't going to burn down after all, the less there was of me there to find the better.

Melanie had no problem with the cameras. She was closeted with the police. As the owner of a burned-out car, she had to file a separate report on that incident as well as making her statement as a tenant about the house fire. Connell too, the one who had signed the rental contract for the Fiat it appeared, would have to file a separate report to complete the paper work.

By then, it was eleven o'clock.

I could be certain of at least one thing. When the *Chanteuse* was picked up, Frank would not be among those found on board. It was also likely that, with all the police activity in and around the Villa Lipp, his squads of hired helpers on land had been withdrawn from the vicinity. Now, they would be waiting at assembly points farther out – waiting to see what my next move would be.

It was time I made it.

I found Krom sitting with Henson and Yves in the drawing-room, and set the ashtray I had been using as a candlestick down on the table nearest to them.

Krom was obviously very tired. However, my hope that fatigue would make him easier to deal with was a vain one.

'We have no electricity,' I began cheerfully; 'and the fireman tells me that someone will shortly arrive to turn off the main water supply. There is still the swimming pool, of course, if you don't mind the taste of chlorine and care to use buckets, but most of it has already been pumped on to the flames by one of the fire trucks.'

He flicked me away contemptuously. 'Spare us. You meant to disperse our gathering. You still mean to disperse it. The enemies outside having been disposed of, you are now ready to dispose of the enemies within. Dr Henson agrees with me.'

Her eyes were unfriendly. 'The relief of the beleaguered city having been completed,' she said, 'the garrison is ready to march out with colours flying. The cavalry are left in possession after their ride to the rescue.'

I knew then what the trouble with *her* was. The quip about cavalry riding to the rescue had been made by Connell while he was in her bed. By inadvertently throwing the word 'cavalry' back at him when he had accused me, facetiously, of trying to escape, I had let them both know that I had invaded their privacy. I could expect no more co-operation from them in dealing with Krom.

'The garrison may march out,' I said, 'but I wouldn't advise flying colours. You don't think Mat Williamson's going to give up just because of a little set-back here, do you?'

Krom's teeth were back in service. 'I too, think it unlikely that the person who made that telephone call to you will give up. Was he the 'Vic' we heard mentioned earlier? I think he must have been. So, he won't give up any more than Kleister and Torten will give up. They want their revenge, and they have waited a long time. Now that someone has shown them how to find you, they can follow you to the ends of the earth if necessary. We are more fortunate.'

'I wouldn't be too sure about that.'

'Oh, but I *am* sure, and my witnesses agree with me. The truth about you will be our protection. All we have to do is publish it. It's you that they want dead, not us. Mr Boularis has made that clear.'

I glanced at Yves. He smiled slightly. His closed session with them had been highly profitable. It was time for me to cut my losses.

I moved over and sat down by Krom. 'I think you have something of mine, Professor,' I pointed to the cassette in his shirt pocket, and then extended my hand as if to grab it. 'That!'

He drew back, clutching it to his breast fiercely. 'Ah, No! No, Mr Firman. If you want *this* back, you'll have to buy it. And I'll tell you what the price is. Don't you want to hear?'

His protective embrace had been passionate enough to smudge beyond recognition any of my fingerprints that might have been left on the thing, but to please him I nodded. 'How much?'

I want two things. I want the rest of the papers you had prepared for me, the ones I would have had if we hadn't been interrupted, and I want a resumption of our meetings by this time next week at the latest. And they will be in Brussels, if you please. We have met discreetly there before, and in a public place. Why not again? I'm sure you know how to protect yourself there from fireworks, and your victims are used to waiting for satisfaction. Besides, they are obviously careful men. They are not likely to attack you in the lobby of the Brussels Westbury. So, in not more than a week's time we can continue, eh? I shall be expecting you. What do you say?'

I stood up. 'I think it's time we thought about leaving, and I at any rate intend to be very careful *how* I leave. With luck, I may be able to persuade the gendarmerie to assist.' I looked at Henson. 'Melanie's still with the local police. The Professor's tired. I'd be glad of some help, but it's up to you.'

She followed me out to the gendarmerie van and stood by while I explained to the sergeant in charge what the fireman had said about going to an hotel.

He pulled a face. 'At this time of year? You won't find anything near here. Monte Carlo might have something of the kind you're used to, but if you just want a place to sleep, Nice is your best chance. One of the commercial places near the central station.'

'Would it be in any way possible, Sergeant, for you to use your radio to call us a taxi?'

Henson gave him a most appealing look. 'Or even two taxis, Sergeant? There are six of us, as you see, and we have baggage.'

He said that taxis might be in short supply on the night of the Quatorze, but that he would use his influence with the radio dispatchers, those who were sober, and see what could be arranged.

The taxis came from Beaulieu, and were there within half an hour.

Melanie left the house keys with the cook's husband before joining me in the back of the second taxi. Henson said that they would take the sergeant's advice and head for Nice. No goodbyes were said. The whip had been cracked. Obviously, I was going to be sensible and safeguard what was left of my reputation by reporting for duty in Brussels the following week. They owed me no courtesies. Why should they pretend that they did?

As they were about to leave, I noticed that Yves wasn't

with them. At the same moment he slid into the front seat beside our driver. He had no bag with him, nothing.

'I said, 'Hallo.'

He didn't turn his head. 'Where are we going?' he asked.

I had already told the driver that we wanted to take a night train to Paris from Monte Carlo. There probably wasn't one, but modern taxi drivers only know about planes. I had no intention of going anywhere by train in any case, only of losing that taxi in a convenient place.

'Monte Carlo,' I said. 'The railway station.'

No more was said until we were up the hill by the Hotel de Paris. Then, Yves suddenly told the driver to stop.

'Leaving us?' I asked.

'I have a bad migraine,' he said as he got out, 'and there's an all-night pharmacy just over there. Won't be a moment.'

I waited until he was out of sight inside the place, and then told the driver to go ahead.

Melanie looked surprised.

'He isn't coming back,' I said, 'just hoping to delay us a few extra minutes. He's telephoning Frank, trying to re-establish credit. His rating must be pretty low at present. They may even believe that he *knew* I was setting the fire. A report that we're on our way out by train may help him for a few hours. If it had been true, if we were going to be there at the station waiting to be picked off like sitting ducks, they could have ended up forgiving him.'

'All this violence, I detest it! When did you suspect him?'

'When he said that he knew people who had worked for Mat Williamson, and that Mat was one to stay away from because he had a habit of ditching them.'

'You mean it's not true?'

'It's true in a way, but "ditching" is Frank's word, part of the formula he always uses when he's briefing someone who mustn't suspect that Mat's the boss. You can see why. Who would ever believe that the man hiring you would talk against his own head man like that? So, I knew that Yves had been briefed by Frank. Incidentally, Mat never speaks of ditching people, even when they have caused him deep distress, only of losing them.'

'Then what do you mean by "true in a way"? What way?'

'When Mat loses someone, it's because the person is being discarded or ditched. That's true enough. But nobody ever talks about it, as a rule, because nobody ever knows it's happened, the losing I mean.'

'Not even the lost one?'

'Least of all the lost one. He's dead.'

'Detestable!'

As we neared the station, I told the driver that we had changed our minds and now wanted to go to the Hotel Mirabeau.

I was quite sure that the Mirabeau wouldn't have rooms for anyone arriving without reservations at that stage of the season, and at that time of night. The driver was of the same opinion. I silenced him by declaring in a lordly way that I would demand a suite, and paid him off the instant he had our bags out. Because he was now in Monaco, and so not allowed to pick up another fare, he was on his way back to Beaulieu even before the Mirabeau's night man was out there to tell us we hadn't a hope.

A hundred francs got us another taxi and we didn't have long to wait. The Monagasque driver had a charming manner, and his price for taking us to Menton, ten minutes away, was only mildly exorbitant.

We stayed in a no-restaurant hotel in a back street near the Sacré Coeur; and we didn't go out more than was necessary.

The only time we went near a main road was to buy a couple of cheap radios. We bought newspapers at a kiosk on the nearby *quai*. There was a café-restaurant at the corner of the street. We had our meals there, and used their pay-phone to make our calls rather than go through the hotel switchboard.

Yves had an apartment in Paris and, since he was a keen skier as well as a highly-paid technician, a chalet near Megève. We took it in turns to call both his phone numbers, and we called three times each day. There was no reply from either until the evening of the fourth day.

It had been Melanie's turn to make the calls, and her blank look as she returned to our table told me that there'd been an answer.

'Paris,' she said as she sat down. 'A man's voice. I asked twice for Yves. He asked who wanted him, and then offered to have Yves call me back. Pressed most flatteringly for my name and number. I hung up.'

'A police voice?'

'An over-friendly, coaxing voice. I thought police. Why don't you try him?'

'I'll take your word for it. They say dialled calls are hard to trace, but that was last year. Who knows how hard or easy it may be now?'

We ate our food because we had ordered it and because it would have looked odd if we'd suddenly paid the bill and left. We couldn't risk drawing attention to ourselves just then.

In our rooms back at the hotel, we stayed glued to the radios. I switched between the hourly France-Inter news from the local transmitter and an Italian FM station. Melanie stayed with Radio Monte Carlo. The first announcement came through on France-Inter, at the end of the ten o'clock local news and before the sports round-up.

Earlier in the evening reports had been received of a bomb incident in the vicinity of Cagnes. They had since been confirmed, though detailed information was still awaited.

The incident involved a car found standing on the scrubland beside a drainage ditch a few metres from the west-bound access road to the autoroute. The driver, a man in the late thirties, appeared to have been '*plastiqué*' inside the car.

A curious feature of the accident was that the car itself

had scarcely been damaged at all, according to Jean-Pierre Something-or-other, the man who had found it. He was a night watchman employed by the contractors working on the adjacent building site. He had seen nothing of the car's arrival. He had been led to it by his dog while making his hourly tour of the area he was there to guard.

The car was the property of an international rental service. It had been signed for earlier that day by a man with a credit card in the name of Yves Boularis and an address in Paris. Other papers found on the victim, along with the credit card in question, identified the dead man as Boularis. There was a description of the car and a request to anyone who had happened to notice it, either in the Cagnes district that evening or earlier in Nice, to contact the police.

At eleven there was a repetition of the same story, but with additional details.

Boularis was a Tunisian who was listed in the central file of foreign residents as an import-export dealer in electronic equipment. The possibility of his having also been involved in the narcotics traffic had not been overlooked. Friends of the dead man and business associates were being sought for questioning.

There was a cryptic tail-piece.

A police spokesman had said that a disquieting feature of the case was the bizarre method that seemed to have been employed by the killer or killers. The dead man had been sitting with his seat belt fastened. The '*plastiqué*' had not been detonated by an ignition-key contact or by any of the other methods commonly used in these cases. A possible suicide? Certainly not. Out of the question.

The newspapers the following morning were a good deal more explicit, and one of them sickeningly so.

There was no doubt that Yves had been driven to the place of execution. He had been unconscious or semi-conscious at the time. There was evidence to suggest that force had been used to make him submit to an injection. The nature of the drug would doubtless be determined later.

He had then been placed in the driving seat of his rented car. The charge of '*plastiqué*' that had killed him had been attached to the diagonal portion of the seat-belt where it crossed his stomach. Both his wrists had been lashed with baling-wire to the steering wheel. A time fuse had been used to explode the charge. It may have been intended that he should regain consciousness and know what was being done to him before he died. A murder of revenge was indicated. It seemed likely that more than one assassin, and certainly a second car, had been needed to commit the crime. The body, which had been eviscerated – indeed, almost cut in half – by the explosive charge, was undergoing the most thorough forensic examination. The autopsy findings, together with scientific investigation of the car's interior, were expected to supply much-needed leads to the identity of those responsible.

'Bestial!' said Melanie. 'They are vile gangsters.'

'I dare say those who did it are. But what do we call those nice people, Mat and Frank, say, who specified exactly what was to be done, *and* paid for the doing of it? What do we call them?'

'Ask Professor Krom. He always has a word for things. Ask him, Paul, and send me a postcard with the answer.'

'You won't be going to Brussels with me?'

'Thank you. I prefer to keep my stomach.' She gave me a sidelong look. 'Will you go?'

I managed a thin smile. 'Mr Williamson seems to have made his position very clear. Until the Placid Island negotiations are safely concluded, I am advised not to show my nose in any of the usual places. I must remain completely unavailable, physically unavailable, for questioning by any inquisitive journalist who may have heard rumours put about by Krom's witnesses or listened to the great man's schnapps-induced ramblings. The same applies to you. My work at Symposia will have to be delegated for a while.'

'To whom? Frank Yamatoku?'

I actually chuckled. 'We'll have to see. Meanwhile I too

would like to keep my stomach. We must both vanish. Of *course* I'm not going to Brussels.'

'Krom won't be pleased.'

'Then I must learn to live with his displeasure.'

Why have I failed?

Possibly because the form taken by Krom's displeasure hasn't greatly encouraged me to try living with it.

Some things are too difficult for a man of my sort ever to learn. Among them is the art of living with the displeasure of a fool.

His anger at my failure to commit suicide – by joining him and his witnesses in Brussels – was promptly expressed.

Two months later, a whole Special Issue of *The New Sociologist* was devoted to a piece by Krom. Its title was: *The Able Criminal*, Notes for a Case-study.

I made no complaint about it at the time.

That wasn't simply because, in order to oblige Mat Williamson, and discourage him from having me murdered, I was making myself scarce. I may have been incommunicado, but I wasn't out of touch. I could have instructed lawyers if I'd wished to, or I could have told my people at Symposia to instruct lawyers. There were, indeed, some of them who urged me to do so. I didn't because I thought it best to ignore the thing. Most international corporation lawyers and accountants are too busy trying to keep abreast of new tax legislation affecting their clients to bother their heads with publications like *The New Sociologist*.

I am not the first person to have made that sort of mistake, and I won't be the last. However, it wasn't until German publication of Krom's book, *Der kompetente Kriminelle,* produced a whole crop of articles on the subject in the international news magazines and business journals, that I knew I had made a mistake.

So, it is against Krom's irresponsible book, not his irresponsible article, that my formal complaint is made.

Not that there's much to choose between them. The book, now being translated into four other languages, is essentially a revamped version of the article, padded to size with long winded footnotes, appendices, a bibliography and an index. There is little new material. The journalistic crossheads used to break the article up into digestible sections – phrases such as *The Anarchy of Extortion* and *The Criminal as Moral Philosopher* – have become chapter headings.

Not many changes otherwise. The inaccuracy, falsity and total dishonesty of the original remain unqualified.

Frits Buhler Krom is a phony.

He came to see me in Brussels with his head full of preconceived notions. Nothing had been permitted to modify them. He knew what he had to say in order to prove his case. He has now said it.

Why, then, did he risk his skin on the battlefield of Cap d'Ail? Though he couldn't have known the kind of danger he would be running into, he was clearly prepared for trouble of some sort. The precautions he took in Brussels against the possibility of my being the kind of man who might like to have him killed tells us that. Why then?

So that he can now apply the respectable label of 'case-study' to the drivel he has written, of course. Why else? Now, he can pretend that, having journeyed bravely into the unknown and observed its wonders, he is simply reporting what he alone has seen for the enlightenment of scholars.

As poor Yves might have said, he is 'all piss and wind'.

For what does this criminological Münchhausen have to tell us about his travels?

Well, once upon a time when he was in Zürich, he identified this man Oberholzer. Years later, he saw him again. Oberholzer, now, as then, the sole and supreme overlord of a vast international extortion conspiracy, agreed to talk and even make written statements about techniques used by able criminals in exchange for immunity from certain pressures Krom was in a position to apply. There were two victims of Oberholzer's extortion racket who happened to be known to Krom. Their code-names were Kleister and Torten, and . . .

And so on, and so. Until we get to the shrewd analysis of my 'papers'.

Sample questions. Why, if the tax-avoidance consultancy service wasn't a mere front, was it necessary to employ informers like the unfortunate Kramer? A genuine tax-consultant would naturally be given access to his clients' banking accounts by the clients themselves. Isn't it obvious that men like Kleister and Torten were never clients, only victims?

It doesn't occur to him that men like K and T – men whom even he is prepared to describe in another part of the book, as 'moneyed psychopaths' – lie to the consultants they employ as readily as they lie to the revenue authorities they hope to cheat. When such clients tell you that they have three accounts, you naturally assume that they have six. For your own sake, if not for theirs, you'd better know for sure just where things stand.

His is a monochrome world of good-and-evil, innocence-and-guilt, truth-and-falsehood. If such a world exists, and perhaps it does exist in the privacy of some minds, then he is welcome to it. What he may not, *must* not, do is people it with real-life human beings such as Paul Oops-nearly-said-it Oberholzer, real-life business enterprises such as S . . . a Inc., and real-life professional bodies such as the Institute of No-I-shouldn't-mention-the-name.

There are some things he's very good at not mentioning. They're the things about which you're not supposed to hear.

There's no mention of Mat Williamson.

No mention of Placid Island.

No mention of Frank Yamatoku.

No mention of the murder of Yves Boularis.

No mention of the gift to us by his colleague, Professor Langridge, of an aerosol spray of ninhydrin and a camera.

There's no mention of a lot of other things.

No one who has read Krom's book, certainly no one who matters in the trust management field, has any doubt about the identity of the man and the Group he is indicting.

And it's no good his retorting: 'If the cap fits, wear it.' As I told him at the Villa Lipp, no one concerned with the management of other people's money can afford to ignore a smear. We're too vulnerable.

I have the scars and mutilations to prove it.

What figure do I put on the damage?

Well, none of the cases against Professor Krom and his various publishers is yet *sub judice* so there can be no harm in my making a rough estimate. There's still plenty of time to settle out of court after withdrawing the book.

To begin with, during a single month following the publication of *Der kompetente Kriminelle*, attendance at the two scheduled Symposia seminars was sixty per cent down. A temporary set-back? Far from it. During the month following, registrations for our big one of the year, the annual Paris get-together, were down seventy per cent. We also received polite notes of regret from all but one of our star speakers.

So, I decided to cancel.

Note that please, *I* decided.

I have spoken of 'my people' in Brussels. I was referring, of course, to my senior staff – the head of research, the internal security man, those I had hand-picked myself – to whom I had always delegated a certain amount of authority. The Mat Williamson 'ultimatum' had made it necessary for me to delegate more, but I had managed.

I had managed by going back to using the methods Carlo and I had used before I'd been fool enough to send those stupid roses to Kramer's funeral.

I used an office accommodation service in a city where I wasn't known. It was a good service, properly equipped with telephones, telex and trained operators, and efficiently run. That was how I kept in touch. That was how I went on making the important decisions. Some wouldn't have called it delegating at all.

That, it seemed, was not what Mat had intended.

I used to go to the accommodation service office every day at noon and look at any telexes that had come in for me during the morning. Then, if I thought it necessary, I would call Brussels and talk to one or two of my people there.

Three months after the publication of Krom's book we had quite a lot to talk about. The virtual boycotting of our seminars had been only the beginning of our troubles. An old and valued associate, a tax lawyer with whom we'd done a lot of business, had described the nature of our ultimate predicament in uncompromising terms.

'No, I daren't do business with Paul Firman any more, nor with anyone connected with him. The banks won't have him. Nobody'll have him. I don't wonder. I've read the Krom book too.'

That's when I decided to take action; after hearing what an intelligent man who knew me was prepared to accept from Krom, a man who didn't know me at all.

It was Wednesday. I was impatient to hear what Symposia's German lawyer had had to say at the meeting that morning. I called Brussels just before noon.

Neither of my people was there.

I waited twenty minutes and then called again. The operator knew my voice of course, but hers sounded odd. I soon understood why. The person she put me through to was Frank.

'Hi, Paul.'

There was a tightening of muscles, but I managed to keep my voice level. 'There seems to be something wrong with the line. I'm calling Brussels.'

'Nothing wrong with the line, Paul, just with your thinking. I'm sitting in what used to be your office.'

'I see.'

'Well, now, that's what seems to be at the heart of the problem. You *don't* see.'

'So you're going to explain. Is that it?'

'No, Paul, it isn't. Nobody's giving you any more explanations. You don't listen to them. Nobody's giving you any more advice. You don't take it. So I have the job of telling you what you *are* going to get from now on.'

'I can hear a squeaking noise, Frank. It isn't just your voice. You must be rocking backwards and forwards in that chair of mine. I wouldn't do that. I keep the spring adjustment on the tight side. If you lean too far back the whole thing's liable to flip right over. You could hurt yourself.'

I tried to make my concern sound genuine. It sounded genuine enough to make him lose his temper.

'Don't get cute with me, Dad. Just shut up and try to listen. You were warned to keep a low profile. You didn't. You blew it. If Krom had taken you seriously a lot of damage could have been done. Luckily, you didn't impress him. But now you've had it. You were warned extra plainly last time. For a while, we thought we'd finally gotten through to you. But no. You're like all the rest of the old farts. You're told, you act like you've heard and then you forget what was said to you.'

'What did I forget, Frank? To fasten my seat belt?'

'Don't joke about serious matters, Paul. You've had your chances and you've been lucky. The Krom situation was contained, no thanks to you. *Now* what happens? You want to start suing that big prick and open the whole can of worms again.'

'You're mixing metaphors on a open line, Frank.'

'You don't have anything left to hide, old-timer. It's all hanging out for everyone to see, including the shareholders, and nobody likes the look of it. So, as of noon today, you're out. No need for you to worry about the chair I'm sitting in. It's been fixed and if you think it can still be unfixed, forget it. You're out on your arse.'

That I could believe. Keeping in touch is never the same as being on the job and Frank has always been an ingenious accountant. He has other skills I'm told. When signatures are needed from persons not immediately available, or willing, to give them, he is able to produce excellent forgeries.

'You're not forgetting that I'm a major shareholder, myself, are you?'

'Twenty per cent is what you have, and I'll tell you what the deal is there. It's been okayed from on high, so you can believe me. Right? Want to hear?'

'I'm listening.'

'Call off the dogs on Krom, buy that nice retirement home you've always dreamed of owning in dear old Senior City, and you get a golden handshake. We'll buy that twenty per cent of yours at book valuation, *your* book valuation. So what do you say?'

'Drop dead.'

There was a pause. Then: 'Paul, that offer's quite genuine. We mean it. Just lay off Krom.' The effort he was having to make to remain civil was nearly audible.

'Drop dead.'

'Paul, I'd like you to reconsider that answer.'

'Okay. I've reconsidered. The answer's no.'

'Because if anyone's going to drop dead, it's not going to be anyone here.'

'Frank,' I said, 'you wasted your money on Yves. Why did you have to hire people to kill him? You should have just tied him down and kept talking to him. The way you're talking to me. It wouldn't have been a pleasant death, any more than the '*plastiqué*' was, but it would have been a whole lot cheaper for Mat. And it would have left no traces. Well, scarcely any. Just the sort of rictus a man gets on his face when he's been hit by a poisoned arrow or dies yawning.'

There was another pause. 'I'm going to read out some numbers to you. You know about communications codes. Well, this is yours, your current one. It places you and your Kraut helper about four hours from here by road, and about three from the guys with the know-how that you tell me is so inefficient and over-priced. So, better take a deep breath. If you're going to run again, this time, you'll have a long way to go. Ready? Okay. This is your code. Prefix reads . . . '

I listened to the first seven figures, just to make sure that my old security man hadn't thought he owed it to me to make a slight error.

He hadn't. The Brussels old-pals act had been repealed. It was time I got moving.

I hung up and called Melanie.

She always knows best how to make travel arrangements.

CHAPTER ELEVEN

Carlo's house smells like a handkerchief out of an old drawer. Even when it was newly built one had been aware of a certain mustiness. Carlo had attributed it then to the brackish water used in mixing the concrete and said that it would gradually go away. It never has gone away; instead, it has ripened. That verbena-scented anti-mildew spray which Melanie gets at the general store on the Out Island only makes it worse.

She does the trip on our boat, with Jake to navigate and nurse the engine, every week; and, every week, she returns with our mail and our groceries and our drinks and a denunciation of the Out Island hairdresser. Every week, too, she says that that is the last time and that next week, no matter what the risk, she is leaving for Nassau or Miami and the joys of Elizabeth Arden. She adds that bad food can kill you just as surely as '*plastiqué*'.

She has my sympathy. Tonight, though, when I've thought everything through again and treble-checked it, it is possible that I may at last have an escape plan to submit to her.

Yesteray, the mail brought back with her consisted of two letters.

One was from a real-estate agent in Kingston, and it was to tell me that my asking price for the island was a bit too high. We get lots of letters like that. I mention it only to explain how we've been operating. Just in case somebody working for Mat and Frank somehow, somewhere, accidentally got on to the fact that I had access, as one of Carlo's trustees, to a Caribbean island, we have an early-warning system. There are hundreds of small island properties around here; and, since the real-estate people know more than the government records office about who really owns what, they're the ones who always know first if anyone starts making enquiries. Who but a prospective buyer would make enquiries? So, although I haven't the slightest right to be, I am a prospective seller. In that way, I get the benefit of the real-estate agents' intelligence network. Thus far, only one prospective buyer has actually reached our dreamy lagoon. After a lunch prepared by Carlo's cook – getting a little old now but still resolutely awful – he left and we heard no more.

We have been reasonably secure against everything except excruciating boredom, malnutrition and the possibility of those conditions becoming permanent features of what's left of our lives.

That's why the second letter was so important.

It was from the man who has helped me prepare this account of the 'siege of the Villa Lipp' for publication.

I had sought him out because I had liked something he had written and deduced from it that he was a person who would be unlikely to strike high-minded or other tedious attitudes. My approach was made by sending him a copy of Krom's book and a commentary I had written on the original *New Sociologist* piece. At the same time I had him vetted as a security risk.

At our first meeting on the Out Island we reached an understanding. Neither of us, I am happy to say, has since had reason to remind the other of the terms of it. Our relationship has developed remarkably. From being my amanuensis, he has become my literary mentor, then a business intermediary dealing on my behalf with publishers, and finally, my trusted legal adviser.

He anticipated that final role on several occasions during the writing of the book by sending me warnings – 'You can't say things like that,' or 'Nobody's going to stand for this' – that I had simply ignored. Then, when the first English language text was submitted to our publisher, the blow fell. The publisher made his acceptance conditional on legal waivers being obtained from those persons whom his lawyers said were libelled in the book as it stood; namely, Connell, Henson, Langridge, Williamson, Yamatoku, Symposia SA and, of course, Krom.

For me, that could have finished it. I was tired and unusually depressed. Indeed, at a gloomy last meeting on the Out Island with my adviser, I told him to have all those expensive typescripts – expensive because they had been done on that special paper that goes black if anyone tries to photograph or photocopy it – retrieved and destroyed.

He persuaded me not to be hasty. Let the publisher, who was willing to persevere with the book, try to get the waivers. If massive deletions or other vital changes were required, we could decide then whether or not they were acceptable. Possibly some name changes would be sufficient. There was nothing to be lost by finding out.

I told him to go ahead and see what happened. He gets a percentage of any royalties that the book may earn, so I could see his point of view. Mine was that, providing the book wasn't totally emasculated, he and the publisher had better be left to do the best they could for what they have been polite enough to refer to as my Cause.

The first reaction we had was encouraging though somewhat surprising. It was from Connell and said simply: 'Publish and be damned.'

An accompanying letter from my adviser explained that Dr Connell was now teaching in a different university and also being divorced by his second wife. However, the lawyer seemed to think that his brief note constituted a waiver.

Dr Henson's reply puzzled me.

'Publish by all means,' she wrote, 'recent school-leavers and college drop-outs should find some passages in the book heartening as well as instructive. Funnier than Smiles's *Self help* and likely to be preferred by modern teenage readers. Probation officers everywhere will love it.'

I wondered if she had been sent the wrong book, but

was assured that she hadn't. It was thought that her reply may have been designed to cause annoyance to the head of her department.

He objected strongly to the use of his name and the attribution to him of certain statements. His name was changed to 'Langridge' and some deletions of references to British security service personnel were made.

The response from Mat was most strange. I was sent a photocopy.

The letter came, beautifully typed, on paper with the heading, GOVERNMENT HOUSE, PLACID ISLAND, in discreet capitals. It was signed by a Personal Assistant.

'I am directed by His Excellency Mathew Tuakana to present his compliments. He has read the manuscript of the book described as the edited recollections of Mr Paul Firman. It may, he agrees, be of some sociological interest to specialists, particularly in the field of psychiatric social work. It is not a field with which His Excellency has had occasion to become familiar. On Placid Island psychiatric illness, even in its milder forms, is virtually unknown. Mr Firman's account of a western criminal sub-culture seems, possibly for that reason, as far fetched as the one he would like to give of Placid and its people. It is to be hoped that his recollections of the former are as unreliably based on hearsay as his speculations about the latter.

'Since His Excellency could not conceivably be the Mr Williamson described in this book, he feels unable to comment at greater length. I am instructed to add for your information that there are no less than twenty families named Williamson with Placid Island nationality. If the author, or Mr Firman himself, cares to communicate direct with our Office of Information, it may be possible to clear up any confusion existing in Mr Firman's mind, at least on that point.

'I am further instructed to say that the only Mr Yamatoku who could be described as being in His Excellency's employ, is financial counsellor to the Placid Island mission at the

296

United Nations. Counsellor Yamatoku is presently stationed in New York.'

My adviser thought the letter quaint; but said that my credibility had suffered a set-back. *Twenty* Williamson families on Placid? Hadn't I known that?

I explained the joke Mat had once explained to me. On Placid, changing family names was a popular sport, far more popular than the European political sport of street-name changing. In 1946 there had had to be a bye-law passed declaring a moratorium on name changing for two years. That was because every family name on Placid was suddenly MacArthur. All those Williamsons simply meant that Mat was becoming a potent cult figure.

And I don't consider that communication in the least quaint. I think it plainly serves notice on me that, book or no book, I'm still on the run; and that if at any time I should feel disposed to think otherwise, I can put my belief to the test by writing direct to Mat's Office of Information.

Well, I may now decide to do that.

The only reply from Symposia SA was a form letter from an official in a tribunal of commerce. It stated that Symposia was in voluntary liquidation and that any claim against it must be made by such-and-such a date. Very sad; but, as my adviser pointed out with unfeeling satisfaction, you can't in Anglo-Saxon law libel the dead.

That left Professor Krom.

He was in no hurry to reply; and, after some weeks of silence, it was feared that he did not intend to do so. Enquiries established, however, that he had been in the United States attending another of his international police conferences, and also absent on vacation.

His reply has now been received. A copy of it was attached to the letter that arrived yesterday.

What I had expected, at best, was a tongue-lashing and a stern demand for the deletion of all references to himself and his work that he considered disrespectful. What I have

297

received instead is – well, I haven't yet quite made up my mind.

The waiver he gives is a conditional one, and my adviser seems to find it in some way entertaining. The conditions the Professor lays down are that, along with my account, there must be published in the same volume and as a postscript or appendix, his own brief Commentary on it. The Commentary must be published exactly as written, in full and as an uninterrupted whole. Furthermore, I may not change or modify it, as a result of anything he has had to say about it or for any other reason. 'All those false hopes, doomed expectations, demonstrable lies and unintentional errors must remain in their original state, unspoilt and undisguised by the scratchings-over of hindsight.' If these conditions are accepted, he will waive any objections he might have had to the submitted text.

There is a supplementary condition. While Professor Krom has the greatest respect for the publishers concerned, of whose reputation for integrity he is well aware, he must still insist upon receiving a final corrected proof of the book before it goes to press. He will wish to see for himself that the nominal price he has asked for his blessing has been fully and properly paid.

The publishers tell me, with evident satisfaction, that the Professor's conditions are entirely acceptable to them.

They assume that his conditions will also be acceptable to me.

Well, of course they are acceptable. They must be. If I want my voice to be heard at all, I obviously have no choice in the matter.

The Professor's Commentary is translated from the original Dutch.

I have read the edited version of Paul Firman's book [he writes] with the keenest pleasure, the liveliest professional interest and yes, a good deal of wry amusement too.

It has in it so much of what I always felt was there but

failed completely to bring out myself. The reasons for my failure are plain. When the investigator-subject relationship is clouded by a basic personality conflict, the best that can be hoped for is that the investigator will ultimately succeed in functioning as a catalyst. To that modest extent, at least, I may claim success. My colleagues, Henson and Connell, both thought this subject exceptionally difficult, the latter going as far as to say, with defences arrayed in such depth, one had to ask oneself not simply what was behind them, but whether there would be room enough for a recognizable fellow creature. The simile he offered, that of a battle tank with armour so thick that it could accommodate a crew consisting only of trained mice, did not seem fanciful.

Well, Mr Firman has now set our minds at rest. The defences are formidable, yes, but there is a human being inside them. What kind of human being still remains, I think, to be seen; but we have available now a much clearer view of him. A self-serving effusion such as this, written by a delinquent of Mr Firman's rare calibre, will always reveal more about its author's internal world than the attempt at self-appraisal of an equally complex but less irresponsible mind. The scatological excesses of a Genet tell us more than the managed insights of a Gide.

Let us take a closer look at the material of Firman's outer defences. At the Villa Lipp, I compared his clouds of verbiage with octopus ink, a comparison which the octopus himself faithfully reports. It is surprising, however, to find the comparison holding good for his written word. Any spoken one – its meaning so easily changed by the voice and body-language of its speaker at the moment – lends itself naturally to deception. Comedians, evangelists, fortune-tellers, demagogues, all who traffic in the human personality, know and depend upon the fact. The written word is usually less obliging. It can be examined more than once. It can be analysed and parsed. Doubters suspecting soft spots may prod and poke at it. Only those accustomed to appealing to the semi-literate, or those as full of bile and adverbs as Mr Firman, can make the mistake of believing that, if a statement is made with sufficient vehemence and a neat turn of phrase, the conviction it seems to carry will always be unquestioned.

At one point in the book, Mr Firman has much to say about the technique of the 'smear'. By no means all of it was said, as he claims at the Villa Lipp, but no matter. To anything Mr Firman has to say about ways of smearing an adversary, I am prepared to listen. He is an expert on the subject.

Consider, for a moment, his descriptions of me and the way that I behave, socially as well as professionally.

Few men are without their vanities, idiosyncrasies and petty weaknesses. Many, I among them, possess visible physical peculiarities as well, although I am in no way abnormally handicapped. About his appearance, a sensible man of my age will have only vestigial illusions; and, if he has been much photographed at conferences and heard his platform voice coming back at him through television and radio, he will probably have dispensed with even those vestiges.

I have a prognathous upper jaw and what are commonly called 'buck' teeth. Because they are so prominent I try always to keep them very clean. I express disgust or disbelief by making a hawking sound in the throat. When we were young, my wife tried unsuccessfully to cure me of the habit which she thought unbecoming, and at times offensive. I also suffer from an arthritic condition of the spine that my doctor calls 'parrot's beak' and is properly known as spondylitis. If afflicts many other people my age, causing discomfort or inconvenience in varying amounts. Long, hot journeys made in small, nervous cars on mountain roads are bad for parrot's beak. In my case, such a journey will result in muscle spasm and lower back pain; and, until I can take recuperative rest, my gait will be affected.

What does Mr Firman make of all this?

A monster, naturally; a staring blue-eyed monster with

gleaming white fangs and circumflected lip, a monster who slobbers down all that lovely wine as if it were water, sprays his flinching companions cheerfully with gobbets of saliva, insults the food and then reels away, supporting himself with practised ease on the furniture as he goes, to sleep it off. The monster does not speak, he only yelps, yaps and blares. The monster does not take a bath, as Dr Henson does for the benefit of the eavesdropping microphones, he only breaks wind.

As the monster's creator himself would say, 'And so on.' Mr Firman must be taken with many grains of salt.

Where then, I may be asked, is the human being we were promised? Is there truth at all here? Is this merely dreamstuff, clinical casebook material that will only become useful when it has been processed and interpreted?

By no means. As Mr Firman admits, indeed claims, many of the conversations he reports are transcribed from the tapes he took with him from the villa. I have consulted my colleagues, Henson and Connell, on the point and both agree with me. As long as one disregards Firman's interpolated comments, though some of them have evidential merit of their own, his accounts of what was said are in the main accurate.

When he is reporting from memory, however, we have to be very much more careful.

The recollections of his adolescence have yet to be checked. The passages concerning his war experiences have been read by a German scholar, a friend of mine who served as an infantry soldier in the Italian theatre from 1943 to 1945. He reports one error. The only German army pistols he can remember as having been issued were the Walther and the Sauer. However, while a prisoner of the Americans, he had heard German pistols referred to as 'Lugers' as if the word were a generic term for every type of German automatic hand-gun. Firman's reference to 'Lugers or Walthers' may be dismissed then as a mistake belonging

301

to another time and place. It is not his memory that is at fault.

The same cannot be said of his mistakes over certain vital dates. All of a sudden he is grossly unreliable. He cannot even place correctly the year of my identification of him in Zürich!

Was the blunder intentional? I really don't think it can have been. Firstly, because I had already published the correct date in my Notes for a Case-study, and I can't see him passing up an opportunity to pour scorn on any factual statement of mine with which he disagreed. Secondly, because Mr Firman is far too astute to make mistakes that look as if they could have been intentional, unless he wished for some reason to draw special attention to them. But why should he? The Zürich date, for one, is among the 'neutral' facts that nobody disputes. A secretarial error then? No, because the rest of his typescript is singularly free of error. The editorial assistant must have accepted those wrong dates too, so presumably they were given him by Mr Firman.

I shall return to this problem. It touches one of Mr Firman's basic contentions concerning the guilt of the man he calls 'Williamson'. Among the charges levelled against me – other than those involving my teeth, my drunkenness, my timidity under fire or my stubborn refusals to concede that black is white – is a list of some of my sins of omission.

In one case, his complaint is certainly justified.

Unfortunately, I did not hear about the murder of Yves Boularis until several months after the event. It was not, I understand, reported outside France. Dr Henson came across a reference to it in a French medico-legal journal that I normally only read in précis. She wrote to me drawing attention both to the oddity of the method employed and to the timing of the murder.

Was it possible after all that the Villa Lipp had really been besieged? And could there really be a wicked Mr Williamson? The political leader who, having gained power and been preclaimed his people's saviour, wishes to obliterate all traces of his corrupt or criminal past is a familiar figure in the history of nations.

The possibility of my having done Mr Firman even a minor injustice was troubling. The true identity of the speaker whom he addresses as 'Mat' in the cassette of the telephone conversation that I took with me from the villa that night proved impossible to establish. I made every effort I could.

Through friends in London, I was able to obtain a copy of a BBC sound archive recording of Mathew Tuakana's voice. It was part of an address of homage and welcome to Chief Tebuke on the occasion of the Chief's inauguration as head of state at the Placid Island independence ceremony. It was in the Placid Island language.

A colleague who specializes in the techniques of 'voice-print' comparison reported to me on the two voices. He identified the man speaking with Firman on the cassette as being British from the English Midlands. Dr Henson had thought Coventry or Birmingham. The Tuakana recording, however, presented difficulties. This wasn't because he couldn't understand the language, but because it couldn't be used for the purposes of comparison. It is the *sounds* of the voice specimens that are analysed and compared. These two lots of sounds were of two completely different orders: one for the most part labial and nasal, the other wholly glottal. One cannot compare a fingerprint with a palmprint, even when they have been made by the same hand. There was no available and authenticated recording of Mr Tuakana speaking English or any other phonetically comparable language.

The doubt nagged at me, however, and, after the San Francisco conference two months ago, my wife agreed to my suggestion that we might spend the vacation due to me in seeing something of the South Pacific. We obtained a visa for Placid in Fiji, and went there, along with some cargo, on one of the bi-weekly island-hopping planes.

A hotel is nearly completed, but not yet in business. The

old rest-house is primitive, but our reception there was warm.

As an outspoken critic of what Mr Firman calls the 'tax-haven business,' I am fairly well known by name among those who earn their livings in it. It did not at all surprise me that the Canadian lawyer, who acts as Placid vice-consul in Suva, and who issued our visas, had sent advance warning of our visit. Letters from Mr Tuakana and from a daughter of Chief Tebuke awaited us on arrival. Both were invitations to lunch the following day. My wife's hostess would be the Principal of the Island's new high school for girls. Mr Tuakana looked forward to meeting me for an informal discussion of matters of mutual interest to us. He hoped to prevail upon me and Vrouw Krom to attend a reception by Chief Tebuke later in the week. Meanwhile, lunch at Government House would be *à deux*. A car and driver would be at my disposal during our stay.

Government House consists of one two-storey house and four bungalows, the accommodation used by the British Resident Commissioner and his senior officials in colonial days. Mr Tuakana, as Chief Minister, occupies the largest bungalow and has his offices in it as well as his private quarters. His domestic staff, I noted, seem to be exceptionally well-trained.

In studying Mr Firman's book, I have tried from the start to remain objective, and to remind myself at regular intervals that all statements in it must be presumed false until there is evidence to the contrary. When I say, then, that the Firman description of Mat Williamson fits Mathew Tuakana like a glove, I mean that the description is not only visually correct – there may be two names but there is only one man – but that it also gives an impression I found recognizable, that of a man somewhat too well aware of his ability to deal with subordinates.

The way in which he introduced himself, however, had little of the charm Firman's account had led me to expect.

'I am the Tuakana whose baptismal name is Mathew

Williamson,' he said. 'I am not the Williamson in this man Firman's book, any more than you, I imagine, consider yourself to be the Professor Krom he caricatures. As long as that is clearly understood, I see no reason why we shouldn't talk fairly freely and frankly.' He rang a small glass bell standing on the table beside him. 'What would you like to drink? Schnapps?'

'No, thank you, Minister.'

When the servant appeared he ordered iced water. I should record that his voice was quite unlike that on the cassette. I can usually tell the difference between American and British spoken English. His *sounded* more American, but I really don't know. Firman's assertion that the man is a clever mimic was obviously uncheckable.

After ascertaining that the rest-house had made us comfortable, he went on: 'Professor, tell me something. You and your wife went for a drive this morning. You saw mainly the port and the old phosphate-company workings. What did you think of the little you were able to see of us?'

'Somewhere in our friend's book this place is described as like a lunar landscape. That seemed a fair description of the mining area. Though I also saw what looked like efforts being made to improve things. Are they yours?'

His fleeting smile of satisfaction suggested that what I had seen had been a show put on for my benefit, and that our driver had been briefed. 'Not mine alone, Professor, As helpers I have a number of those persons of whom you so steadfastly disapprove.' He poured me a glass of water from the jug that had been brought. 'I mean the ones you call tax-dodgers.'

I was wilfully dense. 'The men operating the earth-moving equipment looked like Islanders to me.'

'They were. But do you know the procedures for registering a corporation or creating a trust on Placid?'

'I could recite the exempt company and trust laws of half a dozen of your competitors in the field, Minister. I would be surprised if yours were much different.'

'Not much different, no, but a little. Part of our corporation and trust registration fees must be paid in kind.'

'A nice gimmick. Plant and machinery?'

'Topsoil. Most of Placid's was stripped away and lost by the mining company. A delivery of five thousand metric tons of good, black topsoil ensures the best of everything here for a newly arrived corporation. In subsequent years we'll take a thousand tons annually as long as the quality remains good. I'll take no sub-soil fill. The only clock we mean to put back here is the ecological one. And I think we have just enough time in which to do it.'

'You have a deadline, Minister?'

I received a cool look. 'People who think as you do are our deadline, Professor. There is writing on the wall. Tax authorities everywhere, especially in the high-tax jurisdictions, are getting tougher every day. And the writing is not only on walls. In the European Common Market Official Journal, the sin we are committing, the crime you so deplore has been given a name of its own – Incitement to Anti-Social Tax-Avoidance! Doesn't that sound wicked? Ten years from now we'll have been legislated out of our economic existence if a career of crime is the only one we're trained to follow. We have no illusions, I can assure you. If the western powers prefer to have us as neo-colonial Third World pensioners rather than as self-respecting exporters of fiscal services, we must look elsewhere for salvation. But where? Yes, we could sell our port facilities to the highest bidder and become somebody's nuclear naval base. Or we could lease ourselves as sites for missile-tracking or microwave stations. Fates worse than death, I'm afraid. No! With sufficient topsoil and a well-researched development programme, surely we can use our sinful tax-avoidance years to purchase a better future. What do you think, Professor?'

'There's a lot in what you say, Minister.'

The arrogance of his answering smile was insufferable. I made a decision. If he could test Firman's verdict on me by making impertinent offerings of schnapps, I could

306

test Firman's gossip about him by asking impertinent questions.

'How active is the Boy Scout movement here on Placid, Minister?'

Not an eyelid flickered. 'There is no Boy Scout movement here as yet. The Legislative Assembly has been asked to authorize the establishment of the movement here. The new Protestant chaplain is interested, I'm told, but we have more important things to do with our time at present.'

Over lunch – canned ham, salad, instant coffee – he told me about the public-works programmes he had scheduled and the problems of getting low-interest loans.

I asked if Mr Yamatoku advised him at all on such matters.

He looked mystified. 'Mr Yamatoku is with our mission at the UN in New York.'

'Minister, I shall be returning home via New York. Would it be possible for me to meet Mr Yamatoku?'

'If you were to call his secretary, I dare say he would try to make time to see you. He is a busy man of course.'

My patience ran out there. I made detailed notes on the conversation that follows as soon as I returned to the rest-house.

'But not as busy as you, Minister, I'm sure. Where and when did you first meet Mr Firman?'

He stared over my right shoulder for a moment in a way that nearly had me turning to see who might be there. Such well-worn interviewing tricks sit oddly on so pretentious a man. When he saw that I wasn't going to respond, he played at folding his napkin carefully as he answered.

'The place of meeting was the one he gives,' he said. 'Port Vila in the New Hebrides. He was calling himself Perry Smythson. Almost everything else he says is, either wholly or in part, a pack of lies. If it were not we wouldn't be talking. I'm quite sure you don't believe that we are sitting here privately like this because I am eager to hear your views on the methodology of international tax planning.'

'No, Minister, but you might be curious about my intentions where Firman's book is concerned. I am naturally curious about yours. I'm hoping that they may help me to make up my mind. For a man in your position, public controversy of the kind that libel actions can generate is a thing to be avoided I imagine.'

'Avoided like the plague, Professor. The same goes for book-banning by injunction, or censorship through legal blackmail. My intention is to do nothing, and I will tell you why. After reading the Firman script, I sent off at once both for your book and the *New Sociologist* essay. The German of the book was a little beyond my understanding, but the essay fascinated me. Yes, fascinated! It confirmed something that I had long suspected.'

'Essays that do that are always fascinating.'

I earned only a fleeting smile. 'Tell me something, Professor. Firman quotes a definition of the able criminal which he says is yours. Is it?'

'It's the simplified, lecture-platform definition I normally give.'

'Then I'm afraid it can't be applied to Smythson-Oberholzer.'

'Shall we just call him Firman, Minister?'

'By all means. He's had too many aliases, I agree. But, whatever name you use, you can't call him the well-adjusted emotionally stable man of your definition. That, Firman certainly is not. It was one of the first things I came to understand about him.'

'Could you be specific?'

'Certainly. The death of Carlo Lech was a great blow to him, I know, because I was with him when he heard the news.' He held up a defensive hand as if I had started to interrupt him. 'Bear with me, please. Lech was never the father-figure whom Firman portrays. There, I'm completely with you. *But,* Firman always chose to *believe* that he was. The child blames a suitable *alter ego* for its own misdeeds. That is natural. The neurotic adult, the boy

308

who will never grow up, continues to project, but he does so on a different scale and uses different mechanisms. One such mechanism is called role-reversal, I believe.'

'Please go on, Minister.' The amateur psychiatrist is rarely as dangerous as he is often made out to be. As long as he has no patients, the injuries he inflicts are usually more painful than serious, like blows on the elbow. The kind of rubbish he talks, however, can tell you a lot about him.

'The Lech you dismiss, rightly, as a figment of the imagination was desperately real to Firman. Is *that* your emotionally stable, well-adjusted man, Professor?'

'It doesn't sound like him, no. Have you any other examples of this instability?'

'There are other examples staring at us from the pages of his book. He quotes you as saying that Lech had died five years previously. Wrong. He himself says that you saw him at the Zürich funeral five years previously. Wrong again. But why?'

'Those dating mistakes puzzled me too, Minister. Lech had died seven years previously, not five. I identified Firman in Zürich eight months before Lech's death. Those facts have never been in dispute. What was so special about the number five? Why the mistake?'

'Shall we call them Freudian slips, Professor?'

'Unintentional mistakes can be made by a copy typist who needs new glasses or an editorial adviser who can't be bothered with details.'

'But not these mistakes, Professor.' He was glad of my stuffiness; it made me a better audience. 'I know for a fact that the five-years-ago we are talking about now was of deep psychological significance to him. I'm no coffee-house analyst, Professor, and I only know what I've read about abnormal behaviour. But no one could have made a mistake about Mr Paul Firman then. It's not the sort of thing you forget. He went nowhere near Zürich or anywhere else in Europe. He spent the year shuttling between Singapore, Sydney and Hong Kong. That was the year his own mysterious Mat Williamson, the man on the telephone speaking with a Birmingham accent, seems to be talking about. He refers to a moment of personal loss and sadness, or sadness and loss. I made a note somewhere. It's on page . . .'

'Thank you, Minister. I know the place you mean. How did you come to see so much of him that year? Was that when your partnership began?'

'Partnership?' He didn't like the word. It occurred to me suddenly that Mr Tuakana was in a position to have me arrested, jailed and charged with insulting his government if he felt like it. 'That's what he calls it now. I was working for him as what he called a talent-spotter. I had no money worth talking about, and lobbying a company like Anglo-Anzac into facing the inevitable, even in a place like this, takes plenty. Firman paid me well, but I had to work for it. He had a short list of companies, corporations, that interested him. Usually they were in trouble. I investigated them for him. He was what some people call an operator. Quickly in, quickly out. Sometimes there were assets to be stripped. Sometimes there was a loss position to be parlayed. Sometimes there were other things. Partnership? I never saw it in that light. I was his hot-shot auditor. We never got around to discussing any of my long-term plans. That was the year of his crack-up.'

'A physical crack-up or a mental one, Minister?'

He placed his smoothed and folded napkin neatly beside his plate.

The hand that had held it twitched for a moment and then was still. He may have decided against rapping the table in time with the words.

'Professor, surely we can see now. Isn't it plain enough how those date mistakes came to be made? Five was the evil-magic number because five years before had been the evil-magic time. That was the year of the most terrible death and of the catastrophic disaster. As a result, it ends up as the year of *all* death and *all* disaster – Lech's death,

310

the Kramer folly, the encounter with you, the exile from Europe, *everything*. The year of ultimate misfortune! And, by the way, that was the year he got himself into trouble with the New South Wales police. In Sydney, at one point, there was serious talk of starting extradition proceedings to winkle him out of Hong Kong.'

'Do you know what for, Minister?'

'Indeed I do. You asked for other examples of his instability. I can given you a perfect one. It's another of his role-switching ploys. Do you remember the long lecture he says he gave to that mythical Mr Williamson? Remember, Professor? The one about the perils of international fraud and the terrible fate that awaited those who didn't obey the laws?'

'I remember.'

'Professor, that was a lecture *I gave him.*'

He paused, shrugged slightly and then gazed into my eyes with the peculiar look of engaging frankness that I have learned to associate with guilt sure of its defences and completely at its ease.

'My job,' he went on, 'was investigation and I could see the overall picture. Some corners of it were pretty murky, believe me. What provoked the lecture was a kind of multi-national thimble-rigging scheme he had going. This was a chain of twenty different corporations, all having what looked like serious assets – mining properties, real estate, palm-nut plantations – and all making paper profits. That chain was just the debris left from his asset-stripping deals. So, he's given the mess a coat of paint. Why? Well, it seems he's acquired this little ex-British insurance company registered in ex-British Singapore and still operating under the old British free-for-all rules. That means minimal regulation by American standards. Most of its business is done in Malaysia and the Islands and it has a cosy Chinese name that means 'faithful tiger'. So guess who ends up owning all those paper corporations. Yes, the faithful tiger, only now he's called Fidelity Lion and does his investigating through nominees. The only mistake Firman made there was to let that mangy lion write annuity business in Australia. He'll never go back there again. They don't like insurance grifters, especially when they can't pin anything on them.'

'No country likes them. But you spoke of a terrible death and a catastrophic disaster, Minister. Was that what you meant? The collapse of a fraudulent insurance scheme?'

'Oh no. His Chinese directors nearly had him in trouble, but he moved fast enough to get out from under that. It was the business of his son that hit him so hard.'

'He mentioned a child by his second marriage.'

'That was a daughter. The son was by his first wife. Brilliant boy, handsome, great charmer. Snapped up by one of the Ivy League colleges. Firman doted. Terribly proud of him. Actually used to carry a photograph of the lad in his wallet.'

'What happened?'

'He died suddenly. All very unfortunate it was.'

'Drugs? Alcohol? A car crash?'

'Nothing as simple. The boy committed suicide, hanged himself. It destroyed Firman completely for a while. I've never seen a crack-up like it. Almost total withdrawal. He'd just sit.'

'Was there any explanation?'

'Of the suicide? The college had one. Overwork, examination pressures, unjustified fears of not meeting the high expectations of others. Most of these places must have a form letter they send out. But Firman thought that he'd been the only one at fault. When he spoke at all then it was always to say the same thing. 'I seem to have made a habit of failing the people who love me.' No arguing with him. I for one would never be surprised if Firman decided to kill himself. There's a suicidal streak somewhere there.'

He stood up. It was time for me to leave. I asked if I could have copies of some of his speeches. A Personal Assistant was instructed to take me to the Office of Information.

I asked for tapes.

Later that day two envelopes were delivered to the rest-house. In one there was a number of Mr Tuakana's speeches translated into English. A covering note from the Information Officer explained that there were no taped recordings of the speeches available in a language I would understand.

The second envelope contained the promised invitations to a reception by Chief Tebuke later in the week.

I had nothing more to do on Placid. There was a plane leaving the following day. With my wife's agreement, I answered the invitation with an apologetic letter explaining that we were expected back in Suva and much regretted our inability to attend the reception.

Firman's Mr Williamson cannot, in my opinion, be described as able.

He is not even a good liar.

Melanie finished reading the Commentary in a state of high excitement.

'If you still have those company accounts,' she said, 'this is a wonderful gift that Krom has sent you.'

Bedtime on the Island had usually been nine-thirty; but that night, with Melanie smoking to keep the insects at bay, we sat up later.

'It's not only a gift,' I said, 'it's a gift horse with a mouth I'm looking into. Oh yes, I have those company accounts all right. I had them all microfilmed in Hong Kong at the time. Mat's accounts were very good, but not to anyone who'd been trained to read figures by Carlo. The only thing I could never discover was the name of the suckers using his nominees. Now, we have the name – Fidelity Lion. No wonder the Australians were treading on Mat's tail.'

Doubts assailed her. 'It's several years ago now. What about statutes of limitations?'

'With our knowledge we could get him in trouble any time we wanted, and he'll know it.'

'The uncrowned king of Placid?'

'*Especially* the uncrowned King of Placid. He's totally vulnerable. There'd be no more topsoil for a man suspected of fraud. No more anything else. All we do is what Professor Krom did in Brussels. We leave copies of all the evidence in sealed envelopes to be opened in case of either of our sudden deaths, particularly if my sudden death looked like a suicide. Then, we just tell Mat. Perfect!'

'If it's perfect, why aren't you happier?'

'Because along with the gift, there comes a disturbing message. Krom has finally confirmed beyond doubt the truth of something that I have resolutely denied. He is telling me again that I have been Number One all the time. The Number One anarchist!'

'Why should that disturb you?'

'It's a lie.'

'You've had too much to drink, Paul.'

'Very likely. They say there's no taste in vodka. There is in *this* vodka. There's a taste of scorched paint.'

She filled her own glass again. 'Did you really say it?'

'What?'

'That thing about always failing the people who loved you.'

'I may have said something to that effect. I was wallowing in self-pity at the time. Even so, Mat's version sounds a bit mawkish to me.'

When Melanie thinks hard, her lower jaw droops a little, giving her a hangdog look. She had it now.

'Failing people who loved me is something I have never done,' she said after a while.

'Good for you.'

'Not good at all.' Her mouth resumed its normal shape. '*I* have always been the one who loved.'

'Oh.'

She disposed of the subject firmly. 'Food, that's the important thing.' She emptied her glass again and banged it down on the table. 'I must tell you, Paul, that I shall think a lot tonight about food. About the good food I'm going to have away from here.'

'Yes. Yes, so shall I.'

I did.

I thought of good food, cold days and decent glasses of wine.

Eric Ambler

The world of espionage and counter-espionage, of sudden violence and treacherous calm; of blackmailers, murderers, gun-runners – and none too virtuous heroes. This is the world of Eric Ambler.

'Unquestionably our best thriller writer.'
Graham Greene

'He is incapable of writing a dull paragraph.'
Sunday Times

'Eric Ambler is a master of his craft.'
Sunday Telegraph

THE MASK OF DIMITRIOS
THE SCHIRMER INHERITANCE
THE NIGHT-COMERS
THE CARE OF TIME
THE DARK FRONTIER
THE LEVANTER
SEND NO MORE ROSES
UNCOMMON DANGER
THE INTERCOM CONSPIRACY

and others

FONTANA PAPERBACKS

Duncan Kyle

'One of the modern masters of the high adventure story.' *Daily Telegraph*

GREEN RIVER HIGH
BLACK CAMELOT
A CAGE OF ICE
FLIGHT INTO FEAR
TERROR'S CRADLE
A RAFT OF SWORDS
WHITEOUT!
STALKING POINT
THE SEMONOV IMPULSE

FONTANA PAPERBACKS

Helen MacInnes

Born in Scotland, Helen MacInnes has lived in the USA since 1937. Her first book, *Above Suspicion*, was an immediate success and launched her on a spectacular writing career that has made her an international favourite.

'She is the queen of spy-writers.' *Sunday Express*

'She can hang up her cloak and dagger right there with Eric Ambler and Graham Greene.'

Newsweek

THE SNARE OF THE HUNTER
HORIZON
ABOVE SUSPICION
MESSAGE FROM MALAGA
REST AND BE THANKFUL
PRELUDE TO TERROR
NORTH FROM ROME
THE HIDDEN TARGET
I AND MY TRUE LOVE
THE VENETIAN AFFAIR
ASSIGNMENT IN BRITTANY
DECISION AT DELPHI
NEITHER FIVE NOR THREE
THE UNCONQUERABLE
CLOAK OF DARKNESS
RIDE A PALE HORSE

FONTANA PAPERBACKS

Alistair MacLean

His first book, HMS *Ulysses*, published in 1955, was outstandingly successful. It led the way to a string of best-selling novels which established Alistair MacLean as the most popular adventure writer of our time.

FONTANA PAPERBACKS

THE DROP